SENIOR
si metric

Dino Dottori B.Sc., M.S.Ed.
Head, Mathematics Department
Hill Park Secondary School
Hamilton, Ontario

George Knill B.Sc., M.S.Ed.
Mathematics Consultant
The Board of Education for the City of Hamilton
Hamilton, Ontario

James Stewart Ph.D.
Associate Professor
Department of Mathematics
McMaster University
Hamilton, Ontario

McGRAW-HILL RYERSON LIMITED

Toronto   Montreal   New York   St. Louis   San Francisco
Auckland   Bogotá   Guatemala   Hamburg   Johannesburg
Lisbon   London   Madrid   Mexico   New Delhi   Panama
Paris   San Juan   São Paulo   Singapore   Sydney   Tokyo

FOUNDATIONS OF MATHEMATICS FOR TOMORROW: SENIOR

ISBN 0-07-82531-9

7890D87654

Illustrations by Frank Zsigo

Printed and bound in Canada

Canadian Cataloguing in Publication Data

DOTTORI, DINO, 1937—
  FMT Senior

THE RYERSON MATHEMATICS PROGRAM
INCLUDES INDEX.
ISBN 0-07-082531-9

1. MATHEMATICS—1961— I. KNILL, GEORGE, 1938.
II. STEWART, JAMES. III. TITLE. IV. TITLE:
FOUNDATIONS OF MATHEMATICS FOR TOMORROW, SENIOR.

QA37.2.D68   510   C79-094688-2

Photos courtesy of:
Canadian National Exhibition, p. 225
IBM Canada Ltd., p. 338
Cambridge University Press, p. 355 (from Science and Civilization in China, III, by Joseph Needham)

The metric usage in this text has been reviewed by the Metric Screening Office of the Canadian Government Specifications Board.

Metric Commission Canada has granted use of the National Symbol for Metric Conversion.

THE RYERSON MATHEMATICS PROGRAM
CORE TEXTS
MATHEMATICS FOR TODAY AND TOMORROW

FOUNDATIONS OF MATHEMATICS FOR TODAY AND TOMORROW
FOUNDATIONS OF MATHEMATICS FOR TOMORROW: AN INTRODUCTION
FOUNDATIONS OF MATHEMATICS FOR TOMORROW: INTERMEDIATE
FOUNDATIONS OF MATHEMATICS FOR TOMORROW: SENIOR

APPLIED MATHEMATICS FOR TODAY: AN INTRODUCTION
APPLIED MATHEMATICS FOR TODAY: INTERMEDIATE
APPLIED MATHEMATICS FOR TODAY: SENIOR

COMPANION BOOKLETS

MATHEMATICS SKILLBUILDING
MATHEMATICS FOR ENRICHMENT
BUSINESS MATH EXERCISES
TECHNICAL MATH EXERCISES

Contents

Functions

The science of Pure Mathematics, in its modern developments, may claim to be the most original creation of the human spirit.

Alfred North Whitehead

CARL FRIEDRICH GAUSS (1777–1855)

There have been several child prodigies in mathematics but the most precocious of them all was Gauss whose astounding intelligence was recognized as early as the age of two. In fact when Gauss was two he observed his father computing a payroll and when the lengthy addition was finished he said, "Father, the sum is wrong. It should be . . . ." Another example of his precocity will be seen in Section 11.5.

Gauss, one of the greatest of all mathematicians, contributed to all branches of mathematics but his favourite branch was number theory. For instance he proved that any positive integer can be written as a sum of 3 triangular numbers. Triangular numbers are those which occur in triangular patterns: 0, 1, 3, 6, 10, 15, 21, ...

1	3	6	10	· · ·

As examples of Gauss's statement we have $4=3+1+0$, $5=3+1+1$, $15=6+6+3$, $37=21+10+6$, but it is difficult to prove, as Gauss did, that *any* natural number is a sum of three of these triangular numbers.

Gauss was the first to prove the Fundamental Theorem of Algebra which says that every polynomial equation has a root if complex numbers are allowed as roots. In geometry he was the first to construct a regular polygon with 17 sides using ruler and compass alone. (If you think that is easy, try it.) He was one of the inventors of non-Euclidean geometry. In fact he showed that it is possible to have a consistent geometry in which the sum of the angles in a triangle is less than 180° and there are infinitely many lines which pass through a given point and are parallel to a given line.

Gauss was interested not only in pure mathematics but also in applying mathematics to physical problems. He is well-known for his work in magnetism and astronomy and in fact he spent much of his life as director of an observatory in Germany. He wrote, "Astronomy and pure mathematics are the magnetic poles toward which the compass of my mind ever turns."

The concept of a function is the basic idea in mathematics and also in most applications of mathematics. A function describes how one quantity depends on another. For example, we say that population is a function of time, pressure is a function of temperature, and so on. In fact functions can be found everywhere.

Therefore it is important to study the nature and properties of functions in this first chapter. Then the common types of functions, such as quadratic functions, polynomial functions, trigonometric functions, exponential functions, and logarithmic functions, will be investigated in more detail in the following chapters.

1.1 FUNCTIONS AND THEIR GRAPHS

The operation of squaring associates with each real number x another real number x^2. Various symbols are used to indicate this correspondence:

$$x \rightarrow x^2 \quad \text{or} \quad y = x^2 \quad \text{or} \quad f(x) = x^2$$

Any such rule or operation which assigns to each element of a given set A an element of a set B is called a function or a mapping

---

Given two sets A and B, a function f is a rule or correspondence that associates with each element x in A an element, called $f(x)$, in B. A is called the domain of f. The range of f is the set $\{y \in B \mid y = f(x), \ x \in A\}$.

The symbol $f(x)$ is read "f of x" or "f at x" and is the value of the function at x. If a function f is given by the formula involving x, then we find $f(3)$, for example, by substituting $x = 3$ in the formula. (However there are some functions which cannot be described by formulas.)

Suppose $A = R$ and $B = R$. Then the equation

$$y = 6x^3 - 5x + 1$$

defines a rule which assigns to each number $x \in R$ another number $y \in R$. Using function notation we have

$$f(x) = 6x^3 - 5x + 1$$
$$f(3) = 6 \times 3^3 - 5 \times 3 + 1 = 148$$
$$f(0) = 6 \times 0^3 - 5 \times 0 + 1 = 1$$
$$f(-0.5) = 6(-0.5)^3 - 5(-0.5) + 1 = 2.75$$
$$f(x-1) = 6(x-1)^3 - 5(x-1) + 1$$
$$= 6(x^3 - 3x^2 + 3x - 1) - 5x + 5 + 1$$
$$= 6x^3 - 18x^2 + 13x$$
$$f\left(\frac{1}{x}\right) = 6\left(\frac{1}{x}\right)^3 - 5\left(\frac{1}{x}\right) + 1$$
$$= \frac{6}{x^3} - \frac{5}{x} + 1$$

Notice that when evaluating f at some number you must first cube the number, multiply by 6, then subtract 5 times the number and add 1, no matter what the number is called.

EXAMPLE 1. *If $A = R$, $B = R$, and we define*

$$f(x) = \begin{cases} 1 & \text{if } x \text{ is an integer} \\ -1 & \text{if } x \text{ is not an integer} \end{cases}$$

evaluate the function at 0, $\frac{1}{2}$, -5, $99\,999$, π.

Solution

$$f(0) = 1$$

$$f(\tfrac{1}{2}) = -1$$

$$f(-5) = 1$$

$$f(99\,999) = 1$$

$$f(\pi) = -1$$

The range of f is $\{1, -1\}$.

Determine the pattern. Find the missing number.

1	2	3	8
2	1	1	3
5	2	3	16
4	2	1	

   Functions describe the way that one quantity varies with another. The following example illustrates this.
   If a ball is thrown straight up in the air with a velocity of 12 m/s, then its height is a function of time. If h is the height of the ball above the ground in metres and t is the time elapsed in seconds, then the equation

$$h = 12t - 4.9t^2$$

is the rule that connects t and h. In function notation we could write

$$h = f(t) = 12t - 4.9t^2.$$

Then $f(1) = 7.1$ means that after 1 s the ball is at a height of 7.1 m.
   In this example h depends on t and so we call t an independent variable and h a dependent variable.

Convention: If the domain of a function is not specified, but a formula is given for $f(x)$, then the domain of f is assumed to be the set of all values of x for which the given expression for $f(x)$ is meaningful.

EXAMPLE 2. *Find the domains of the functions*

$$\text{(a) } f(x) = \sqrt{x - 3} \qquad \text{(b) } g(x) = \frac{1}{x^2 - 2}$$

functions   3

Solution

(a) The expression $\sqrt{x-3}$ is defined if $x-3\geq0$, i.e., $x\geq3$.
So the domain of f is $\{x\in R \mid x\geq3\}$.

(b) The expression $\dfrac{1}{x^2-2}$ is defined if $x^2-2\neq0$, i.e., $x^2\neq2$.
The domain of g is $\{x\in R \mid x\neq\sqrt{2},\ x\neq-\sqrt{2}\}$.

A function can be pictured by an arrow diagram as in Figure 1-1. For

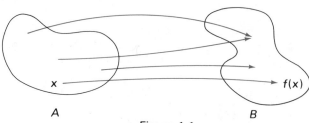

A B

Figure 1-1

each x in A we imagine an arrow drawn from x to its associated $y=f(x)$ in B. Notice that two arrows can end at the same y, but two arrows cannot begin at the same x. The element $f(x)$ in B is called the image of x.

Because of these arrow diagrams, we sometimes write $f: A \rightarrow B$ to indicate that f is a function which maps the set A into the set B. If it happens that every element y in B is the image of some x in A, then the range of f is equal to B and we say that f maps A onto B.

EXAMPLE 3. *Which of the following functions map A onto B?*

(a) $f: A\rightarrow B$, $A=R$, $B=R$, $f(x)=x^2$
(b) $f: A\rightarrow B$, $A=\{-1,0,1,2,\}$, $B=\{0,1,4\}$, $f(x)=x^2$

Solution

(a) The range of f is $\{y\in R,\ y\geq0\}$ which is not equal to R.
So f is not onto.

(b)

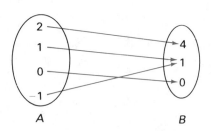

A B

Here the range of f is $\{0,1,4\}=B$.
So f is onto.

A function $f : A \rightarrow B$, where A and B are both subsets of R, is called a real-valued function of a real variable. Such functions can also be pictured by drawing their graphs.

> The graph of f is the set of ordered pairs $\{(x, y) \mid y = f(x), x \in A\}$.

To draw the graph of f we plot all points in the plane such that $f(x \text{ component}) = y$ component.

The graph of a function gives one of the best ways to understand a function because it provides us at a glance with the "life history" of the function.

EXAMPLE 4. *Sketch the graph of the function*

$$f(x) = x^2 + 2x - 1, x \in R$$

Solution

We choose a representative set of numbers from the domain R, calculate their images, and arrange them as in Table 1-1. Then we plot these ordered pairs. It then appears that the complete graph will be smooth and connected as shown.

x	$y = f(x)$
−4	7
−3	2
−2	−1
−1	−2
0	−1
1	2
2	7

Table 1-1

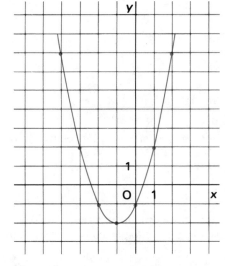

In general, choosing a reasonably representative set of numbers from the domain of a function in order to draw its graph depends on experience in working with functions. The exercises will help you to gain experience.

A relation is any set of ordered pairs. The graph of a function is a special relation because for each first component x there is only one second component, namely $f(x)$. Therefore in order to decide whether the graph of a given relation is the graph of a function we use the vertical line test.

In Figure 1-2 each vertical line intersects (b) only once. However in (a) and (c) the indicated vertical lines intersect the figures more than once. Thus only (b) represents a function.

(a)

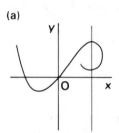

(b)

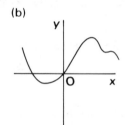

(c)

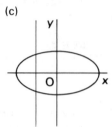

Figure 1-2

EXERCISE 1-1

A 1. If $f(x) = 2x - 3$, state

(a) $f(1)$ (b) $f(0)$ (c) $f(17)$ (d) $f(-3)$ (e) $f(\frac{1}{2})$
(f) $f(1.5)$ (g) $f(-9)$ (h) $f(100)$ (i) $f(a)$ (j) $f(-a)$

2. If $g(x) = \dfrac{1}{x-1}$, state

(a) $g(2)$ (b) $g(25)$ (c) $g(0)$ (d) $g(-2)$ (e) $g(\pi)$

3. State $f(4)$ for each of the following functions.

(a) $f(x) = 4 + 5x$ (b) $f(x) = x^2 - 6$ (c) $f(t) = 9 - t$
(d) $f(x) = 10$ (e) $f(z) = z^3$ (f) $f(x) = 8(5 - x)$
(g) $f : x \to \dfrac{1}{x}$ (h) $f(x) = \sqrt{13 - x}$ (i) $f(t) = \dfrac{1}{t^2}$

4. State the domain and range of the functions represented by the following arrow diagrams. Which of them map A onto B?

(a)

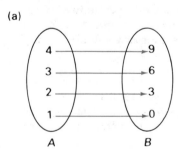

(b)

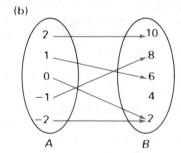

(c)

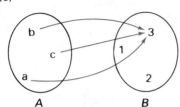

A   B

(d)

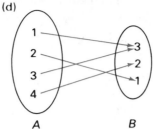

A   B

5. State the domains and ranges of the functions whose graphs are given.

(a)

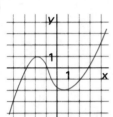

(b)

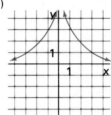

(c)

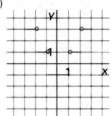

6. Which of the following figures are graphs of functions?

(a)

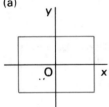

(b)

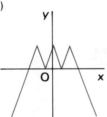

(c)

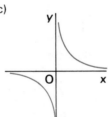

(d)

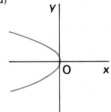

B 7. If $f(x) = x^2 - 3x + 1$, find
(a) $f(4)$ (b) $f(-4)$ (c) $f(0.1)$ (d) $f(12)$
(e) $f(t)$ (f) $f(x+1)$ (g) $f(t^2)$ (h) $f(-x)$

8. If $g(x) = x^3 - x^2 + x - 1$, find
(a) $g(1)$ (b) $g(-1)$ (c) $g(5)$ (d) $g(-0.2)$
(e) $g(\sqrt{2})$ (f) $g(1-t)$ (g) $g(x^2)$ (h) $g(x+1) - g(x)$

9. If $F(x) = \sqrt{x^2 + 1}$, find
(a) $F(0)$ (b) $F(4)$ (c) $F(-4)$ (d) $F(7)$
(e) $F(2\sqrt{6})$ (f) $F(-x)$ (g) $F(x^2)$ (h) $F(3x)$

10. Find $f(8)$ for each of the following functions.
(a) $f(x) = \sqrt{100 - x^2}$ (b) $f(t) = \sqrt[3]{t}$ (c) $f : x \to x^3 - 2x^2$

(d) $f(u) = \dfrac{u-2}{3u+4}$ (e) $f(z) = \sqrt{\dfrac{z-4}{z+1}}$ (f) $f(x) = 2^x$

11. Find the domains of the following functions.

(a) $f(x) = 2x - 37$ (b) $g(x) = x^5 - x$ (c) $h(x) = \sqrt{x}$

(d) $F(x) = \sqrt{8 - x}$ (e) $G(x) = \dfrac{x}{3x - 5}$ (f) $H(x) = \dfrac{1}{\sqrt{x + 4}}$

(g) $f(x) = \dfrac{x^2 + 3}{(x - 1)(x - 3)}$ (h) $g(x) = \sqrt{4 - x^2}$ (i) $h(x) = \sqrt{4 + x^2}$

(j) $F(x) = \sqrt{x^2 - 4}$ (k) $G(x) = \sqrt[3]{x^2 - 4}$ (l) $H(x) = \dfrac{1}{x^2 + x - 6}$

12. Find the range of the following functions.

(a) $f(x) = x + 5$, domain $A = R$
(b) $f(x) = x^2$, domain $A = \{x \in R \mid -5 \leqslant x \leqslant 2\}$
(c) $f(x) = x^2 + 5$, domain $A = R$
(d) $y = x^3$, domain $A = \{x \in R \mid x \leqslant 0\}$
(e) $y = x^3$, domain $A = \{x \in R \mid -3 \leqslant x \leqslant 2\}$
(f) $f(x) = |x| - 1$, domain $A = R$

13. Which of the following functions are onto?

(a) $f : R \to R, \ f(x) = 2x + 1$
(b) $f : R \to R, \ f(x) = -x^2$
(c) $f : A \to B, \ f(x) = x^2 + 2x, \ A = \{-1, 0, 1\}, \ B = \{-1, 0, 3\}$
(d) $f : A \to B, \ f(x) = x^2 + 2|x|, \ A = \{-1, 0, 1\}, \ B = \{-1, 0, 3\}$
(e) $f : A \to A, \ f(x) = \sqrt{x}, \ A = \{x \in R \mid x \geqslant 0\}$
(f) $f : A \to R, \ f(x) = -\sqrt{x}, \ A = \{x \in R \mid x \geqslant 0\}$

14. Draw the graphs of the following functions.

(a) $f(x) = 4 - x, \ -1 \leqslant x \leqslant 3$ (b) $f(x) = 3x - 2, \ x \in R$

(c) $f(x) = 3 - 2x, \ x \in R$ (d) $f(t) = -2(t + 1), \ t \in R$

(e) $y = \dfrac{x + 1}{2}, \ x \in R$ (f) $g(x) = |x + 1|, \ x \in R$

(g) $g(x) = 4 - x^2, \ -2 \leqslant x \leqslant 3$ (h) $h(x) = (x - 1)(x - 3), \ -1 \leqslant x \leqslant 5$

(i) $y = 2x^2 + x - 1, \ x \in R$ (j) $F(t) = \sqrt{t}, \ t \geqslant 0$

(k) $y = \dfrac{1}{x - 1}, \ x \neq 1$ (l) $f(u) = u^3, \ u \in R$

(m) $g(x) = x^4, \ x \in R$ (n) $h(x) = |x^2 - 1|, \ -3 \leqslant x \leqslant 3$

15. Define $p(x)$ to be the number of primes which are less than or equal to x. (By definition, 1 is not a prime.) Find

(a) $p(2)$ (b) $p(9)$ (c) $p(18)$ (d) $p(37)$ (e) $p(\sqrt{97})$

16. A ball is thrown straight up in the air with a velocity of 24.5 m/s. If $h(t)$ is the height of the ball above the ground after t seconds, then $h(t) = 24.5t - 4.9t^2$ while the ball is above ground.

(a) How many seconds is the ball in the air?
(b) Draw the graph of h as a function of t.
(c) How high does the ball go?

C 17. If $f(x) = x^2 + 2$ and $g(x) = 3 - 5x$, find

(a) $f(g(3))$ (b) $g(f(3))$ (c) $f(g(-2))$
(d) $g(f(-2))$ (e) $f(g(x))$ (f) $g(f(x))$

18. If $f(x) = 1 - x$ and $g(x) = \dfrac{x}{1 - x}$, find

(a) $f(g(2))$ (b) $g(f(2))$ (c) $f(g(\tfrac{1}{2}))$
(d) $g(f(\tfrac{1}{2}))$ (e) $f(g(x))$ (f) $g(f(x))$

19. The following functions are defined by different formulas in different parts of their domains. In each case find

(i) $f(-1)$ (ii) $f(0)$ (iii) $f(1)$

and graph the function.

(a) $f(x) = \begin{cases} 0 \text{ if } x < 0 \\ 1 \text{ if } x \geqslant 0 \end{cases}$ (b) $f(x) = \begin{cases} -x \text{ if } x < 0 \\ x^2 \text{ if } x \geqslant 0 \end{cases}$

(c) $f(x) = \begin{cases} -1 \text{ if } -3 \leqslant x \leqslant 1 \\ 1 \text{ if } 1 < x < 2 \\ 4 \text{ if } 2 \leqslant x \leqslant 4 \end{cases}$ (d) $f(x) = \begin{cases} -1 \text{ if } x \leqslant -1 \\ x \text{ if } -1 < x < 1 \\ 1 \text{ if } x \geqslant 1 \end{cases}$

(e) $f(x) = \begin{cases} -3-x \text{ if } -3 \leqslant x < -2 \\ 1+x \text{ if } -2 \leqslant x < 0 \\ 1-x \text{ if } \ 0 \leqslant x < 2 \\ -3+x \text{ if } \ 2 \leqslant x \leqslant 3 \end{cases}$ (f) $f(x) = \begin{cases} (x+1)^2 \text{ if } x < 0 \\ 0 \quad\quad \text{ if } x = 0 \\ (x-1)^2 \text{ if } x > 0 \end{cases}$

20. A worker's weekly pay P is a function of the number of hours t that he works. Suppose that he gets paid \$6/h and he gets "time and a half" for overtime (hours over 40).

(a) Give an expression for $P(t)$ using a divided definition as in question 19.

(b) Use the expression in (a) to find the worker's pay for 35 h and 45 h.

(c) Draw the graph of the function P.

21. If $f(x) = \dfrac{x^7 - x^5}{\sqrt{1 + x^4 + x^8}}$, find the following correct to 5 decimal places.

(a) $f(3)$ (b) $f(1.1)$ (c) $f(2.345)$ (d) $f(-0.86)$

22. Graph the following functions.

(a) $f(x) = \dfrac{10x(x+8)}{(x+10)^2}$, $-30 \leqslant x \leqslant 30$

(b) $g(x) = \sqrt{7.63x^2 - 5.82x + 3.56}$

(c) $h(x) = \sqrt[3]{\dfrac{x-1}{(x+2)^2}}$

1.2 PROPERTIES OF FUNCTIONS

In this section we shall deal with some useful properties of real-valued functions of a real variable. These properties concern continuity, symmetry (even or odd), and whether a function is increasing or decreasing. Each property has a simple geometric interpretation.

> A function $f : A \rightarrow R$ is called
> (i) increasing if whenever x_1 and x_2 are in A and $x_1 < x_2$, then $f(x_1) < f(x_2)$;
> (ii) decreasing if whenever x_1 and x_2 are in A and $x_1 < x_2$, then $f(x_1) > f(x_2)$.

Geometrically, the graph of an increasing function rises as we move from left to right and the graph of a decreasing function falls as we

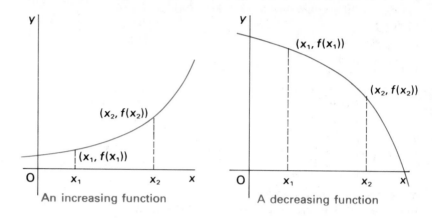

An increasing function   A decreasing function

move from left to right. Many functions are neither increasing nor decreasing but they may be increasing on certain intervals of their domains and decreasing on other intervals.

EXAMPLE 1.   *The graph of a function f is given. On which intervals is f increasing and on which intervals is it decreasing?*

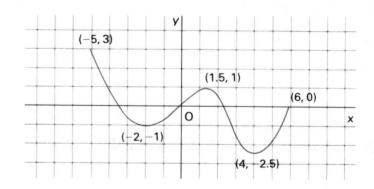

Solution
From the graph we see that

f is decreasing when $-5 \leqslant x \leqslant -2$,
f is increasing when $-2 \leqslant x \leqslant 1.5$,
f is decreasing when $1.5 \leqslant x \leqslant 4$,
f is increasing when $4 \leqslant x \leqslant 6$.

EXAMPLE 2.   *Use the rules for working with inequalities to prove that*
$f(x) = 1 - \dfrac{1}{x}$ *is an increasing function on $A = \{x \in R \mid x > 0\}$.*

Solution

If $0 < x_1 < x_2$, then $\dfrac{1}{x_1} > \dfrac{1}{x_2}$.

$\therefore \quad -\dfrac{1}{x_1} < -\dfrac{1}{x_2}$

$\therefore \quad 1 - \dfrac{1}{x_1} < 1 - \dfrac{1}{x_2}$

$\therefore \quad f(x_1) < f(x_2)$

$\therefore \quad f$ is increasing

The graph of f confirms this calculation:

$x_1 < x_2$

$\therefore \quad \dfrac{x_1}{x_1 x_2} < \dfrac{x_2}{x_1 x_2}$

$\dfrac{1}{x_2} < \dfrac{1}{x_1}$

$\dfrac{1}{x_1} < \dfrac{1}{x_2}$

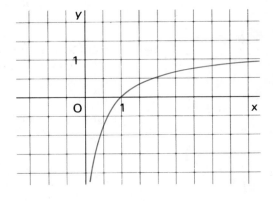

SYMMETRY

The graphs of $f(x) = x^2$ and $f(x) = x^3$ in Figure 1-3 are both symmetric. The one on the left is symmetric in the y-axis, i.e., the graph is mapped onto itself when reflected in the y-axis. The one on the right is symmetric about the origin, i.e., the graph is mapped onto itself when rotated through $180°$ about the origin. Notice that in either case we need only plot the graph of the function for $x \geqslant 0$. The rest of the graph is then obtained by symmetry. So our work is cut in half.
$(-x, y)$

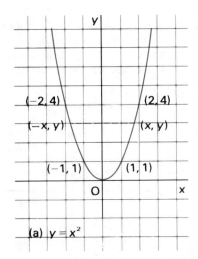

(a) $y = x^2$

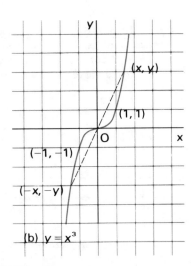

(b) $y = x^3$

Figure 1-3

$(x, y) \rightarrow (-x, y)$ for reflection in the y-axis.

$(x, y) \rightarrow (-x, -y)$ for rotation of $180°$ about the origin.

Notice that if the graph of f is symmetric in the y-axis and (x, y) is on the graph, then so is $(-x, y)$. Thus $f(x) = f(-x)$. Functions which satisfy this condition are called even functions.

Likewise if the graph of f is symmetric about the origin and (x, y) is on the graph, then so is $(-x, -y)$. Thus $f(-x) = -f(x)$. Functions which satisfy this condition are called odd functions.

An even function f satisfies $f(-x) = f(x)$ for all x in its domain. The graph of an even function is symmetric in the y-axis.
An odd function f satisfies $f(-x) = -f(x)$ for all x in its domain. The graph of an odd function is symmetric about the origin.

EXAMPLE 3. *Determine whether each of the following functions is even, odd, or neither.*

(a) $f(x) = x^5$ (b) $g(x) = 1 - x^2$ (c) $h(x) = x^2 + x$

Solution

(a) $f(-x) = (-x)^5$
$\quad\quad\quad = (-1)^5 x^5$
$\quad\quad\quad = -x^5$
$\quad\quad\quad = -f(x)$
$\therefore$ f is odd

(b) $g(-x) = 1 - (-x)^2$
$\quad\quad\quad = 1 - x^2$
$\quad\quad\quad = g(x)$
$\therefore$ g is even

(c) $h(-x) = (-x)^2 + (-x)$
$\quad\quad\quad = x^2 - x$
$h(-x) \neq h(x)$
$h(-x) \neq -h(x)$
$\therefore$ h is neither even nor odd

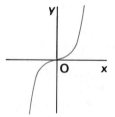 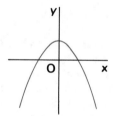 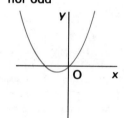

CONTINUITY

Intuitively speaking, a continuous function is one whose graph has no breaks or holes in it. Thus the graph of a continuous function can be drawn without lifting the pencil from the paper. If f is continuous, then as x gets close to any number a in the domain of f, $f(x)$ gets close to $f(a)$.

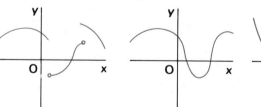

discontinuous function   continuous function   discontinuous function

EXERCISE 1-2

A **1.** On which intervals are the functions, whose graphs are given, increasing or decreasing?

(a)

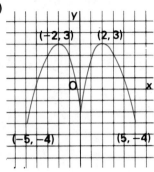

(b)

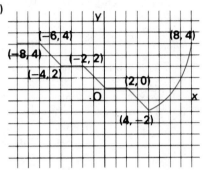

2. State whether the functions whose graphs are given are even, odd, or neither.

(a)

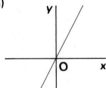

(b)

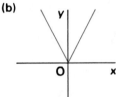

(c)

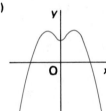

(d)

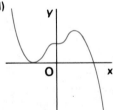

(e)

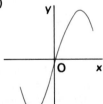

(f)

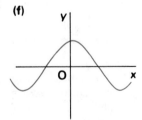

3. Which of the functions whose graphs are given are continuous?

(a)

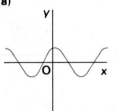

(b)

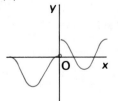

(c)

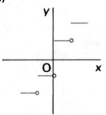

(d)

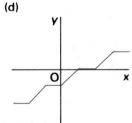

B **4.** Prove using inequalities (i.e., without looking at graphs) that the following functions are increasing.

(a) $f(x) = 3x - 4$ (b) $g(x) = x + 3$ (c) $h(x) = x^2, x \geq 0$

(d) $f(x) = -2x^2, x \leq 0$ (e) $g(x) = \dfrac{1}{1-x}, x > 1$

5. Prove using inequalities that the following functions are decreasing.

(a) $f(x) = 5 - 2x$ (b) $g(x) = \dfrac{1}{x+1}, x > 0$ (c) $h(x) = x^2, x \leq 0$

6. Graph the following functions and find the intervals on which they are increasing or decreasing.

(a) $f(x) = x^2 + 4x + 3, -5 \leq x \leq 1$ (b) $g(x) = 6x - x^2, -1 \leq x \leq 7$

(c) $h(x) = |x - 2|$ (d) $F(x) = 2 - |x + 2|$

(e) $f(x) = \begin{cases} x & \text{if } -3 \leq x < -1 \\ -x^2 & \text{if } -1 \leq x < 0 \\ x^2 & \text{if } 0 \leq x < 1 \\ 2 - x & \text{if } 1 \leq x < 2 \\ x - 2 & \text{if } 2 \leq x \leq 3 \end{cases}$

7. The figures below show parts of the graph of a function. Sketch the remaining parts given that the functions have domain $A = \{x \in R \mid -4 \leq x \leq 4\}$ and are

  (i) odd, (ii) even.

(a)

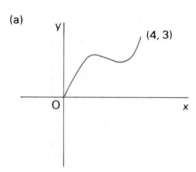

(4, 3)

(b)

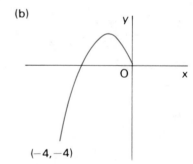

(−4, −4)

8. (a) Find $f(-x)$ for each of the following functions.

(b) Determine whether the function is even, odd, or neither.

(c) Use symmetry to sketch the graphs of those functions that are even or odd.

  (i) $f(x) = 2x^2 + 5$ (ii) $f(x) = 2x^2 - x$

  (iii) $f(x) = x^4$ (iv) $f(x) = x^3 - x$

  (v) $f(x) = x^4 - x^3$ (vi) $f(x) = \dfrac{1}{x^2}$

(vii) $f(x) = x^5$ (viii) $f(x) = |1 - x^2|$

9. Determine whether each of the following functions is even, odd, or neither.

(a) $f(x) = \dfrac{1}{x^2 + 1}$ (b) $g(x) = \dfrac{1}{x^3 + 1}$

(c) $h(x) = 2x^4 + 3x^2$ (d) $F(x) = x^5 + x^3 + x$

(e) $G(x) = \dfrac{x}{x^2 + 1}$ (f) $G(x) = \left(\dfrac{1}{x^3 + x}\right)^5$

10. If $f(x)$ is defined to be the largest integer which is less than or equal to x, draw the graph of f. Is f continuous?

C **11.** Prove that the function $f(x) = x^n$ is an even function if n is an even integer and an odd function if n is an odd integer.

1.3   THE ALGEBRA OF FUNCTIONS

Two real-valued functions f and g can be combined to form new functions $f + g$, $f - g$, fg, and $\dfrac{f}{g}$ in a manner similar to the way we add, subtract, multiply and divide real numbers.

If we define the sum $f + g$ by the equation

$$①\qquad\qquad (f + g)(x) = f(x) + g(x)$$

then the right side of equation ① makes sense if both $f(x)$ and $g(x)$ are defined. In other words x must belong to the domain of f and it must also belong to the domain of g. Therefore if the domain of f is A and the domain of g is B, then the domain of $f + g$ is $A \cap B$.

Notice that the $+$ sign on the left side of equation ① stands for the operation of addition of *functions* but the $+$ sign on the right side of equation ① stands for addition of the *real numbers* $f(x)$ and $g(x)$.

Similarly we can define the difference $f - g$ and the product fg and their domains will also be $A \cap B$. But in defining the quotient $\dfrac{f}{g}$ we must remember not to divide by 0:

$$\left(\frac{f}{g}\right)(x) = \frac{f(x)}{g(x)} \quad \text{where } x \in A \cap B \text{ and } g(x) \neq 0$$

Operations on Functions
Let the domain of f be A and the domain of g be B.

Addition	$(f + g)(x) = f(x) + g(x)$	Domain $= A \cap B$
Subtraction	$(f - g)(x) = f(x) - g(x)$	Domain $= A \cap B$
Multiplication	$(fg)(x) = f(x)g(x)$	Domain $= A \cap B$
Division	$\left(\dfrac{f}{g}\right)(x) = \dfrac{f(x)}{g(x)}$	Domain $= \{x \in A \cap B \mid g(x) \neq 0\}$

EXAMPLE 1. If $f(x) = x^2 - 5x - 1$, where $x \in A = \{x \mid -4 \leqslant x \leqslant 1\}$, and $g(x) = 2x + 3$, where $x \in B = \{x \mid -2 \leqslant x \leqslant 5\}$, find the functions $f + g$, $f - g$, fg, and $\dfrac{f}{g}$.

Solution

$$
\begin{aligned}
(f + g)(x) &= f(x) + g(x) \\
&= (x^2 - 5x - 1) + (2x + 3) \\
&= x^2 - 3x + 2
\end{aligned}
\qquad
\begin{aligned}
&\text{Domain} = A \cap B \\
&= \{x \mid -2 \leqslant x \leqslant 1\}
\end{aligned}
$$

$$(f-g)(x) = f(x) - g(x)$$
$$= (x^2 - 5x - 1) - (2x + 3)$$
$$= x^2 - 7x - 4$$

Domain $= A \cap B$
$$= \{x \mid -2 \leqslant x \leqslant 1\}$$

$$(fg)(x) = f(x)g(x)$$
$$= (x^2 - 5x - 1)(2x + 3)$$
$$= 2x^3 - 7x^2 - 17x - 3$$

Domain $= A \cap B$
$$= \{x \mid -2 \leqslant x \leqslant 1\}$$

$$\frac{f}{g}(x) = \frac{f(x)}{g(x)}$$
$$= \frac{x^2 - 5x - 1}{2x + 3}$$

Domain $= \{x \in A \cap B \mid 2x + 3 \neq 0\}$
$$= \{x \mid -2 \leqslant x \leqslant 1, x \neq -1.5\}$$

There is a method called graphical addition which enables us to draw the graph of the function $f + g$ directly from the graphs of f and g. The idea behind the method is illustrated in Figure 1-4. We take two

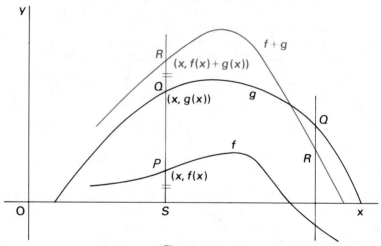

Figure 1-4

points P and Q on the same vertical line such that $P(x, f(x))$ lies on the graph of f and $Q(x, g(x))$ lies on the graph of g. Assume first that $f(x) > 0$. Construct $R(x, y)$ above Q on the same vertical line so that $RQ = PS$. Then

$$y = RS = RQ + QS$$
$$= PS + QS$$
$$= f(x) + g(x)$$

and so $R(x, f(x) + g(x))$ lies on the graph of $f + g$. (Note that if $f(x) < 0$, then R lies below Q.) In effect, we have added the y-coordinates of P and Q to get R. By repeating this procedure for several values of x we obtain enough points to sketch the graph of $f + g$.

EXAMPLE 2. *Given the graphs of f and g, draw the graph of f + g.*

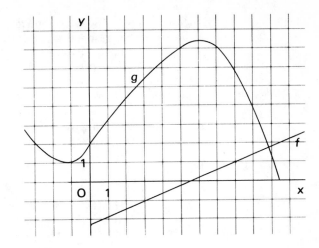

Solution

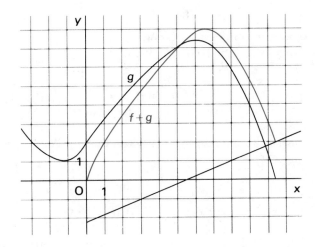

A similar procedure can be used to draw the graph of $f - g$. The graphs of fg and $\dfrac{f}{g}$ are not easily obtained from those of f and g. If formulas are given for f and g, we just compute fg and $\dfrac{f}{g}$ and draw their graphs in the usual way.

EXERCISE 1-3

A 1. Given $f(x) = x^2 + 3x + 1$ and $g(x) = x$, both defined on R.

(a) State

(i) $(f+g)(x)$ (ii) $(f-g)(x)$ (iii) $(g-f)(x)$ (iv) $(fg)(x)$

(v) $\left(\dfrac{f}{g}\right)(x)$

(b) State the domains of the functions in (a).

functions   17

2. For each of the following pairs of functions f and g defined on A and B respectively, state

(a) $(f+g)(x)$ (b) $(f-g)(x)$ (c) the domain of $f+g$

(i) $f(x) = x+2$, $A = R$, $g(x) = x^3 - 1$, $B = \{x \mid 0 \leqslant x \leqslant 1\}$

(ii) $f(x) = 8x^7$, $A = \{x \mid 0 \leqslant x \leqslant 5\}$, $g(x) = x^7 - x$, $B = \{x \mid -4 \leqslant x \leqslant 4\}$

(iii) $f(x) = x^3 - x^2 + 2x - 1$, $A = \{x \mid 1 < x < 4\}$, $g(x) = x^3 + 1$,
    $B = \{x \mid 0 < x < 2\}$

3. For each of the following pairs of functions f and g defined on A and B respectively, state

(a) $(fg)(x)$ (b) the domain of fg

(c) $\left(\dfrac{f}{g}\right)(x)$ (d) the domain of $\dfrac{f}{g}$

(i) $f(x) = x+1$, $A = R$, $g(x) = x-1$, $B = R$

(ii) $f(x) = x$, $A = \{x \mid -3 < x < 3\}$, $g(x) = x^2 - 4$, $B = \{x \mid -5 < x < 5\}$

(iii) $f(x) = \sqrt{x+1}$, $A = \{x \mid x \geqslant -1\}$, $g(x) = \sqrt{x}$, $B = \{x \mid x \geqslant 0\}$

B **4.** For each of the following pairs of functions f and g defined on A and B respectively, find

(a) $f+g$ (b) $f-g$ (c) $g-f$ (d) fg (e) $\dfrac{f}{g}$

and the domains of these functions.

(i) $f(x) = x^2 + 2$, $A = R$, $g(x) = x^2 - 3x + 2$, $B = R$

(ii) $f(x) = x^3 - 1$, $A = R$, $g(x) = x^2 + 4$, $B = \{x \mid x < 87\}$

(iii) $f(x) = x^4 + x^2 + 1$, $A = R$, $g(x) = x^4$, $B = R$

(iv) $f(x) = \sqrt{x^2 - 1}$, $A = \{x \mid |x| \geqslant 1\}$, $g(x) = \sqrt{4 - x^2}$, $B = \{x \mid |x| \leqslant 2\}$

(v) $f(x) = x^4 - 3x^3 + x^2 - 2x - 8$, $A = R$, $g(x) = x^2 - 2x - 8$,
    $B = \{x \mid -2 \leqslant x \leqslant 4\}$

5. Copy each of the following graphs and use graphical addition to sketch the graph of $f + g$.

(a)

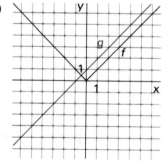

(b)

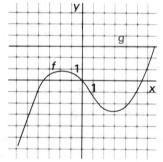

(c)

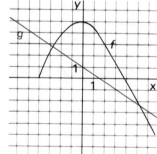

(d)

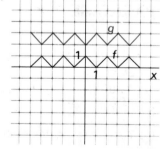

(e)
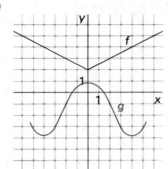

(f)
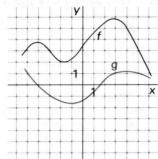

6. Copy each of the graphs in question 5 and sketch the graph of $f - g$.

7. Given the following functions with the indicated domains,
(a) graph f and g on the same axes;
(b) use graphical addition to sketch the graph of $f + g$;
(c) give a formula for $f + g$;
(d) state the domain of $f + g$.
  (i) $f(x) = 2x$, $g(x) = 1 - x$, $x \in R$
 (ii) $f(x) = x^2$, $g(x) = 2x$, $x \in R$
(iii) $f(x) = x^2$ for $-2 \leqslant x \leqslant 2$, $g(x) = 1$ for $x \geqslant 0$
(iv) $f(x) = x$ for $x \in R$, $g(x) = \sqrt{x}$ for $x \geqslant 0$
 (v) $f(x) = x^3$, $g(x) = -x$, $x \in R$
(vi) $f(x) = \sqrt{16 - x^2}$ for $|x| \leqslant 4$, $g(x) = x$ for $x \in R$.

8. Given $f(x) = x^2$ and $g(x) = 2$, $-2 \leqslant x \leqslant 2$.
(a) Sketch the graphs of f and g on the same axes.
(b) Sketch the graph of $f + g$.
(c) Sketch the graph of gf.
(d) How are the graphs of $f + g$ and gf related to the graph of f?

9. If $f(x) = x^2 - 4$ and $g(x) = x$, find the values of x for which
$(f + g) \times (x) = 2$.

10. Let $f(x) = \dfrac{1}{x^2 - 4}$ and $g(x) = \dfrac{2x}{x - 2}$.
(a) What are the domains of the functions f, g, $f + g$?
(b) For what value of x is $(f + g)(x) = 2$?

11. If $f(x) = \sin x$, $0 \leqslant x \leqslant 2\pi$,

$$g(x) = \tan x, -\frac{\pi}{2} < x < \frac{\pi}{2},$$

find

(a) $f + g$,   (b) $f - g$,   (c) fg,   (d) $\dfrac{f}{g}$,

and state the domains of these functions.
Sketch the graphs of (a) and (b).

12. Suppose that f and g are both increasing functions.
(a) Show that $f + g$ is an increasing function.
(b) Is $f - g$ necessarily an increasing function?
(c) Is fg necessarily an increasing function? What if it is known that
$f(x) > 0$ and $g(x) > 0$?

1.4 COMPOSITION OF FUNCTIONS

In the last section we combined functions by the operations of arithmetic, namely addition, subtraction, multiplication, and division. There is another important way of combining two functions which is called composition.

Suppose that the domain of g is A, the domain of f is B, and the range of g is contained in B. If $x \in A$, then $g(x) \in B$ and so it makes sense to consider $f(g(x))$. The result is a new function $h(x) = f(g(x))$ obtained by substituting g into f. It is called the composition (or composite) of f and g and is denoted by $h = f \circ g$.

If $g: A \to B$ and $f: B \to C$ then the composition (or composite) of f and g is the function

$$f \circ g : A \to C$$

defined by

$$(f \circ g)(x) = f(g(x)).$$

The best way to think of composition is in terms of mapping diagrams:

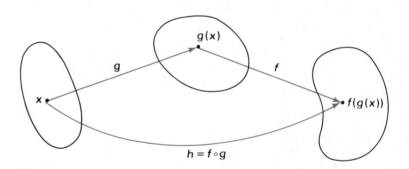

or, more briefly,

$$f \circ g : A \xrightarrow{g} B \xrightarrow{f} C$$

Note: The notation $f \circ g$ means that the map g is performed first and then f is performed second.

EXAMPLE 1. *If f and g are given by the following arrow diagrams, draw an arrow diagram for f∘g.*

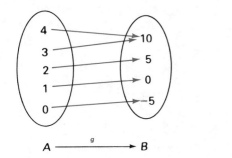
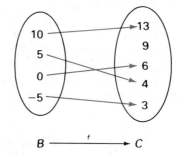

Solution
Combining the two diagrams we get

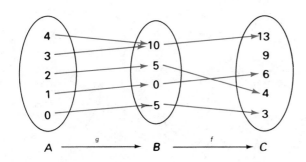

which gives

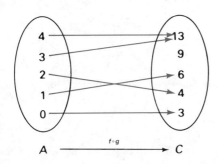

EXAMPLE 2. *If $f(x) = 2x^2 - x$ and $g(x) = 4x + 1$, find the functions $f \circ g$ and $g \circ f$.*

Solution

$$(f \circ g)(x) = f(g(x))$$
$$= f(4x + 1)$$
$$= 2(4x + 1)^2 - (4x + 1)$$
$$= 2(16x^2 + 8x + 1) - 4x - 1$$
$$= 32x^2 + 12x + 1$$

$$(g \circ f)(x) = g(f(x))$$
$$= g(2x^2 - x)$$
$$= 4(2x^2 - x) + 1$$
$$= 8x^2 - 4x + 1$$

In Example 2, notice that

$$f \circ g \neq g \circ f.$$

In the preceding section order was unimportant because $f + g = g + f$ and $fg = gf$. But in combining f and g by composition to get $f \circ g$, the order *is* important.

EXERCISE 1-4

A 1. Given f and g as defined by the following arrow diagrams.

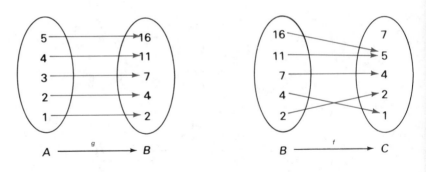

State

(a) $f(g(1))$ (b) $f(g(4))$ (c) $f(g(3))$ (d) $f(g(5))$

(e) $g(f(2))$ (f) $g(f(16))$ (g) $f(g(2))$ (h) $g(f(4))$

2. Let $m(x) =$ mother of x $f(x) =$ father of x

          $s(x) =$ oldest son of x $d(x) =$ oldest daughter of x

          $h(x) =$ husband of x $w(x) =$ wife of x

The family tree of the O'Connor family is as follows.

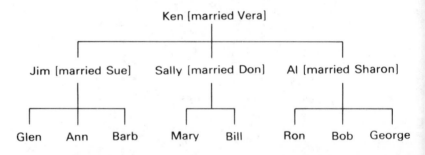

State

(a) $f(m(\text{Bill}))$

(b) $w(f(\text{Jim}))$

(c) $f(f(\text{George}))$

(d) $d(h(\text{Vera}))$

(e) $h(d(\text{Vera}))$

(f) $d(m(\text{Barb}))$

(g) $s(d(\text{Ken}))$

(h) $d(s(\text{Ken}))$

(i) $s(f(\text{Sally}))$

(j) $s(f(\text{Glen}))$

(k) $m(m(\text{Mary}))$

(l) $w(h(\text{Sue}))$

(m) $f(h(\text{Sharon}))$

(n) $d(d(\text{Ken}))$

(o) $s(s(\text{Ken}))$

B 3. If f and g are defined by the following arrow diagrams, then draw arrow diagrams for $f \circ g$ and $g \circ f$.

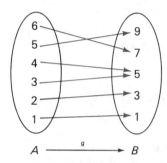 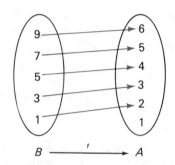

4. In each of the following cases, find $f \circ g$, $g \circ f$, $f \circ f$, and $g \circ g$.

(a) $f(x) = 5x + 6$ $\qquad g(x) = 8x - 9$

(b) $f(x) = 2x - 1$ $\qquad g(x) = x^3$

(c) $f(x) = 7x - 6$ $\qquad g(x) = \frac{1}{7}x + \frac{6}{7}$

(d) $f(x) = 17$ $\qquad g(x) = x^2 - 9$

(e) $f(x) = \dfrac{1}{x}$ $\qquad g(x) = \dfrac{1}{x^2}$

(f) $f(x) = x^2 - x + 3$ $\qquad g(x) = 1 - x$

(g) $f(x) = 3x - 4$ $\qquad g(x) = \dfrac{1}{x^2 + 1}$

(h) $f(x) = |x|$ $\qquad g(x) = x^2$

(i) $f(x) = \sqrt{x}$ $\qquad g(x) = x^2 + 1$

(j) $f(x) = \dfrac{x^2 + 2}{x^2 + 1}$ $\qquad g(x) = \dfrac{x^2 + 1}{x^2 + 2}$

Find unequal rational numbers other than 2 and 4 such that

$$a^b = b^a$$

5. Let $f(x) = x^2 + 2$, $g(x) = \sqrt{1 - x^2}$.

(a) Find the domain and range of f and g.

(b) Are the functions $g \circ f$ and $f \circ g$ defined? Explain.

6. If $g(x) = |x|$, then $(g \circ f)(x) = g(f(x)) = |f(x)|$.

Sketch the graphs of g, f, and $g \circ f = |f|$ for the following functions.

(a) $f(x) = x - 3$ $\qquad$ (b) $f(x) = 1 - 2x$ $\qquad$ (c) $f(x) = \dfrac{1}{x}$

(d) $f(x) = 4 - x^2$ $\qquad$ (e) $f(x) = x^3$

7. Let $f(x) = x + 4$ and $h(x) = 4x - 1$. Find a function g such that $f \circ g = h$.

8. Let $f(x) = 3x + 5$ and $h(x) = 3x^2 + 3x + 2$. Find a function g such that $f \circ g = h$.

C 9. Let $f(x) = x + 4$ and $h(x) = 4x - 1$. Find a function g such that $g \circ f = h$.

10. (a) Prove that the associative law

$$f \circ (g \circ h) = (f \circ g) \circ h$$

holds, assuming that all the compositions are defined.

(b) If $f(x) = x + \dfrac{1}{x}$, find $f \circ f$ and $f \circ f \circ f$.

11. In each of the following cases find $f \circ g$, $g \circ f$, $f \circ f$, and $g \circ g$.
(a) $f(x) = \sin x$ $g(x) = 5x$
(b) $f(x) = x^2 + 3$ $g(x) = \cos x$

12. Let $f(x) = \sqrt{x^2 - 2}$ and $g(x) = \sin x$.
(a) Find the domain and range of f and g.
(b) Are the functions $g \circ f$ and $f \circ g$ defined? Explain.

1.5 TRANSFORMED FUNCTIONS

In this section we shall see how the use of transformations, such as translations and reflections, can reduce the amount of work in graphing functions.

VERTICAL AND HORIZONTAL SHIFTS

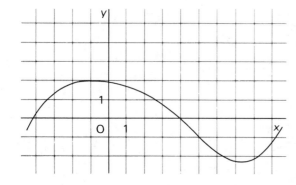

EXAMPLE 1. *Given the graph of $y = f(x)$, use graphical addition to find the graphs of*
(a) $y = f(x) + 3$
(b) $y = f(x) + 5$
(c) $y = f(x) - 2$

Solution
(a) In graphing $y = f(x) + 3$ we just apply graphical addition to find the sum $f + g$ where $g(x) = 3$, i.e., g is a constant function.

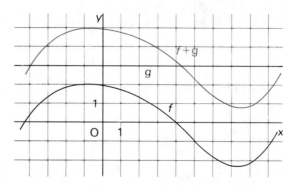

(b) and (c) Similarly by taking $g(x) = 5$ and then $g(x) = -2$, we

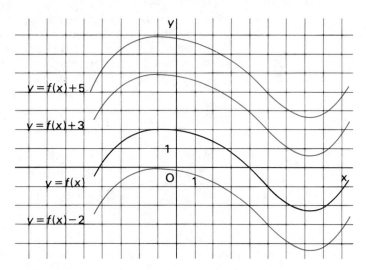

$y = f(x) + 5$

$y = f(x) + 3$

$y = f(x)$

$y = f(x) - 2$

obtain the graphs of $y = f(x) + 5$ and $y = f(x) - 2$. From Example 1 we see that if c is a constant, then to get the graph of $y = f(x) + c$ we just shift the graph of $y = f(x)$ by c units in a vertical direction.

> Let $c > 0$.
> (a) The graph of $y = f(x) + c$ is the graph of $y = f(x)$ translated *upward* by c units.
> (b) The graph of $y = f(x) - c$ is the graph of $y = f(x)$ translated *downward* by c units.

EXAMPLE 2. (a) *Given the graph of $y = f(x)$, compare the graph of $y = h(x)$, where $h(x) = f(x - 6)$, with the graph of $y = f(x)$.* (b) *Draw the graph of $y = f(x + 9)$.*

Note $h(x) = (f \circ g)(x)$ where $g(x) = x - 6$

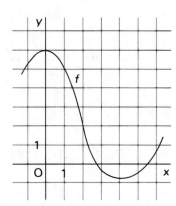

f

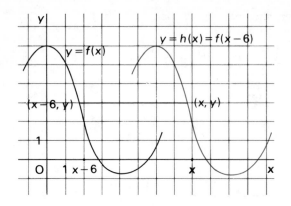

(a) We have $h(x) = f(x-6)$, i.e., the value of h at x is the same as the value of f at $x-6$. In other words the value of h at a point is the same as the value of f, 6 units to the left of the point. So the graph of h is just the graph of f shifted 6 units to the right.

(b) Similar reasoning shows that the graph of $y = f(x+9)$ is the graph of $y = f(x)$ shifted 9 units to the left.

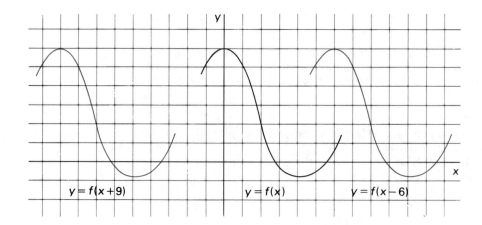

Let $c > 0$.
(a) The graph of $y = f(x+c)$ is the graph of $y = f(x)$ translated to the *left* by c units.
(b) The graph of $y = f(x-c)$ is the graph of $y = f(x)$ translated to the *right* by c units.

Let us summarize our results on translating the graphs of functions as follows.

Let $c > 0$. The graph of

$$\left.\begin{array}{l} y = f(x) + c \\ y = f(x) - c \\ y = f(x+c) \\ y = f(x-c) \end{array}\right\} \text{ is the graph of } y = f(x) \text{ shifted } c \text{ units } \left\{\begin{array}{l} \text{upward} \\ \text{downward} \\ \text{to the left} \\ \text{to the right.} \end{array}\right.$$

EXAMPLE 3. *Given the graph of* $y = f(x)$, *draw the graphs of the following functions.*

(a) $y = 2f(x)$ (b) $y = \frac{1}{2}f(x)$
(c) $y = -f(x)$ (d) $y = -2f(x)$
(e) $y = -\frac{1}{2}f(x)$

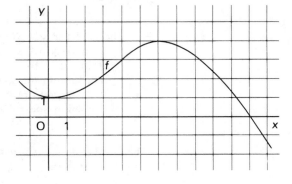

Solution
Notice that in this example we are really finding the product of two functions f and g where g is a constant function. In (a) $g(x) = 2$ and $y = (fg)(x) = f(x)g(x) = 2f(x)$. In general, to obtain the graph of $y = cf(x)$ from the graph of $y = f(x)$ we replace each point (x, y) by (x, cy), i.e., we stretch by a factor of c in the y-direction.

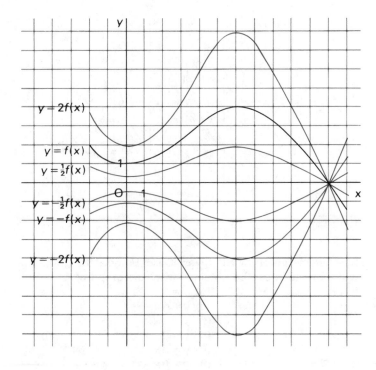

The graph of $y = -f(x)$ is obtained from the graph of $y = f(x)$ by reflection in the x-axis because each point (x, y) is replaced by the point $(x, -y)$.

In general if c is any constant and f is a given function, then the function cf defined by $(cf)(x) = cf(x)$ can be graphed using the following rules.

> The graph of $y = cf(x)$ is obtained from the graph of $y = f(x)$ by
>
> | | |
> |---|---|
> | stretching in the y-direction | if $c > 1$ |
> | shrinking in the y-direction | if $0 < c < 1$ |
> | reflection in the x-axis | if $c = -1$ |
> | shrinking and reflecting in the x-axis | if $-1 < c < 0$ |
> | stretching and reflecting in the x-axis | if $c < -1$ |

EXAMPLE 4. *Use the transformations of this section to draw the graph of* $y = 3(x+4)^2 + 2$.

Solution

There are four steps.

① We first draw the graph of $y = x^2$.
② We shift it 4 units to the left to get the graph of $y = (x+4)^2$.
③ We stretch it vertically by a factor of 3 to get the graph of $y = 3(x+4)^2$.
④ We shift it 2 units upward to get the graph of $y = 3(x+4)^2 + 2$.

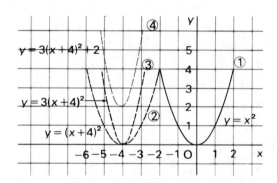

EXERCISE 1-5

A 1. Suppose that the graph of f is given. Describe how the graphs of the following functions can be obtained from the graph of f.

(a) $y = f(x) + 6$ (b) $y = f(x+6)$

(c) $y = f(x) - 8$ (d) $y = f(x-8)$

(e) $y = 3f(x)$ (f) $y = -f(x)$

(g) $y = -5f(x)$ (h) $y = \frac{1}{5}f(x)$

(i) $y = -\frac{1}{3}f(x)$ (j) $y = f(x-2)$

(k) $y = f(x) + 3$ (l) $y = f(x+1)$

(m) $y = 2f(x)$ (n) $y = 2f(x) + 1$

(o) $y = f(x+1)$ (p) $y = 2f(x+1)$

(q) $y = -4f(x)$ (r) $y = -4f(x) - 3$

(s) $y = \frac{1}{2}f(x)$ (t) $y = \frac{1}{2}f(x) - 1$

B 2. The graphs of three functions $y = f(x)$ are given

(i)

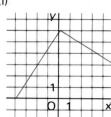

(ii)

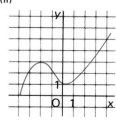

(iii)

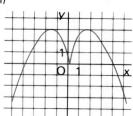

In each case draw the graphs of the following functions.
(a) $y = f(x) - 4$ (b) $y = f(x) + 2$
(c) $y = 3f(x)$ (d) $y = 3f(x) - 2$
(e) $y = \frac{1}{3}f(x)$ (f) $y = \frac{1}{3}f(x) + 5$
(g) $y = f(x - 6)$ (h) $y = f(x + 4)$

3. The graphs of three functions $y = f(x)$ are given.

(i)

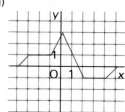

(ii)

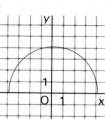

(iii)

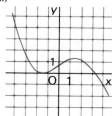

In each case draw the graphs of the following functions.
(a) $y = f(x - 6)$ (b) $y = f(x) - 6$
(c) $y = f(x - 6) - 6$ (d) $y = -f(x)$
(e) $y = 2f(x)$ (f) $y = -2f(x - 6)$
(g) $y = -2f(x - 6) - 6$ (h) $y = 3f(x + 8) + 4$

4. Use transformations to graph the following functions starting from the graph of $y = x^2$.
(a) $y = 3x^2 - 1$ (b) $y = -2x^2$
(c) $y = -\frac{1}{2}(x - 3)^2$ (d) $y = -2(x + 3)^2 + 4$

5. Sketch the graph of the function $f(x) = (x - 10^{10})^2 + 1$.
[*Hint*: Sketch only the *interesting* part of the graph.]

6. Use transformations to graph the following functions starting from the graph of $y = x^3$.
(a) $y = -x^3$ (b) $y = x^3 - 1$
(c) $y = \frac{1}{3}x^3$ (d) $y = (x + 5)^3$

7. Use transformations to graph the following functions starting from the graph of $y = |x|$.
(a) $y = |x - 4|$ (b) $y = -|x| + 1$
(c) $y = \frac{1}{2}|x + 2|$ (d) $y = |x - 3| - 5$

8. Use transformations to graph the following functions starting from the graph of $y = \dfrac{1}{x}$

(a) $y = \dfrac{1}{x-1}$

(b) $y = \dfrac{1}{x} - 1$

(c) $y = \dfrac{2}{x} + 3$

(d) $y = -\dfrac{1}{x+2}$

9. The graph of f is given:

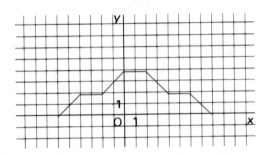

(a) If $h(x) = f(2x)$, find $h(-3)$, $h(-2)$, $h(-1)$, $h(0)$, $h(1)$, $h(2)$, $h(3)$, $h(4)$.

(b) Draw the graph of $y = f(2x)$.

(c) Draw the graph of $y = f(\tfrac{1}{2}x)$.

10. If $g(x) = cx$, where c is constant, and $h = f \circ g$, then $h(x) = f(g(x)) = f(cx)$. As question 9 illustrates, the graph of $y = f(cx)$ is obtained from the graph of $y = f(x)$ by shrinking in the x-direction if $c > 1$ and by stretching in the x-direction if $0 < c < 1$. The graphs of two functions f are given:

(i)

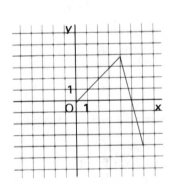

(ii)

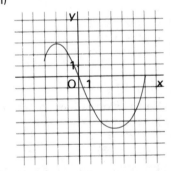

In each case draw the graphs of the following functions.

(a) $y = f(2x)$ (b) $y = f(3x)$ (c) $y = f(\tfrac{1}{2}x)$ (d) $y = f(\tfrac{1}{3}x)$

11. (a) How is the graph of $y = f(-x)$ related to the graph of $y = f(x)$? Draw the graph of $y = f(-x)$ for the two functions in question 10.

(b) How is the graph of $y = f(cx)$, $c < 0$, related to the graph of $y = f(x)$? For each of the functions in question 10 draw the graphs of

(i) $y = f(-2x)$ (ii) $y = f(-\tfrac{1}{2}x)$.

12. In each of the following cases describe how the graph of the given function can be obtained from the graph of *f*.

(a) $y = 3f(x) + 2$ (b) $y = 1 - f(x)$

(c) $y = f(x + 5)$ (d) $y = f(5x)$

(e) $y = 3f(5x)$ (f) $y = f\left(\dfrac{x}{4}\right) - 1$

(g) $y = -f(x)$ (h) $y = f(-x)$

(i) $y = -f(-x)$ (j) $y = \frac{1}{2}f(2x) + 3$

C 13. Describe how the graph of $y = f(cx + d)$ is related to the graph of $y = f(x)$. Consider the following cases separately.

(a) $c > 1, d > 0$ (b) $c > 1, d < 0$

(c) $0 < c < 1, d > 0$ (d) $0 < c < 1, d < 0$

$$\left[\text{Hint: If } g(x) = f(cx) \text{ and } h(x) = g\left(x + \frac{d}{c}\right), \text{ then} \right.$$

$$\left. h(x) = f\left(c\left(x + \frac{d}{c}\right)\right) = f(cx + d). \right]$$

Using six 2's we can write 13 as follows.

$$2^2 - 2 + \frac{22}{2} = 13$$

Write 1000 using eight 8's.

1.6 ONE-TO-ONE FUNCTIONS AND THEIR INVERSES

Compare the functions *f* and *g* whose arrow diagrams are given in Figure 1-5. The most important difference between *f* and *g* is that *f*

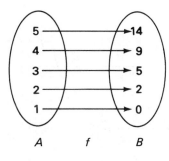 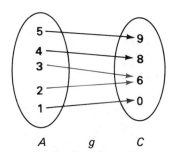

Figure 1-5

maps the elements of *A* into *different* elements of *B* (i.e., any two elements of the domain have different images) whereas *g* maps two elements of *A* into the *same* element of *C* (i.e., there are two elements of *A* with the same image). In symbols

$$g(2) = g(3)$$

but

$$f(x_1) \neq f(x_2) \quad \text{whenever} \quad x_1 \neq x_2.$$

Functions which have this same property as *f* are called one-to-one.

> A function f with domain A and range B is called a one-to-one (or 1-1) function if no two elements of A have the same image, i.e., every element of B is the image of only one element of A. In symbols
>
> $$f(x_1) \neq f(x_2) \quad \text{whenever} \quad x_1 \neq x_2.$$

EXAMPLE 1. *Which of the following functions are 1-1?*
(a) $f(x) = x^2$ (b) $g(x) = x^3$

Solution
(a) $f(x) = x^2$ is not 1-1 because, for example,

$$f(1) = 1^2 = 1$$

and $$f(-1) = (-1)^2 = 1$$

Thus 1 and -1 have the same image.
(b) If $x_1 \neq x_2$, then $x_1^3 \neq x_2^3$

$$g(x_1) \neq g(x_2)$$

$$\therefore \quad g \text{ is 1-1}$$

This example can also be done graphically:

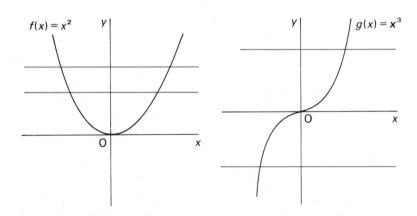

Any horizontal line intersects the graph of g only once. This means that g takes on each value in its range only once, so it is 1-1. But you can see that there are horizontal lines that intersect the graph of f more than once. This means that f takes on the same value at two different points, so it is not 1-1.

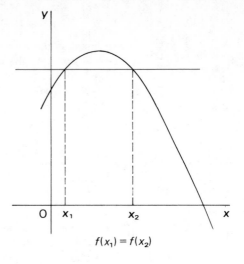

$$f(x_1) = f(x_2)$$

In Figure 1-6 each horizontal line intersects the graphs of f and h only once. However the indicated horizontal line intersects the graph of g more than once. Therefore f and h are 1-1 functions but g is not 1-1. Notice that functions which are either increasing or decreasing must be one-to-one.

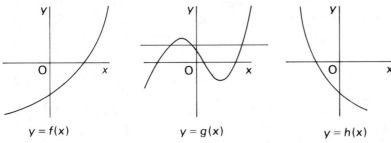

$$y = f(x) \qquad y = g(x) \qquad y = h(x)$$

Figure 1-6

INVERSE FUNCTIONS

Figure 1-7 shows the arrow diagram for a 1-1 function f. If we reverse the direction of the arrows we get a new function g whose arrow diagram is given in Figure 1-8.

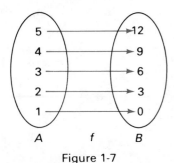

Figure 1-7

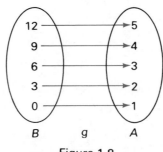

Figure 1-8

f^{-1} does *not* mean $\frac{1}{f}$.

g is called the *inverse function* of f and is usually denoted by f^{-1}. (If f were not 1-1, then by reversing the arrows we would not get a function, but f^{-1} could be defined as a relation.)

Notice that

$$f(1) = 0 \quad \text{and} \quad g(0) = 1$$
$$f(2) = 3 \quad \text{and} \quad g(3) = 2$$
$$f(3) = 6 \quad \text{and} \quad g(6) = 3$$

In general

$$f(x) = y \quad \text{and} \quad g(y) = x.$$

If f maps x into y, then g maps y back into x. In other words the inverse function f^{-1} undoes what f does.

Notice also that

$$\text{domain of } f = A = \text{range of } g$$
$$\text{range of } f = B = \text{domain of } g$$

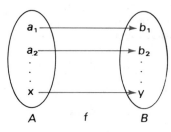

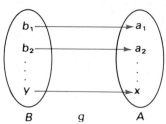

If f is a 1-1 function with domain A and range B, then its inverse function $g = f^{-1}$ has domain B and range A and is defined by

$$g(y) = x \quad \text{if} \quad f(x) = y$$

for any $y \in B$.

EXAMPLE 2. *Find the inverse function of* $f(x) = 4x - 3$.

Solution
Let $g = f^{-1}$.

$$g(y) = x \iff f(x) = y$$
$$4x - 3 = y$$
$$4x = y + 3$$
$$x = \frac{y + 3}{4}$$

But

$$x = g(y)$$
$$g(y) = \frac{y + 3}{4}$$

Usually we use x as the independent variable. So replacing y by x, we have

$$g(x) = \frac{x+3}{4}$$

or

$$f^{-1}(x) = \frac{x+3}{4}$$

$f(x) = 4x - 3$

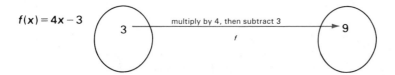

$f^{-1}(x) = \dfrac{x+3}{4}$

In Example 2 if we use the notation $y = 4x - 3$ for the original function and then solve for x, we get $x = \dfrac{y+3}{4}$. If we now interchange x and y we have $y = \dfrac{x+3}{4}$ which is the defining equation of the inverse function.

> The defining equation for f^{-1} is found by solving the equation $y = f(x)$ for x and then interchanging x and y.

EXAMPLE 3. *Find the inverse of the function* $y = \dfrac{1}{x-1}$.

Solution I
First solve the equation for x.

$$y = \frac{1}{x-1}$$

$$x - 1 = \frac{1}{y}$$

$$x = 1 + \frac{1}{y}$$

Now interchange x and y.

$y = 1 + \dfrac{1}{x}$ is the defining equation of the inverse.

Solution II
Interchange x and y.

$$x = \frac{1}{y-1}$$

Then solve for y.

$$y - 1 = \frac{1}{x}$$

$$y = 1 + \frac{1}{x}$$

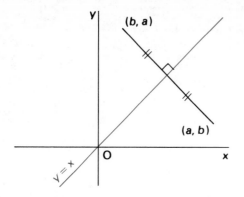

The principle of interchanging x and y to find the inverse function also gives us the method for obtaining the graph of f^{-1} from the graph of f. Recall that the transformation

$$(x, y) \rightarrow (y, x)$$

which interchanges the coordinates of a point is just reflection in the line $y = x$. So if we reflect the graph of f in the line $y = x$, we get the graph of f^{-1}.

> The graph of f^{-1} is the reflection of the graph of f in the line $y = x$.

EXAMPLE 4. Let $f(x) = x^2 + 1$, $x \geqslant 0$.
(a) *Sketch the graph of f^{-1}.*
(b) *Find an expression for f^{-1}.*

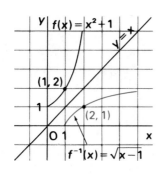

Solution
(a) We know what the graph of $y = x^2 + 1 (x \geqslant 0)$ looks like.
So we need only draw its reflection in the line $y = x$.
(b) Solve $y = x^2 + 1$ for x.

$$x^2 = y - 1$$
$$x = \pm\sqrt{y - 1}$$
$$x = \sqrt{y - 1} \text{ since } x \geqslant 0.$$

Interchange x and y.

$$y = \sqrt{x - 1}$$
$$\therefore \quad f^{-1}(x) = \sqrt{x - 1}$$

EXERCISE 1-6

A 1. Which of the functions represented by the following arrow diagrams are 1-1?

(a)

(b)

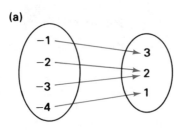
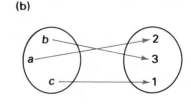

(c)

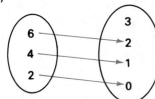

(d)

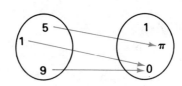

2. Which of the functions whose graphs are given are one-to-one functions?

(a)

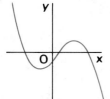

(b)

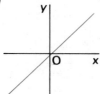

(c)

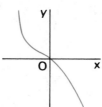

(d)

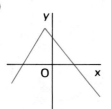

(e)

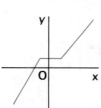

(f)

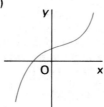

B 3. Which of the following functions are 1-1?

(a) $f(x) = x + 1$ (b) $g(x) = |x|$ (c) $y = 3 - 2x$

(d) $h(x) = \dfrac{1}{x}$ (e) $F(x) = \dfrac{1}{x^2}$ (f) $y = 1 - x^2$

(g) $f(t) = -t^3$ (h) $G(t) = t^4$ (i) $y = \sqrt{x}$

(j) $f(x) = \dfrac{1}{x^2}, x \leqslant 0$ (k) $g(x) = 1 - x^2, x \geqslant 6$

4. Draw arrow diagrams for the inverse of those functions in question 1 which are 1-1.

5. In each of the following cases find f^{-1} and state the domain and range of f^{-1}.

(a) $f(x) = 2 - 5x$ (b) $f(x) = 13x + 6$

(c) $f(x) = x^2, x \geqslant 0$ (d) $f(x) = \dfrac{1}{x}$

(e) $f(x) = x^3$ (f) $f(x) = 3x - 2, o \leqslant x \leqslant 4$

6. Find the inverses of the following functions.

(a) $y = \frac{1}{2}(x - 7)$ (b) $y = \frac{1}{6}(36 - x)$

(c) $y = 5x^3 - 6$ (d) $y = \sqrt{x}$

(e) $y = \sqrt{x - 3}$

(f) $y = 1 + \dfrac{1}{x}$

(g) $y = \dfrac{1}{1 + x}$

(h) $y = \dfrac{1 - x}{1 + x}$

(i) $y = \dfrac{4x - 1}{3x + 2}$

(j) $y = \dfrac{\pi - 3x}{x}$

(k) $y = x^4,\ x \geqslant 0$

(l) $y = 3(x - 1)^2,\ x \geqslant 1$

(m) $y = \sqrt{x^2 + 9},\ x \geqslant 0$

(n) $y = \sqrt{25 - x^2},\ x \geqslant 0$

7. In each of the following cases find f^{-1} and then calculate $f \circ f^{-1}$ and $f^{-1} \circ f$.

(a) $f(x) = 5x - 8$

(b) $f(x) = \sqrt{x}$

(c) $f(x) = \dfrac{1}{2x + 3}$

8. Copy the following graphs of functions and use them to draw the graphs of their inverse functions.

(a)

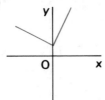

(b)

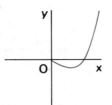

(c)

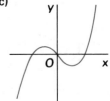

9. For each of the following functions,
   (i) draw the graph of f,
   (ii) use it to draw the graph of f^{-1},
   (iii) find the expression for $f^{-1}(x)$.

(a) $f(x) = 2x + 1$

(b) $f(x) = x^2 + 2,\ x \geqslant 0$

(c) $f(x) = x^3$

(d) $f(x) = -\dfrac{1}{x}$

REVIEW EXERCISE

A 1. If $f(x) = x^2 - 2$ and $g(x) = 2(x - 3)$, state

(a) $f(3)$ (b) $g(3)$ (c) $f(-4)$ (d) $g(8)$
(e) $f(1)$ (f) $f(10)$ (g) $g(-2)$ (h) $g(0)$
(i) $g(-3)$ (j) $f(0)$ (k) $f(-8)$ (l) $f(\pi)$

2. State the domain and range of the functions represented by the following arrow diagrams. Which of them map A onto B? Which of them are 1-1?

(a)

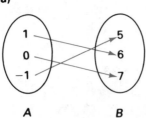

(b)

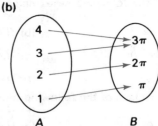

(c)

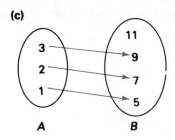

A   B

(d)

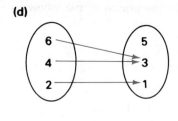

3. Which of the following figures are graphs of functions? Which of the functions are 1-1?

(a)

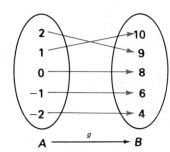

(b)

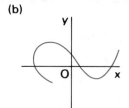

(c)

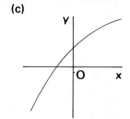

(d)

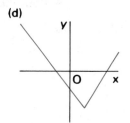

4. The functions f and g are defined by the following arrow diagrams.

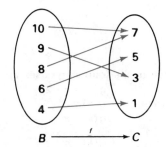

A ——g——→ B   B ——f——→ C

State

(a) $f(g(-1))$ (b) $f(g(2))$ (c) $f(g(1))$ (d) $f(g(0))$
(e) $g^{-1}(9)$ (f) $g^{-1}(4)$ (g) $g^{-1}(10)$ (h) $g(f(4))$

5. In each of the following cases describe how the graph of the given function can be obtained from the graph of f.

(a) $y = f(x) - 4$ (b) $y = f(x-4)$
(c) $y = 3f(x)$ (d) $y = f(3x)$
(e) $y = -f(x)$ (f) $y = 2f(x+1)$
(g) $y = f(x-1) + 2$ (h) $y = \frac{1}{3}f(x) - 5$

B 6. If $f(x) = x^3 + 3x^2 - 2$ and $g(x) = \dfrac{x^2+1}{x+1}$, find

(a) $f(3)$ (b) $g(3)$ (c) $f(-0.1)$ (d) $g(0)$
(e) $f(1.5)$ (f) $g(1.5)$ (g) $f(t-1)$ (h) $g(t-1)$

7. Draw the graphs of the following functions. Use transformations where appropriate.

(a) $f(x) = 5 - 4x$

(b) $f(t) = (t-1)^2 + 3$

(c) $y = \sqrt{x}$

(d) $y = \sqrt{x-3}$

(e) $f(x) = x^4$

(f) $g(x) = (x+2)^4 - 1$

(g) $y = 3|x-1|$

(h) $y = \dfrac{1}{x+3}$

(i) $y = \dfrac{1}{x^2}$

(j) $y = 1 - \dfrac{1}{x^2}$

8. Determine whether each of the following functions is even, odd, or neither.

(a) $f(x) = 2x^3 + x^5$

(b) $g(t) = t^2 + t^6$

(c) $y = x^3 + 1$

(d) $y = \dfrac{2}{x^2 + 1}$

9. Copy the following graphs and use graphical addition to sketch the graph of $f + g$.

(a)

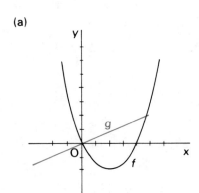

(b)

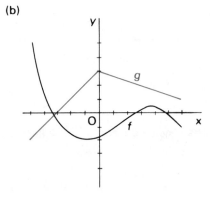

10. In each of the following cases find $f \circ g$, $g \circ f$, $f \circ f$, and $g \circ g$.

(a) $f(x) = x^2$ $g(x) = x - 2$

(b) $f(x) = x^2 + 1$ $g(x) = x^2 - 1$

(c) $f(x) = \sqrt{x}$ $g(x) = x^2$

(d) $f(x) = \dfrac{1}{x+1}$ $g(x) = \dfrac{x}{x-1}$

11. Which of the following functions are 1-1? Find the inverse of each function that is 1-1.

(a) $y = 2x + 9$

(b) $y = (x+2)^2 + 3$

(c) $y = \sqrt{x+1}$

(d) $y = 1 - x^3$

(e) $y = 1 - x^4$

(f) $y = (x+2)^2$, $x \geqslant -2$

(g) $y = \dfrac{x+5}{x-5}$

(h) $y = \dfrac{1}{x^2}$

C 12. Graph the function f defined by

$$f(x) = \begin{cases} 6(x+2) & \text{if} \quad -4 \leqslant x < -2 \\ 1 - (x+1)^2 & \text{if} \quad -2 \leqslant x < 0 \\ 1 - (x-1)^2 & \text{if} \quad 0 \leqslant x < 2 \\ 6(x-2) & \text{if} \quad 2 \leqslant x \leqslant 4 \end{cases}$$

REVIEW AND PREVIEW TO CHAPTER 2

EXERCISE 1   EQUATIONS OF LINES

Slope point form	$y - y_1 = m(x - x_1)$
Slope y-intercept form	$y = mx + b$
Slope x-intercept form	$y = m(x - a)$
Two intercept form	$\dfrac{x}{a} + \dfrac{y}{b} = 1$
Slope $m = \dfrac{y_2 - y_1}{x_2 - x_1}$	$\begin{cases} \text{Parallel lines } m_1 = m_2 \\ \text{Perpendicular lines } m_1 m_2 = -1 \end{cases}$

1. Find the equation of the line
(a) with slope -3, passing through $(2, -5)$.
(b) with slope 2 and x-intercept 3.
(c) with slope -3 and y-intercept 1.
(d) with x-intercept 5 and y-intercept -2.

2. Find the slope and y-intercept of each of the following lines.
(a) $y = 2x - 3$ (b) $2x + y = 1$ (c) $2x - 3y + 5 = 0$
(d) $\dfrac{x}{2} + \dfrac{y}{3} = 1$ (e) $3x + y = 3$ (f) $2y = 3(x - 2)$

3. Find the equation of the line
(a) passing through $(2, -3)$, parallel to $y = 3x - 2$
(b) passing through $(-1, 5)$, perpendicular to $y = -2x + 5$
(c) passing through $(0, 4)$ and perpendicular to $2x + y = 5$.
(d) passing through $(-2, 0)$ and parallel to $x - y = 3$
(e) passing through $(3, 4)$ and parallel to $y = 2$.
(f) passing through $(-5, 2)$ and perepndicular to $y = 2$.

> $y = 2x + b$ represents the family of lines with slope 2.
> $y = mx + 3$ represents the family of lines with y-intercept 3.

4. Find the equation of the family of lines
(a) with y-intercept 2
(b) with slope 3
(c) parallel to $y = -2x + 3$
(d) perpendicular to $y = 3x - 5$
(e) passing through $(2, 5)$
(f) passing through $(2, -5)$
(g) passing through $(-1, -3)$
(h) perpendicular to the x-axis
(i) passing through the point of intersection of $y = 2x + 1$ and $y = x + 2$
(j) parallel to the line segment joining $(1, 5)$ to $(2, 3)$
(k) passing through the origin

EXERCISE 2   GRAPHING

1. Sketch the graph of each of the following, $x, y \in R$

(a) $y \geqslant x + 3$ (b) $y < 2x - 1$

(c) $y \leqslant 3 - x$ (d) $y > 2 - 2x$

(e) $x + y \geqslant 4$ (f) $2x - y < 4$

(g) $3y - 2x > 6$ (h) $4x + 3y \leqslant -12$

2. Graph the following, $x, y \in R$.

(a) $\{(x, y) \mid y \leqslant x - 3 \text{ and } y \geqslant x + 2\}$

(b) $\{(x, y) \mid y > 2x + 1 \text{ and } y \leqslant 3 + x\}$

(c) $\{(x, y) \mid 2x + y < 4 \text{ and } 3x - y > 6\}$

(d) $\{(x, y) \mid y \geqslant 2 \text{ and } x \leqslant -1\}$

(e) $\{(x, y) \mid y > x + 2 \text{ and } x \geqslant 0\}$

(f) $\{(x, y) \mid x + y > 4 \text{ or } x - y < 2\}$

(g) $\{(x, y) \mid 3x + 2y \leqslant 12 \text{ and } x \geqslant 0 \text{ and } y \geqslant 0\}$

EXERCISE 3   FACTORING

1. Complete the following

(a) $5x + 30 = 5(\rule{2cm}{0.3cm})$

(b) $7x^2y - 14x^3y^2 = 7x^2y(\rule{2cm}{0.3cm})$

(c) $6abc - 4ab = 2ab(\rule{2cm}{0.3cm})$

(d) $6x^2 - 4x = 3x(\rule{2cm}{0.3cm})$

(e) $6mn - 7m^2n = -2mn(\rule{2cm}{0.3cm})$

(f) $x + 5y = x(\rule{2cm}{0.3cm})$

(g) $5x^2 - 9x = 5(\rule{2cm}{0.3cm})$

(h) $-3x^2 + 4x = -3(\rule{2cm}{0.3cm})$

(i) $-6x^2 + 8x = -6x(\rule{2cm}{0.3cm})$

(j) $4x - 7x^2 = 7x(\rule{2cm}{0.3cm})$

(k) $-x^2 - 6x = -(\rule{2cm}{0.3cm})$

(l) $\frac{1}{2}x^2 - 3x = \frac{1}{2}(\rule{2cm}{0.3cm})$

(m) $-\frac{2}{3}x^2 + 4x = -\frac{2}{3}(\rule{2cm}{0.3cm})$

(n) $-\frac{5}{3}x^2 - 10x = -\frac{5}{3}(\rule{2cm}{0.3cm})$

CHAPTER 2

Quadratic Functions

When we cannot use the compass of mathematics or the torch of experience ... it is certain we cannot take a single step forward.

Voltaire

In Chapter 1 we studied the characteristics of functions in general. In this chapter we shall study the quadratic function in detail.

2.1 PARABOLAS IN STANDARD FORM

A function determined by a second degree polynomial is called a quadratic function. Examples of quadratic functions are $y = 2x^2$, $y = -3x^2 + 4x$, $y = x^2 - 3x + 1$. The graph of a quadratic function is called a parabola.

We graph the function $f(x) = x^2$ by first determining a set of ordered pairs, then plotting the points and joining them by a smooth curve.

x	y
0	0
1	1
−1	1
2	4
−2	4
3	9
−3	9

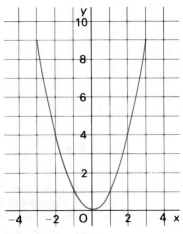

The graph of the parabola is symmetric about the y-axis since $f(x) = f(-x)$. The axis of symmetry of a parabola is the line such that the parabola is mapped onto itself by reflection in the line. In this case the axis of symmetry is the y-axis. The vertex, or turning point, of the parabola is the point where the graph intersects the axis of symmetry. In this example the vertex is $(0, 0)$.

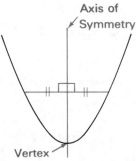

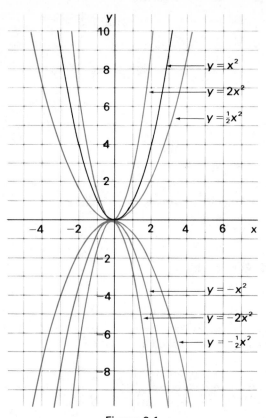

Figure 2-1

Figure 2-1 illustrates the change in the parabola $y = ax^2$ for different values of a. If $a > 0$ the parabola opens upward. If $a < 0$ the parabola opens downward. Compare the functions to $y = x^2$.

(i) If $|a| > 1$ there is a stretch in the y-direction.

(ii) If $|a| < 1$ there is a shrink in the y-direction.

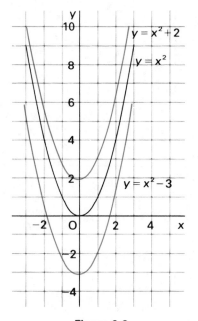

Figure 2-2

Figure 2-2 illustrates that the graphs of

$$y = x^2 + 2$$

and

$$y = x^2 - 3$$

are congruent to $y = x^2$.

All three have the same size and shape, but different positions. The graph of $y = x^2 + 2$ is the graph of $y = x^2$ shifted up 2 units. The graph of $y = x^2 - 3$ is the graph of $y = x^2$ shifted down 3 units.

In general, if $c > 0$,

(i) the graph of $y = ax^2 + c$ is the graph of $y = ax^2$ translated upward by c units.

(ii) the graph of $y = ax^2 - c$ is the graph of $y = ax^2$ translated downward by c units.

EXAMPLE 1. *Sketch the graphs of*

(a) $y = 2x^2 - 4$

(b) $y = -\frac{1}{2}x^2 + 3$

Solution

(a) The graph of $y = 2x^2 - 4$ is the graph of $y = 2x^2$ translated downward by 4 units.

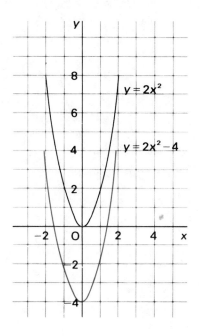

(b) The graph of $y = -\frac{1}{2}x^2 + 3$ is the graph of $y = -\frac{1}{2}x^2$ translated upward by 3 units.

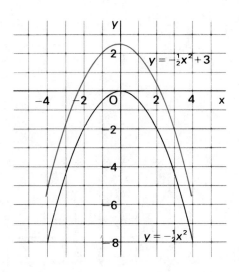

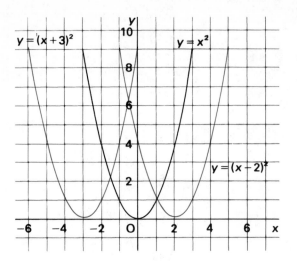

Figure 2-3

Figure 2-3 illustrates that the graphs of

$$y = (x-2)^2$$

and

$$y = (x+3)^2$$

are congruent to

$$y = x^2$$

but have different positions.   The graph of $y = (x-2)^2$ is the graph of $y = x^2$ shifted 2 units to the right. The graph of $y = (x+3)^2$ is the graph of $y = x^2$ shifted 3 units to the left.

In general, if $h > 0$,
(i) the graph of $y = a(x+h)^2$ is the graph of $y = ax^2$ translated to the left by h units
(ii) the graph of $y = a(x-h)^2$ is the graph of $y = ax^2$ translated to the right by h units.

EXAMPLE 2.   *Sketch the graphs of*

(a) $y = 2(x-3)^2$

(b) $y = -3(x+2)^2$

and find the vertex and the equation of the axis of symmetry.

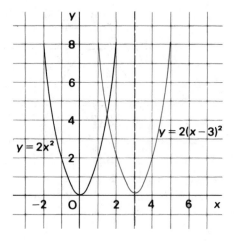

Solution

(a) The graph of $y = 2(x-3)^2$ is the graph of $y = 2x^2$ translated to the right by 3 units. The vertex is $(3, 0)$.

   The equation of the axis of symmetry is $x = 3$.

(b) The graph of $y = -3(x+2)^2$ is the graph of $y = -3x^2$ translated to the left by 2 units.

The vertex is $(-2, 0)$.

The equation of the axis of symmetry is $x = -2$.

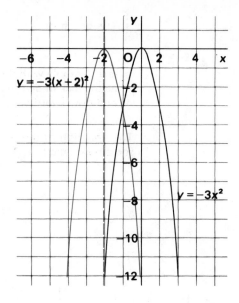

Figure 2-4 illustrates that the graphs of $y = (x-4)^2 + 3$ and $y = (x+3)^2 - 5$ are congruent to $y = x^2$. The graph of $y = (x-4)^2 + 3$ is the graph of $y = x^2$ shifted right 4 units and up 3 units. The graph of $y = (x+3)^2 - 5$ is the graph of $y = x^2$ shifted left 3 units and down 5 units.

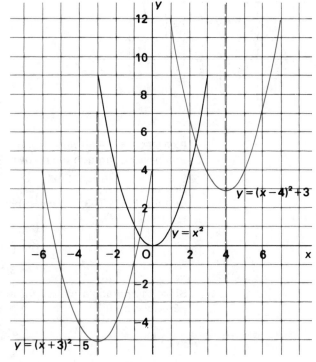

Figure 2-4

The graph of

$$y = a(x-h)^2 + k$$

is a parabola with the point (h, k) as the vertex and the line $x = h$ as the axis of symmetry. The parabola opens upward when $a > 0$ and downward when $a < 0$.

The equation of the form $y = a(x-h)^2 + k$ is called the standard form for a quadratic function.

EXAMPLE 3. *Sketch the graph of* $y = 2(x+4)^2 - 1$

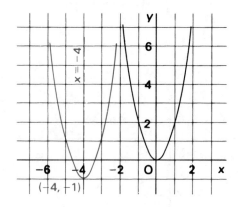

Solution

The graph of $y = 2(x+4)^2 - 1$ is congruent to the graph of $y = 2x^2$. The vertex is $(-4, -1)$, the equation of the axis of symmetry is $x = -4$. Since $a > 0$, the parabola opens upward.

EXAMPLE 4. *Find an equation for the parabola with vertex $(-3, -2)$ and passing through the point $(-2, 0)$.*

Solution
Setting $(h, k) = (-3, -2)$ we substitute in the formula

$$y = a(x-h)^2 + k \quad \text{to obtain}$$
$$y = a(x-(-3))^2 + (-2)$$
$$= a(x+3)^2 - 2$$

Since the parabola passes through the point $(-2, 0)$, we replace x by -2 and y by 0.

$$0 = a(-2+3)^2 - 2$$
$$0 = a - 2$$
$$a = 2$$

$\therefore$ the equation is $y = 2(x+3)^2 - 2$

EXERCISE 2-1

A 1. For each of the following parabolas state
  (i) the direction of the opening (up or down)
  (ii) the coordinates of the vertex
  (iii) the equation of the axis of symmetry

(a) $y = 4x^2$
(b) $y = x^2 + 3$
(c) $y = -\frac{1}{2}x^2$
(d) $y = -3x^2 + 5$
(e) $y = 2(x+1)^2$
(f) $y = 3(x-4)^2 + 2$
(g) $y = -5(x+6)^2$
(h) $y = x^2 - 6$
(i) $y = -\frac{1}{2}(x-1)^2 - 6$
(j) $y = 2x^2 + 7$
(k) $y = 4(x-3)^2$
(l) $y = -(x+5)^2$
(m) $y = -7x^2 - 7$
(n) $y = 2(x+6)^2 - 10$
(o) $y = -3(x-3)^2 - 3$
(p) $y = 3(x-\frac{1}{2})^2$
(q) $y = 0.5(x-3)^2 - 0.7$
(r) $y = -1.2x^2 - 3.4$
(s) $y = -0.009x^2$
(t) $y = -2(x+5)^2 - 10$
(u) $y = 6(x-1)^2 + 8$

B 2. Write an equation for a parabola with the given vertex and value for a.

(a) $(0,0)$, $a = 4$
(b) $(0,0)$, $a = -3$
(c) $(0,0)$, $a = -\frac{1}{2}$
(d) $(0,4)$, $a = 1$
(e) $(0,-3)$, $a = -2$
(f) $(0,-4)$, $a = 6$
(g) $(5,0)$, $a = 2$
(h) $(-4,0)$, $a = -3$
(i) $(-6,0)$, $a = \frac{1}{2}$
(j) $(3,2)$, $a = 1$
(k) $(-3,5)$, $a = -2$
(l) $(4,-3)$, $a = 4$
(m) $(0,6)$, $a = -3$
(n) $(-6,-7)$, $a = -5$
(o) $(-5,0)$, $a = \frac{1}{3}$
(p) $(0,0)$, $a = -\frac{1}{3}$
(q) $(6,6)$, $a = -\frac{1}{2}$
(r) $(-7,2)$, $a = -5$
(s) $(0,-7)$, $a = 4$
(t) $(-3,-4)$, $a = -7$
(u) $(-6,0)$, $a = -11$

3. Without making a table of values, sketch the graph of each of the following.

(a) $y = 3x^2$
(b) $y = -2x^2 + 4$
(c) $y = 3(x+2)^2$
(d) $y = 2(x+1)^2 - 5$
(e) $y = 3x^2 - 5$
(f) $y = -2(x-3)^2 - 4$
(g) $y = -3(x-5)^2$
(h) $y = -\frac{1}{2}x^2 - 9$
(i) $y = -(x+5)^2$
(j) $y = 4(x+3)^2 - 1$
(k) $y = -2x^2 - 6$
(l) $y = -\frac{1}{2}(x-1)^2 + 6$
(m) $y = x^2 + 3 - 0$
(n) $y = 2(x+6)^2$
(o) $y = -2(x+3)^2 - 4$
(p) $y = \frac{1}{2}(x+3)^2 + 1$
(q) $y = -4(x-1)^2 + 3$
(r) $y = 6(x-2)^2 + 7$

4. Find an equation for the parabola with the given vertex and passing through the given point.

(a) vertex: $(3,2)$, point: $(1,6)$
(b) vertex: $(-1,-3)$, point: $(-2,-5)$
(c) vertex: $(-3,6)$, point: $(-2,10)$
(d) vertex: $(2,-4)$, point: $(1,-7)$
(e) vertex: $(2,-6)$, point: $(4,-4)$
(f) vertex: $(-4,3)$, point: $(-3,2)$

C 5. Determine the values of h or k so that the graph of the parabola will pass through the given point.

(a) $y = 2(x-1)^2 + k$; $(2,7)$
(b) $y = 3(x-h)^2 + 2$; $(1,14)$
(c) $y = -3(x+2)^2 + k$; $(-3,-7)$
(d) $y = -2(x-h)^2 + 5$; $(2,3)$
(e) $y = -\frac{1}{2}(x-h)^2 - 4$; $(4,-6)$
(f) $y = 3(x+2)^2 + k$; $(-3,-4)$

6. Find a and k so that the given points will lie on the parabola.

(a) $y = a(x-1)^2 + k$; $(2,4)$, $(3,10)$
(b) $y = a(x+3)^2 + k$; $(-2,3)$, $(0,-13)$
(c) $y = a(x-2)^2 + k$; $(1,8)$, $(-1,32)$

7. Graph $y = |x^2 - 4|$

8. Graph $y = |x^2 - 9|$

ADDITION

$$
\begin{array}{r}
\text{TWO} \\
\text{THREE} \\
\text{SEVEN} \\
\hline
\text{TWELVE}
\end{array}
$$

2.2 GRAPHING BY COMPLETING THE SQUARE

In the previous section we graphed quadratic functions written in standard form. Functions of this type may be rewritten as follows.

$$y = 2(x-3)^2 - 7 \quad\longleftarrow\text{standard form}$$
$$= 2(x^2 - 6x + 9) - 7$$
$$= 2x^2 - 12x + 18 - 7$$
$$= 2x^2 - 12x + 11 \quad\longleftarrow\text{general form}$$

The equation $y = 2x^2 - 12x + 11$ is written in *the general form of a quadratic function.* Many quadratic functions appear in this form, but it is easier to graph a quadratic function when it is expressed in the standard form $y = a(x-h)^2 + k$. To make the transition from general to standard we use a procedure called completing the square. In order to understand the process we first square two binomials.

$$(x+3)^2 = x^2 + 6x + 9$$
$$(x+t)^2 = x^2 + 2tx + t^2$$

Notice that the constant term, 9 or t^2, is the square of half the coefficient of x. We use this fact when we complete the square.

EXAMPLE 1. *Express $y = x^2 - 6x - 1$ in standard form*

Solution

$$y = x^2 - 6x - 1$$

We first determine what must be added to $x^2 - 6x$ to make it a square trinomial.
The square of half the coefficient of x is 9. Since we add 9 to the original function we must also subtract 9 to keep the value of the function the same.

$$\left(\frac{-6}{2}\right)^2 = 9$$

$$y = x^2 - 6x + 1$$
$$= x^2 - 6x + 9 - 9 + 1$$
$$= (x^2 - 6x + 9) - 9 + 1$$
$$= (x-3)^2 - 8$$

EXAMPLE 2. *Sketch the graph of* $y = x^2 + 8x + 11$

Solution
We first complete the square to put the function in standard form.

$$y = x^2 + 8x + 11$$
$$= x^2 + 8x + 16 - 16 + 11$$
$$= (x+4)^2 - 5$$

The coordinates of the vertex are $(-4, -5)$ and the parabola opens upward.

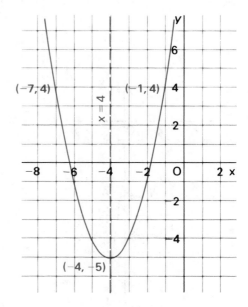

In Examples 1 and 2 we expressed quadratic functions of the form $y = x^2 + bx + c$ in standard form. We shall now consider quadratic functions of the form $y = ax^2 + bx + c$ where $a \neq 1$.

EXAMPLE 3. *Express* $y = 3x^2 - 12x + 7$ *in standard form.*

Solution
We factor the coefficient of x^2 from the first two terms.

$$y = 3x^2 - 12x + 7$$
$$= 3[x^2 - 4x] + 7$$
$$= 3[x^2 - 4x + 4 - 4] + 7 \qquad \text{(complete the square)}$$
$$= 3[(x^2 - 4x + 4) - 4] + 7$$
$$= 3[(x - 2)^2 - 4] + 7$$
$$= 3(x - 2)^2 - 12 + 7 \qquad \text{(remove square brackets)}$$
$$= 3(x - 2)^2 - 5$$

quadratic functions   51

EXAMPLE 4. (a) *Sketch the graph of* $y = -3x^2 - 4x - 3$.
(b) *Determine the y-intercept and plot the appropriate point on the graph.*

Solution
(a) We first rewrite the equation in standard form.

$$y = -3x^2 - 4x - 3$$
$$= -3[x^2 + \tfrac{4}{3}x] - 3$$
$$= -3[x^2 + \tfrac{4}{3}x + \tfrac{4}{9} - \tfrac{4}{9}] - 3$$
$$= -3[(x + \tfrac{2}{3})^2 - \tfrac{4}{9}] - 3$$
$$= -3(x + \tfrac{2}{3})^2 + \tfrac{4}{3} - 3$$
$$= -3(x + \tfrac{2}{3})^2 - \tfrac{5}{3}$$

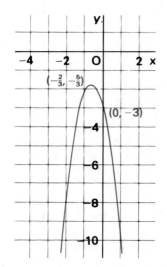

The coordinates of the vertex are $(-\tfrac{2}{3}, -\tfrac{5}{3})$ and the parabola opens downward.
(b) We determine the y-intercept by setting $x = 0$ in the original equation.

$$y = -3x^2 - 4x - 3$$
$$= -3(0)^2 - 4(0) - 3$$
$$= -3$$

$\therefore$ the y-intercept is -3.

EXERCISE 2-2

A 1. Complete the square in each of the following.

(a) $x^2 + 8x$ (b) $x^2 + 6x$ (c) $x^2 - 12x$
(d) $x^2 - 2x$ (e) $x^2 + 10x$ (f) $x^2 - 14x$
(g) $x^2 + x$ (h) $x^2 - 3x$ (i) $x^2 - 5x$
(j) $x^2 + \tfrac{1}{2}x$ (k) $x^2 - \tfrac{6}{5}x$ (l) $x^2 - 0.8x$
(m) $x^2 + \tfrac{1}{4}x$ (n) $x^2 + \tfrac{2}{3}x$ (o) $x^2 + 0.2x$
(p) $x^2 - 1.2x$ (q) $x^2 - \tfrac{1}{3}x$ (r) $x^2 + 2.4x$

B 2. Without making a table of values, sketch the graph of each of the following functions. State the range of each function.

(a) $y = x^2 + 6x + 7$ (b) $y = x^2 - 4x - 1$ (c) $y = x^2 + 10x + 9$
(d) $y = x^2 - 8x$ (e) $y = x^2 + 3x$ (f) $y = x^2 - x + 1$
(g) $y = x^2 - \tfrac{1}{2}x - 1$ (h) $y = x^2 + \tfrac{2}{3}x - 2$ (i) $u = x^2 - \tfrac{3}{5}x$

3. Without making a table of values, sketch the graph of each of the following functions, State the range of each.

(a) $y = 2x^2 + 8x + 5$ (b) $y = 3x^2 - 6x + 4$ (c) $y = -2x^2 + 4x - 2$
(d) $y = -x^2 + 6x + 3$ (e) $y = -2x^2 + 5x + 2$ (f) $y = -3x^2 - 12x - 1$
(g) $y = 5x^2 - 15x - 1$ (h) $y = \tfrac{1}{2}x^2 + 3x - 2$ (i) $y = -\tfrac{1}{3}x^2 - 2x + 4$
(j) $y = -4x^2 + 6x$ (k) $y = -0.2x^2 + 2x + 7$ (l) $y = \tfrac{2}{3}x^2 - x + 2$
(m) $y = 2x^2 + \tfrac{1}{2}x + 1$ (n) $y = -6x^2 - x - \tfrac{1}{3}$ (o) $y = -2x^2 - 0.8x - 2$

4. Sketch the graph of each of the following.

(a) $y + 3 = x^2 + 2x + 1$ (b) $y - 2 = 2x^2 - 6x - 1$

(c) $\frac{1}{2}y = x^2 - 3x - 1$ (d) $4y = -2x^2 + 6x - 8$

(e) $y = 3 - 4x - x^2$ (f) $y - 1 = 3x - 2x^2 + 5$

2.3 APPLICATIONS: MAXIMUM AND MINIMUM

The function $f(x) = 2x - 3$ (or $y = 2x - 3$) is graphed in Figure 2-5. The function has a value of 5 when $x = 4$, 1 when $x = 2$, -1 when $x = 1$ and so on. *The ordinates of points on the graph of a function are the values of the functions.* For example, the value of

$$y = x^2 + 2x + 1$$

when $x = 2$ is $(2)^2 + 2(2) + 1$ or 9. The corresponding ordered pair is $(2, 9)$.

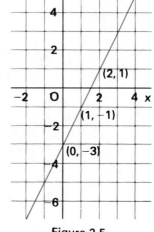

Figure 2-5

Consider the function $y = 2x^2 - 4x + 5$. Expressed in standard form it becomes $y = 2(x - 1)^2 + 3$. The point $(1, 3)$ is called the minimum point of the graph because it is the lowest point on the graph. The minimum value of the function is 3 when $x = 1$ because $f(x) \geqslant 3$ for $x \in R$.

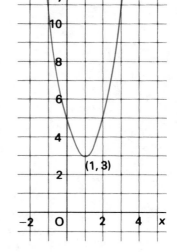

For the general function $y = a(x - h)^2 + k$, when $a > 0$ the parabola opens upward. Clearly $a(x - h)^2 \geqslant 0$. Therefore

$$a(x - h)^2 + k \geqslant k$$

and the minimum occurs when $a(x - h)^2 = 0$ or $x = h$.

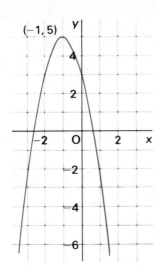

Similarly, the function $y = -2x^2 - 4x + 3$ expressed in standard form becomes $y = -2(x+1)^2 + 5$. The point $(-1, 5)$ is called the **maximum point** of the graph. The **maximum value** of the function is 5 when $x = -1$. For the general function $y = a(x-h)^2 + k$, when $a < 0$ the parabola opens downward. Clearly $a(x-h)^2 \leq 0$. Therefore $a(x-h)^2 + k \leq k$ and the maximum occurs when $a(x-h)^2 = 0$ or $x = h$.

EXAMPLE 1. *Determine the maximum or minimum value of the function* $y = -\frac{1}{2}x^2 + 6x - 13$.

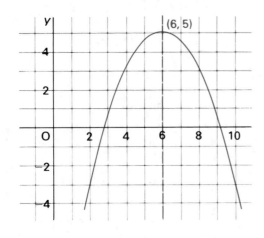

Solution
We first complete the square.

$$y = -\tfrac{1}{2}x^2 + 6x - 13$$
$$= -\tfrac{1}{2}[x^2 - 12x] - 13$$
$$= -\tfrac{1}{2}[x^2 - 12x + 36 - 36] - 13$$
$$= -\tfrac{1}{2}[(x-6)^2 - 36] - 13$$
$$= -\tfrac{1}{2}(x-6)^2 + 18 - 13$$
$$= -\tfrac{1}{2}(x-6)^2 + 5$$

Since $-\frac{1}{2}(x-6)^2 \leq 0$
$\therefore \quad -\frac{1}{2}(x-6)^2 + 5 \leq 5$
Therefore the function has a maximum value of 5 when $-\frac{1}{2}(x-6)^2 = 0$ or when $x = 6$.

EXAMPLE 2. *During the summer months Terry makes and sells necklaces on the beach. Last summer he sold the necklaces for $10 each. His sales averaged 20 per day. Considering a price increase, he took a small survey and found that for every dollar increase he would lose two sales per day. If the material for each necklace costs Terry $6, what should the selling price be to maximize profits? Determine the profit.*

Solution

Let x be the number of dollars that Terry increases the selling price from $10.

Income from sales is (number sold) $\times$ (selling price), or

$$(20-2x)(10+x)$$

Expenses are $6(20-2x)$

$$\text{Profit} = \text{Income} - \text{Expenses}$$

$$P = (20-2x)(10+x) - 6(20-2x)$$

$$= -2x^2 + 12x + 80$$

$$= -2[x^2 - 6x + 9 - 9] + 80$$

$$= -2[(x-3)^2 - 9] + 80$$

$$= -2(x-3)^2 + 18 + 80$$

$$= -2(x-3)^2 + 98$$

Since $-2(x-3)^2 \leqslant 0$

$\therefore \quad -2(x-3)^2 + 98 \leqslant 98$

The function reaches a maximum value of 98 when $-2(x-3)^2 = 0$ or when $x = 3$.

The profit reaches a maximum of $98 when $x = 3$. Therefore the selling price should be $13.

In how many ways is it possible to make change for a dollar?

EXERCISE 2-3

1. Determine the maximum or minimum of the following functions. State the value of x where each occurs.

(a) $y = 2x^2 - 12x - 7$ (b) $y = -3x^2 - 18x + 4$

(c) $y = 5x^2 - 10x + 4$ (d) $y = -x^2 + 2x - 3$

(e) $y = -\frac{1}{2}x^2 + 6x - 3$ (f) $y = \frac{1}{5}x^2 + 2x + 1$

(g) $y = \frac{1}{2}x^2 - 3x + 1$ (h) $y = -4x^2 + 2x - 1$

(i) $y = 0.1x^2 + 2x + 1$ (j) $y = -0.3x^2 - 0.6x - 0.1$

2. Find two numbers whose sum is 32 and whose product is a maximum.

3. Find two numbers whose difference is 6 and whose product is a minimum.

4. If a pistol bullet is fired vertically at an initial speed of 100 m/s, the height in metres after t seconds is given by $h = 100t - 5t^2$. Find the maximum height attained by the bullet.

5. A rectangular field is to be enclosed with 600 m of fencing. What dimensions will produce a maximum area?

6. A rectangular field bounded on one side by a lake is to be fenced on 3 sides by 800 m of fence. What dimensions will produce a maximum area?

7. A large car dealership has been selling new cars at $600 over the factory price. Sales have been averaging 80 cars per month. Due to inflation the $600 markup is going to be increased. The marketing manager has determined that for every $10 increase there will be one less car sold each month. What should the new markup be in order to maximize income?

8. Mary is an artist who works at a shopping centre drawing "pencil portraits". She charges $20 per portrait and she has been averaging 30 portraits per week. She decides to increase the price but realizes that for every one dollar increase she will lose one sale per week. If materials cost her $10 per portrait, what should she set the price at in order to maximize her profit?

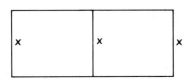

9. A rectangular field is to be enclosed by a fence and divided into two rectangular fields by a fence parallel to one side of the field. If 1200 m of fence are available, find the dimensions of the field giving the maximum area.

10. The TruTime watch company has been selling 1200 watches per week at $18 each. They are planning a price increase. A survey indicates that for every dollar increase in price there will be a drop of 40 sales per week. If it costs $10 to make each watch, what should the selling price be in order to maximize profit?

11. The effectiveness of a T.V. commercial depends on how many times a viewer sees it. A television advertising agency has determined that if effectiveness (e) is put on a scale from 0 to 10 where 10 is *maximum positive effect,* then $e = -\frac{1}{90}n^2 + \frac{2}{3}n$ where n is the number of times a viewer sees a particular commercial. Determine how many times a viewer should see a commercial to attain maximum positive effect.

12. A rocket is fired down a practice range. The height in metres after t seconds is given by

$$h = \tfrac{1}{4}t^2 + 3t + 45$$

Find the maximum height attained by the rocket.

C   **13.** A rocket is launched vertically upward with an initial velocity of v. The height h of the rocket at time t is equal to the height it would attain in the absence of gravity (vt) minus the free fall distance due to gravity $\left(\dfrac{gt^2}{2}\right)$.

Thus $$h = vt - \frac{gt^2}{2}$$

Neglecting air resistance and the variation of g with altitude, show that the rocket attains a maximum height of $\dfrac{v^2}{2t}$ at time $\dfrac{v}{g}$.

2.4 QUADRATIC REGIONS

The parabola $y = ax^2 + bx + c$ divides the plane into three regions.

$y > ax^2 + bx + c$ describes the points above the parabola		
$y = ax^2 + bx + c$ describes the points on the parabola		
$y < ax^2 + bx + c$ describes the points below the parabola		

EXAMPLE 1. *Draw the graph of* $y \geqslant x^2 - 4x + 7$

Solution
First we express $y = x^2 - 4x + 7$ in standard form.

$$y = x^2 - 4x + 7$$
$$= x^2 - 4x + 4 - 4 + 7$$
$$= (x - 2)^2 + 3$$

The parabola has its vertex at $(2, 3)$. The equation of the axis of symmetry is $x = 2$. The required graph is the set of points on or above the parabola.

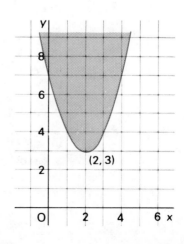

EXAMPLE 2. *Graph the solution set of the system of inequalities*

$$y < -x^2 - 2x + 2$$

$$\text{and } y > -\tfrac{1}{2}x - 2.$$

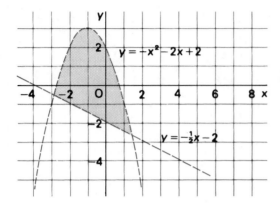

Solution
The solution set is the intersection of the solution sets of each inequality. For $y < -x^2 - 2x + 2$ the region is below the parabola. For $y > -\tfrac{1}{2}x - 2$ the region is above the straight line. The intersection is represented by the shaded area.

EXERCISE 2-4

B **1.** Draw the graphs of the following.

(a) $y \geq 2x^2$ (b) $y < x^2 + 4$
(c) $y > -x^2 - 3$ (d) $y \leq (x+3)^2 - 4$
(e) $y < -2(x-1)^2 + 5$ (f) $y \geq 4(x+2)^2 - 7$
(g) $y > x^2 + 4x + 1$ (h) $y < x^2 - 6x + 5$
(i) $y \leq -x^2 + 6x - 11$ (j) $y \geq -x^2 - 8x - 14$
(k) $y < 2x^2 - 12x + 14$ (l) $y > -2x^2 - 4x - 6$
(m) $y \geq -\tfrac{1}{3}x^2 + 2x + 3$ (n) $y < \tfrac{2}{3}x^2 - 4x + 1$

2. Graph the solution set of the following systems.

(a) $y > x^2 + 2$ and $y < x + 4$
(b) $y \geq x^2 - 4x + 6$ and $y < \tfrac{1}{2}x + 4$
(c) $y \leq -x^2 - 2x + 2$ and $y \geq x$
(d) $y > x^2 - 4x + 1$ and $y < -\tfrac{2}{3}x + 2$
(e) $y < -x^2 + 6x - 7$ and $y \geq -3$
(f) $y \leq -2x^2 + 4$ and $y > 0$
(g) $y > 2x^2 + 12x + 18$ and $y \leq -\tfrac{1}{2}x + 4$
(h) $y \geq 2x^2 - 4x + 2$ and $x \geq 1$

C **3.** Graph the solution set of the following.

(a) $y \leq -x^2 + 5$ and $y \geq x^2 - 4$
(b) $y < -x^2 + 4x$ and $y \geq 2x^2 - 4x + 2$

2.5 QUADRATIC RELATIONS WHOSE GRAPHS ARE PARABOLAS

In Section 1.6 we found that the graph of a function and its inverse were symmetric about the line $y = x$. Given points on the graph of a function the points on the graph of the inverse relation are found by interchanging the x and y values.

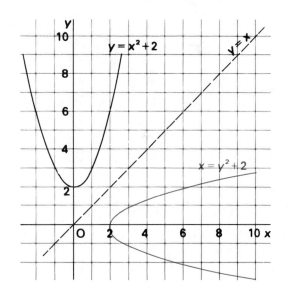

For example the inverse of the function $y = x^2 + 2$ is $x = y^2 + 2$. Its graph is found by reflecting the graph of $y = x^2 + 2$ in the line $y = x$.

Although $x = y^2 + 2$ does not define y as a function of x, it does define y as two functions of x, namely

$$y = \sqrt{x-2}$$
$$\text{and } y = -\sqrt{x-2}$$

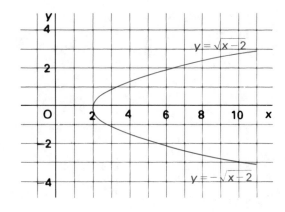

The techniques used to graph quadratic functions can also be used to graph quadratic relations whose graphs are parabolas. These relations are of the form $x = ay^2 + by + c, \quad a \neq 0$

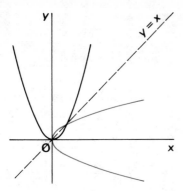

For such parabolas

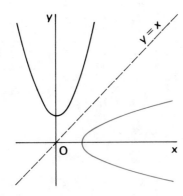

(a) an "upward translation" becomes a "translation to the right",

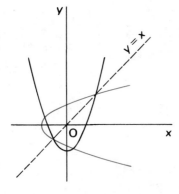

(b) a "downward translation" becomes a "translation to the left,

(c) a "translation to the right" becomes an "upward translation",

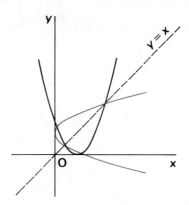

(d) a "translation to the left" becomes a "downward translation".

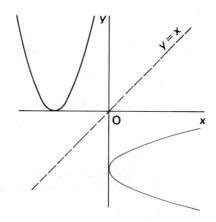

EXAMPLE 1. *Sketch the graph of* $x = 2y^2 - 4y + 5$

Solution
We first complete the square to put the relation in standard form.

$$x = 2y^2 - 4y + 5$$
$$= 2[y^2 - 2y] + 5$$
$$= 2[y^2 - 2y + 1 - 1] + 5$$
$$= 2[(y-1)^2 - 1] + 5$$
$$= 2(y-1)^2 - 2 + 5$$
$$= 2(y-1)^2 + 3$$

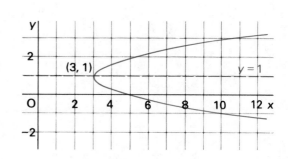

The co-ordinates of the vertex are (3, 1) and the equation of the axis of symmetry is $y = 1$.

EXERCISE 2-5

A　**1.** State the coordinates of the vertex and the equation of the axis of symmetry for each of the following.

(a) $x = y^2 - 2$　　　　(b) $x = 3y^2$　　　　(c) $x = -y^2 + 4$

(d) $x = -2y^2 + 5$　　　(e) $x = (y + 3)^2 + 2$　　(f) $x = (y - 1)^2 - 4$

(g) $x = 2(y + 2)^2 + 7$　(h) $x = -(y - 4)^2 - 1$　(i) $x = 3(y + 1)^2 + 6$

(j) $x = -\frac{1}{2}(y + 5)^2 - 3$　(k) $x = 4(y - 3)^2 - 8$　(l) $x = \frac{1}{3}(y - 6)^2 - 9$

B　**2.** Without making a table of values, sketch the graph of each of the following. State the domain of each.

(a) $x = 2y^2$　　　　(b) $x = -y^2$　　　　(c) $x = y^2 + 2$

(d) $x = y^2 - 4$　　　(e) $x = -y^2 + 3$　　　(f) $x = (y + 2)^2$

(g) $x = -2(y - 3)^2$　(h) $x = 2(y + 1)^2 + 1$　(i) $x = -(y - 2)^2 - 4$

3. Without making a table of values, sketch the graph of each of the following.

(a) $x = y^2 + 4y$　　　　(b) $x = y^2 - 6y + 7$　　(c) $x = 2y^2 + 4y$

(d) $x = -y^2 + 8y$　　　(e) $x = 2y^2 - 4y - 1$　　(f) $x = -2y^2 + 8y + 1$

(g) $x = 3y^2 - 12y - 2$　(h) $x = -4y^2 - 16y + 3$　(i) $x = \frac{1}{2}y^2 + y + 2$

(j) $x = 2y^2 + y - 3$　　(k) $x = -\frac{1}{3}y^2 + 2y + 1$　(l) $x = 3y^2 - 2y + 1$

2.6　THE GENERAL QUADRATIC FUNCTION

We shall now apply the technique of completing the square to express the general quadratic function, $y = ax + bx + c$, in standard form

$$y = ax^2 + bx + c$$

$$= a\left[x^2 + \frac{b}{a}x\right] + c$$

$$= a\left[x^2 + \frac{b}{a}x + \frac{b^2}{4a^2} - \frac{b^2}{4a^2}\right] + c$$

$$= a\left[\left(x + \frac{b}{2a}\right)^2 - \frac{b^2}{4a^2}\right] + c$$

$$= a\left(x + \frac{b}{2a}\right)^2 - \frac{b^2}{4a} + c$$

$$= a\left(x + \frac{b}{2a}\right)^2 + c - \frac{b^2}{4a}$$

$$y = a\left(x + \frac{b}{2a}\right)^2 + \frac{4ac - b^2}{4a}$$

Comparing this equation with $y = a(x - h)^2 + k$ we conclude:

The graph of the general quadratic function $y = ax^2 + bx + c$ is a parabola with vertex $\left(-\dfrac{b}{2a}, \dfrac{4ac - b^2}{4a}\right)$. The equation of the axis of symmetry is $x = -\dfrac{b}{2a}$. The parabola opens upward when $a > 0$ and downward when $a < 0$.

EXAMPLE 1. *Determine the vertex and the equation of the axis of symmetry of the parabola*

$$y = -2x^2 + 3x - 4$$

Solution
For $y = -2x^2 + 3x - 4$, $a = -2$, $b = 3$ and $c = -4$

Vertex:

$$x\text{-coordinate} = -\frac{b}{2a}$$

$$= -\frac{3}{2(-2)}$$

$$= \tfrac{3}{4}$$

$$y\text{-coordinate} = \frac{4ac - b^2}{4a}$$

$$= \frac{4(-2)(-4) - (3)^2}{4(-2)}$$

$$= -\tfrac{23}{8}$$

$\therefore$ the coordinates of the vertex are $(\tfrac{3}{4}, -\tfrac{23}{8})$

Axis of Symmetry:

$$x = -\frac{b}{2a}$$

$$x = \tfrac{3}{4}$$

EXAMPLE 2. *Find a quadratic function f that satisfies the given conditions*

$$f(1) = 0, \qquad f(3) = 2, \qquad f(-2) = 12$$

Solution
The quadratic function is defined by

$$f(x) = ax^2 + bx + c$$

WORD LADDER

Start with the word "snail" and change one letter at a time to form a new word until you reach "boat". The best solution has the fewest steps.

s a i l
_ _ _ _
_ _ _ _
_ _ _ _
_ _ _ _
_ _ _ _
b o a t

quadratic functions   63

$$f(1) = a(1)^2 + b(1) + c = 0 \quad \text{or} \quad a + b + c = 0$$
$$f(3) = a(3)^2 + b(3) + c = 2 \quad \text{or} \quad 9a + 3b + c = 2$$
$$f(-2) = a(-2)^2 + b(-2) + c = 12 \quad \text{or} \quad 4a - 2b + c = 12$$

We now solve the resulting linear system.

$$a + b + c = 0 \quad ①$$
$$9a + 3b + c = 2 \quad ②$$
$$4a - 2b + c = 12 \quad ③$$

Eliminate c from ① and ②

$$a + b + c = 0 \quad ①$$
$$9a + 3b + c = 2 \quad ②$$

Subtract $\quad -8a - 2b = -2 \quad ④$

or $\qquad\quad 4a + b = 1 \quad ④$

Eliminate c from ② and ③

$$9a + 3b + c = 2 \quad ②$$
$$4a - 2b + c = 12 \quad ③$$

Subtract $\quad 5a + 5b = -10 \quad ⑤$

or $\qquad\quad a + b = -2 \quad ⑤$

Eliminate b from ④ and ⑤

$$4a + b = 1 \quad ④$$
$$a + b = -2 \quad ⑤$$

Subtract $\quad 3a = 3$

$$a = 1$$

Substitute $a = 1$ in ④

$$4a + b = 1$$
$$4(1) + b = 1$$
$$4 + b = 1$$
$$b = -3$$

Substitute $a = 1$, $b = -3$ in ①

$$a + b + c = 0$$
$$(1) + (-3) + c = 0$$
$$c = 2$$

$$\therefore \quad f(x) = x^2 - 3x + 2$$

EXERCISE 2-6

A **1.** State the values of a, b and c for the following quadratic functions
(a) $y = 2x^2 + 3x - 7$ (b) $y = 2x^2 - x - 3$ (c) $y = -x^2 - 4x$
(d) $y = 3x^2 - 4$ (e) $y + 3 = x^2 + 2x$ (f) $y - 7 = 2x^2$
(g) $y = 7 - 3x + 5x^2$ (h) $y = 3x - 4x^2 - 2$ (i) $y = 5x - 3 + 7x^2$

B **2.** Find the vertex and axis of symmetry of each of the following.
(a) $y = x^2 - x - 12$ (b) $y = x^2 + 2x + 3$ (c) $y = 2x^2 - 4x - 1$
(d) $y = -x^2 - 2x + 5$ (e) $y = -2x^2 + x - 5$ (f) $y = 3x^2 - x + 4$
(g) $y = \frac{1}{2}x^2 - 2x + 1$ (h) $y = -\frac{1}{4}x^2 + 3x - 1$ (i) $y = 4x^2 - 7$
(j) $y = 2x^2 - 6x$

3. Find a quadratic function that satisfies the given conditions.
(a) $f(1) = 2$, $f(-1) = 4$, $f(2) = 4$
(b) $f(1) = 0$, $f(3) = -2$, $f(-1) = 10$
(c) $f(1) = 2$, $f(-1) = -4$, $f(2) = 8$
(d) $f(0) = 2$, $f(-2) = 12$, $f(3) = 2$

Write 100 using four 9's.

C **4.** Determine without graphing if the following will cross the x-axis.
(a) $y = x^2 - 2x - 8$ (b) $y = 2x^2 + 4x + 3$
(c) $y = -x^2 - 7x - 12$ (d) $y = -2x^2 + 6x - 5$
(e) $y = -\frac{1}{2}x^2 + 3x - 4$ (f) $y = 3x^2 - 10x - 8$

5. If $y = ax^2 + bx + c$ crosses the x-axis, does $y = -ax^2 - bx - c$ cross the x-axis? Explain.

6. If $f(x) = ax^2 + bx + c$ and $f(x) = f(-x)$ for all x, show that $b = 0$.

REVIEW EXERCISE

A **1.** For each of the following parabolas state
(i) the direction of the opening
(ii) the coordinates of the vertex
(iii) the equation of the axis of symmetry
(a) $y = 3x^2$ (b) $y = x^2 - 4$ (c) $y = -x^2 + 3$
(d) $y = -2(x - 1)^2$ (e) $y = 2(x + 3)^2 + 4$ (f) $y = 3(x - 4)^2 - 3$
(g) $y = -\frac{1}{2}x^2 - 5$ (h) $y = -3(x + 1)^2 + 2$ (i) $y = -5(x - 4)^2 - 7$

2. Complete the square for each of the following.
(a) $x^2 - 8x$ (b) $x^2 - 12x$ (c) $x^2 - 10x$
(d) $x^2 - x$ (e) $x^2 + 3x$ (f) $x^2 - \frac{4}{3}x$
(g) $x^2 - 0.4x$ (h) $x^2 + \frac{1}{3}x$ (i) $x^2 + 5x$

B **3.** Sketch the graph of each of the following.
(a) $y = 2x^2$ (b) $y = -x^2 + 3$ (c) $y = 2(x - 1)^2$
(d) $y = -3(x + 1)^2$ (e) $y = -(x - 2)^2 - 1$ (f) $y = -2(x + 2)^2 + 5$
(g) $y = 2x^2 - 2$ (h) $y = 3(x - 4)^2 - 2$ (i) $y = 4(x + 3)^2 - 2$

4. Sketch the graph of each of the following.
(a) $y = 2x^2 - 8x - 1$ (b) $y = 3x^2 + 6x + 7$ (c) $y = -x^2 - 4x - 2$
(d) $y = -2x^2 + x - 1$ (e) $y = \frac{1}{2}x^2 + 3x - 2$ (f) $y = x^2 - 3x + 5$
(g) $y = -3x^2 + 12x + 5$ (h) $y = -\frac{1}{3}x^2 + x - 3$ (i) $y = \frac{2}{3}x^2 - 4x - 1$

5. Determine the maximum or minimum of each of the following functions. State the value of x where each occurs.

(a) $y = x^2 - 2x + 5$ (b) $y = -x^2 + 4x + 2$ (c) $y = 3x^2 - 6x + 1$

(d) $y = \frac{1}{2}x^2 + x + 7$ (e) $y = -2x^2 - x - 1$ (f) $y = \frac{3}{2}x^2 + 6x$

6. A rectangular field, bounded on one side by a river, is to be fenced on 3 sides by 1200 m of fence. Determine the dimensions of the field that will produce a maximum area.

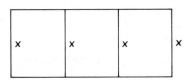

7. A rectangular field is to be enclosed by a fence. Two fences, parallel to one side of the field, divide the field into 3 rectangular fields. If 2400 m of fence are available, find the dimensions of the field giving the maximum area.

8. Draw the graphs of the following.

(a) $y < x^2$

(b) $y \geq x^2 - 2$

(c) $y > -x^2 + 3$

(d) $y \leq (x - 1)^2 + 4$

(e) $y \geq -2(x + 2)^2 - 1$

(f) $y < x^2 - 2x + 5$

(g) $y > 2x^2 - 6x - 2$

(h) $y \leq -x^2 + 4x - 1$

(i) $y \geq -3x^2 - 6x - 2$

(j) $y > \frac{1}{2}x^2 + x + 4$

Determine the pattern. Find the missing number

8	7	4	5
10	9	5	6
3	2	6	7
	7	5	11

REVIEW AND PREVIEW TO CHAPTER 3

EXERCISE 1. EQUATIONS AND INEQUALITIES

1. Solve the following
(a) $3x + 16 = x - 28$
(b) $4t - 3 = t - 45$
(c) $3(x - 4) - 6 = 5x - 12$
(d) $4(2w - 1) - (w - 5) = 11$
(e) $2(1 - 3t) - 2(4t - 5) = -2$
(f) $0 = 5 - 3(s - 5) + 4(2 - s)$
(g) $(x - 1)(x + 3) = (x + 2)(x + 1)$
(h) $4 - (w - 3) + 2(3w - 5) = 6$
(i) $\dfrac{x}{3} - \dfrac{x}{4} = \dfrac{1}{2}$
(j) $\dfrac{x + 1}{2} - \dfrac{x - 1}{4} = 5$
(k) $\dfrac{2w + 3}{3} - 1 = \dfrac{w}{2}$
(l) $5x - 3(2x - 3) + 7 = 2(1 + x)$
(m) $\dfrac{4t + 3}{2} - 2 = \dfrac{3t + 5}{5}$
(n) $0.2(x - 3) + 1 = 0.3(x + 2)$
(o) $1.2(2x - 1) - 0.2(x - 2) = 3$
(p) $\dfrac{3 - x}{4} - \dfrac{x + 1}{3} = \dfrac{x - 2}{2}$

2. Solve the following inequalities.
(a) $5x + 7 > 3x + 9$
(b) $3(w - 1) - 2 < 2w + 1$
(c) $3 - 3(t + 1) \geq 5(t - 8)$
(d) $7 - 3(x + 5) - 2(1 - 2x) \leq 2(x + 1)$
(e) $4(2 - 3t) - 5 > t - 6$
(f) $\dfrac{x}{2} + 1 < \dfrac{x}{3}$
(g) $3(2x + 1) - 2(1 - x) \leq 5$
(h) $\dfrac{x + 1}{3} \geq \dfrac{x - 2}{2}$

EXERCISE 2 RADICALS

1. Simplify the following
(a) $\sqrt{2} + 3\sqrt{2} - 5\sqrt{3} + 8\sqrt{3}$
(b) $\sqrt{8} + 3\sqrt{18} - 3\sqrt{32}$
(c) $4\sqrt{27} - 5\sqrt{12} - 3\sqrt{80} - 2\sqrt{45}$
(d) $2\sqrt{90} + 5\sqrt{40} - 3\sqrt{75} + 2\sqrt{48}$
(e) $5\sqrt{63} - 2\sqrt{54} + 2\sqrt{28} - 3\sqrt{24}$
(f) $2\sqrt{68} - 5\sqrt{13} - 2\sqrt{153} - 4\sqrt{52}$
(g) $5\sqrt{363} - 2\sqrt{300} + 6\sqrt{27}$
(h) $6\sqrt{20} - 4\sqrt{125} + 8\sqrt{45} - \sqrt{500}$

2. Expand and simplify.
(a) $(3\sqrt{2} - 4)(5\sqrt{3} + 2\sqrt{2})$
(b) $(2\sqrt{3} - \sqrt{2})^2$
(c) $(5\sqrt{6} - \sqrt{3})(5\sqrt{6} + \sqrt{3})$
(d) $(2 - 3\sqrt{2})(2 + 3\sqrt{2})$
(e) $(2 + 4\sqrt{5})(\sqrt{3} - \sqrt{15})$
(f) $(6\sqrt{2} - \sqrt{5})(6\sqrt{2} + \sqrt{5})$

3. Rationalize the denominator of each of the following.

(a) $\dfrac{3}{2\sqrt{2}}$

(b) $\dfrac{3\sqrt{2}-1}{\sqrt{3}}$

(c) $\dfrac{2+3\sqrt{5}-\sqrt{2}}{2\sqrt{5}}$

(d) $\dfrac{2}{\sqrt{3}-\sqrt{2}}$

(e) $\dfrac{\sqrt{3}}{1+3\sqrt{2}}$

(f) $\dfrac{4\sqrt{3}-1}{2\sqrt{5}-\sqrt{3}}$

(g) $\dfrac{1+\sqrt{6}}{2\sqrt{5}+3\sqrt{7}}$

(h) $\dfrac{-\sqrt{7}}{3\sqrt{5}-1}$

(i) $\dfrac{-2\sqrt{3}+1}{\sqrt{8}+2\sqrt{2}-3}$

4. Expand and simplify.

(a) $(\sqrt{x}+3)(\sqrt{x}-1)$

(b) $(\sqrt{x}-4)^2$

(c) $(2\sqrt{x}-1)(\sqrt{x}-3)$

(d) $(\sqrt{x+1}+2)(\sqrt{x+1}+3)$

(e) $(\sqrt{x-5}+1)^2$

(f) $(3\sqrt{x+2}-1)^2$

(g) $(1-\sqrt{x-3})^2$

(h) $(2-\sqrt{x+3})^2$

(i) $(1+2\sqrt{x-1})^2$

Using only the digits 2, 3, 5 or 7, find the product.

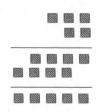

Quadratic Equations

CHAPTER 3

I'm very well acquainted too with matters mathematical,
I understand equations, both simple and quadratical,
About binomial theorem I'm teeming with a lot o' news—
With many cheerful facts about the square of the hypotenuse.

    —sung by the model of a modern Major-General
    in Gilbert and Sullivan's The Pirates of Penzance

3.1 SOLVING QUADRATIC EQUATIONS BY GRAPHING

A linear-quadratic system such as

$$y = x^2 - 2x - 3$$

$$y = 5$$

may be solved graphically by plotting the graph of each equation. The points of intersection will give the solution, namely $(-2, 5)$ and $(4, 5)$.

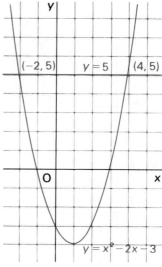

In Figure 3-1 the system

$$y = x^2 - 2x - 3$$

$$y = 0$$

is solved graphically. The points of intersection are $(-1, 0)$ and $(3, 0)$. Note that the x-intercepts of the quadratic function

$$y = x^2 - 2x - 3$$

are -1 and 3.

The roots of the corresponding quadratic equation,

$$x^2 - 2x - 3 = 0$$

are -1 and 3.

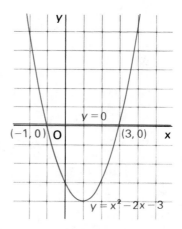

Figure 3-1

The quadratic equation

$$x^2 - 4x - 5 = 0$$

may be solved graphically.
First we set y equal to both sides of the equation

$$y = x^2 - 4x - 5$$

$$y = 0$$

We then plot the graph of each equation to find the points of intersection.
Since the original equation, $x^2 - 4x - 5 = 0$, involved only x, we only need the x coordinates of the points of intersection, namely -1 and 5. We verify by substitution that -1 and 5 are the roots of $x^2 - 4x - 5 = 0$.

$$\text{L.S.} = (-1)^2 - 4(-1) - 5 \quad \text{R.S.} = 0$$

$$= 1 + 4 - 5$$

$$= 0$$

$$\text{and L.S.} = (5)^2 - 4(5) - 5 \qquad \text{R.S.} = 0$$

$$= 25 - 20 - 5$$

$$= 0$$

$\therefore$ the roots are -1 and 5.

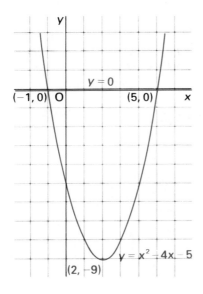

EXAMPLE 1. Solve $x^2 - 2x - 8 = 0$ graphically.

Solution
Draw the graph of $y = x^2 - 2x - 8$.
The graph intersects the x-axis at $(4, 0)$ and $(-2, 0)$. Therefore the solution set for the corresponding quadratic equation $x^2 - 2x - 8 = 0$ is $\{-2, 4\}$
Check

$$x = -2 \qquad\qquad x = 4$$

$$\text{L.S.} = x^2 - 2x - 8 \qquad \text{L.S.} = x^2 - 2x - 8$$

$$= (-2)^2 - 2(-2) - 8 \qquad = (4)^2 - 2(4) - 8$$

$$= 4 + 4 - 8 \qquad\qquad = 16 - 8 - 8$$

$$= 0 \qquad\qquad\qquad = 0$$

$$\text{R.S.} = 0 \qquad\qquad \text{R.S.} = 0$$

$\therefore$ the roots are -2 and 4.

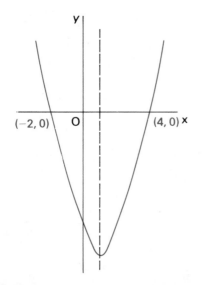

The zeros of the quadratic function are the roots of the corresponding quadratic equation.

Figures 3-2, 3-3, and 3-4 show cases where the associated quadratic equation has (i) two distinct real roots, (ii) two equal real roots and (iii) no real roots.

(i)

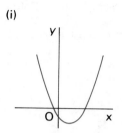

Figure 3-2

(ii)

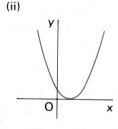

Figure 3-3

(iii)

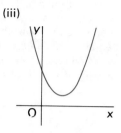

Figure 3-4

Case (iii) will be studied in Section 3.8.

In general, if we let $y = 0$ in the quadratic function $y = ax^2 + bx + c$ we have the general quadratic equation

$$ax^2 + bx + c = 0$$

The solution for this equation may be found by graphing the quadratic function $y = ax^2 + bx + c$ to locate the zeros of the function.

EXERCISE 3-1

B **1.** Solve each equation by graphing. Check each root by substitution.
(a) $x^2 + 2x - 8 = 0$
(b) $x^2 + 4x - 5 = 0$
(c) $x^2 + 6x - 7 = 0$
(d) $x^2 - x - 2 = 0$
(e) $x^2 + 4x + 3 = 0$
(f) $x^2 - 6x + 8 = 0$
(g) $x^2 + x - 20 = 0$
(h) $x^2 + 6x + 5 = 0$
(i) $x^2 - 4 = 0$
(j) $x^2 + 8x + 15 = 0$
(k) $x^2 + 6x = -8$
(l) $x^2 - 6x + 1 = -4$

C **2.** Solve graphically. Check your solutions.
(a) $-x^2 - 2x + 3 = 0$
(b) $9 - x^2 = 0$
(c) $2x^2 + 3x - 2 = 0$
(d) $x^2 - 6x + 9 = 0$
(e) $3x^2 + 5x = -2$
(f) $2x^2 - 12x + 10 = 0$

3. For the quadratic function $y = x^2 - 4$ determine the values of x so that $5 \leqslant y \leqslant 12$.

3.2 FACTORING QUADRATIC EXPRESSIONS

One method of solving quadratic equations is the *factor method*. Before using this method we shall review factoring trinomials over the integers. When factoring over the integers we restrict factors to those having only integral coefficients.

We first consider polynomials of the form $ax^2 + bx + c$ where $a = 1$. An analysis of a general expansion simplifies factoring.

$$(x + r)(x + s) = x^2 + sx + rx + rs$$
$$= x^2 + (s + r)x + rs$$
$$= x^2 + bx + c$$

Here $b = (s + r)$ and $c = rs$.

To write $x^2 - 2x - 15$ in the form $(x + r)(x + s)$,

$$b = (s + r) = -2$$

and

$$c = rs = -15$$

Hence $r = -5$ and $s = 3$ and the factors of $x^2 - 2x - 15$ are $(x - 5)$, $(x + 3)$.

$$\therefore \qquad x^2 - 2x - 15 = (x - 5)(x + 3)$$

EXAMPLE 1. *Factor* $x^2 - x - 72$

Solution
For $x^2 - x - 72$

$$b = -1 = r + s$$
$$c = -72 = rs$$

The two integers that add to give -1 and multiply to give -72 are -9 and 8.

$$x^2 - x - 72 = (x - 9)(x + 8)$$

Factoring trinomials where $a \neq 1$, such as $6x^2 + x - 2$, is simplified if we break up the middle term into two parts.

$$6x^2 + x - 2 = 6x^2 - 3x + 4x - 2$$
$$= (6x^2 - 3x) + (4x - 2)$$
$$= 3x(2x - 1) + 2(2x - 1)$$
$$= (2x - 1)(3x + 2)$$

In order to factor by grouping, x was replaced by $-3x + 4x$. The decision as to what two terms must be used to replace the middle term will be clarified if we analyze the general expansion.

$$(px + r)(qx + s) = pqx^2 + psx + qrx + rs$$
$$= pqx^2 + (ps + qr)x + rs$$
$$= ax^2 + bx + c$$

If we break up the middle term bx into two terms, say mx and nx, then

$$m + n = ps + qr = b$$

and
$$mn = pqrs = ac.$$

EXAMPLE 2. *Factor* $6x^2 - 11x - 10$

Solution
For $6x^2 - 11x - 10$, $a = 6$, $b = -11$, $c = -10$.
   To replace $-11x$ by $mx + nx$ we first determine m and n.

$$m + n = b = -11$$
$$mn = ac = -60$$

Therefore m and n are -15 and 4.

$$6x^2 - 11x - 10 = 6x^2 - 15x + 4x - 10$$
$$= (6x^2 - 15x) + (4x - 10)$$
$$= 3x(2x - 5) + 2(2x - 5)$$
$$= (2x - 5)(3x + 2)$$

EXERCISE 3-2

A **1.** Factor

(a) $x^2 + 7x + 12$ (b) $x^2 + 7x + 10$ (c) $y^2 - 7y + 10$
(d) $w^2 - 8w + 15$ (e) $x^2 - 2x - 8$ (f) $s^2 - 4s - 21$
(g) $x^2 + 3x - 10$ (h) $x^2 - 16$ (i) $x^2 - 25$
(j) $x^2 + 10x + 25$ (k) $x^2 - 14x + 49$ (l) $w^2 + 3w - 70$
(m) $x^2 + 2x - 15$ (n) $t^2 - t - 12$ (o) $r^2 + 2r - 24$
(p) $w^2 - 4w - 45$ (q) $t^2 - 2t + 1$ (r) $x^2 + 7x - 30$
(s) $x^2 + 11x + 28$ (t) $w^2 - 14w + 40$ (u) $x^2 + 6x - 27$
(v) $t^2 - t - 20$ (w) $x^2 + 3x - 88$ (x) $x^2 - 100$

2. If possible, determine integer values for m and n.

(a) $m + n = -1$, $mn = -12$ (b) $m + n = 7$, $mn = 10$
(c) $m + n = -2$, $mn = -42$ (d) $m + n = 5$, $mn = -50$
(e) $m + n = -5$, $mn = -36$ (f) $m + n = -2$, $mn = -10$
(g) $m + n = 15$, $mn = 44$ (h) $m + n = -12$, $mn = 20$
(i) $m + n = -2$, $mn = 1$ (j) $m + n = 3$, $mn = -18$
(k) $m + n = 0$, $mn = -36$ (l) $m + n = -8$, $mn = 16$

B **3.** Factor over the integers, if possible.

(a) $2x^2 + 7x + 3$ (b) $2x^2 - 7x + 5$ (c) $6w^2 - 7w - 3$
(d) $3w^2 - 11w - 20$ (e) $6y^2 + y - 1$ (f) $3x^2 - 3x - 4$
(g) $4x^2 + 12x + 9$ (h) $10w^2 - w - 2$ (i) $2w^2 + 9w + 10$

(j) $4x^2 - 9$ (k) $30t^2 + t - 20$ (l) $14s^2 + 41s + 15$

(m) $24x^2 - 46x + 21$ (n) $12w^2 + 29w + 15$ (o) $12t^2 - 25t + 12$

(p) $4x^2 + 20x + 25$ (q) $10 - 11x + 3x^2$ (r) $36x^2 + 1$

3.3 SOLVING QUADRATIC EQUATIONS BY FACTORING

Many quadratic equations can be solved by factoring. A solution by factoring depends on the following fact.

> For any two real numbers a and b, $ab = 0$ if, and only if, $a = 0$ or $b = 0$.

This includes the possibility that both a and $b = 0$.

EXAMPLE 1. *Solve* $3x^2 - 10x - 8 = 0$

Solution

$$3x^2 - 10x - 8 = 0$$
$$(3x + 2)(x - 4) = 0$$

Since the product of the two factors is zero, one or both of the factors must be zero.

$$3x + 2 = 0 \quad \text{or} \quad x - 4 = 0$$
$$3x = -2 \qquad\qquad x = 4$$
$$x = -\tfrac{2}{3}$$

The solution is checked by substitution.

Check

$$x = -\tfrac{2}{3}$$
$$\text{L.S.} = 3x^2 - 10x - 8$$
$$= 3(-\tfrac{2}{3})^2 - 10(-\tfrac{2}{3}) - 8$$
$$= \tfrac{4}{3} + \tfrac{20}{3} - 8$$
$$= 0$$
$$\text{R.S.} = 0$$

$$x = 4$$
$$\text{L.S.} = 3x^2 - 10x - 8$$
$$= 3(4)^2 - 10(4) - 8$$
$$= 48 - 40 - 8$$
$$= 0$$
$$\text{R.S.} = 0$$

The roots are $-\tfrac{2}{3}$ and 4.

EXAMPLE 2. *Solve* $10x^2 - 9x = -2$

Solution

We rewrite the equation so that one side of the equation is zero.

$$10x^2 - 9x = -2$$
$$10x^2 - 9x + 2 = 0$$
$$(5x - 2)(2x - 1) = 0$$
$$5x - 2 = 0 \quad \text{or} \quad 2x - 1 = 0$$
$$x = \tfrac{2}{5} \qquad\qquad x = \tfrac{1}{2}$$

The solution set is $\{\tfrac{2}{5}, \tfrac{1}{2}\}$

The following rules summarize the procedure for solving quadratic equations by factoring.

1. Clear fractions.
2. Transform the equation so that one side is zero.
3. Divide both sides by any numerical common factors.
4. Factor.
5. Set each factor equal to zero and solve the resulting linear equations.

EXAMPLE 3. *Solve* $10x^2 + 24 = -38x$

Solution

$$10x^2 + 24 = -38x$$
$$10x^2 + 38x + 24 = 0$$
$$5x^2 + 19x + 12 = 0 \qquad\qquad \text{Divide by 2}$$
$$(5x + 4)(x + 3) = 0$$
$$5x + 4 = 0 \quad \text{or} \quad x + 3 = 0$$
$$x = -\tfrac{4}{5} \qquad\qquad x = -3$$

The roots are $-\tfrac{4}{5}$ and -3

```
  ADDITION

    BASE
    BALL
   -------
   GAMES
```

EXAMPLE 4. *Solve* $\dfrac{4}{x-1} - \dfrac{3}{x+2} = 2$

Solution

$$\frac{4}{x-1} - \frac{3}{x+2} = 2$$

$$4(x+2) - 3(x-1) = 2(x-1)(x+2) \qquad \text{Clear fractions}$$

$$4x + 8 - 3x + 3 = 2(x^2 + x - 2) \qquad \text{(multiply by } (x-1)(x+2))$$

$$x + 11 = 2x^2 + 2x - 4$$

$$2x^2 + x - 15 = 0$$

$$(x+3)(2x-5) = 0$$

$$x + 3 = 0 \quad \text{or} \quad 2x - 5 = 0$$

$$x = -3 \qquad\qquad x = \tfrac{5}{2}$$

The roots are -3 and $\tfrac{5}{2}$

EXERCISE 3-3

A **1.** State the roots of the following quadratic equations.

(a) $(x+3)(x-1) = 0$ (b) $(x-1)(x-4) = 0$

(c) $(x+5)(x-4) = 0$ (d) $(w-7)(w+9) = 0$

(e) $(t-11)(t-7) = 0$ (f) $(x+7)(x+8) = 0$

(g) $(3x-1)(3x+5) = 0$ (h) $(4w-3)(w-5) = 0$

(i) $(2t+5)(3t+10) = 0$ (j) $(4s+7)(3s+1) = 0$

(k) $(8x+3)(7x-5) = 0$ (l) $(9w+11)(3w+14) = 0$

B **2.** Solve by factoring. Check your solution.

(a) $x^2 - x - 12 = 0$ (b) $x^2 + 9x + 18 = 0$ (c) $x^2 - x - 20 = 0$

(d) $x^2 + 8x + 15 = 0$ (e) $x^2 - 4x = 77$ (f) $x^2 + 117 = -22x$

(g) $x^2 - 23x + 126 = 0$ (h) $x^2 + 8x + 16 = 0$ (i) $x^2 + 3x = 40$

3. Solve by factoring. Check your solution.

(a) $2x^2 + 3x - 2 = 0$ (b) $3x^2 + 7x + 2 = 0$ (c) $2t^2 - 7t + 5 = 0$

(d) $6x^2 - 7x + 2 = 0$ (e) $12y^2 + 29y + 15 = 0$ (f) $2x^2 + 11x - 21 = 0$

(g) $3w^2 - 4w - 32 = 0$ (h) $6x^2 + 5x - 50 = 0$ (i) $6s^2 + 11s + 5 = 0$

(j) $8x^2 + 30x + 7 = 0$ (k) $4t^2 - 11t - 45 = 0$ (l) $2w^2 - 13w - 7 = 0$

(m) $15x^2 + 19x - 10 = 0$ (n) $8w^2 - 2w - 15 = 0$ (o) $5t^2 + 23t + 24 = 0$

4. Solve by factoring.

(a) $2x^2 - 5x = 12$ (b) $10w^2 = 7w + 12$ (c) $6t^2 + 10 = 19t$

(d) $4x^2 - 18x - 10 = 0$ (e) $6x^2 + 27x + 12 = 0$ (f) $10s^2 = 17s + 20$

(g) $30w^2 + 73w + 7 = 0$ (h) $56t^2 + 14 = 65t$ (i) $5x^2 + 21x - 54 = 0$

5. Solve

(a) $3x(x-2) - x(x+1) + 5 = 0$ (b) $x^2 + (x+1)^2 = 13$

(c) $x^2 + \tfrac{9}{2}x - 2\tfrac{1}{2} = 0$ (d) $w^2 + (w+1)^2 + (w+2)^2 = 50$

(e) $3(x-1)(x+4) - 2(2x+1)^2 = -18$ (f) $3(x-1)(x+2) - (x+1)^2 = -4$

6. Solve

(a) $\dfrac{3}{x+1} + \dfrac{4}{x+2} = 2$ (b) $\dfrac{4}{x+2} - 4 = \dfrac{3}{x-3}$

(c) $\dfrac{x}{x+1} - \dfrac{5}{x+4} = -\dfrac{1}{6}$ (d) $\dfrac{30}{x+15} + 1 = \dfrac{30}{x}$

(e) $\dfrac{2x}{x-2} - 3x + 8 = 0$ (f) $\dfrac{5}{x-1} + \dfrac{6}{x+1} - 7 = 0$

7. Write a quadratic equation whose roots are

(a) 3, 4   (b) -2, 5   (c) -7, -4

(d) $\frac{1}{2}, \frac{1}{3}$ (e) $-\frac{3}{4}, -\frac{1}{5}$ (f) r, s

3.4 SOLVING QUADRATIC EQUATIONS—SPECIAL CASES

A quadratic equation is written in the form $ax^2 + bx + c = 0$ where a, b and c may have any real values except $a \neq 0$. When one or more of these coefficients is 0, the resulting equations have relatively simple solutions.

Case 1. If $c = 0$, the equation becomes $ax^2 + bx = 0$. This type can be solved by factoring and 0 is always one of the roots.

EXAMPLE 1.   Solve $3x^2 - 5x = 0$

Solution

$$3x^2 - 5x = 0$$
$$x(3x - 5) = 0$$
$$x = 0 \quad \text{or} \quad 3x - 5 = 0$$
$$3x = 5$$
$$x = \tfrac{5}{3}$$

$\therefore$ the roots are 0 and $\frac{5}{3}$

Case 2. If $b = 0$, the equation becomes $ax^2 + c = 0$. The roots are numerically equal but opposite in sign.

EXAMPLE 2. solve $4x^2 - 7 = 0$

Solution

$$4x^2 - 7 = 0$$
$$4x^2 = 7$$
$$4x^2 = 7$$
$$x^2 = \tfrac{7}{4}$$
$$x = \pm\tfrac{1}{2}\sqrt{7}$$

If $x^2 - d = 0$

then $x^2 = d$

and $x = \pm\sqrt{d}$

$\therefore$ the roots are $\frac{1}{2}\sqrt{7}$ and $-\frac{1}{2}\sqrt{7}$

Case 3. If $b = c = 0$. the equation becomes $ax^2 = 0$. In this case both roots are 0.

If $a = 0$, the equation is linear and has only one root.

$$0x^2 + bx + c = 0$$

$$bx = -c$$

$$x = -\frac{c}{b}$$

EXERCISE 3-4

B **1.** Solve the following.

(a) $2x^2 + 7x = 0$　　(b) $x^2 - 16 = 0$　　(c) $5x^2 = 0$

(d) $3t^2 - 12 = 0$　　(e) $3x^2 - 2x = 0$　　(f) $4w^2 - 25 = 0$

(g) $-6w^2 = 0$　　(h) $5t^2 = 4t$　　(i) $100x^2 = 9$

(j) $\dfrac{w^2}{3} = 27$　　(k) $6s - 7s^2 = 0$　　(l) $25x^2 - 1 = 0$

(m) $\dfrac{3x^2 - 2x}{4} = 0$　　(n) $0 = -3w^2$　　(o) $\frac{1}{2}x^2 + \frac{1}{3}x = 0$

3.5 SOLVING QUADRATIC EQUATIONS BY COMPLETING THE SQUARE

Not all quadratic equations can be solved by factoring, so we must develop other methods of solution which are more generally applicable.

The principle of completing the square, which was used in graphing quadratic functions, is also used to solve quadratic equations.

The equation $x^2 - 9 = 0$ may be solved by factoring

$$x^2 - 9 = 0$$

$$(x - 3)(x + 3) = 0$$

$$x - 3 = 0 \quad \text{or} \quad x + 3 = 0$$

$$x = 3 \qquad\qquad x = -3$$

The equation may also be solved by taking the square root of both sides

$$x^2 - 9 = 0$$

$$x^2 = 9$$

$$x = \pm 3$$

This method may be used to solve equations of the following form.

$$(x + 3)^2 = 16$$

EXAMPLE 1. *Solve*

$$(x+3)^2 = 16$$

Solution

$$(x+3)^2 = 16$$
$$x+3 = \pm 4$$
$$x+3 = 4 \quad \text{or} \quad x+3 = -4$$
$$x = 1 \qquad\qquad x = -7$$

Check

$x = 1$	$x = -7$
L.S. $= (x+3)^2$	L.S. $= (x+3)^2$
$= (1+3)^2$	$= (-7+3)^2$
$= 16$	$= 16$
R.S. $= 16$	R.S. $= 16$

$\therefore$ the roots are 1 and -7.

Example 1 suggests that a quadratic equation can be solved if we express it in the form

$$(x+m)^2 = d$$

or
$$x^2 + 2mx + m^2 = d$$

This can be done using the principle of completing the square.

EXAMPLE 2. *Solve $x^2 - 6x + 4 = 0$*

Solution

$$x^2 - 6x + 4 = 0$$
$$x^2 - 6x + 4 - 4 = 0 - 4 \qquad \left\{ \text{Subtract the constant term from both sides} \right.$$
$$x^2 - 6x = -4$$
$$x^2 - 6x + 9 = -4 + 9 \qquad \left\{ \text{Add the square of half the coefficient of } x \right.$$
$$x^2 - 6x + 9 = 5$$
$$(x-3)^2 = 5$$
$$x - 3 = \pm\sqrt{5} \qquad \left\{ \text{Write the left side as a perfect square} \right.$$
$$x - 3 = \sqrt{5} \quad \text{or} \quad x - 3 = -\sqrt{5} \qquad \left\{ \begin{array}{l} \text{Take the square root of both sides and} \\ \text{proceed as in Example 1} \end{array} \right.$$
$$x = 3 + \sqrt{5} \qquad\quad x = 3 - \sqrt{5}$$

The solution set is $\{3+\sqrt{5}, 3-\sqrt{5}\}$

If the coefficient of x^2 is not 1, a preliminary step is required.

EXAMPLE 3. *Solve* $2x^2 - 3x - 1 = 0$

Solution

$$2x^2 - 3x - 1 = 0$$

$$x^2 - \tfrac{3}{2}x - \tfrac{1}{2} = 0 \qquad \text{Divide by 2}$$

$$x^2 - \tfrac{3}{2}x = \tfrac{1}{2} \qquad \text{Add } \tfrac{1}{2} \text{ to each side}$$

$$x^2 - \tfrac{3}{2}x + \tfrac{9}{16} = \tfrac{1}{2} + \tfrac{9}{16} \qquad \text{Complete the square}$$

$$(x - \tfrac{3}{4})^2 = \tfrac{17}{16} \qquad \text{Simplify}$$

$$x - \tfrac{3}{4} = \pm \frac{\sqrt{17}}{4} \qquad \text{Square root}$$

$$x = \tfrac{3}{4} \pm \frac{\sqrt{17}}{4}$$

$$x = \frac{3 \pm \sqrt{17}}{4}$$

The solution set is $\left\{ \dfrac{3+\sqrt{17}}{4}, \dfrac{3-\sqrt{17}}{4} \right\}$

This method of solving quadratic equations must be understood because it leads to the derivation of the quadratic formula which will be discussed in the next section.

EXERCISE 3-5

A **1.** State the value of k that makes each trinomial a perfect square.

(a) $x^2 + 6x + k$ (b) $x^2 - 8x + k$ (c) $x^2 - 10x + k$

(d) $x^2 - 2x + k$ (e) $x^2 + 4x + k$ (f) $x^2 - 12x + k$

(g) $x^2 + 18x + k$ (h) $x^2 - 22x + k$ (i) $x^2 - 3x + k$

(j) $x^2 + x + k$ (k) $x^2 - 7x + k$ (l) $x^2 + \tfrac{1}{2}x + k$

(m) $x^2 - \tfrac{2}{3}x + k$ (n) $x^2 + \tfrac{1}{5}x + k$ (o) $x^2 - \tfrac{3}{5}x + k$

B **2.** Solve.

(a) $(x+4)^2 = 9$ (b) $(x-2)^2 = 3$ (c) $(x+1)^2 = 7$

(d) $(x-5)^2 = 8$ (e) $(x+7)^2 = 27$ (f) $(x-6)^2 = 12$

(g) $(x+\tfrac{1}{2})^2 = 6$ (h) $(x-\tfrac{1}{2})^2 = \tfrac{3}{4}$ (i) $(x+\tfrac{1}{3})^2 = \tfrac{5}{9}$

(j) $(x-\tfrac{3}{4})^2 = \tfrac{7}{16}$ (k) $(x+\tfrac{5}{2})^2 = \tfrac{3}{8}$ (l) $(x-\tfrac{4}{3})^2 = \tfrac{6}{27}$

3. Solve by completing the square.

(a) $x^2 - 2x - 8 = 0$ (b) $x^2 - 4x + 1 = 0$ (c) $x^2 + 6x - 2 = 0$

(d) $2w^2 + 8w + 5 = 0$ (e) $2x^2 - 8x + 3 = 0$ (f) $3t^2 - 6t + 2 = 0$

(g) $5x^2 + 5x - 2 = 0$ (h) $2s^2 - 3s - 5 = 0$ (i) $-x^2 + 3x + 1 = 0$

(j) $\tfrac{1}{2}x^2 + x - 1 = 0$ (k) $3t^2 + 4t - 2 = 0$ (l) $7x^2 - 2x - 2 = 0$

3.6 THE QUADRATIC FORMULA

The method of completing the square can be used to solve the general quadratic equation $ax^2 + bx + c = 0$, $a \neq 0$.

$$ax^2 + bx + c = 0$$

$$x^2 + \frac{b}{a}x + \frac{c}{a} = 0 \qquad \text{Divide by } a$$

$$x^2 + \frac{b}{a}x + \frac{c}{a} - \frac{c}{a} = 0 - \frac{c}{a} \qquad \text{Subtract } \frac{c}{a}$$

$$x^2 + \frac{b}{a}x = -\frac{c}{a}$$

$$x^2 + \frac{b}{a}x + \frac{b^2}{4a^2} = \frac{b^2}{4a^2} - \frac{c}{a} \qquad \text{Complete the square}$$

$$\left(x + \frac{b}{2a}\right)^2 = \frac{b^2 - 4ac}{4a^2} \qquad \text{Simplify}$$

$$x + \frac{b}{2a} = \pm\sqrt{\frac{b^2 - 4ac}{4a^2}} \qquad \text{Square root}$$

$$x + \frac{b}{2a} = \pm\frac{\sqrt{b^2 - 4ac}}{2a}$$

$$x + \frac{b}{2a} - \frac{b}{2a} = -\frac{b}{2a} \pm \frac{\sqrt{b^2 - 4ac}}{2a} \qquad \text{Subtract } \frac{b}{2a}$$

$$x = -\frac{b}{2a} \pm \frac{\sqrt{b^2 - 4ac}}{2a} \qquad \text{Simplify}$$

$$x = \frac{-b \pm \sqrt{b^2 - 4ac}}{2a}$$

The solution for a quadratic equation $ax^2 + bx + c = 0$ is given by the quadratic formula

$$x = \frac{-b \pm \sqrt{b^2 - 4ac}}{2a}$$

EXAMPLE 1. *Solve $3x^2 - 5x + 2 = 0$ using the quadratic formula.*

Solution

For $3x^2 - 5x + 2 = 0$,

$$a = 3, \qquad b = -5, \qquad c = 2$$

$$x = \frac{-b \pm \sqrt{b^2 - 4ac}}{2a}$$

$$= \frac{-(-5) \pm \sqrt{(-5)^2 - 4(3)(2)}}{2(3)}$$

$$= \frac{5 \pm \sqrt{25 - 24}}{6}$$

$$= \frac{5 \pm \sqrt{1}}{6}$$

$$= \frac{5 \pm 1}{6}$$

Therefore

$$x = \frac{5 + 1}{6} \quad \text{or} \quad x = \frac{5 - 1}{6}$$

$$= 1 \qquad\qquad = \tfrac{2}{3}$$

The solution set is $\{1, \tfrac{2}{3}\}$

EXAMPLE 2. *Solve*

$$5x^2 + 2x - 2 = 0$$

Solution

For $5x^2 + 2x - 2 = 0$

$$a = 5, \qquad b = 2, \qquad c = -2$$

$$x = \frac{-b \pm \sqrt{b^2 - 4ac}}{2a}$$

$$= \frac{-(2) \pm \sqrt{(2)^2 - 4(5)(-2)}}{2(5)}$$

$$= \frac{-2 \pm \sqrt{4 + 40}}{10}$$

$$= \frac{-2 \pm \sqrt{44}}{10} = \frac{-2 \pm 2\sqrt{11}}{10}$$

$$= \frac{-1 \pm \sqrt{11}}{5}$$

The roots are $\dfrac{-1 + \sqrt{11}}{5}$ and $\dfrac{-1 - \sqrt{11}}{5}$

EXAMPLE 3. *Solve*

$$\frac{2}{x} - \frac{3}{x+1} = 1$$

Solution

$$\frac{2}{x} - \frac{3}{x+1} = 1$$

$$2(x+1) - 3x = x(x+1) \qquad \text{Multiply by } x(x-1) \text{ to clear fractions}$$

$$2x + 2 - 3x = x^2 + x$$

$$-x^2 - 2x + 2 = 0$$

$$x^2 + 2x - 2 = 0 \qquad \text{Multiply by } -1$$

Here $a = 1$, $b = 2$ and $c = -2$

$$x = \frac{-b \pm \sqrt{b^2 - 4ac}}{2a}$$

$$= \frac{-(2) \pm \sqrt{(2)^2 - 4(1)(-2)}}{2(1)} \qquad \text{Find an integer } x \text{ such that}$$
$$\frac{x}{2} \text{ is a perfect square and } \frac{x}{3}$$
$$= \frac{-2 \pm \sqrt{4+8}}{2} \qquad \text{is a perfect cube.}$$

$$= \frac{-2 \pm \sqrt{12}}{2}$$

$$= \frac{-2 \pm 2\sqrt{3}}{2}$$

$$= -1 \pm \sqrt{3}$$

The roots are $-1 + \sqrt{3}$ and $-1 - \sqrt{3}$

The roots may be expressed to the nearest tenth as follows

$$x = -1 + \sqrt{3} \qquad\qquad x = -1 - \sqrt{3}$$

$$\doteq -1 + 1.73 \qquad\qquad \doteq -1 - 1.73$$

$$\doteq 0.73 \qquad\qquad\quad\; \doteq -2.7$$

$$\doteq 0.7$$

EXERCISE 3-6

A 1. State values for a, b and c for each of the following.

(a) $2x^2 + 7x - 1 = 0$ (b) $4x - 7 + 5x^2 = 0$ (c) $3x^2 + 2x = 7$

(d) $9x^2 - 7 = 4x$ (e) $0 = x^2 - 7x + 1$ (f) $4 - 2x^2 = 9x$

(g) $2x^2 - 7 = 0$ (h) $5x^2 = 9x$ (i) $4 - x^2 + \sqrt{2}x = 0$

B 2. Solve using the quadratic formula.

(a) $x^2 + 6x + 8 = 0$ (b) $x^2 - 2x - 15 = 0$ (c) $2w^2 - 3w + 1 = 0$

(d) $10t^2 - 21t + 9 = 0$ (e) $7w^2 - 3w = 0$ (f) $5x^2 - 16 = 0$

(g) $4s^2 + 4s + 1 = 0$ (h) $x^2 - 2x - 4 = 0$ (i) $x^2 - x - 5 = 0$

(j) $x^2 + 2x - 6 = 0$ (k) $2x^2 + 8x - 3 = 0$ (l) $7x^2 - 2x - 2 = 0$

3. Solve using the quadratic formula.

(a) $2x^2 - x = 3$ (b) $6x = 2 - x^2$ (c) $3w^2 = 2w + 2$

(d) $2s^2 = 8s - 7$ (e) $2 = 3x^2 + 8x$ (f) $10x^2 - 4x - 4 = 0$

(g) $6x + 6 = 15x^2$ (h) $-x^2 - 7x - 1 = 0$ (i) $1 = 8x + 3x^2$

(j) $1 = 3t^2 + 7t$ (k) $1 = 5x^2$ (l) $4x^2 + 4x = 14$

4. Solve.

(a) $x^2 - 0.1x - 0.06 = 0$ (b) $w^2 + 2.76 = 3.5w$

(c) $t^2 + 3t - 14.56 = 0$ (d) $3.1x + 0.66 = x^2$

(e) $0.1t^2 + 0.2 = 0.45t$ (f) $0.02x^2 + 0.13x - 0.57 = 0$

5. Solve.

(a) $\frac{1}{2}x^2 - x = \frac{5}{2}$ (b) $2t(t - 1) - 3 = 0$

(c) $2(1 - x^2) - 3x(1 - x) = 7$ (d) $\frac{x^2}{3} - x - 1\frac{2}{3} = 0$

(e) $\frac{1}{2}w^2 - \frac{w}{4} - 1 = 0$ (f) $2(x - 2)(x + 1) - (x + 3) = 0$

(g) $(3x - 2)(x - 3) = (x - 4)(x - 1)$ (h) $\frac{2}{x - 1} + \frac{3}{x + 2} = 1$

(i) $\frac{3}{x + 2} + \frac{2}{x - 3} = 2$ (j) $\frac{x + 3}{2x - 1} = \frac{x - 3}{x + 4}$

(k) $\frac{4}{w - 2} + \frac{2}{w + 2} = 3$ (l) $\frac{x + 4}{x + 5} - \frac{2x + 1}{x + 2} = 0$

(m) $\frac{2x}{x + 1} - \frac{3}{x - 1} = \frac{4}{x^2 - 1}$ (n) $\frac{x^2 + 5x + 6}{2x^2 + 3x - 2} = \frac{x - 1}{x + 2}$

6. Solve and express irrational roots to the nearest tenth.

(a) $x^2 - 2x - 5 = 0$ (b) $2w^2 - 3w = 3$

(c) $\frac{x}{4} - \frac{x^2}{2} = -1$ (d) $\frac{3}{x} - \frac{4}{x + 2} = 2$

(e) $\frac{1}{2x - 1} = \frac{3}{4x^2 + 4x - 7}$ (f) $\frac{x + 2}{x - 1} = \frac{2x + 3}{x + 2}$

7. Solve for x.

(a) $\sqrt{2}x^2 - x - 3\sqrt{2} = 0$ (b) $2x^2 - \sqrt{3}x - 1 = 0$

(c) $\sqrt{2}x^2 - \sqrt{3}x - \sqrt{2} = 0$ (d) $x^2 - kx + k - 1 = 0$

3.7 APPLICATIONS OF QUADRATIC EQUATIONS

Many problems can be solved by translating the problem into an equation and then solving the equation. In this section we shall consider problems that give rise to quadratic equations.

EXAMPLE 1. *The sum of the squares of two consecutive even integers is 452. Find the integers.*

Solution
Let x represent the first even integer. Then $x+2$ represents the next even integer. The sum of their squares is 452.

$$x^2+(x+2)^2=452, x \in I$$
$$x^2+x^2+4x+4=452$$
$$2x^2+4x-448=0$$
$$x^2+2x-224=0$$
$$(x-14)(x+16)=0$$
$$x=14 \quad \text{or} \quad x=-16$$

Since x represents the first even integer, we see that there are two solutions.
When $x=14$, $x+2=16$ and $14^2+16^2=452$
When $x=-16$, $x+2=-14$ and $(-16)^2+(-14)^2=452$
The two integers are 14 and 16 or -16 and -14

EXAMPLE 2. *A rectangular supermarket, 90 m by 60 m is to be built on a city block having an area of 9000 m². There is to be a uniform strip around the building for parking. How wide is the strip?*

Solution
Let the width of the strip be x metres. Then $x>0$. The dimensions of the city block are $(90+2x)$ metres by $(60+2x)$ metres. The area of the block is 9000 m²

$$(90+2x)(60+2x)=9000$$
$$5400+180x+120x+4x^2=9000$$
$$4x^2+300x-3600=0$$
$$x^2+75x-900=0$$

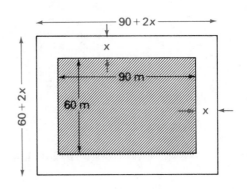

$$x = \frac{-b \pm \sqrt{b^2 - 4ac}}{2a}$$

$$= \frac{-(75) \pm \sqrt{(75)^2 - 4(1)(-900)}}{2(1)}$$

$$= \frac{-75 \pm \sqrt{9225}}{2}$$

$$= \frac{-75 \pm 15\sqrt{41}}{2} \quad \text{and} \quad x > 0$$

$$\therefore \quad x = \frac{-75 + 15\sqrt{41}}{2}$$

$$\left(\text{We reject the root } \frac{-75 - 15\sqrt{41}}{2} \text{ since } x > 0.\right)$$

To determine the width to the nearest tenth of a metre, we evaluate $\sqrt{41}$ to the nearest hundredth and substitute.

$$x \doteq \frac{-75 + 15(6.40)}{2}$$

$$\doteq \frac{-75 + 96.00}{2}$$

$$\doteq 10.50$$

$\therefore$ the width of the strip is 10.5 m.

EXAMPLE 3. *A jet flew from New York to Los Angeles, a distance of 4200 km. On the return trip the speed was increased by 100 km/h. If the total trip took 13 h, what was the speed from New York to Los Angeles?*

Solution

Let x represent the speed from New York to Los Angeles, $x > 0$.
Then $x + 100$ represents the speed from Los Angeles to New York.
Complete the DST table.

D S T	Distance km	Speed km/h	Time h
N.Y. TO L.A.	4200	x	$\dfrac{4200}{x}$
L.A. TO N.Y.	4200	$x + 100$	$\dfrac{4200}{x + 100}$

The total time is 13 h.

$$\frac{4200}{x} + \frac{4200}{x+100} = 13$$

$4200(x+100) + 4200x = 13x(x+100)$ Multiply by $x(x+100)$

$4200x + 420\,000 + 4200x = 13x^2 + 1300x$

$13x^2 - 7100x - 420\,000 = 0$

$(13x + 700)(x - 600) = 0$

$$x = -\frac{700}{13} \quad \text{or} \quad x = 600$$

Since we reject $-\frac{700}{13}$

∴ the speed from New York to Los angeles is 600 km/h.

EXERCISE 3-7

1. The product of two consecutive even integers is 224. Find the integers.

2. The product of two consecutive odd integers is 323. Find the integers.

3. The sum of a number and its square is 272. Find the number.

4. The sum of the squares of two consecutive positive integers is 481. Find the integers.

5. The sum of the squares of three consecutive integers is 434. Find the integers.

6. The difference between a number and its square is 420. Find the number.

7. The sum of two numbers is 20 and the sum of their squares is 272. Find the numbers.

8. The sum of two numbers is 30 and their product is 209. Find the numbers.

9. The product of two consecutive even integers is 528. Find the integers.

10. The product of two consecutive positive odd integers is 195. Find the integers.

11. The sum of a number and twice its square is 300. Find the number.

12. The sum of twice a number and three times its square is 261. Find the number.

13. The sum of the squares of three consecutive even integers is 116. Find the integers.

14. The difference between three times a number and its square is 378. Find the number.

15. Two numbers differ by seven and the sum of their squares is 389. Find the numbers.

16. The hypotenuse of a right triangle is 15 cm. The sum of the legs is 21 cm. Find the legs of the triangle.

17. The hypotenuse of a right triangle is 26 cm. The sum of the legs is 34 cm. Find the legs of the triangle.

18. The length of a rectangle is 6 m longer than the width. If the area of the rectangle is 91 m², find the dimensions of the rectangle.

19. The hypotenuse of a right triangle is 6 cm and one leg is 2 cm longer than the other. Find the length of each leg to the nearest tenth of a centimetre.

20. A lidless box is constructed from a square piece of tin by cutting a 10 cm square from each corner and bending up the sides for the box. If the volume of the box is 1200 cm³, find the dimensions to the nearest tenth of a centimetre.

21. A rectangular piece of tin 40 cm by 30 cm is to be made into an open box with a base of 900 cm² by cutting equal squares from the four corners and then bending up the sides. Find, to the nearest tenth, the length of the side of the square cut from each corner.

22. A playground, which measures 60 m by 40 m, is to be doubled in area by extending each side an equal amount. By how much should each side be extended?

Determine the pattern.
Find the missing number.

21	62	74	55
29	45	61	▨
33	18	25	21
25	35	38	58

23. A rectangular skating rink measuring 30 m by 20 m is to be doubled in area by adding a strip at one end and a strip of the same width along one side. Find the width of the strips.

24. A local building code requires that all factories must be surrounded by a lawn. The width of the lawn must be uniform and the area of the lawn must equal to the area of the factory. What must be the width of a lawn surrounding a rectangular factory that measures 120 m by 80 m?

25. A factory is to be built on a lot that measures 80 m by 60 m. A lawn of uniform width and equal in area to the factory must surround the factory. What dimensions must the factory have?

26. A jet flew from Montreal to San Francisco, a distance of 4000 km. On the return trip the speed was increased by 300 km/h. If the total trip took 13 h, what was the speed from Montreal to San Francisco?

27. Pete drove from Buffalo to Boston, a distance of 720 km. On the return trip he increased his speed by 10 km/h. If the total trip took 17 h, what was his speed from Boston to Buffalo?

28. Mary drove from Dry Creek to Cactus, a distance of 250 km. She increased her speed by 10 km/h for the 360 km trip from Cactus to Spur. If the total trip took 11 h, what was her speed from Dry Creek to Cactus?

29. A jet flew from Tokyo to Bangkok, a distance of 4800 km. On the return trip the speed was decreased by 200 km/h. If the difference in the times of the flights was 2 h, what was the speed from Bangkok to Tokyo?

30. If a rock is thrown down a well, the distance, d, travelled in metres after t seconds is given by the formula

$$d = 5t^2 + vt$$

where v is the initial velocity in metres per second.
(a) How deep is the well if $v = 0$ (the rock is dropped not thrown) and the splash is heard after 3 s?
(b) How long will it take until the splash is heard if $d = 200$ m and $v = 0$?
(c) How long will it take until the splash is heard if $v = 4$ m/s and $d = 300$ m?

31. It took a crew $2\frac{2}{3}$ h to row 6 km upstream and back again. If the rate of flow of the stream was 3 km/h, what was the rowing rate of the crew in still water?

3.8 COMPLEX NUMBERS

The equation $x + 1 = 0$ has no solution in the set of whole numbers. However it does have a solution in the set of integers. Similarly the equation $x^2 + 1 = 0$ has no solution over the real numbers since for any real number $x^2 \geqslant 0$. We wish to enlarge the replacement set of x to obtain a set over which $x + 1 = 0$ does have a solution. We do this by introducing a number i, called the imaginary unit, with the property that

$$i^2 = -1$$

> The imaginary unit i is a number whose square is -1; that is,
>
> $$i^2 = -1$$
>
> or $\quad i = \sqrt{-1}$

The equation $x^2 + 1 = 0$ has i as a solution.

$$\begin{aligned}
\text{L.S.} &= x^2 + 1 & \text{R.S.} = 0 \\
&= (i)^2 + 1 \\
&= (\sqrt{-1})^2 + 1 \\
&= -1 + 1 \\
&= 0
\end{aligned}$$

It will be necessary to combine i with real numbers so that expressions such as $4 + 3i$ and $5 - 2i$ have meaning. We want the sum of a real number and an imaginary number to be a number. This new number is called a *complex number*.

> A complex number is a number of the form $a + bi$ where a and b are real numbers and $i^2 = -1$

If $b = 0$ then $a + bi = a$. In other words a real number can also be considered to be a complex number since 5 can be written as $5 + 0i$. If $a = 0$ then $a + bi = bi$. Numbers such as $7i$ are called *pure imaginary numbers*.

Complex numbers may be summarized as follows.

<table>
<tr><td colspan="3">Complex Numbers C
$C = a + bi$, a, b real numbers and $i^2 = -1$</td></tr>
<tr><th>Restriction</th><th>Type</th><th>Example</th></tr>
<tr><td>$b = 0$</td><td>real</td><td>5</td></tr>
<tr><td>$a = 0$</td><td>pure imaginary</td><td>$7i$</td></tr>
<tr><td>$a, b \neq 0$</td><td>imaginary</td><td>$4 + 3i$</td></tr>
</table>

Consider the following example.

$$(2i)^2 = (2i) \times (2i) = 4i^2 = 4(-1) = -4$$

More generally, for any $x > 0$

$$(\sqrt{x}\,i)^2 = (\sqrt{x})^2 \times i^2 = x(-1) = -x,$$

and so we make the following definition.

> For every positive real number x, $\sqrt{-x} = \sqrt{x}\,i$

EXAMPLE 1. *Simplify the following.*

(a) $\sqrt{-81}$ (b) $\sqrt{-20}$

Solution

(a) $\sqrt{-81} = \sqrt{81} \times i$ (b) $\sqrt{-20} = \sqrt{20} \times i$
$\qquad = 9i$ $\qquad = 2\sqrt{5} \times i$
$\qquad = 2i\sqrt{5}$

EXAMPLE 2. *Simplify the following.*

(a) $(3 + 2i) + (5 - 4i)$ (b) $(1 + 3i)(1 - 3i)$ (c) i^6

Solution

(a) $(3 + 2i) + (5 - 4i) = (3 + 5) + (2i - 4i)$
$\qquad = 8 - 2i$

We assume that the laws that hold for real numbers also apply to complex numbers.

(b) $(1+3i)(1-3i) = 1-3i+3i-9i^2$

$\qquad\qquad = 1-9i^2$

$\qquad\qquad = 1-9(-1)$

$\qquad\qquad = 10$

(c) $i^6 = i^2 \times 1^2 \times 1^2$

$\qquad = (-1) \times (-1) \times (-1)$

$\qquad = -1$

EXAMPLE 3. *Solve* $x^2 - 2x + 5 = 0$, $x \in C$

Solution

$$x^2 - 2x + 5 = 0$$

$$x = \frac{-b \pm \sqrt{b^2 - 4ac}}{2a}$$

$$= \frac{-(-2) \pm \sqrt{(-2)^2 - 4(1)(5)}}{2(1)}$$

$$= \frac{2 \pm \sqrt{-16}}{2}$$

$$= \frac{2 \pm 4i}{2}$$

$$= 1 \pm 2i$$

$\therefore$ the roots are $1 + 2i$ and $1 - 2i$.

EXAMPLE 4. *Solve* $\dfrac{3}{x+3} - \dfrac{2}{x+2} = 1$, $x \in C$

Solution

$$\frac{3}{x+3} - \frac{2}{x+2} = 1$$

$$3(x+2) - 2(x+3) = (x+3)(x+2) \qquad \text{Multiply by } (x+3)(x+2)$$

$$3x + 6 - 2x - 6 = x^2 + 5x + 6$$

$$x^2 + 4x + 6 = 0$$

$$x = \frac{-b \pm \sqrt{b^2 - 4ac}}{2a}$$

$$= \frac{-(4) \pm \sqrt{4^2 - 4(1)(6)}}{2(1)}$$

$$= \frac{-4 \pm \sqrt{-8}}{2}$$

$$= \frac{-4 \pm 2i\sqrt{2}}{2}$$

$$= -2 \pm i\sqrt{2}$$

$\therefore$ the roots are $-2 + i\sqrt{2}$ and $-2 - i\sqrt{2}$

The concept of imaginary numbers can be illustrated further by the following example.

EXAMPLE 5. *Sketch the graph of* $y = x^2 - 4x + 6$

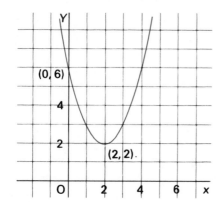

Solution

$$y = x^2 - 4x + 6$$
$$= x^2 - 4x + 4 - 4 + 6$$
$$= (x - 2)^2 + 2$$

To determine the y-intercept we let $x = 0$

$$y = x^2 - 4x + 6$$

When $x = 0$, $y = 6$

To determine the x-intercepts, if they exist, we let $y = 0$

When $y = 0$,

$$x^2 - 4x + 6 = 0$$

$$x = \frac{4 \pm \sqrt{16 - 24}}{2}$$

$$= \frac{4 \pm \sqrt{-8}}{2}$$

$$= \frac{4 \pm 2i\sqrt{2}}{2}$$

$$= 2 \pm i\sqrt{2}$$

The corresponding quadratic equation has no real roots and hence the parabola has no x-intercepts.

The Argand Plane

Complex numbers can be represented geometrically in the complex plane, often called the Argand plane after Jean R. Argand who gave the representation in 1806.

The complex number $3+2i$ is represented by the directed line segment, or vector, from the origin to the point $(3, 2)$. The horizontal axis is the real axis, and the vertical axis is the imaginary axis. Real numbers, such as 5, are written in the form $5+0i$ and are represented by points on the real axis. Pure imaginary numbers such as $3i$, are written $0+3i$ and are represented by points on the imaginary axis.

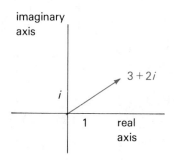

Multiplying the complex number $z = 3+4i$ by i,

$$(3+4i)i = 3i+4i^2$$
$$= -4+3i$$

results in another complex number whose vector representation has the same magnitude. This new vector has been rotated $90°$ in a counterclockwise direction.

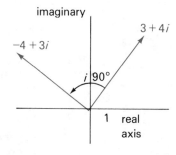

What is the result of multiplying a complex number by i^2? i^3? i^4? 2? 3? 4?

EXERCISE 3-8

1. Simplify.
(a) $(3-i)+(2+4i)$ (b) $(2+5i)+(3-2i)$
(c) $(5-2i)+(3+4i)$ (d) $(3+4i)-(2+2i)$
(e) $(5-3i)-(2+4i)$ (f) $(3+4i)+(2-4i)$

2. Simplify the following.
(a) $\sqrt{-4}$ (b) $\sqrt{-25}$ (c) $\sqrt{-2}$ (d) $\sqrt{-100}$
(e) $\sqrt{-5}$ (f) $\sqrt{-20}$ (g) $\sqrt{-12}$ (h) $\sqrt{-18}$
(i) $\sqrt{-16}$ (j) i^2 (k) $2i^2$ (l) $(\sqrt{-3})^2$
(m) $(\sqrt{-5})^2$ (n) $\sqrt{(-5)^2}$ (o) i^3 (p) i^4
(q) $(\sqrt{-7})^2$ (r) $(5i)(2i)$ (s) $(-3i)(7i)$ (t) i^5

3. Expand and express in the form $a+bi$.
(a) $(2i-1)(2i+1)$ (b) $(1-i)(1+i)$ (c) $(1+i)^2$
(d) $(2+i)(3-i)$ (e) $(i^2-1)^2$ (f) $(5+2i)(1-i)$
(g) $3i(2i^2-5i+2)$ (h) i^{100} (i) $(i^2+1)(i^2-1)$

4. Solve for x, $x \in C$.

(a) $x^2 - 2x + 4 = 0$ (b) $x^2 - 2x + 6 = 0$ (c) $x^2 + 7 = 2x$

(d) $x^2 - 2x - 6 = 0$ (e) $2x^2 + 8x + 9 = 0$ (f) $x^2 + 9 = 0$

(g) $2x^2 + 7 = 0$ (h) $5x^2 + 2 = 2x$ (i) $0 = 3x^2 - 2x + 2$

(j) $7x^2 - 2x + 2 = 0$ (k) $2x^2 + x + 4 = 0$ (l) $3x^2 - 14x - 5 = 0$

C   **5.** Solve, $x \in C$.

(a) $x^2 + (x+1)^2 + (x+2)^2 = -1$ (b) $\dfrac{1}{x-1} - \dfrac{2}{x-2} = 1$

(c) $\dfrac{x-2}{3x} = \dfrac{x-4}{x+2}$ (d) $\dfrac{x^2 - 2x + 1}{x^2 - 1} = \dfrac{3x - 1}{x + 2}$

3.9 THE DISCRIMINANT

Using the quadratic formula we found the roots of $ax^2 + bx + c = 0$ to be

$$r_1 = \frac{-b + \sqrt{b^2 - 4ac}}{2a}, \qquad r_2 = \frac{-b - \sqrt{b^2 - 4ac}}{2a}$$

The quantity under the radical sign, $b^2 - 4ac$, is called the discriminant of the quadratic equation. The discriminant is useful because it enables us to determine the nature of the roots of $ax^2 + bx + c = 0$ without solving the equation.

There are three possibilities for the roots of a quadratic equation.

(a) imaginary

(b) real and distinct

(c) real and equal

We know that the value of the discriminant must be positive, zero or negative. We shall now consider each case.

$$r_1 = \frac{-b + \sqrt{b^2 - 4ac}}{2a}$$

$$r_2 = \frac{-b - \sqrt{b^2 - 4ac}}{2a}$$

(a) $b^2 - 4ac$ is negative. If $b^2 - 4ac < 0$, the expression $\pm\sqrt{b^2 - 4ac}$ represents the square root of a negative number. The equation has no real roots. The roots are imaginary.

(b) $b^2 - 4ac$ is positive. If $b^2 - 4ac > 0$, the expression $\pm\sqrt{b^2 - 4ac}$ has two values, one positive and one negative. Hence the quadratic formula will give two real numbers and there will be two real roots of the quadratic equation.

$$r_1 = \frac{-b + 0}{2a}$$

$$r_2 = \frac{-b - 0}{2a}$$

(c) $b^2 - 4ac$ is zero. If $b^2 - 4ac = 0$, the expression $\pm\sqrt{b^2 - 4ac}$ has the value zero. Both roots of the quadratic equation will have the same value, $-\dfrac{b}{2a}$. The quadratic equation has equal roots.

EXAMPLE 1. *Determine the nature of the roots of the quadratic equations*

$$\text{(a) } x^2 - 6x + 9 = 0$$

$$\text{(b) } 3x^2 + 5x - 2 = 0$$

$$\text{(c) } 2x^2 + x = -5$$

Solution

(a) $b^2 - 4ac = (-6)^2 - 4(1)(9)$

$$= 36 - 36$$

$$= 0$$

∴ roots are real and equal

(b) $b^2 - 4ac = (5)^2 - 4(3)(-2)$

$$= 25 + 24$$

$$= 49$$

∴ roots are real and distinct

(c) $b^2 - 4ac = (1)^2 - 4(2)(5)$ $c = 5$

$$= 1 - 40$$

$$= -39$$

∴ roots are imaginary

EXAMPLE 2. *Given that the quadratic equation $kx^2 + (k+8)x + 9 = 0$ has equal roots, find k.*

Solution

$$b^2 - 4ac = (k+8)^2 - 4(k)(9)$$

$$= k^2 + 16k + 64 - 36k$$

$$= k^2 - 20k + 64$$

Since the roots are equal, the discriminant is zero.

$$k^2 - 20k + 64 = 0$$

$$(k - 4)(k - 16) = 0$$

∴ $k = 4$ or $k = 16$

The discriminant can also be used to describe the relationship of the graph of the function $y = ax^2 + bx + x$ to the x-axis. Since the x-intercepts are found by letting $y = 0$, the discriminant determines whether the graph of $y = ax^2 + bx + c$ will intersect the x-axis

(a) not at all
(b) in two distinct points
(c) in one point.

(a)

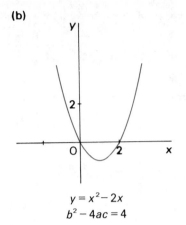

$$y = x^2 - 4x + 5$$
$$b^2 - 4ac = -4$$

(b)

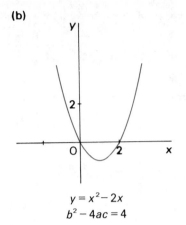

$$y = x^2 - 2x$$
$$b^2 - 4ac = 4$$

(c)

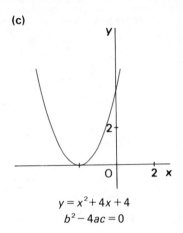

$$y = x^2 + 4x + 4$$
$$b^2 - 4ac = 0$$

The following is a summary of the three cases.

Parabola	Equation	Discriminant	Roots	Graph
$y = x^2 - 6x + 11$	$x^2 - 6x + 11 = 0$	$(-6)^2 - 4(1)(11)$ $= -8$	Imaginary	
$y = x^2 - 6x + 7$	$x^2 - 6x + 7 = 0$	$(-6)^2 - 4(1)(7)$ $= 8$	Real, Distinct	
$y = x^2 - 6x + 9$	$x^2 - 6x + 9 = 0$	$(-6)^2 - 4(1)(9)$ $= 0$	Real, Equal	

EXERCISE 3-9

A **1.** If the discriminant of a quadratic equation has the given value, state the characteristics of the roots.

(a) -15 (b) 16 (c) 35 (d) -9
(e) 42 (f) 121 (g) 36 (h) 0
(i) -22 (j) 3.4 (k) -1.5 (l) 1.44

2. Assuming that a, b, and c are real numbers, how many times would the graph of $y = ax^2 + bx + c$ intersect the x-axis if

(a) the discriminant of $ax^2 + bx + c = 0$ is positive?
(b) the discriminant of $ax^2 + bx + c = 0$ is negative?
(c) the discriminant of $ax^2 + bx + c = 0$ is zero?

B **3.** Find the discriminant and determine the nature of the roots of the following equations.

(a) $x^2 - 8x + 16 = 0$ (b) $x^2 - x - 5 = 0$ (c) $x^2 + 3x + 10 = 0$
(d) $x^2 + 2x + 7 = 0$ (e) $4x^2 + 9 = 12x$ (f) $x^2 - 16 = 0$
(g) $3x^2 - x + 4 = 0$ (h) $2x^2 + x = 5$ (i) $5x^2 + 7x = 0$
(j) $12x^2 - x = 6$ (k) $x^2 + 5 = 3x$ (l) $9x^2 = 5x$

4. Determine the characteristics of the roots of the following equations.

(a) $\dfrac{x^2}{2} + 4x + 4 = 0$ (b) $\frac{1}{3}x^2 + \frac{1}{2}x - 1 = 0$ (c) $\dfrac{x-1}{2} - x^2 - 3 = 0$

(d) $(x+1)(x-2) = 4$ (e) $4(x^2 - 5x + 5) = -5$ (f) $\dfrac{x^2}{5} = 5$

(g) $2(x^2 - 3) = 4x$ (h) $2x^2 - \sqrt{5}x = 4$ (i) $3\sqrt{2}x^2 - x - \sqrt{2} = 0$

5. Determine the value of k that will give the indicated solution.

(a) $x^2 - 4x + k = 0$; equal roots
(b) $x^2 + 3x - 2k = 0$; imaginary roots
(c) $kx^2 - 2x + 1 = 0$; real distinct roots
(d) $3kx^2 - 3x + 1 = 0$; imaginary roots
(e) $x^2 + kx + 16 = 0$; real distinct roots
(f) $x^2 + 4kx + 1 = 0$; equal roots
(g) $(k+1)x^2 - 2x - 3 = 0$; imaginary roots
(h) $x^2 + (k+2)x + 2k = 0$; equal roots
(i) $x^2 + (k+3)x + 1 = 0$; equal roots
(j) $x^2 + (k-1)x + 1 = 0$; real distinct roots

6. Find k such that the graph of $y = 9x^2 + 3kx + k$
(a) is tangent to the x-axis
(b) intersects the x-axis in two points
(c) has no intersection with the x-axis.

3.10 RADICAL EQUATIONS

A radical equation is an equation in which a variable appears under a radical sign.

Before solving radical equations we shall review the operation of squaring radicals. Recall that
(a) squaring a quantity and
(b) determining its square root
are inverse operations like multiplication and division. Thus when we determine the square root of a quantity and then square the result, the quantity we obtain must be exactly the same as the one with which we started.

For example

$$(\sqrt{5})^2 = 5$$
$$(\sqrt{x-1})^2 = x-1$$

EXAMPLE 1. *Square the following*

$$(a)\ 3\sqrt{x+1}$$
$$(b)\ \sqrt{x-1}-3$$

Solution

$$(a)\quad (3\sqrt{x+1})^2 = 9(x+1)$$
$$= 9x+9$$
$$(b)\ (\sqrt{x-1}-3)^2 = (\sqrt{x-1}-3)(\sqrt{x-1}-3)$$
$$= (\sqrt{x-1})^2 - 6\sqrt{x-1}+9$$
$$= x-1-6\sqrt{x-1}+9$$
$$= x+8-6\sqrt{x-1}$$

To solve a radical equation we use the operation that is the inverse of taking a root. However, squaring both sides of an equation does not always produce equivalent equations so all solutions must be verified.

EXAMPLE 2. *Solve* $\sqrt{x-1}-5=0$

Solution

$$\sqrt{x-1}-5=0$$
$$\sqrt{x-1}=5 \qquad \text{Isolate the radical}$$
$$(\sqrt{x-1})^2 = 5^2 \qquad \text{Square both sides}$$
$$x-1=25$$
$$x=26$$

Check

$$\text{L.S.} = \sqrt{x-1} - 5 \qquad \text{R.S.} = 0$$
$$= \sqrt{26-1} - 5$$
$$= 5 - 5$$
$$= 0$$

∴ the root is 26.

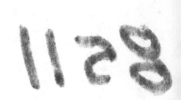

Write 1000 using five 9's.

EXAMPLE 3. *Solve* $x + \sqrt{x-2} = 4$

Solution

$$x + \sqrt{x-2} = 4$$
$$\sqrt{x-2} = 4 - x \qquad \text{Isolate the radical}$$
$$(\sqrt{x-2})^2 = (4-x)^2 \qquad \text{Square both sides}$$
$$x - 2 = 16 - 8x + x^2$$
$$x^2 - 9x + 18 = 0$$
$$(x-3)(x-6) = 0$$

$x = 3$ or $x = 6$

Check   Check

$$x = 3 \qquad\qquad\qquad\qquad x = 6$$
$$\text{L.S.} = x + \sqrt{x-2} \qquad \text{L.S.} = x + \sqrt{x-2}$$
$$= 3 + \sqrt{3-2} \qquad\qquad = 6 + \sqrt{6-2}$$
$$= 3 + 1 \qquad\qquad\qquad = 6 + 2$$
$$= 4 \qquad\qquad\qquad\qquad = 8$$
$$\text{R.S.} = 4 \qquad\qquad\qquad \text{R.S.} = 4$$

∴ the solution set is {3}

Since 6 does not satisfy the original equation it is called an *extraneous root*.

EXAMPLE 4. *Solve*

$$\sqrt{4x+5} - \sqrt{2x-6} = 3$$

Solution

$$\sqrt{4x+5} - \sqrt{2x-6} = 3$$

When a radical equation contains more than one radical we rewrite the equation with one radical on each side.

$$\sqrt{4x+5} = 3+\sqrt{2x-6}$$

$$(\sqrt{4x+5})^2 = (3+\sqrt{2x-6})^2 \qquad \text{Square both sides}$$

$$4x+5 = 9+6\sqrt{2x-6}+2x-6$$

$$2x+2 = 6\sqrt{2x-6} \qquad \text{Isolate the radical}$$

$$x+1 = 3\sqrt{2x-6} \qquad \text{Divide by 2}$$

$$(x+1)^2 = (3\sqrt{2x-6})^2 \qquad \text{Square both sides}$$

$$x^2+2x+1 = 9(2x-6)$$

$$x^2+2x+1 = 18x-54$$

$$x^2-16x+55 = 0$$

$$(x-11)(x-5) = 0$$

$x = 11$ or $x = 5$

Check   Check

$$x = 11 \qquad\qquad\qquad\qquad\qquad x = 5$$

$$\text{L.S.} = \sqrt{4x+5}-\sqrt{2x-6} \qquad\qquad \text{L.S.} = \sqrt{4x+5}-\sqrt{2x-6}$$

$$= \sqrt{4(11)+5}-\sqrt{2(11)-6} \qquad\qquad = \sqrt{4(5)+5}-\sqrt{2(5)-6}$$

$$= \sqrt{49}-\sqrt{16} \qquad\qquad\qquad\qquad = \sqrt{25}-\sqrt{4}$$

$$= 3 \qquad\qquad\qquad\qquad\qquad\qquad = 3$$

$$\text{R.S.} = 3 \qquad\qquad\qquad\qquad\qquad\quad \text{R.S.} = 3$$

$\therefore$ the solution set is $\{5, 11\}$

EXERCISE 3-10

A **1.** State the solution set of each of the following.

(a) $\sqrt{x+1} = 3$ (b) $\sqrt{x-1} = 4$ (c) $\sqrt{x+2} = -3$

(d) $\sqrt{3x-2} = 4$ (e) $\sqrt{x-2}-2 = 0$ (f) $\sqrt{x+12} = 3$

(g) $\sqrt{x+3}-3 = 0$ (h) $\sqrt{5x+6} = 4$ (i) $2\sqrt{x} = 3$

B **2.** Solve.

(a) $2\sqrt{x-1}-1 = 9$ (b) $\sqrt{x+7}-\sqrt{x} = 1$

(c) $\sqrt{x-5}+\sqrt{x+4} = 9$ (d) $\sqrt{x+2}-\sqrt{x+5} = 3$

(e) $\sqrt{3x-5}+1 = \sqrt{3x}$ (f) $\sqrt{x+1} = 1+\sqrt{x-4}$

(g) $\sqrt{x}-\sqrt{x-5} = 5$ (h) $\sqrt{x}-\sqrt{x-16} = 2$

3. Solve.

(a) $\sqrt{x+2} = x$ (b) $5\sqrt{x-6} = x$

(c) $\sqrt{x+4}+8 = x$ (d) $\sqrt{x-1}-x = -1$

(e) $7-x = -\sqrt{x-1}$ (f) $x+\sqrt{x+7} = 5$

(g) $x = 3+\sqrt{x-1}$ (h) $\sqrt{14-10x}+3 = x$

4. Solve.

(a) $\sqrt{2x-1}+\sqrt{x-1} = 1$ (b) $\sqrt{3x-2}-1 = \sqrt{2x-3}$

(c) $\sqrt{x+1}+\sqrt{3x+1} = 2$ (d) $\sqrt{x^2-4x+3}+\sqrt{x^2-2x+2} = 1$

(e) $\sqrt{3x-2}-2\sqrt{x} = 1$ (f) $2\sqrt{x+6}+\sqrt{2x+10} = 2$

5. Solve.

(a) $\sqrt[3]{x-1}=3$

(b) $\sqrt[3]{x-2}=2$

(c) $\sqrt{x+1}+\dfrac{2}{\sqrt{x+1}}=\sqrt{x+6}$

(d) $\sqrt{x-7}+\sqrt{x}=\dfrac{21}{\sqrt{x-7}}$

(e) $\sqrt{x+2}+\sqrt{x-1}=\sqrt{4x+1}$

(f) $\sqrt{x^2+4x+4}-\sqrt{x^2+3x}=1$

(g) $\sqrt{x}+\sqrt{3}=\sqrt{x+3}$

(h) $\dfrac{1}{1-x}+\dfrac{1}{1+\sqrt{x}}=\dfrac{1}{1-\sqrt{x}}$

6. Solve.

(a) $x=\sqrt{2x+1}$

(b) $\sqrt{2x+2}=x$

3.11 QUADRATIC INEQUALITIES

The solution of quadratic inequalities $ax^2+bx+c>0$ and $ax^2+bx+c<0$ is best understood if we consider the graph of $y=ax^2+bx+c$. The next two examples illustrate this.

EXAMPLE 1. *Sketch the graph of* $y=x^2-4x-5$ *and indicate where*

(i) $x^2-4x-5=0$

(ii) $x^2-4x-5>0$

(iii) $x^2-4x-5<0$

Solution

We complete the square to sketch the graph of $y=x^2-4x-5$

$$y=x^2-4x-5$$
$$=x^2-4x+4-4-5$$
$$=(x-2)^2-9$$

(i) The function is zero ($x^2-4x-5=0$) when $x=5$ or $x=-1$

(ii) The function is positive ($x^2-4x-5>0$) when $x>5$ or $x<-1$

(iii) The function is negative ($x^2-4x-5<0$) when $x<5$ *and* $x>-1$, that is, when $-1<x<5$

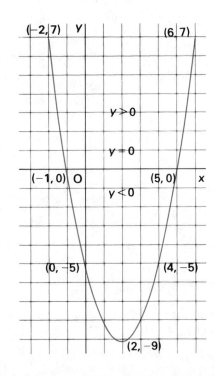

EXAMPLE 2. *Use a graph to find x for which* $-x^2+4x-2 \geqslant 0$.

Solution

We first sketch the graph of $y = -x^2+4x-2$.

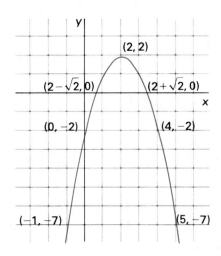

$$y = -x^2+4x-2$$
$$= -(x^2-4x+4-4)-2$$
$$= -(x-2)^2+4-2$$
$$= -(x-2)^2+2$$

When $y = 0$,

$$-x^2+4x-2=0$$
$$x^2-4x+2=0$$

$$x = \frac{4 \pm \sqrt{16-8}}{2}$$

$$= 2 \pm \sqrt{2}$$

From the graph we see that $-x^2+4x-2 \geqslant 0$, $(y \geqslant 0)$, for all points (x, y) which are on the parabola and. also on or above the x-axis. Thus $-x^2+4x-2 \geqslant 0$ if $2-\sqrt{2} \leqslant x \leqslant 2+\sqrt{2}$.

The solution set for a quadratic inequality may also be found algebraically.

EXAMPLE 3. *Solve* $x^2-2x-15>0$

Solution

First we factor

$$x^2-2x-15>0$$
$$(x-5)(x+3)>0$$

The product of the two factors must be positive. Hence both factors must be positive or both factors must be negative. This means that we have two cases to consider.

Case I—Both Positive

$x-5>0$ and $x+3>0$

$x>5$ and $x>-3$

The intersection of the solution sets of these inequalities is

$$\{x \mid x>5\}$$

or Case II—Both Negative

$x-5<0$ and $x+3<0$

$x<5$ and $x<-3$

The intersection of the solution sets of these inequalities is

$$\{x \mid x<-3\}$$

∴ the solution set of the given inequality is

$$\{x \mid x > 5\} \cup \{x \mid x < -3\}$$

whose graph is

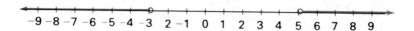

EXAMPLE 4. *Solve* $2x^2 + x - 6 < 0$

Solution

$$2x^2 + x - 6 < 0$$
$$(2x - 3)(x + 2) < 0$$

The product of the two factors must be negative. Hence, one of the factors must be positive and the other one must be negative. There are two cases to consider.

Case I

$$2x - 3 > 0 \quad \text{and} \quad x + 2 < 0$$
$$x > \tfrac{3}{2} \quad \text{and} \quad x < -2$$

There is no intersection for these inequalities.

Case II

$$2x - 3 < 0 \quad \text{and} \quad x + 2 > 0$$
$$x < \tfrac{3}{2} \quad \text{and} \quad x > -2$$

The intersection of the solution sets of these inequalities is

$$\{x \mid -2 < x < \tfrac{3}{2}\}$$

∴ the solution set of the given inequality is

$$\{x \mid -2 < x < \tfrac{3}{2}\}$$

whose graph is

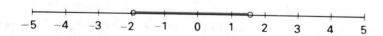

EXERCISE 3-11

B **1.** Sketch the graph of $y = x^2 - 2x - 3$ and indicate where
  (i) $x^2 - 2x - 3 = 0$
  (ii) $x^2 - 2x - 3 > 0$
  (iii) $x^2 - 2x - 3 < 0$

2. Sketch the graph of $y = -x^2 + 4x - 3$ and indicate where
  (i) $-x^2 + 4x - 3 = 0$
  (ii) $-x^2 + 4x - 3 > 0$
  (iii) $-x^2 + 4x - 3 < 0$

3. Graph the solution for each of the following.

(a) $x^2 + 6x + 5 > 0$

(b) $x^2 - 6x + 8 < 0$

(c) $x^2 + 2x - 15 < 0$

(d) $x^2 - 4 > 0$

(e) $x^2 + 2x > 0$

(f) $x^2 - 4x + 4 < 0$

(g) $x^2 + x - 12 \geqslant 0$

(h) $x^2 - 7x + 12 \leqslant 0$

(i) $x^2 + 9x + 20 < 0$

(j) $x^2 + 5x - 14 \geqslant 0$

4. Graph the solution set for each of the following.

(a) $x^2 + 7x > -12$

(b) $x^2 + 6 > 5x$

(c) $x^2 - 5x + 4 \geqslant 0$

(d) $x^2 - x - 12 \leqslant 0$

(e) $x^2 - 9 \leqslant 0$

(f) $x^2 - 5x \geqslant 0$

(g) $2x^2 + 5x - 3 > 0$

(h) $2x^2 - 13x + 15 \leqslant 0$

(i) $2x^2 - 5x < 12$

(j) $2x^2 - 7x + 5 > 0$

5. Graph the solution set.

(a) $2x^2 + 3x - 15 < 2x$

(b) $x^2 - 2x - 2 \geqslant 0$

(c) $x^2 - 2x - 1 > 0$

(d) $\dfrac{x^2}{2} - \frac{3}{2}x - 2 < 0$

(e) $x^2 - \dfrac{x-1}{3} \leqslant 15$

(f) $x^2 + (x+1)^2 + (x+2)^2 > 14$

(g) $\dfrac{x^2 + 4}{2} < \dfrac{2x(x-1)}{3}$

(h) $\dfrac{4}{x-2} \geqslant 3$

REVIEW EXERCISE

A **1.** Factor, if possible.

(a) $x^2 + 8x + 15$

(b) $16x^2 - 9$

(c) $x^2 + 5x + 5$

(d) $t^2 - 2t - 35$

(e) $x^2 - 3x - 80$

(f) $w^2 + 27w + 180$

(g) $z^2 + 3z - 108$

(h) $t^2 - 17t + 70$

(i) $x^2 + 26x + 169$

2. State the roots of the following equations.

(a) $(x - 6)(x + 7) = 0$

(b) $(x + 5)(x + 11) = 0$

(c) $(w - 10)(w + 3) = 0$

(d) $(2x + 1)(x - 4) = 0$

(e) $(3t - 4)(2t - 5) = 0$

(f) $(5w + 7)(3w + 11) = 0$

(g) $x(3x - 4) = 0$

(h) $(5w + 12)w = 0$

(i) $(4x + 5)^2 = 0$

3. Simplify the following.

(a) $\sqrt{-9}$

(b) $\sqrt{-8}$

(c) $3i^2$

(d) i^7

(e) $(\sqrt{-6})^2$

(f) $(2i)(7i)$

(g) i^6

(h) $(-2i)(-5i)$

4. If the discriminant of a quadratic equation has the given value, state the characteristics of the roots.

(a) 15

(b) 0

(c) -13

(d) 25

(e) 20

5. State the solution set of each of the following.

(a) $\sqrt{x+2} = 3$

(b) $\sqrt{x-1} = 4$

(c) $\sqrt{x+2} = 1$

(d) $2\sqrt{x} = 5$

B **6.** Factor over the integers, if possible.

(a) $6x^2 + 11x + 3$

(b) $6t^2 - 41t - 7$

(c) $15w^2 + 28w + 12$

(d) $20x^2 - 56x + 15$

(e) $28t^2 + 48t + 9$

(f) $8x^2 - 29x - 12$

(g) $12x^2 - 52x + 35$

(h) $10x^2 - 35x - 12$

(i) $8t^2 + 38t + 35$

7. Solve by factoring.

(a) $2x^2 - 7x - 30 = 0$
(b) $9x^2 - 4 = 0$
(c) $6t^2 - 25t + 4 = 0$
(d) $10x^2 + 27x + 18 = 0$
(e) $2w^2 - 7w + 5 = 0$
(f) $2x^2 + 16x + 30 = 0$
(g) $18t^2 + 24t - 10 = 0$
(h) $14w^2 - 17w + 5 = 0$
(i) $16x^2 + 34x - 15 = 0$

8. Solve.

(a) $5x^2 + 14x = 0$
(b) $x^2 - 5x + 3 = 0$
(c) $6t^2 + 13t + 7 = 0$
(d) $2w^2 + 5 = 0$
(e) $2(x^2 + 3) - 4x = 5$
(f) $2x^2 - 3x = -6$
(g) $(x + 1)^2 - 3(x + 1) = 0$
(h) $(2z + 5)(z + 2) = 6$

9. Solve.

(a) $\dfrac{x+1}{2} + \dfrac{x-1}{3} = x^2$
(b) $w^2 + w + 1 = 0$

(c) $\dfrac{2}{x-1} + \dfrac{3}{x+2} = 2$
(d) $x^2 + 6 = -2x$

(e) $\dfrac{x+1}{x-2} = \dfrac{2x+3}{x-3}$
(f) $2t^2 + t + 3 = 0$

(g) $2w(3w - 4) + 6 = 0$
(h) $\frac{2}{3}x^2 + x = 2$

10. Solve.

(a) $(x - 3)(x - 4) - (2x + 1)(x - 5) = 8$
(b) $x^2 + 0.1x - 0.2 = 0$

(c) $\dfrac{3x+1}{x} - \dfrac{x}{2} = 6$
(d) $\dfrac{3}{x} - \dfrac{4}{x-3} = 2$

(e) $0.1x^2 + 0.3x = 1$
(f) $1.2x^2 = 0.3x + 0.2$

11. The sum of the squares of two consecutive integers is 145. Find the integers.

12. The sum of the squares of three consecutive integers is 302. Find the integers.

13. The sum of a number and three times its square is 200. Find the number.

14. A rectangular building 100 m by 80 m is to be surrounded by a lawn of uniform width. The area of the lawn must be equal to the area of the building. Find the width of the lawn to the nearest tenth of a metre.

15. Julie drove from Dog's Nest to Bullet, a distance of 270 km. For the 300 km trip from Bullet to Dust she increased her speed by 10 km/h. If the total trip took 6 h, what was her speed from Bullet to Dust?

16. Use the discriminant to determine the nature of the roots of the following.

(a) $2x^2 + x - 3 = 0$
(b) $9w^2 + 4 = 12w$
(c) $2x^2 - x + 4 = 0$
(d) $3x^2 = -5x - 2$
(e) $2(x^2 - 1) + 3x = -4$
(f) $(x - 1)(x - 2) = -3x$

17. Determine the value of k that will give the indicated solution.

(a) $x^2 - 3x + k = 0$; equal roots
(b) $2x^2 + x - 2k + 1 = 0$; imaginary roots
(c) $2kx^2 + x^2 - x - 3 = 0$; real distinct roots.

18. Solve.

(a) $\sqrt{x+1} + \sqrt{x-2} = 3$
(b) $\sqrt{x-3} = 2 - \sqrt{x+5}$
(c) $\sqrt{x-2} = 4 - x$
(d) $x = 10 - \sqrt{x+2}$
(e) $\sqrt{x+6} = 1 + \sqrt{x-1}$
(f) $\sqrt{x-3} + \sqrt{x} = \sqrt{2}$

19. Graph the solution set for each of the following.

(a) $x^2 - x - 12 \leq 0$
(b) $x^2 - 6x > 0$
(c) $x^2 - 3x < 10$
(d) $x^2 + 8x + 15 \geq 0$
(e) $2w^2 - 5w - 3 > 0$
(f) $3x^2 \leq 10x + 8$

REVIEW AND PREVIEW TO CHAPTER 4

EXERCISE 1 FACTORING

Factor the following.
(a) $2x^2 - 7x - 15$
(b) $8x^2 - 14x + 3$
(c) $3x^2 - 26x + 35$
(d) $6x^2 + 23x + 20$
(e) $6x^2 + x - 7$
(f) $6x^2 + 29x + 28$
(g) $12x^2 - 22x + 8$
(h) $18x^2 - 15x - 75$
(i) $2x^3 - 5x^2 - 42x$
(j) $18x^2 - 51x + 8$

EXERCISE 2 QUADRATIC EQUATIONS

Solve the following.
(a) $2x^2 + 5x - 3 = 0$
(b) $3x^2 + 11x + 10 = 0$
(c) $4x^2 - 23x + 15 = 0$
(d) $6x^2 + 7x + 2 = 0$
(e) $10x^2 - 19x + 6 = 0$
(f) $4x^2 - 25 = 0$
(g) $6x^2 - 11x = 0$
(h) $x^2 + 3x - 1 = 0$
(i) $2x^2 - x - 5 = 0$
(j) $2x^2 + 2x + 5 = 0$
(k) $\frac{1}{2}x^2 + 3x + 6 = 0$
(l) $10x^2 - x + 0.2 = 0$

EXERCISE 3 SIMPLIFICATION

1. Expand and simplify.
(a) $(x+3)(2x^2 - 7x + 4)$
(b) $(x^2 - x - 6)(x^2 + 5x + 7)$
(c) $2(x-1)(x+5) - 4(x-5)^2$
(d) $3(2x-1)^2 - 4(x+6)(x-7) - 5(x+3)$
(e) $(3x^2 - 4x + 2)(2x + 3)$
(f) $(x^2 + 3)(2x^2 - x - 5)$
(g) $3(3x+2)(x-4) - 5(x-7)(2x+3)$
(h) $4(2x+1)^2 - (3x-2)^2 - (2x+1)(x-6)$
(i) $(x^2 + x - 1)(3x^3 - 2x^2 - x + 1)$
(j) $2(2x-3)(x^2 + x + 1) - (3x+4)^2$
(k) $5(x-3) - (2x-1)^2 + 7x$
(l) $(3x^2 - x - 2)(x^2 + 3x - 4)$

2. Simplify
(a) $\dfrac{3x^2 - 6x + 9}{3}$
(b) $\dfrac{4x^5 - 6x^4 + 10x^3}{2x^2}$
(c) $\dfrac{15xy^2 - 25x^2y^3 + 30x^5y^2}{-5xy^2}$
(d) $\dfrac{28x^2y^3z - 14xy^4z^2 - 35xy^3z^2}{7xy^2z}$
(e) $\dfrac{27x^4y^5 - 36x^3y^6 - 18x^2y^4}{-3x^2y^4}$
(f) $\dfrac{30x^5z^3 - 25x^4z^2 - 5xz + 40x^2z}{-5xz}$

EXERCISE 4 QUADRATIC FUNCTIONS

Determine the coordinates of the vertex for each of the following.
(a) $y = x^2 - 4$
(b) $y = (x-1)^2 + 5$
(c) $y = -2(x+3)^2 - 2$
(d) $y = x^2 + 2x - 1$
(e) $y = 2x^2 - 8x + 13$
(f) $y = -2x^2 + 6x - 4$
(g) $y = -\frac{1}{3}x^2 + 2x + 3$
(h) $y = -x^2 + 5x - 3$
(i) $y = -3x^2 + 5x + 1$
(j) $y = -4x^2 + x + \frac{1}{2}$
(k) $y = 0.2x^2 + 0.4x + 1$
(l) $y = -0.3x^2 - 0.6x - 0.1$
(m) $y = 2x^2 - x - 2$
(n) $y = -3x^2 - 2x + 4$

Polynomials

Mathematicians are like lovers.... Grant a mathematician the least principle, and he will draw from it a consequence which you must also grant him, and from this consequence another.

Fontenelle

Algebraic expressions such as

$$3x + 5, \ 2x^2 - 7x + 5 \quad \text{and} \quad 8x^4 - 2$$

are called polynomials.

> A polynomial is a function of the form
> $$f(x) = a_n x^n + a_{n-1} x^{n-1} + \cdots + a_1 x^1 + a_0$$
> where n is a non-negative integer, x is a variable and $a_i (i = n, n-1, \ldots, 1, 0)$ is a real number.

In the first section we shall deal with second degree polynomials.

4.1 ROOTS AND COEFFICIENTS OF A QUADRATIC EQUATION

The roots of the quadratic equation $ax^2 + bx + c = 0$ are

$$r_1 = \frac{-b + \sqrt{b^2 - 4ac}}{2a} \quad \text{and} \quad r_2 = \frac{-b - \sqrt{b^2 - 4ac}}{2a}$$

We shall now determine expressions for $r_1 + r_2$ (sum of roots) and $r_1 \times r_2$ (product of roots) in terms of a, b and c.

SUM

$$r_1 + r_2 = \left(\frac{-b + \sqrt{b^2 - 4ac}}{2a} \right) + \left(\frac{-b - \sqrt{b^2 - 4ac}}{2a} \right)$$

$$= -\frac{b}{2a} + \frac{\sqrt{b^2 - 4ac}}{2a} - \frac{b}{2a} - \frac{\sqrt{b^2 - 4ac}}{2a}$$

$$= -\frac{2b}{2a}$$

$$= -\frac{b}{a}$$

PRODUCT

$(p+q)(p-q)$
$= p^2 - q^2$

$$r_1 \times r_2 = \left(\frac{-b + \sqrt{b^2 - 4ac}}{2a}\right) \times \left(\frac{-b - \sqrt{b^2 - 4ac}}{2a}\right)$$

$$= \left(-\frac{b}{2a} + \frac{\sqrt{b^2 - 4ac}}{2a}\right) \times \left(-\frac{b}{2a} - \frac{\sqrt{b^2 - 4ac}}{2a}\right)$$

$$= \frac{b^2}{4a^2} - \frac{b^2 - 4ac}{4a^2}$$

$$= \frac{b^2 - b^2 + 4ac}{4a^2}$$

$$= \frac{c}{a}$$

> If r_1 and r_2 are the roots of the quad-
> ratic equation $ax^2 + bx + c = 0$, then
>
> $$r_1 + r_2 = -\frac{b}{a} \quad \text{and} \quad r_1 \times r_2 = \frac{c}{a}$$

EXAMPLE 1. *Find the sum and product of the roots of* $2x^2 - 6x - 7 = 0$

Solution

$$r_1 + r_2 = -\frac{b}{a} \qquad\qquad r_1 \times r_2 = \frac{c}{a}$$

$$= -\frac{(-6)}{2} \qquad\qquad = \frac{(-7)}{2}$$

$$= 3 \qquad\qquad = -\frac{7}{2}$$

If we divide the quadratic equation $ax^2 + bx + c = 0$ by a we have

$$x^2 + \frac{b}{a}x + \frac{c}{a} = 0$$

This equation can be written as

$$x^2 - \left(-\frac{b}{a}\right)x + \frac{c}{a} = 0$$

or

> $$x^2 - (\text{sum of roots})x + (\text{product of roots}) = 0$$

Another way of illustrating this follows.

If the roots of a quadratic equation are r_1 and r_2 and x satisfies the equation, then

$$x = r_1 \quad \text{or} \quad x = r_2$$

$$x - r_1 = 0 \quad \text{or} \quad x - r_2 = 0$$

$$\therefore \qquad (x - r_1)(x - r_2) = 0$$

$$x^2 - r_1 x - r_2 x + r_1 r_2 = 0$$

$$x^2 - (r_1 + r_2)x + r_1 r_2 = 0$$

or $\qquad x^2 - (\text{sum of roots})x + (\text{product of roots}) = 0$

EXAMPLE 2. *Determine a quadratic equation whose roots are 7 and −3*

Solution

(i)
$$r_1 + r_2 = 7 + (-3) = 4$$

$$r_1 \times r_2 = 7 \times (-3) = -21$$

$$x^2 - (\text{sum})x + (\text{product}) = 0$$

$$x^2 - 4x - 21 = 0$$

(ii) Since 7 and −3 are roots of a quadratic equation $(x - 7)$ and $(x + 3)$ are factors of the corresponding quadratic. Hence

$$(x - 7)(x + 3) = 0$$

and

$$x^2 - 4x - 21 = 0$$

EXAMPLE 3. *Determine a quadratic equation whose roots are*

(a) $2 + \sqrt{3}, 2 - \sqrt{3}$ \qquad (b) $3 - 2i, 3 + 2i$

Solution

(a) $r_1 + r_2 = (2 + \sqrt{3}) + (2 - \sqrt{3}) = 4$

$\quad r_1 \times r_2 = (2 + \sqrt{3})(2 - \sqrt{3}) = 4 - 3 = 1$

$\quad x^2 - (\text{sum})x + (\text{product}) = 0$

$\quad x^2 - 4x + 1 = 0$

(b) $r_1 + r_2 = (3 - 2i) + (3 + 2i) = 6$

$\quad r_1 \times r_2 = (3 - 2i)(3 + 2i) = 9 + 4 = 13$

$\quad x^2 - (\text{sum})x + (\text{product}) = 0$

$\quad x^2 - 6x + 13 = 0$

EXAMPLE 4. *Without solving the given equation, find an equation whose roots are the reciprocals of the roots of $x^2 + 5x - 7 = 0$.*

Solution

Let the roots of $x^2 + 5x - 7 = 0$ be r_1 and r_2. Then

$$r_1 + r_2 = -\frac{b}{a} = -5$$

and

$$r_1 \times r_2 = \frac{c}{a} = -7$$

Let the roots of the new equation be R_1 and R_2.

Then $R_1 = \dfrac{1}{r_1}$ and $R_2 = \dfrac{1}{r_2}$.

The sum of the roots of the new equation is

$$R_1 + R_2 = \frac{1}{r_1} + \frac{1}{r_2}$$

$$= \frac{r_2 + r_1}{r_1 r_2}$$

$$= \frac{-5}{-7}$$

$$= \tfrac{5}{7}$$

The product of the roots of the new equation is

$$R_1 \times R_2 = \frac{1}{r_1} \times \frac{1}{r_2}$$

$$= \frac{1}{r_1 r_2}$$

$$= -\tfrac{1}{7}$$

$$x^2 - (\text{sum})x + (\text{product}) = 0$$
$$x^2 - (\tfrac{5}{7})x + (-\tfrac{1}{7}) = 0$$
$$7x^2 - 5x - 1 = 0$$

$\therefore$ the required equation is $7x^2 - 5x - 1 = 0$

EXERCISE 4-1

A **1.** State the sum and product of the roots of the following quadratic equations.

(a) $x^2 + 6x + 8 = 0$

(b) $x^2 - 3x - 4 = 0$

(c) $2z^2 - 8z + 3 = 0$

(d) $3y^2 + 4y - 3 = 0$

(e) $6t^2 - 5 = 0$

(f) $2z^2 + 7z = 0$

(g) $-3x^2 + 2x - 5 = 0$

(h) $-x^2 - 6x + 5 = 0$

(i) $3x^2 - 6x = 4$

(j) $5x^2 + 7 = 6x$

(k) $0 = 7 - 6x + 9x^2$

(l) $4x = 3x^2 - 7$

2. State a quadratic equation whose roots have the given sum and product.

(a) sum: 4; product: 3

(b) sum: −5; product: 6

(c) sum: −9; product: −7

(d) sum: 0; product: −9

(e) sum: −5; product: 0

(f) sum: −7 product: −7

3. Find the sum and product of the roots of the following equations

(a) $2(x-3)=3x^2$

(b) $(x-3)(x+2)=5$

(c) $3-(x^2-2x)=4x$

(d) $2(2x-1)(x+3)=x^2+4$

4. Write a quadratic equation having the given roots and integral coefficients.

(a) 4 and 7

(b) −6 and 3

(c) $\frac{1}{2}$ and −4

(d) $-\frac{2}{3}$ and $-\frac{1}{4}$

(e) $\frac{3}{5}$ and 0

(f) −6 and 6

(g) $1+\sqrt{3}$ and $1-\sqrt{3}$

(h) $3+2\sqrt{2}$ and $3-2\sqrt{2}$

(i) $2i$ and $-2i$

(j) $1+3i$ and $1-3i$

(k) $\dfrac{2-\sqrt{5}}{2}$ and $\dfrac{2+\sqrt{5}}{2}$

(l) $\dfrac{3+i\sqrt{2}}{3}$ and $\dfrac{3-i\sqrt{2}}{3}$

5. If 3 is one root of $2x^2+bx+3=0$, find the other root and the value of b.

6. Without solving the given equation, find an equation whose roots are each one less than the roots of $x^2-3x-6=0$.

7. If −2 is one root of $5x^2+9x+c=0$, find the other root and the value of c.

8. Without solving the given equation, find an equation whose roots are the negatives of the roots of $x^2-4x+9=0$.

9. If $2-\sqrt{2}$ is one root of $x^2+bx+2=0$, find the other root and the value of b.

10. Without solving the given equation, find an equation whose roots are the negative reciprocals of the roots of $2x^2-3x+5=0$.

11. If $2kx^2-(k-6)x-5=0$,

(a) find k if the sum of the roots is 2

(b) find k if the product of the roots is −7

(c) find k if the sum of the roots is 0

(d) find k if the reciprocal of the product of the roots is 4.

12. Without solving the given equation, find an equation whose roots are the squares of the roots of $x^2+4x+2=0$.

13. Show that $\dfrac{1}{r_1}+\dfrac{1}{r_2}=-\dfrac{b}{c}$

4.2 EQUATIONS IN QUADRATIC FORM

The quartic equation $x^4-5x^2+4=0$ can be solved using quadratic methods.

If we let $z=x^2$, then the equation can be rewritten as follows

$$x^4-5x^2+4=0$$

$$(x^2)^2-5(x^2)+4=0$$

$$z^2-5z+4=0$$

This equation can be solved by factoring

$$z^2 - 5z + 4 = 0$$

$$(z - 4)(z - 1) = 0$$

$$z = 4 \quad \text{or} \quad z = 1$$

Replace z by x^2

$$x^2 = 4 \quad \text{or} \quad x^2 = 1$$

$$x = \pm 2 \quad \text{or} \quad x = \pm 1$$

The roots of the equations are $1, 2, -1, -2$.

We have expressed a non-quadratic equation in *quadratic form*. An equation is in quadratic form if it can be written as

$$a[f(x)]^2 + b[f(x)] + c = 0$$

where $a \neq 0$ and $f(x)$ is some function of x. We solve such an equation for $f(x)$ and then, if possible, solve the resulting equations for x.

EXAMPLE 1. *Solve* $\left(x + \dfrac{2}{x}\right)^2 - 7\left(x + \dfrac{2}{x}\right) + 12 = 0$

Solution

Let $z = x + \dfrac{2}{x}$

The given equation becomes

$$z^2 - 7z + 12 = 0$$

$$(z - 3)(z - 4) = 0$$

$$z = 3 \quad \text{or} \quad z = 4$$

Replace z by $x + \dfrac{2}{x}$

$$x + \frac{2}{x} = 3 \quad \text{or} \quad x + \frac{2}{x} = 4$$

$$x^2 + 2 = 3x \qquad\qquad x^2 + 2 = 4x$$

$$x^2 - 3x + 2 = 0 \qquad\qquad x^2 - 4x + 2 = 0$$

$$(x - 2)(x - 1) = 0$$

$$x = 2 \quad \text{or} \quad x = 1 \qquad\qquad x = \frac{4 \pm \sqrt{8}}{2}$$

$$= \frac{4 \pm 2\sqrt{2}}{2}$$

$$= 2 \pm \sqrt{2}$$

The roots are $1, 2, 2 + \sqrt{2}, 2 - \sqrt{2}$.

EXERCISE 4-2

B **1.** Solve the following equations.

(a) $x^4 - 13x^2 + 36 = 0$

(b) $x^4 + 3x^2 - 4 = 0$

(c) $\left(x + \dfrac{4}{x}\right)^2 - 9\left(x + \dfrac{4}{x}\right) + 20 = 0$

(d) $\left(x + \dfrac{1}{x}\right)^2 - 5\left(x + \dfrac{1}{x}\right) + 6 = 0$

(e) $x + 3\sqrt{x} - 10 = 0$

(f) $(x^2 + 1)^2 - 7(x^2 + 1) + 10 = 0$

2. Solve.

(a) $(x^2 - 2x)^2 - 2(x^2 - 2x) - 3 = 0$

(b) $(x^2 - 5x)^2 - 36 = 0$

(c) $(x^2 - 3x)^2 - 2(x^2 - 3x) - 8 = 0$

(d) $x^4 - 3x^2 - 4 = 0$

(e) $x^4 - 2x^2 - 24 = 0$

(f) $x^6 - 9x^3 + 8 = 0$

3. Solve.

(a) $(x^2 - 2x)^2 - 5(x^2 - 2x) = 6$

(b) $(x^2 + 2)^2 - 17(x^2 + 2) = -66$

(c) $6\left(\dfrac{1}{x - 1}\right)^2 - \left(\dfrac{1}{x - 1}\right) - 1 = 0$

(d) $2x^4 + 17x^2 - 9 = 0$

(e) $(x^2 + 1)^2 - 7(x^2 + 1) + 10 = 0$

(f) $(2x^2 + x)^2 - 7(2x^2 + x) + 6 = 0$

C **4.** Solve.

(a) $x^4 - 4x^2 + 1 = 0$

(b) $x^4 - 10x^2 + 17 = 0$

4.3 GRAPHS OF POLYNOMIAL FUNCTIONS

In Chapter 2 we graphed the quadratic function $y = ax^2 + bx + c$. In this section we shall graph polynomial functions of degree higher than two. We first look at the simplest polynomial graphs, those in the form $y = ax^n$. The graphs, where $n = 1, \ldots, 6$ and $a = 1$ and $a = -1$ follow.

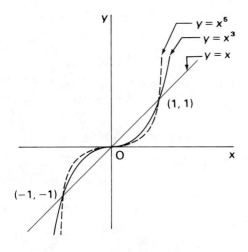

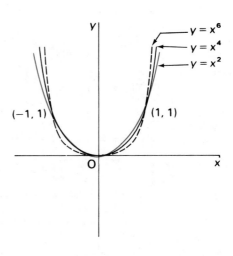

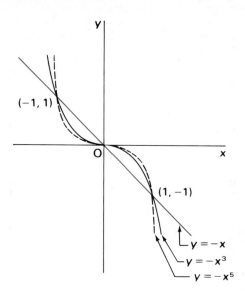

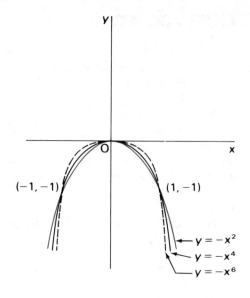

We shall now consider the graphs of cubic functions in the form $y = ax^3 + bx^2 + cx + d$ where b, c and d are not necessarily 0. If the polynomial can be factored into linear factors the graph is easily sketched.

EXAMPLE 1.   *Sketch the graph of $y = (x-1)(x-3)(x+2)$*

Solution

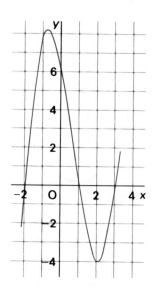

$$y = (x-1)(x-3)(x+2)$$

(i) In order to determine the x-intercepts we set $y = 0$ and solve the cubic equation.

$$(x-1)(x-3)(x+2) = 0$$

$$x - 1 = 0 \text{ or } x - 3 = 0 \text{ or } x + 2 = 0$$

$$x = 1 \quad x = 3 \quad x = -2$$

Hence the x-intercepts are 1, 3 and -2.

(ii) To determine the y-intercept we set $x = 0$.

$$y = (0-1)(0-3)(0+2) = 6$$

$\therefore$ the y-intercept is 6.

(iii) $y > 0$ when $x > 3$ since $(x-1)$, $(x-3)$ and $(x+2)$ are all positive when $x > 3$.

(iv) $y < 0$ when $1 < x < 3$ since $(x-3)$ is negative in this area and the other two factors are positive.

(v) $y > 0$ when $-2 < x < 1$ since $(x-3)$ and $(x-1)$ are negative in this area and $(x+2)$ is positive.

(vi) $y < 0$ when $x < -2$ since all factors are negative in this area.

In this example the graph crosses the x-axis at three points and the corresponding equation has three real roots.

In general the graph of a cubic function where $a > 0$ extends from the third to the first quadrant and so must cross the x-axis at least once. Hence the corresponding equation must have at least one real root.

When $a < 0$ the graph extends from the second quadrant to the fourth, crossing the x-axis at least once. As before, the corresponding equation has at least one real root.

The following graphs illustrate the four possible cases for a cubic function when $a > 0$.

I

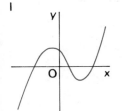

II

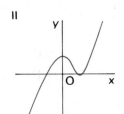

III

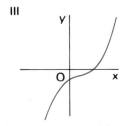

IV

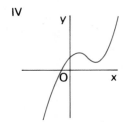

Case I: The graph crosses the x-axis at three points and the corresponding equation has three real unequal roots.

Case II: The graph crosses the x-axis at one point and touches it at another. The equation has three real roots, two of which are equal.

Case III: This case shows the graph of the function whose corresponding equation has three real and equal roots.

Case IV: The graph crosses the x-axis at one point and the corresponding equation has one real and two imaginary roots.

These four cases also apply when $a < 0$.

EXAMPLE 2. *Sketch the graph of $y = 2x^3 + 7x^2 + 2x - 3$.*

Solution

x	y
1	8
0	−3
−1	0
−2	5
−3	0
−4	−27

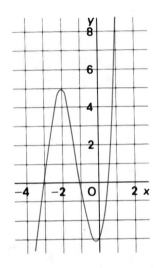

We see that the graph crosses the x-axis at $(-3, 0)$, $(-1, 0)$. We can estimate the other point where the graph crosses the x-axis as $(\frac{1}{2}, 0)$. This can be checked by substitution.

$$y = 2x^3 + 7x^2 + 2x - 3$$
$$= 2(\tfrac{1}{2})^3 + 7(\tfrac{1}{2})^2 + 2(\tfrac{1}{2}) - 3$$
$$= \tfrac{1}{4} + \tfrac{7}{4} + 1 - 3$$
$$= 0$$

∴ the roots of the equation $2x^3 + 7x^2 + 2x - 3 = 0$ are $\frac{1}{2}$, −1 and −3.

Not all x-intercepts can be accurately determined from a graph. In Section 4.6 we shall develop an algebraic method for solving polynomial equations.

Like the graph of a cubic function, the graph of a quartic function, $y = ax^4 + bx^3 + cx^2 + dx + e$, is easily drawn if the quartic can be expressed as the product of linear factors.

EXAMPLE 3. *Sketch the graph of $y = (x + 1)(x + 4)(x - 1)(x - 3)$.*

Solution

(i) In order to determine where the graph crosses the *x*-axis we solve the quartic equation that results when $y = 0$.

$$(x+1)(x+4)(x-1)(x-3) = 0$$

∴ $x = -1$ or $x = -4$ or $x = 1$ or $x = 3$.

(ii) $y > 0$ when $x > 3$ since all factors are positive when $x > 3$.

(iii) $y < 0$ when $1 < x < 3$ since $(x-3)$ is negative in this area.

(iv) Both $(x-3)$ and $(x-1)$ are negative when $-1 < x < 1$ so y is positive in this area.

(v) When $-4 < x < -1$ three factors are negative, so $y < 0$.

(vi) When $x < -4$, all factors are negative, so $y > 0$.

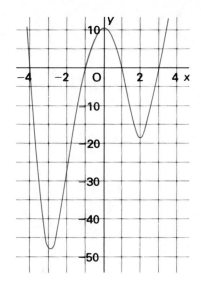

We summarize the above in the following table.

x	$x+1$	$x+4$	$x-1$	$x-3$	y
$x > 3$	+	+	+	+	+
$1 < x < 3$	+	+	+	−	−
$-1 < x < 1$	+	+	−	−	+
$-4 < x < -1$	−	+	−	−	−
$x < -4$	−	−	−	−	+

In general the graph of a quartic function where $a > 0$ extends from the second quadrant to the first. The following graphs illustrate the seven possible cases for a quartic function when $a > 0$.

Case I. The graph touches the *x*-axis at one point and the corresponding equation has four equal real roots.

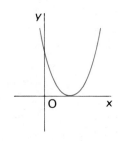

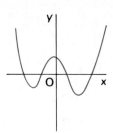

Case II. The graph crosses the *x*-axis at four distinct points and the corresponding equation has four real unequal roots.

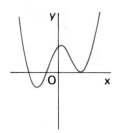

Case III. The equation has four real roots, two of which are equal.

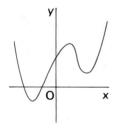

Case IV. The equation has two real unequal roots and two imaginary roots.

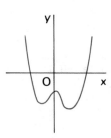

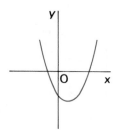

Case V. The equation has two pairs of equal roots.

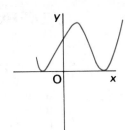

Case VI. The equation has two equal roots and two imaginary roots.

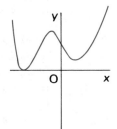

Case VII. The equation has four imaginary roots.

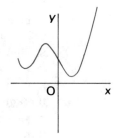

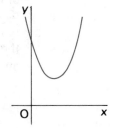

These seven cases also apply when $a < 0$. For $a < 0$ the graph is shaped like the letter m.

EXERCISE 4-3

B **1.** Sketch the graph of each of the following and state the roots of the corresponding equation.
(a) $y = (x-1)(x-3)(x+1)$
(b) $y = x(x+2)(x-2)$
(c) $y = (x-2)(x+2)^2$
(d) $y = -(x+1)(x-2)(x+2)$
(e) $y = -(x-3)(x-1)(x+1)$
(f) $y = (x+2)^3$
(g) $y = (x+2)(x+4)(x-1)(x-4)$
(h) $y = -x(x+3)(x-2)(x-4)$
(i) $y = (x+1)(x+3)(x-2)^2$
(j) $y = -x(x-3)^3$
(k) $y = x(x+4)(x+2)(x-2)(x-4)$

2. Sketch the graph of each of the following and state any real roots of the corresponding equation.
(a) $y = x^3 - 9x$
(b) $y = x^3 + 2x^2 - 5x - 6$
(c) $y = x^4 - 10x^2 + 9$
(d) $y = -x^3 - 6x^2 - 8x$
(e) $y = x^3 + 2x^2 + 2x + 1$
(f) $y = -x^3 - x^2 + x + 1$
(g) $y = x^4 - 2x^2 + 1$
(h) $y = -x^4 - 3x^3 - 3x^2 - 2x$
(i) $y = (x+3)^4$
(j) $y = x^4 + 3$

3. Find an equation of the cubic function whose graph passes through $(-4, 0)$, $(-1, 0)$ and $(3, 0)$.

4. Find an equation of the cubic function whose graph passes through $(-2, 0)$ and which touches the x-axis at $(1, 0)$.

5. Find an equation of the cubic function whose graph passes through $(-3, 0)$, $(0, 0)$ and $(2, 0)$ and is negative when $0 < x < 2$.

6. Find an equation of the quartic function whose graph passes through $(-4, 0)$, $(-2, 0)$, $(1, 0)$ and $(2, 0)$.

7. Find an equation of the quartic function whose graph passes through $(-3, 0)$, $(-1, 0)$ and which touches the x-axis at $(2, 0)$.

8. Find an equation of the quartic function which touches the x-axis at $(0, 0)$ and $(3, 0)$.

C **9.** Determine an equation of a cubic function whose graph passes through $(1, 0)$, $(0, -1)$, $(-1, -4)$ and $(2, 5)$.

10. Use a calculator to sketch the graph of

$$y = x^5 + 4x^4 - 10x^3 - 40x^2 + 9x + 36$$

WORD LADDER

Start with the word "foot" and change one letter at a time to form a new word until you reach "ball". The best solution has the fewest steps.

f o o t
– – – –
– – – –
– – – –
– – – –
– – – –
b a l l

4.4 DIVISION OF POLYNOMIALS

Before developing an algebraic method of solving polynomial equations we shall first review the division of polynomials.

EXAMPLE 1. *Divide* $x^3 + x^2 - 3x - 1$ *by* $x + 2$, $x \neq -2$.

Solution

$$
\begin{array}{r}
x^2 - x - 1 \\
x+2\overline{)x^3 + x^2 - 3x - 1} \\
\underline{x^3 + 2x^2} \\
-x^2 - 3x \\
\underline{-x^2 - 2x} \\
-x - 1 \\
\underline{-x - 2} \\
1
\end{array}
$$

We continue dividing until the remainder is a polynomial of degree less than the divisor.
The division statement is

$$x^3 + x^2 - 3x - 1 = (x + 2)(x^2 - x - 1) + 1$$

When dividing by $x - n$ where the coefficient of x is 1, division is simplified by using a process called synthetic division. It is derived from the standard division procedure by working with only the numerical coefficients. The process is illustrated in the following example.

EXAMPLE 2. *Divide* $-3x^2 - 10x + 2x^3 + 5$ *by* $x - 3$, $x \neq 3$

Solution
We first rearrange the terms of the dividend in descending powers of x

$$2x^3 - 3x^2 - 10x + 5$$

Copy the coefficients and place the n number (in this case 3) as shown

$$3 \, \lfloor \, 2 \; -3 \; -10 \; 5$$

Repeat the first coefficient of the dividend as shown.

$$3 \, \lfloor \, \underset{\downarrow}{2} \; -3 \; -10 \; 5$$
$$2$$

Multiply the number below the line by n, put the product above the line in the second column, and add.

$$
3 \, \lfloor \, 2 \quad -3 \; -10 \; 5
$$

Multiply the last number below the line by n and continue the above process.

$$
3 \, \lfloor \, 2 \; -3 \quad -10 \quad 5
$$

When the process is complete, the last number on the row is the remainder and the other numbers are the coefficients of the quotient.

Thus when $2x^3 - 3x^2 - 10x + 5$ is divided by $x - 3$ the quotient is $2x^2 + 3x - 1$ and the remainder is 2.

We now compare the two methods of division.

$$\begin{array}{r}
③\,|\ \ 2\ \ -3\ \ -10\ \ \ 5 \\
\ \ \ \ \ \ \ \ 6\ \ \ \ \ 9\ \ -3 \\
②\ \ ③\ \ ⊝1\ \ ② \\[4pt]
②x^2{+}3x\ ⊝1 \\
x{-}③)\,2x^3 - 3x^2 - 10x + 5 \\
\underline{2x^3 - 6x^2} \\
3x^2 - 10x \\
\underline{3x^2 - 9x} \\
-x + 5 \\
\underline{-x + 3} \\
②
\end{array}$$

EXAMPLE 3. *Use synthetic division to divide $x^3 - x + 28$ by $x + 3$ and write the division statement. State any restrictions on the variable.*

Solution

We are dividing by $x + 3$ or $x - (-3)$, so $n = -3$. An x^2 term is missing from the dividend so we use a 0 coefficient as a placeholder.

$$\begin{array}{r|rrrr}
-3 & 1 & 0 & -1 & 28 \\
   &   & -3 & 9 & -24 \\
\hline
   & 1 & -3 & 8 & 4
\end{array}$$

$\therefore\ \ x^3 - x + 28 = (x + 3)(x^2 - 3x + 8) + 4$

In order to avoid division by 0 we stipulate that $x \neq -3$.

The traditional method of division is used when the coefficient of the variable in the divisor is not 1.

EXAMPLE 4. *Divide $18x - 19x^2 + 6x^3 - 22$ by $2x - 5$ and state any restrictions on the variable.*

Solution

We first rearrange the terms of the dividend in descending (or ascending) powers of x.

$$(6x^3 - 19x^2 + 18x - 22) \div (2x - 5)$$

$$\begin{array}{r}
3x^2 - 2x + 4 \\
2x - 5)\overline{6x^3 - 19x^2 + 18x - 22} \\
\underline{6x^3 - 15x^2} \\
-4x^2 + 18x \\
\underline{-4x^2 + 10x} \\
8x - 22 \\
\underline{8x - 20} \\
-2
\end{array}$$

$\therefore\ \ 6x^3 - 19x^2 + 18x - 22 = (2x - 5)(3x^2 - 2x + 4) - 2$

Since division by 0 is not defined,

$$2x - 5 \neq 0$$
$$2x \neq 5$$
$$x \neq \tfrac{5}{2}$$

EXERCISE 4-4

1. Divide and state any restrictions on the variables.
(a) $(x^3 - 2x^2 + 2x - 15) \div (x - 3)$
(b) $(x^3 + 3x^2 - 9x - 20) \div (x + 4)$
(c) $(x^3 + 2x^2 - 5x - 7) \div (x + 3)$
(d) $(5w^2 - 4w - 2 + w^3) \div (w - 1)$
(e) $(11x^2 - 22 + 26x + x^3) \div (6 + x)$
(f) $(3t - 6 - 2t^2 + t^3) \div (t - 2)$
(g) $(24 + 6x - 7x^2 + x^3) \div (x - 5)$
(h) $(5x^2 + x^3 - 4x - 20) \div (5 + x)$
(i) $(x^4 + 4x^3 + 2x^2 - 3x + 2) \div (x + 2)$
(j) $(2w - 4w^2 + 2w^4 - 5w^3 + 3) \div (w - 3)$

Write 30 using four 5's.

2. Divide and state any restrictions on the variables.
(a) $(2x^3 + x^2 + x - 1) \div (2x - 1)$
(b) $(21w - 11w^2 + 3w^3 - 7) \div (3w - 2)$
(c) $(2 + 5t - t^2 + 6t^3) \div (1 + 3t)$
(d) $(6z^3 + 13z^2 - 9) \div (2z + 3)$
(e) $(9x^2 - 8 + 4x^3) \div (2 + x)$
(f) $(4x^3 + 5x + 21) \div (2x + 3)$
(g) $(2w - 1 + 9w^3) \div (3w - 2)$
(h) $(10 + 9x + x^3) \div (2 + x)$

3. Divide. No divisors are zero.
(a) $(x^4 + x^3 - 13x^2 - 25x - 12) \div (x^2 + 2x + 1)$
(b) $(2w^3 - 4 - 8w - 3w^2 + w^4) \div (w^2 - w - 2)$
(c) $(t^4 - 17t^2 - 36t - 20) \div (t^2 - 3t - 10)$

4.5 THE REMAINDER AND FACTOR THEOREMS

In order to illustrate the remainder theorem we first divide the polynomial $P(x) = x^3 + 2x^2 + 3x - 15$ by $x - 2$ and then find $P(2)$.

$$
\begin{array}{r}
x^2 + 4x + 11 \\
x - 2 \overline{)\, x^3 + 2x^2 + 3x - 15} \\
\underline{x^3 - 2x^2} \\
4x^2 + 3x \\
\underline{4x^2 - 8x} \\
11x - 15 \\
\underline{11x - 22} \\
7
\end{array}
$$

$$P(x) = x^3 + 2x^2 + 3x - 15$$
$$P(2) = (2)^3 + 2(2)^2 + 3(2) - 15$$
$$= 8 + 8 + 6 - 15$$
$$= 7$$

The fact that $P(2)$ is the remainder when $P(x)$ is divided by $x - 2$ illustrates the Remainder Theorem, which says:

> If a polynomial in x is divided by $x - a$, the remainder obtained is equal to the value of the polynomial when $x = a$.

When $P(x)$ is divided by $x - a$, the quotient is $Q(x)$ and the remainder is R. The division statement

$$P(x) = (x - a) \times Q(x) + R$$

is an identity which can be proven true for all values of x.

Substituting a for x we have

$$P(a) = (a - a) \times Q(a) + R$$
$$= 0 \times Q(a) + R$$
$$= R$$

> Remainder Theorem: If a polynomial P(x) is divided by $x - a$, the remainder is $P(a)$.

EXAMPLE 1. *Find the remainder when $x^3 - 2x^2 - x + 13$ is divided by $x + 3$.*

Solution

$$P(x) = x^3 - 2x^2 - x + 13$$
$$P(-3) = (-3)^3 - 2(-3)^2 - (-3) + 13$$
$$= -27 - 18 + 3 + 13$$
$$= -29$$

The remainder is -29 when $x^3 - 2x^2 - x - 13$ is divided by $x + 3$.

EXAMPLE 2. *Find the remainder when $x^3 - 7x^2 - 9x + 2$ is divided by $x - 2$ and write the division statement.*

Solution

$$P(x) = x^3 - 7x^2 + 9x + 2$$

$$P(2) = (2)^3 - 7(2)^2 + 9(2) + 2$$
$$= 8 - 28 + 18 + 2$$
$$= 0$$

$$
\begin{array}{r|rrrr}
2 & 1 & -7 & +9 & +2 \\
  &   & 2 & -10 & -2 \\
\hline
  & 1 & -5 & -1 & 0
\end{array}
$$

$$x^3 - 7x^2 + 9x + 2 = (x + 2)(x^2 - 5x - 1)$$

Since division gives zero as a remainder, both $x - 2$ and $x^2 - 5x - 1$ are factors of $x^3 - 7x^2 + 9x + 2$. This illustrates the factor theorem.

> Factor Theorem: A polynomial $P(x)$ has $x - a$ as a factor if and only if $P(a) = 0$.

If a polynomial $P(x)$ has $x - a$ as a factor, then

$$P(x) = (x - a) \times Q(x)$$

Substituting a for x we have

$$P(a) = (a - a) \times Q(a)$$
$$P(a) = 0$$

Conversely, if $P(a) = 0$, then by the Remainder Theorem when $P(x)$ is divided by $x - a$ the remainder is 0, i.e., $x - a$ is a factor of $P(x)$.

EXAMPLE 3. *Factor* $4x^3 + 16x^2 + 9x - 9$

Solution

$$P(x) = 4x^3 + 16x^2 + 9x - 9$$
$$P(1) = 4(1)^3 + 16(1)^2 + 9(1) - 9 = 20$$
$$P(-1) = 4(-1)^3 + 16(-1)^2 + 9(-1) - 9 = -6$$
$$P(3) = 4(3)^3 + 16(3)^2 + 9(3) - 9 = 270$$
$$P(-3) = 4(-3)^3 + 16(-3)^2 + 9(-3) - 9 = 0$$

In this example we only substitute numbers that are factors of 9. Why?

$\therefore$ $x + 3$ is a factor.
Another factor is found by division

$$
\begin{array}{r|rrrr}
-3 & 4 & 16 & 9 & -9 \\
   &   & -12 & -12 & 9 \\
\hline
   & 4 & 4 & -3 & 0
\end{array}
$$

$\therefore$ $4x^3 + 16x^2 + 9x - 9 = (x + 3)(4x^2 + 4x - 3)$

In this example $4x^2 + 4x - 3$ may be factored using the methods of Section 3.2.
$\therefore$ $4x^3 + 16x^2 + 9x - 9 = (x + 3)(2x + 3)(2x - 1)$.

EXERCISE 4-5

B **1.** Use the Remainder Theorem to find the remainders.
(a) $(x^2 - 5x + 4) \div (x + 2)$
(b) $(w^2 + 3w - 7) \div (w - 3)$
(c) $(t^3 - 3t^2 + t - 1) \div (t - 1)$
(d) $(z^3 - 2z^2 + 3z - 4) \div (z + 3)$
(e) $(2x^3 + 3x^2 - x - 5) \div (x + 1)$
(f) $(3x^3 - 2x - 7) \div (x - 2)$
(g) $(x^4 - x^3 + 2x^2 - x + 1) \div (x + 2)$
(h) $(w^4 - w + 5) \div (w - 4)$

2. Determine whether the second polynomial is a factor of the first.
(a) $x^3 + 5x^2 + 8x + 4,\ x + 2$
(b) $w^3 - 3w^2 + 2,\ w - 1$
(c) $t^3 + 3t^2 - 2t - 9,\ t + 3$
(d) $2x^3 - 3x^2 - 2x - 21,\ x - 3$
(e) $x^3 - 3x^2 + 3x - 4,\ x - 2$
(f) $5x^4 + 3x^3 - 2x^2 + 3x + 3,\ x + 1$

3. Factor.
(a) $x^3 + 4x^2 + x - 6$
(b) $x^3 + 6x^2 + 11x + 6$
(c) $x^3 + 2x^2 - 9x - 18$
(d) $t^3 + 4t^2 - 17t - 60$
(e) $x^3 + 3x^2 + 3x + 2$
(f) $x^3 - 4x^2 + 2x + 3$

4. Factor.
(a) $2w^3 - 5w^2 + w + 2$
(b) $2t^3 + 9t^2 + 7t - 6$
(c) $6x^3 + x^2 - 10x + 3$
(d) $x^3 - 7x + 6$
(e) $x^3 - 2x^2 + 2x - 15$
(f) $2w^3 - 2w^2 - w - 6$
(g) $4x^3 + 12x^2 - x - 3$
(h) $6x^3 - 11x^2 - 57x + 20$

5. Determine the value of m so that $x + 2$ is a factor of $x^3 + x^2 + mx + 6$

6. Determine the value of n so that $x - 2$ is a factor of $x^3 - 3x + n$.

7. Factor the following.
(a) $x^4 + 4x^3 - x^2 - 16x - 12$
(b) $x^4 - 2x^3 - 17x^2 + 18x + 72$
(c) $x^4 + x^3 - 8x^2 - 9x - 9$

8. Find the values of a and b if $ax^3 + bx^2 + 3x - 4$ has a remainder of -2 when divided by $(x - 1)$, and a remainder of 2 when divided by $x - 2$.

9. When a polynomial $P(x)$ is divided by $2x - 1$ the quotient is $x^2 - 2x - 1$ and the remainder is -4. Find $P(x)$.

C **10.** Show that $x - a$ is a factor of $x^n - a^n$.

11. Show that $x + a$ is a factor of $x^n + a^n$ if n is odd.

12. Use the Factor Theorem to show that $x - c$ is a factor of $x^2(c - b) + c^2(b - x) + b^2(x - c)$.

13. Use the Factor Theorem to show that $x - a$ is a factor of $(a - x)^3 + (x - b)^3 + (b - a)^3$.

4.6 SOLVING POLYNOMIAL EQUATIONS BY FACTORING

In Section 3.3 we solved second degree or quadratic equations by factoring. In this section we will see how the factor theorem is used to solve equations of degree higher than two.

EXAMPLE 1. *Solve* $2x^3 - 3x^2 - 5x + 6 = 0$

Solution

We use the factor theorem to factor $2x^3 - 3x^2 - 5x + 6$

$$P(x) = 2x^3 - 3x^2 - 5x + 6$$
$$P(1) = 2(1)^3 - 3(1)^2 - 5(1) + 6$$
$$= 2 - 3 - 5 + 6$$
$$= 0$$

∴ $x - 1$ is a factor.

Division yields another factor.

```
1 | 2  -3  -5   6
  |    2  -1  -6
  ---------------
    2  -1  -6   0
```

$$2x^3 - 3x^2 - 5x + 6 = (x - 1)(2x^2 - x - 6)$$
$$= (x - 1)(2x + 3)(x - 2)$$

∴ $(x - 1)(2x + 3)(x - 2) = 0$
and $x - 1 = 0$ or $2x + 3 = 0$ or $x - 2 = 0$

$$x = 1 \qquad x = -\tfrac{3}{2} \qquad x = 2$$

∴ $x = -\tfrac{3}{2}, 1, 2$

The roots may be checked by substitution.

EXAMPLE 2. *Solve* $x^3 - 4x^2 - x + 12 = 0$

Solution

$$P(x) = x^3 - 4x^2 - x + 12$$
$$P(3) = (3)^3 - 4(3)^2 - (3) + 12$$
$$= 27 - 36 - 3 + 12$$
$$= 0$$

∴ $x - 3$ is a factor of $x^3 - 4x^2 - x + 12$

Division yields $x^3 - 4x^2 - x + 12 = (x - 3)(x^2 - x - 4)$

∴ $(x - 3)(x^2 - x - 4) = 0$

Determine the pattern. Find the missing number.

3	4	5	2
2	3	3	3
1	7	13	4
5	5	2	

$x^2 - x - 4$ is not readily factored. However we can use the quadratic formula to solve $x^2 - x - 4 = 0$

$$x - 3 = 0 \quad \text{or} \quad x^2 - x - 4 = 0$$

$$x = 3 \qquad\qquad x = \frac{-b \pm \sqrt{b^2 - 4ac}}{2a}$$

$$= \frac{1 \pm \sqrt{1 + 16}}{2}$$

$$= \frac{1 \pm \sqrt{17}}{2}$$

The roots are $3, \dfrac{1 + \sqrt{17}}{2}, \dfrac{1 - \sqrt{17}}{2}$.

EXAMPLE 3. *Solve $x^3 - 2x - 4 = 0$*

Solution

$$P(x) = x^3 - 2x - 4$$
$$P(2) = (2)^3 - 2(2) - 4$$
$$= 8 - 4 - 4$$
$$= 0$$

$\therefore \quad x - 2$ is a factor.

Division yields $x^3 - 2x - 4 = (x - 2)(x^2 + 2x + 2)$

$\therefore \quad (x - 2)(x^2 + 2x + 2) = 0$

and $\quad x - 2 = 0 \quad \text{or} \quad x^2 + 2x + 2 = 0$

$$x = 2 \qquad\qquad x = \frac{-2 \pm \sqrt{4 - 8}}{2}$$

$$= \frac{-2 \pm \sqrt{-4}}{2}$$

$$= \frac{-2 \pm 2i}{2}$$

$$= -1 \pm i$$

$\therefore \quad$ the roots are $2, -1 + i, -1 - i$.

Note that the imaginary roots occur in conjugate pairs. In general if $a + bi$ is one root then $a - bi$ is another.

EXERCISE 4-6

B **1.** Solve.

(a) $x^3 - 3x^2 - 4x + 12 = 0$ (b) $x^3 - 4x^2 + x + 6 = 0$

(c) $t^3 - t^2 - 16t - 20 = 0$ (d) $3w^3 + w^2 - 3w - 1 = 0$

(e) $2z^3 - z^2 - 15z + 18 = 0$ (f) $4t^3 - 7t^2 - 21t + 18 = 0$

(g) $2x^3 - 9x^2 - 8x + 15 = 0$ (h) $x^3 - 3x^2 - 16x + 48 = 0$

2. Solve.

(a) $x^3 - 5x + 2 = 0$ (b) $t^3 - 2t^2 - 2t + 1 = 0$

(c) $w^3 + 4w^2 + 7w + 6 = 0$ (d) $x^3 - 1 = 0$

(e) $t^3 + 8 = 0$ (f) $x^3 + 2x^2 - 8x - 15 = 0$

3. Solve.

(a) $x^4 - x^3 - 11x^2 + 9x + 18 = 0$ (b) $x^4 - x^3 - 13x^2 + x + 12 = 0$

(c) $x^4 - 1 = 0$ (d) $6t^3 + 7t^2 - 43t - 30 = 0$

4. Solve.

(a) $x^4 - 27x = 0$ (b) $x^2(x + 1) = 12 + 8x$

C **5.** Solve.

(a) $x(x^2 - 4) = -3(x^2 - 4)$ (b) $x^5 + 3x^4 - 5x^3 - 15x^2 + 4x + 12 = 0$

4.7 GRAPHING RATIONAL FUNCTIONS

Polynomial functions are obtained by a number of multiplications, additions, and subtractions of variables and constants. When division of expressions is permitted, the result is a class of functions called rational functions.

A rational function f is the quotient of two polynomial functions:

$$f(x) = \frac{P(x)}{Q(x)}$$

where P and Q are polynomials.

Examples of rational functions are

$$y = \frac{x+1}{x-1}, \qquad y = \frac{1}{x^2} \quad \text{and} \quad y = \frac{x^2 + 2x + 7}{x^3 + 4}$$

EXAMPLE 1. *Sketch the graph of* $y = \dfrac{x}{x-3}$.

Solution

(i) The zero of the numerator is 0 so the zero of the function is 0

(ii) The zero of the denominator is 3. Although 3 is not in the domain of the function its graph approaches the vertical line $x = 3$ as x approaches 3 from above and below. The line $x = 3$ is called a vertical asymptote.

x	y
6	2
5	$2\frac{1}{2}$
4	4
2	-2
1	$-\frac{1}{2}$
0	0
-1	$\frac{1}{4}$
-2	$\frac{2}{5}$

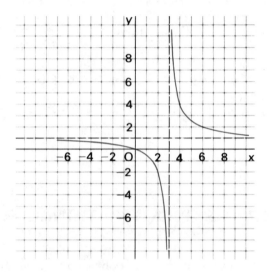

(iii) By letting $x = 0$ we see that the y-intercept is 0.

(iv) Solving the equation for x gives $x = \dfrac{3y}{y-1}$. Hence, $y \neq 1$ and a horizontal asymptote is drawn at $y = 1$. The function approaches 1 as $|x|$ gets very large.

Two important properties of rational functions are:

1. The zeros of the function are the zeros of the numerator (provided that they are not also zeros of the denominator)

2. Vertical asymptotes are found by determining zeros of the denominator.

EXAMPLE 2. *Sketch the graph of* $y = \dfrac{4}{x^2 + 1}$

Solution

(i) Since there are no zeros for the numerator there are no zeros for the function. (The graph doesn't cross the x-axis.)

(ii) There are no zeros for the denominator so there are no vertical asymptotes.

(iii) By letting $x = 0$ we see that the y-intercept is 4.

x	y
0	4
1	2
−1	2
2	$\frac{4}{5}$
−2	$\frac{4}{5}$
3	$\frac{2}{5}$
−3	$\frac{2}{5}$

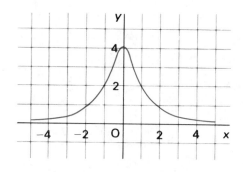

(iv) As $|x|$ increases the value of the function decreases rapidly. As $|x|$ get very large, the value of $\frac{4}{x^2+1}$ approaches zero but never reaches zero. Therefore the x-axis is a horizontal asymptote.

(v) From the graph we see that the range is $0 < y \leqslant 4$.

EXAMPLE 3. *Sketch the graph of* $y = \frac{1}{x^2-9}$.

Solution

$$y = \frac{1}{x^2-9} = \frac{1}{(x-3)(x+3)}$$

(i) There are no zeros for the numerator so there are no zeros for the function.

(ii) The zeros of the denominator are 3 and −3 so vertical asymptotes are drawn at $x = 3$ and $x = -3$.

(iii) When $x = 0$, $y = -\frac{1}{9}$. Hence the y-intercept is $-\frac{1}{9}$.

(iv) For values of x between 3 and −3 the function is negative.

(v) For values of x greater than 3 and less than −3 the function is positive.

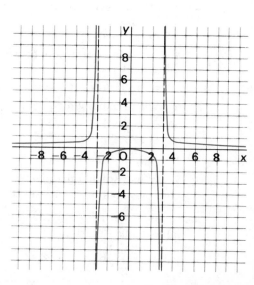

EXERCISE 4-7

B　**1.** Sketch the graph of each of the following.

(a) $y = \dfrac{x}{x-2}$

(b) $y = \dfrac{x}{x+3}$

(c) $y = \dfrac{x+1}{x}$

(d) $y = \dfrac{x+3}{x}$

(e) $y = \dfrac{1}{x}$

(f) $y = -\dfrac{1}{x}$

(g) $y = \dfrac{2}{x+3}$

(h) $y = -\dfrac{2}{x-4}$

(i) $y = \dfrac{1}{x^2+2}$

(j) $y = -\dfrac{2}{x^2+1}$

2. Sketch the graph of each of the following.

(a) $y = \dfrac{1}{x^2-4}$

(b) $y = \dfrac{x^2}{x-3}$

(c) $y = \dfrac{1}{x^2-x-2}$

(d) $y = \dfrac{x}{x^2+1}$

(e) $y = \dfrac{x+2}{x-3}$

(f) $y = \dfrac{x-1}{x+4}$

C　**3.** Sketch the graph of each of the following.

(a) $y = \dfrac{x}{x^2-9}$

(b) $y = \dfrac{x^2-5x+4}{x^2-2x-3}$

REVIEW EXERCISE

A　**1.** State the sum and product of the roots of the following quadratic equations.

(a) $x^2-5x+5=0$

(b) $2x^2+3x-7=0$

(c) $7x^2-6x=0$

(d) $13x^2+8=0$

2. State a quadratic equation whose roots have the given sum and product.

(a) sum: 6; product: -2

(b) sum: -7; product: 6

(c) sum: 0; product: -5

(d) sum: -2; product: 0

B　**3.** Write a quadratic equation having the given roots and integral coefficients

(a) -5 and -8

(b) $\frac{1}{3}$ and $-\frac{1}{4}$

(c) $2+2\sqrt{3}$ and $2-2\sqrt{3}$

(d) $2+3i$ and $2-3i$

4. If 4 is one root of $3x^2-11x+c=0$, find the other root and the value of c.

5. Without solving the given equation, find an equation whose roots are two more than the roots of $x^2+2x-5=0$.

6. Solve the following equations.

(a) $x^4-10x^2+9=0$

(b) $(x^2-2x)^2-11(x^2-2x)+24=0$

(c) $\left(x+\dfrac{1}{x}\right)^2 - 6\left(x+\dfrac{1}{x}\right)+8=0$

(d) $(x^2-3x)^2-16=0$

7. Graph the following and state the roots of the corresponding equation.

(a) $y = (x+3)(x+1)(x-2)$

(b) $y = (x+1)(x-3)^2$

(c) $y = -x(x+3)(x-1)$

(d) $y = (x-3)(x-1)(x+1)(x+4)$

(e) $y = x^3 - 4x$

(f) $y = (x+2)^4$

(g) $y = x^4 - 5x^3 + 2x^2 + 8x$

8. Divide and state any restrictions on the variables.

(a) $(x^3 + 2x^2 - 10x + 5) \div (x-2)$

(b) $(6t^3 + 7t^2 - 2t - 2) \div (2t+1)$

(c) $(6 + 6w^3 - 5w^2) \div (3w+2)$

(d) $(3x^3 - 10x^2 + 6 - x + 2x^4) \div (x+3)$

9. Use the Remainder Theorem to find the remainders.

(a) $(x^2 - 3x + 5) \div (x-2)$

(b) $(w^3 - 3w^2 + 2w - 4) \div (w-1)$

(c) $(3x^3 - 2x^2 + x - 5) \div (x+2)$

(d) $(2t^3 - t^2 - 3t + 1) \div (t-3)$

10. Factor.

(a) $w^3 - 3w^2 - 4w + 12$

(b) $x^3 + 2x^2 - 11x - 12$

(c) $2x^3 + x^2 - 13x + 6$

(d) $2x^3 - 3x^2 - 18x + 27$

11. Determine the value of k so that $x - 2$ is a factor of $x^3 + x^2 + x + k$.

12. Solve.

(a) $x^3 + 8x^2 + 19x + 12 = 0$

(b) $t^3 - 9t^2 + 26t - 24 = 0$

(c) $w^2 + 2w^2 - 9w - 18 = 0$

(d) $4x^3 - 8x^2 + x + 3 = 0$

(e) $x^3 - 6x + 4 = 0$

(f) $t^3 - 10t - 3 = 0$

(g) $x^3 + 3x^2 - 3x + 4 = 0$

(h) $6t^3 + t^2 - 31t + 10 = 0$

(i) $x^4 + 3x^3 - x^2 - 6x = 0$

(j) $x^3 + 27 = 0$

13. Sketch the graph of each of the following.

(a) $y = \dfrac{x}{x-1}$

(b) $y = \dfrac{x}{x+2}$

(c) $y = \dfrac{x+2}{x}$

(d) $y = \dfrac{3}{x+3}$

(e) $y = \dfrac{5}{x^2+1}$

(f) $y = \dfrac{4}{x^2-4}$

(g) $y = \dfrac{x-1}{x+3}$

(h) $y = \dfrac{1}{x^2-x-12}$

ADDITION

```
      C A B
      C A B
      C A B
      C A B
      ―――――
      R A C E
```

REVIEW AND PREVIEW TO CHAPTER 5

EXERCISE 1　ALGEBRAIC OPERATIONS ON RATIONAL EXPRESSIONS

Simplify.

1. $\dfrac{1}{x+1}+\dfrac{1}{x-1}$

2. $\dfrac{1}{x+1}-\dfrac{1}{x-1}$

3. $\dfrac{1}{x+1}\times\dfrac{1}{x-1}$

4. $\dfrac{1}{x+1}\div\dfrac{1}{x-1}$

5. $\dfrac{2}{x-3}+\dfrac{5}{x+4}$

6. $\dfrac{x}{x-5}-\dfrac{x+1}{x-2}$

7. $\dfrac{3+2x}{2+3x}-\dfrac{3-2x}{2-3x}$

8. $\dfrac{1}{a-b}-\dfrac{1}{a+b}$

9. $\dfrac{a}{b^2c^2}\div\dfrac{a^2b}{c}$

10. $\dfrac{x}{y}\div\dfrac{y}{z}\cdot\dfrac{1}{zx^2}$

11. $\dfrac{3x-3}{7-x}-\dfrac{11-2x}{49-x^2}$

12. $\dfrac{x-3}{x^2+x-2}+\dfrac{x-2}{x+2}$

13. $\dfrac{x^2+x-2}{x^2-x-6}\times\dfrac{x^2-9}{x^2+2x-3}$

14. $\dfrac{x^2+4x}{x^2-16}\times\dfrac{x^2+3x-28}{x^2+14x+49}$

15. $\dfrac{2x^2-3x-2}{3x^2-7x+2}\div\dfrac{4x^2+12x+5}{2x^2+x-10}$

16. $\dfrac{4x^2-4}{2x^2+5x-7}\div\dfrac{3x^2-2x-5}{4x^2+8x-21}$

17. $\dfrac{2x+1}{x^2-1}-\dfrac{2x+3}{x^2-x-2}$

18. $\dfrac{1}{x-1}+\dfrac{x^2+5x+2}{x^3-1}$

19. $\dfrac{a^3-b^3}{a}\times\dfrac{ab}{a-b}$

20. $a-\dfrac{b}{\dfrac{a}{b}+\dfrac{b}{a}}$

21. $\left(3a-\dfrac{2ab+b^2}{a}\right)\div\dfrac{a^2-ab}{a^2b^2}$

22. $\dfrac{1+\dfrac{1}{a-1}}{1-\dfrac{1}{a-1}}$

23. $\left(x-\dfrac{2x}{2-x}\right)\left(x-3+\dfrac{2}{x}\right)$

24. $\dfrac{\dfrac{m-n}{m}-\dfrac{m+n}{n}}{\dfrac{m-n}{n}+\dfrac{m+n}{m}}$

25. $1+\dfrac{1}{1+\dfrac{1}{1+x}}$

26. $2x+\dfrac{3}{4+\dfrac{x}{x+\dfrac{1}{x}}}$

Exponential and Logarithmic Functions

Strange as it may seem, the power of mathematics rests on its evasion of all unnecessary thought and on its wonderful saving of mental operations.

Ernest Mach

JOHN NAPIER (1550–1617)

John Napier was a Scottish lord, the Baron of Merchiston, who spent most of his time managing his estates and writing books on a great variety of topics, especially religion. As an amateur mathematician he was mainly interested in computation and trigonometry. He started to work on his greatest achievement, the invention of logarithms, in about 1594, but it was not until 1614 that he published a book containing the first table of logarithms. This book was immediately hailed as a great labour-saving device by mathematicians, astronomers, and other scientists.

We have studied relatively simple functions such as polynomials and rational functions. We shall now turn our attention to two of the most important functions in mathematics, the exponential function and its inverse, the logarithmic function. As we shall see, these functions have a wide variety of applications in such sciences as biology, chemistry, physics, geology, sociology, and economics.

5.1 LAWS OF EXPONENTS

If $a \in R$ and $n \in N$, then the nth power of a is written

$$a^n = \underbrace{a \times a \times a \times \cdots \times a}_{n \text{ factors}}$$

and n is called the exponent, a is called the base. For example

$$8^2 = 8 \times 8 = 64 \quad \text{and} \quad 2^8 = 2 \times 2 \times 2 \times 2 \times 2 \times 2 \times 2 \times 2 = 256$$

There are five laws of exponents which we shall illustrate by examples.

1. To multiply two powers of the same number we add the exponents.

$$5^4 \times 5^2 = (5 \times 5 \times 5 \times 5)(5 \times 5)$$
$$= 5 \times 5 \times 5 \times 5 \times 5 \times 5$$
$$= 5^6$$

$$a^m \times a^n = \underbrace{(a \times a \times \ldots \times a)}_{m \text{ factors}}\underbrace{(a \times a \times \ldots \times a)}_{n \text{ factors}}$$
$$= \underbrace{a \times a \times a \times \ldots \times a}_{m + n \text{ factors}}$$
$$= a^{m+n}$$

2. To divide two powers of the same number we subtract the exponents.

$$\frac{3^5}{3^3} = \frac{3 \times 3 \times 3 \times 3 \times 3}{3 \times 3 \times 3}$$
$$= 3 \times 3$$
$$= 3^2$$

$$\frac{a^m}{a^n} = \frac{\overbrace{a \times a \times a \times \ldots \times a}^{m \text{ factors}}}{\underbrace{a \times a \times \ldots \times a}_{n \text{ factors}}} \qquad (m > n, a \neq 0)$$
$$= \underbrace{a \times a \times \ldots \times a}_{m - n \text{ factors}}$$
$$= a^{m-n}$$

3. To raise a power to a new power we multiply the exponents.

$$(7^3)^2 = (7 \times 7 \times 7)^2$$
$$= (7 \times 7 \times 7) \times (7 \times 7 \times 7)$$
$$= 7 \times 7 \times 7 \times 7 \times 7 \times 7$$
$$= 7^6$$

$$(a^m)^n = (\underbrace{a \times a \times \ldots \times a}_{m \text{ factors}})^n$$
$$= \underbrace{(\underbrace{a \times a \times \ldots \times a}_{m \text{ factors}}) \times (\underbrace{a \times a \times \ldots \times a}_{m \text{ factors}}) \ldots (\underbrace{a \times a \times \ldots \times a}_{m \text{ factors}})}_{n \text{ times}}$$
$$= \underbrace{a \times a \times a \times \ldots \times a}_{mn \text{ factors}}$$
$$= a^{mn}$$

4. To raise a product to a power we raise each of the factors to the power.

$$(4 \times 5)^3 = (4 \times 5) \times (4 \times 5) \times (4 \times 5)$$
$$= 4 \times 4 \times 4 \times 5 \times 5 \times 5$$
$$= 4^3 \times 5^3$$

$$(ab)^n = \underbrace{(ab) \times (ab) \times \ldots \times (ab)}_{n \text{ factors}}$$

$$= \underbrace{(a \times a \times \ldots \times a)}_{n \text{ factors}} \times \underbrace{(b \times b \times \ldots \times b)}_{n \text{ factors}}$$

$$= a^n b^n$$

5. To raise a quotient to a power we raise both numerator and denominator to the power.

$$\left(\frac{2}{3}\right)^4 = \frac{2}{3} \times \frac{2}{3} \times \frac{2}{3} \times \frac{2}{3}$$

$$= \frac{2 \times 2 \times 2 \times 2}{3 \times 3 \times 3 \times 3}$$

$$= \frac{2^4}{3^4}$$

$$\left(\frac{a}{b}\right)^n = \underbrace{\frac{a}{b} \times \frac{a}{b} \times \ldots \times \frac{a}{b}}_{n \text{ factors}}$$

$$= \frac{\overbrace{a \times a \times \ldots \times a}^{n \text{ factors}}}{\underbrace{b \times b \times \ldots \times b}_{n \text{ factors}}}$$

$$= \frac{a^n}{b^n}$$

Laws of Exponents

If $a \in R$ and $m, n \in N$, then

1. $a^m \times a^n = a^{m+n}$

2. $\dfrac{a^m}{a^n} = a^{m-n}$ (if $m > n$, $a \neq 0$)

3. $(a^m)^n = a^{mn}$

4. $(ab)^n = a^n b^n$

5. $\left(\dfrac{a}{b}\right)^n = \dfrac{a^n}{b^n}$ $(b \neq 0)$

EXAMPLE 1. *Express the following as powers of 2*

(a) 4^7 (b) $2^8 \times 8^2$ (c) $\dfrac{2^9}{16}$

Solution

(a) $4^7 = (2^2)^7$ (b) $2^8 \times 8^2 = 2^8 \times (2^3)^2$ (c) $\dfrac{2^9}{16} = \dfrac{2^9}{2^4}$

    $= 2^{14}$ $= 2^8 \times 2^6$ $= 2^5$

                                          $= 2^{14}$

EXAMPLE 2. *Simplify the expressions.*

(a) $\dfrac{(x^2 y)^5}{(xy)^4}$ (b) $\dfrac{(2x)^4}{x^9}$

Solution

$\dfrac{a^m}{a^n} = \dfrac{1}{a^{n-m}}$

if $n > m$

(a) $\dfrac{(x^2 y)^5}{(xy)^4} = \dfrac{(x^2)^5 y^5}{x^4 y^4}$ (b) $\dfrac{(2x)^4}{x^9} = \dfrac{2^4 x^4}{x^9}$

           $= \dfrac{x^{10}}{x^4} \times \dfrac{y^5}{y^4}$ $= \dfrac{16}{x^5}$

           $= x^6 y$

EXAMPLE 3. *Simplify $3^5 \times 2^7$ if possible.*

Solution

$3^5 \times 2^7$ cannot be simplified.

The first law of exponents cannot be used here since it only applies when both factors have the *same base.*

EXAMPLE 4. *Solve the equation*

$$5^{x-2} = 125$$

Solution

If $a^m = a^n$ $(a \neq 1, 0, -1)$ then $m = n$.

$$5^{x-2} = 125$$
$$5^{x-2} = 5^3$$
$$\therefore \quad x - 2 = 3$$
$$\therefore \quad x = 5$$

EXERCISE 5-1

Assume $m, n, p \in N$.

A **1.** State the following numbers as powers of 2

(a) 16   (b) 2   (c) $(2^4)^7$ (d) $2^8 \times 2^7$

(e) 32   (f) $2^9 \times 2^3$ (g) $(2^9)^3$ (h) 2×2^9

(i) 4×2^5 (j) $2^4 \times 2^m$ (k) $(2^4)^m$ (l) $(2^m)^4$

2. State the following numbers as powers of 3

(a) 27   (b) $3^4 \times 3^6$ (c) $3^8 \times 3$ (d) 81

(e) $(3^6)^6$ (f) $\dfrac{3^{10}}{3^7}$ (g) $(3^p)^m$ (h) $\dfrac{3^{12}}{3^5}$

3. Use the Laws of Exponents to express the following in another form, if possible.

(a) $(9 \times 13)^4$ (b) $(9x)^4$ (c) $(\frac{5}{6})^{18}$ (d) $\left(\dfrac{x}{6}\right)^5$

(e) $7^8 \times 9^8$ (f) $(6 \times 72)^5$ (g) $2^6 \times 5^4$ (h) $(xy)^3$

(i) $\pi^2 \times \pi^3$ (j) $(\pi^2)^3$ (k) $(\frac{2}{3})^{10}$ (l) $\left(\dfrac{x}{y}\right)^6$

(m) $\dfrac{(2.78)^{12}}{(2.78)^4}$ (n) $\dfrac{(-2)^{100}}{(-2)^{93}}$ (o) $\left(\dfrac{3}{a}\right)^2$ (p) $\dfrac{a^8}{b^8}$

(q) $4^9 \times 5^6$ (r) $(2x^2)^3$ (s) $x^9 \times x^6$ (t) $(-x^3)^4$

(u) $(x^3)^n$ (v) $x^3 \times x^n$ (w) $x^n \times x^n$ (x) $(x^n)^n$

4. Simplify the following expressions.

(a) $(-3x^6)^3$ (b) $(-3x^6)(4x^3)$ (c) $3^8 \times 3^6 \times 3^4$

(d) $a^m \times a^n \times a^p$ (e) $((2^3)^2)^4$ (f) $((a^m)^n)^p$

(g) $\dfrac{4^7 \times 4^3}{4^6}$ (h) $\dfrac{x^{m+n} \times x^{2m}}{x^n}$ (i) $\dfrac{(x^4)^n}{x^3}$

B   **5.** Simplify the following.

(a) $\dfrac{7^{10} \times 7^{12} \times 7^6}{(7^3)^9}$ (b) $\dfrac{3^6 \times 3^5 \times 3^4}{3^8 \times 3^9}$

(c) $\dfrac{56^4}{14^4}$ (d) $\dfrac{2^{n+2} \times 4^{n+1}}{8^n}$

(e) $\dfrac{125^{16}}{5^{47}}$ (f) $\dfrac{a^{27} \times a^{18} \times a^4}{a^7 \times (a^3)^{14}}$

6. Simplify the following.

(a) $a^{2+p} \times a^{2p} \times (-a)^7$ (b) $x^n \times (x^2)^{n+1} \times (x^3)^{n+2}$

(c) $\left(\dfrac{2}{3}\right)^8 \left(\dfrac{5}{8}\right)^3 \left(\dfrac{6}{10}\right)^4$ (d) $\dfrac{(3^6)^n \times (81)^{2n}}{(3^n)^4}$

(e) $\dfrac{2^n \times 4^{n-1} \times 8^{3n-2}}{16^{2n-1}}$

7. Simplify if possible.

(a) $(x^5 y^3)(x^2 y^6)$ (b) $x^8 y^9$

(c) $(\frac{1}{2}x^3)^2 (x^8 y^2)^4$ (d) $(-xy)^3 (x^4 y)^9$

(e) $\dfrac{2xy^4}{3x^3 y^2} \times \dfrac{15x^2 y^3}{12x^4 y^2}$ (f) $\dfrac{a^2 b^4}{a^3 b^2} \times \left(\dfrac{a^4}{b^2}\right)^3$

(g) $\dfrac{(2x^2 y^2)^5}{8x^4 y^3 (x^2 y)^3}$ (h) $\left(\dfrac{x}{y}\right)^5 \left(\dfrac{2}{x}\right)^4 \left(\dfrac{y}{4}\right)^3$

(i) $\dfrac{3^n \times 3^{4n} \times 9^{n-1}}{27^{2n+1}}$ (j) $\dfrac{(x^2)^m \times (x^3)^n}{x^{m+n} \times x^{m-n}}$

(k) $(b^3 c^8) \div (b^6 c^9)$ (l) $(a^2 b^3)^n \div (ab)^{2n}$

(m) $\left(\dfrac{a}{b}\right)^m \left(\dfrac{b}{c}\right)^m \left(\dfrac{c}{a}\right)^m$ (n) $\dfrac{(xy)^4 (2yz)^3 (-xz)^5}{xyz}$

8. Solve the following equations. ($x \in N$)

(a) $2^x = 64$

(b) $6^{x+3} = 6^{2x}$

(c) $9^x = 729$

(d) $2^x = 16^4$

(e) $2^x = 4^{x-1}$

(f) $2(5^x) = 1250$

(g) $9^{2x-6} = 3^{x+6}$

(h) $4^{2x-1} = 64$

(i) $1^x = 1$

(j) $(-1)^x = 1$

C **9.** Simplify.

(a) $\dfrac{7^{15} + 7^{14}}{8 \times 7^8}$

(b) $\dfrac{3^{2n+2} + 3^{2n}}{3^n + 3^{n+1}}$

(c) $\dfrac{3^n + 6^n}{1 + 2^n}$

(d) $\dfrac{2^{100} + 2^{95}}{2^{100} - 2^{95}}$

5.2 NEGATIVE EXPONENTS

We have defined a^n if $a \in R$ and $n \in N$, but how can we give a meaning to a^n if n is 0 or a negative integer? For example $5^4 = 5 \times 5 \times 5 \times 5$, but is it impossible to give a reasonable definition of 5^0 or 5^{-3}? If so, we would still like all the Laws of Exponents to be true. If the second law of exponents

$$\frac{a^m}{a^n} = a^{m-n}$$

is to be true, then we would have

$$\frac{2^3}{2^3} = 2^{3-3} = 2^0$$

But

$$\frac{2^3}{2^3} = 1$$

So 2^0 must be 1.

Similarly a^0 must be 1 if $a \neq 0$. Note that if we define $a^0 = 1$, then

$$a^m \times a^0 = a^m \times 1 = a^m = a^{m+0}$$

So the first law of exponents is also true.

0^0 is not defined because

$0^0 = 0^{1-1}$

$= \dfrac{0^1}{0^1}$

$= \dfrac{0}{0}$ which is

undefined.

If $a \neq 0$, we define $a^0 = 1$

If the first law is to hold for negative exponents, then

$$5^3 \times 5^{-3} = 5^{3+(-3)} = 5^0 = 1$$

$$\therefore \quad 5^{-3} = \frac{1}{5^3} \qquad \text{(divide both sides by } 5^3\text{)}$$

Similarly, under the same assumption,

$$a^n \times a^{-n} = a^{n+(-n)} = a^0 = 1 \qquad \text{(if } a \neq 0\text{)}$$

$$\therefore \quad a^{-n} = \frac{1}{a^n} \qquad \text{(divide both sides by } a^n\text{)}$$

> If $a \neq 0$ and $n \in N$, we define
>
> $$a^{-n} = \frac{1}{a^n}$$

With these definitions we can show that all the previous laws of exponents still hold for any integer exponents. For example

$$(3 \times 5)^{-4} = \frac{1}{(3 \times 5)^4} = \frac{1}{3^4 \times 5^4} = \frac{1}{3^4} \times \frac{1}{5^4} = 3^{-4} \times 5^{-4}$$

$$\therefore \quad (3 \times 5)^{-4} = 3^{-4} \times 5^{-4}$$

Laws of Exponents for Integral Exponents

If $a \in R$, $a \neq 0$, and $m, n \in I$, then

1. $a^m \times a^n = a^{m+n}$
2. $\dfrac{a^m}{a^n} = a^{m-n}$
3. $(a^m)^n = a^{mn}$
4. $(ab)^n = a^n b^n$
5. $\left(\dfrac{a}{b}\right)^n = \dfrac{a^n}{b^n}$

EXAMPLE 1. *Evaluate.*

(a) $\left(\frac{2}{3}\right)^{-2}$ 　　(b) $\dfrac{(-12)^0}{2^{-4}}$ 　　(c) $\dfrac{2^{-8}+2^{-10}}{2^{-9}+2^{-7}}$

Solution

(a) $\left(\frac{2}{3}\right)^{-2} = \dfrac{1}{\left(\frac{2}{3}\right)^2}$

$= \dfrac{1}{\frac{4}{9}}$

$= \dfrac{9}{4}$

(b) $\dfrac{(-12)^0}{2^{-4}} = \dfrac{1}{2^{-4}}$

$= \dfrac{1}{\frac{1}{2^4}}$

$= 2^4$

(c) $\dfrac{2^{-8}+2^{-10}}{2^{-9}+2^{-7}} = \dfrac{2^{10}}{2^{10}} \times \dfrac{2^{-8}+2^{-10}}{2^{-9}+2^{-7}}$

$= \dfrac{2^{10} \times 2^{-8} + 2^{10} \times 2^{-10}}{2^{10} \times 2^{-9} + 2^{10} \times 2^{-7}}$

$= \dfrac{2^2 + 2^0}{2^1 + 2^3}$

$= \dfrac{4+1}{2+8}$

$= \dfrac{5}{10}$

$= \dfrac{1}{2}$

EXERCISE 5-2

A **1.** State the value of each of the following.

(a) 6^0 (b) 9^{-1} (c) 2^{-3} (d) 3^{-2}

(e) $(-1)^{-1}$ (f) $(-\pi)^0$ (g) 10^{-4} (h) 837^{-1}

(i) $\dfrac{1}{8^{-1}}$ (j) 4^{-3} (k) $\dfrac{1}{6^{-2}}$ (l) $(\tfrac{1}{2})^{-5}$

2. State the following using only positive exponents.

(a) x^{-8} (b) x^2y^{-2} (c) $a^{-3}b^{-4}$ (d) $a^3 \times a^{-5}$

(e) $\dfrac{1}{a^{-10}}$ (f) $\left(\dfrac{x}{y}\right)^3$ (g) $\dfrac{a^{-2}}{b^{-3}}$ (h) $\dfrac{x^3}{y^{-5}}$

3. State the following with the variables in the numerator.

(a) $\dfrac{1}{x^3}$ (b) $2\dfrac{a}{b^4}$ (c) $\pi\dfrac{x^2}{y^{-1}}$

(d) $\dfrac{3}{a^2b^{-4}}$ (e) $\dfrac{2x}{x^2y^2}$ (f) $\dfrac{x^3}{xy^2z^{-3}}$

B **4.** Evaluate.

(a) $2^{-1} \times 3^0 \times 4^2 \times 5^{-2}$ (b) $(2^3 \times 4^{-4})^{-2}$ (c) $(3^{-3} \times 5^2)^{-1}$

(d) $4^{10} \times 2^{-18}$ (e) $\dfrac{(27)^{-2}}{3^{-8}}$ (f) $\dfrac{(5^3 + 3^5)^0}{2^{-1}}$

(g) $\dfrac{7^{-1} + 7^{-2}}{7^{-3} + 7^{-4}}$ (h) $\dfrac{4^{-2} - 3^{-3}}{4^{-1} - 3^{-1}}$ (i) $\dfrac{3^{-12} + 3^{-14}}{3^{-12} - 3^{-14}}$

(j) $\dfrac{(7 \times 5^{-1})^{-1}}{(2 \times 3^{-1})^{-1}}$ (k) $\left(\dfrac{3^{-1} - 4^{-1}}{2^{-1} - 3^{-1}}\right)^{-1}$ (l) $(5^{-4} \times (25)^3)^2$

(m) $1 + \dfrac{1}{2^{-1} + \dfrac{1}{3^{-1} + \dfrac{1}{4^{-1}}}}$ (n) $\{1 - [(2 + 3^{-1})^{-1}]\}^{-1}$

MYRIAD

The Greeks called the number 10 000 a myriad. Which is larger

10^{myriad} or myriad^{10}?

5. Rewrite the following using only positive exponents. Simplify where possible.

(a) $(7x^2y^{-3})^3$ (b) $(3a^{-1}b^{-2})^{-5}$

(c) $(4ab^{-2}c^3d^{-4})^3$ (d) $\dfrac{a^{-3}b^2}{a^{-5}b^5}$

(e) $\dfrac{a^2x^3y^{-2}}{b^{-2}xy^{-6}}$ (f) $(a^2b^{-1} - 1)^2$

(g) $a^4(a^2 + a - 5a^{-2})$ (h) $(x^2 - 1)(x^{-2} + 2)$

(i) $(b^{-2})^{n-2} \div b^4$ (j) $(x^{-n} + y^{-m})(x^{-n} - y^{-m})$

(k) $(a^n b^{-2n} c^{n^2})^{-n}$ (l) $\dfrac{x^{-1} - y^{-1}}{x^{-1} + y^{-1}}$

(m) $\dfrac{x^{-2} - y^{-2}}{x^{-1} + y^{-1}}$ (n) $\dfrac{x^{-1} + y^{-1}}{(x+y)^{-1}}$

(o) $\left(\dfrac{x+y}{x}\right)^{-1} + \left(\dfrac{x-y}{y}\right)^{-1}$ (p) $\dfrac{a^{-1} - b^{-1}}{a^{-2} - b^{-2}}{(ab)^{-2}}$ (q) $\dfrac{a}{a^{-1} - b^{-1}} - \dfrac{b}{a^{-2} - b^{-2}}$

6. Solve the following equations for $x \in I$.

(a) $6^{3x-6} = 1$ (b) $2^{-x} = 128$

(c) $5^{4-x} = \frac{1}{5}$ (d) $(-1)^x = 1$

5.3 APPLICATION: SCIENTIFIC NOTATION

The nearest star beyond the sun, Proxima Centauri, is 40 000 000 000 000 km away. The mass of a hydrogen atom is about 0.000 000 000 000 000 000 000 001 66 g.

Scientists who work with such very large or very small numbers usually write them in a more convenient way called scientific notation.

For example they would write

$$40\ 000\ 000\ 000\ 000 = 4 \times 10^{13}$$

and

$$0.000\ 000\ 000\ 000\ 000\ 000\ 000\ 001\ 66 = 1.66\ 10^{-24}$$

> A positive real number x is said to be written in scientific notation (or standard form) if it is expressed as
>
> $$x = a \times 10^n$$
>
> where $1 \leq a < 10$ and $n \in I$.

Thus a number in scientific notation is a single nonzero digit followed by a decimal point and other digits, all multiplied by a power of 10.

EXAMPLE 1. *Write the following numbers using scientific notation.*

         (a) 1786 000   (b) 0.000 043 12

Solution

(a) $1\ 786\ 000 = 1.786 \times 1\ 000\ 000$

                $= 1.786 \times 10^6$

The exponent, $n = 6$, indicates that the decimal point is 6 places to the *right* of the standard position of the decimal point

                                             1 786 000

(b) $0.000\ 043\ 12 = 4.312 \times 0.000\ 01$

                       $= 4.312 \times \dfrac{1}{100\ 000}$

                       $= 4.312 \times \dfrac{1}{10^5}$

                       $= 4.312 \times 10^{-5}$

The exponent, $n = -5$, indicates that the decimal point is 5 places to the *left* of the standard position of the decimal point

                                       0.000 043 12

One of the advantages of scientific notation is the relative ease of computing with large and small numbers (as well as those in between) if we first put all of them in standard form and then use the laws of exponents. Many calculators do this automatically. In such computations it must be remembered to express the final answer to the least number of decimal places found among the original numbers.

EXAMPLE 2. *Approximate* $\dfrac{ab}{c}$ *where* $a \doteq 521$, $b \doteq 0.000\,415$, $c \doteq 71\,640$

Solution

First we express the numbers in scientific notation.

$$a \doteq 521 = 5.21 \times 10^2$$

$$b \doteq 0.000\,415 = 4.15 \times 10^{-4}$$

$$c \doteq 71\,640 = 7.164 \times 10^4$$

$$\therefore \quad \frac{ab}{c} \doteq \frac{(5.21 \times 10^2)(4.15 \times 10^{-4})}{7.164 \times 10^4}$$

$$= \frac{(5.21)(4.15)}{7.164} \times \frac{10^2 \times 10^{-4}}{10^4}$$

$$= \frac{21.165}{7.164} \times 10^{2-4-4}$$

$$\doteq 3.02 \times 10^{-6}$$

$$\frac{ab}{c} \doteq 3.02 \times 10^{-6}$$

or, in more conventional notation,

$$\frac{ab}{c} \doteq 0.000\,003\,02$$

EXERCISE 5-3

B   **1.** Express in scientific notation.

(a) 2000 (b) 363 (c) 723.4 (d) 0.001
(e) 0.000 72 (f) 3.5 (g) 246 000 (h) 0.045
(i) 1984 (j) 0.123 (k) 0.000 08 (l) 12 345
(m) 140.61 (n) −100 (o) 0.008 34 (p) 37×10^4

2. The following numbers are given in scientific notation. Express them in the usual decimal notation.

(a) 2×10^3 (b) 7.4×10^2 (c) 2.3×10^{-1} (d) 3.7×10^{-3}
(e) 1×10^6 (f) 1.23×10^4 (g) 9.99×10^{-2} (h) 5.456×10^{-4}

B **3.** Rewrite the numbers in the following statements in scientific form.

(a) A light-year, the distance that light travels in one year, is about 9 410 000 000 000 km.

(b) The light from the sun is equivalent to about 3 000 000 000 000 000 000 000 000 000 cd.

(c) The mass of the earth is approximately 5 970 000 000 000 000 000 000 000 kg.

(d) Light travels one metre in about $\dfrac{1}{300\,000\,000}$ s.

(e) The distance from the sun to the earth is approximately one hundred fifty million kilometres.

(f) The diameter of an electron is approximately 0.000 000 000 000 4 cm.

4. Express the following numbers in scientific notation.

(a) 69 000 000 000
(b) 634×10^{19}
(c) 0.000 000 078
(d) 0.000 019 83
(e) 183 555 000
(f) 2635.84
(g) 0.000 006 8
(h) 123 456 789 000 000
(i) $\dfrac{17}{1\,000\,000}$
(j) $\dfrac{832}{100\,000\,000}$

5. Write the following numbers in conventional notation.

(a) 3.12×10^5
(b) 8.57×10^{-3}
(c) 2.67×10^{-8}
(d) 6.853×10^{10}
(e) 1.495×10^{-10}
(f) 9×10^{12}
(g) 1.1111×10^{-9}
(h) 4.337×10^{11}
(i) 6.5×10^{-7}

6. Express the following products and quotients in scientific notation.

(a) $(3.7 \times 10^5)(8 \times 10^7)$
(b) $5\,000\,000 \times 10^{-14}$
(c) $(3 \times 10^{12})(9.1 \times 10^{-7})$
(d) $0.000\,006 \times 300$
(e) $60(1.5 \times 10^8)$
(f) $(800\,000)^2$
(g) $\dfrac{6\,400\,000}{0.008}$
(h) $\dfrac{5.5 \times 10^{12}}{5 \times 10^4}$
(i) $\dfrac{120 \times 10^{-9}}{4 \times 10^{-3}}$
(j) $\dfrac{0.000\,16}{2\,000\,000\,000}$
(k) $61\,000\,000 \times 0.009$
(l) $\dfrac{240\,000 \times 0.000\,000\,5}{0.006}$

7. Use scientific notation to approximate $\dfrac{ab}{c}$ where $a \doteq 73.1$, $b \doteq 816\,000\,000$, $c \doteq 0.000\,014$

8. If $r \doteq 1.62$, $s \doteq 9.13 \times 10^9$, $t \doteq 5.545 \times 10^{-23}$, find an approximate value for $\dfrac{r}{st}$.

9. Find an approximate value for

$$\frac{(0.000\,345\,61)(870\,513\,000)}{(78.91)(0.000\,000\,000\,172\,3)}$$

5.4 RATIONAL EXPONENTS

So far we have defined a^n where $a \neq 0$ and $n \in I$. We shall see in this section that it is also possible to define powers where the exponent is a rational number, such as $5^{\frac{1}{2}}$ or $8^{\frac{3}{5}}$, in such a way that the laws of exponents are still true.

If the third law of exponents

$(\sqrt{3})^2 = 3$
$(3^{\frac{1}{2}})^2 = 3^{\frac{1}{2} \times 2}$
$\qquad = 3$

$$(a^m)^n = a^{mn}$$

is to be true, then putting $m = \dfrac{1}{n}$ we would have

$$(a^{\frac{1}{n}})^n = a^{\frac{1}{n} \times n} = a^1 = a$$

If $a \geq 0$, we can take nth roots of both sides of the equation

$$(a^{\frac{1}{n}})^n = a$$

we get

$$a^{\frac{1}{n}} = \sqrt[n]{a}$$

This suggests the following definition.

$$\boxed{a^{\frac{1}{n}} = \sqrt[n]{a}, \ n \in N}$$

Note that if n is even, then we must have $a \geq 0$, but if n is odd, then a can be any real number.

EXAMPLE 1. *Find*

$$\text{(a)} \ 16^{\frac{1}{4}} \qquad \text{(b)} \ (-27)^{\frac{1}{3}}$$

Solution

$$\text{(a)} \ 16^{\frac{1}{4}} = \sqrt[4]{16} \qquad \text{(b)} \ (-27)^{\frac{1}{3}} = \sqrt[3]{-27}$$
$$\qquad = 2 \qquad\qquad\qquad\qquad = -3$$

To see how we should define $a^{\frac{m}{n}}$ when $m, n \in N$ we again use the third law of exponents:

$8^{\frac{2}{3}} = 8^{\frac{1}{3} \times 2}$
$\quad = (8^{\frac{1}{3}})^2$
$\quad = 2^2$
$\quad = 4$

$$a^{\frac{m}{n}} = a^{m \times \frac{1}{n}} \qquad a^{\frac{m}{n}} = a^{\frac{1}{n} \times m}$$
$$= (a^m)^{\frac{1}{n}} \qquad = (a^{\frac{1}{n}})^m$$
$$= \sqrt[n]{a^m} \qquad = (\sqrt[n]{a})^m$$

Therefore we make the following definition for rational exponents.

$$\boxed{a^{\frac{m}{n}} = \sqrt[n]{a^m} = (\sqrt[n]{a})^m, \ m, n \in N}$$

Again, if n is even then we must have $a \geq 0$.

Notice that in calculating $a^{\frac{m}{n}}$ you can either raise a to the mth power and then take the nth root, or first take the nth root and then raise the result to the mth power. With these definitions we can show that all of the previous laws of exponents are still true for rational exponents.

Laws of Exponents for Rational Exponents

If $a \in R$, $a \geqslant 0$, and $r, s \in Q$, then

1. $a^r \times a^s = a^{r+s}$

2. $\dfrac{a^r}{a^s} = a^{r-s}$

3. $(a^r)^s = a^{rs}$

4. $(ab)^r = a^r b^r$

5. $\left(\dfrac{a}{b}\right)^r = \dfrac{a^r}{b^r}$ $\qquad (b \neq 0)$

6. $a^0 = 1$

7. $a^{-r} = \dfrac{1}{a^r}$

8. $a^{\frac{r}{s}} = \sqrt[s]{a^r} = (\sqrt[s]{a})^r$

EXAMPLE 2. *Find* $4^{\frac{3}{2}}$

Solution

There are several methods.

(i) $\quad 4^{\frac{3}{2}} = (\sqrt{4})^3$ $\qquad$ (ii) $\quad 4^{\frac{3}{2}} = \sqrt{4^3}$

$\qquad\qquad = 2^3$ $\qquad\qquad\qquad\qquad = \sqrt{64}$

$\qquad\qquad = 8$ $\qquad\qquad\qquad\qquad\ \ = 8$

(iii) $\quad 4^{\frac{3}{2}} = (4^{\frac{1}{2}})^3$ $\qquad$ (iv) $\quad 4^{\frac{3}{2}} = (2^2)^{\frac{3}{2}}$

$\qquad\qquad = 2^3$ $\qquad\qquad\qquad\qquad = 2^{2 \times \frac{3}{2}}$

$\qquad\qquad = 8$ $\qquad\qquad\qquad\qquad = 2^3$

$\qquad\qquad\qquad\qquad\qquad\qquad\qquad\ \ = 8$

EXAMPLE 3. *Simplify*

(a) $125^{-\frac{2}{3}}$ $\qquad$ (b) $(2x^2y^4)^{\frac{3}{2}}$

Solution

(a) $\quad 125^{-\frac{2}{3}} = \dfrac{1}{125^{\frac{2}{3}}}$ $\qquad$ (b) $\quad (2x^2y^4)^{\frac{3}{2}} = 2^{\frac{3}{2}}(x^2)^{\frac{3}{2}}(y^4)^{\frac{3}{2}}$

$\qquad\qquad\ \ = \dfrac{1}{(\sqrt[3]{125})^2}$ $\qquad\qquad\qquad\qquad\ = (\sqrt{2})^3 x^{2 \times \frac{3}{2}} y^{4 \times \frac{3}{2}}$

$\qquad\qquad\ \ = \dfrac{1}{5^2}$ $\qquad\qquad\qquad\qquad\ = 2\sqrt{2}x^3y^6$

$\qquad\qquad\ \ = \frac{1}{25}$

EXERCISE 5-4

A **1.** State the following using radicals.
(a) $2^{\frac{1}{9}}$ (b) $37^{\frac{1}{2}}$ (c) $x^{\frac{1}{3}}$ (d) $2^{\frac{2}{3}}$
(e) $2^{\frac{3}{2}}$ (f) $3^{\frac{3}{4}}$ (g) $a^{\frac{2}{5}}$ (h) $x^{\frac{4}{7}}$
(i) $2^{-\frac{1}{2}}$ (j) $7^{-\frac{1}{5}}$ (k) $a^{-\frac{3}{2}}$ (l) $9^{\frac{2}{11}}$

2. State the following using exponents.
(a) $\sqrt{3}$ (b) $\sqrt{19}$ (c) $\sqrt[7]{23}$ (d) $\sqrt[4]{x}$
(e) $(\sqrt[3]{7})^2$ (f) $\sqrt[3]{7^2}$ (g) $(\sqrt[5]{6})^4$ (h) $(\sqrt[3]{13})^5$
(i) $\sqrt[5]{a^2}$ (j) $(\sqrt[6]{a})^5$ (k) $\dfrac{1}{\sqrt{5}}$ (l) $\dfrac{1}{(\sqrt[3]{7})^3}$

3. Evaluate.
(a) $4^{\frac{1}{2}}$ (b) $64^{\frac{1}{3}}$ (c) $9^{\frac{3}{2}}$ (d) $1^{\frac{9}{7}}$
(e) $36^{-\frac{1}{2}}$ (f) $8^{\frac{2}{3}}$ (g) $9^{0.5}$ (h) $8^{-\frac{1}{3}}$
(i) $16^{-\frac{1}{4}}$ (j) $4^{-\frac{3}{2}}$ (k) $(-8)^{\frac{1}{3}}$ (l) $(-32)^{\frac{2}{5}}$

B **4.** Evaluate.
(a) $32^{\frac{4}{5}}$ (b) $8^{2\frac{1}{3}}$ (c) $100\ 000^{\frac{2}{5}}$
(d) $64^{-\frac{1}{3}}$ (e) $81^{\frac{3}{4}}$ (f) $625^{-\frac{3}{4}}$
(g) $128^{\frac{8}{7}}$ (h) $3^{\frac{2}{7}}\times3^{\frac{5}{7}}$ (i) $(6^{0.4})^5$
(j) $(49^6)^{\frac{1}{4}}$ (k) $2^{\frac{1}{5}}\times4^{\frac{2}{5}}$ (l) $9^{\frac{1}{2}}\div36^{-\frac{1}{2}}$
(m) $(\frac{8}{27})^{\frac{1}{3}}$ (n) $(\frac{49}{144})^{-\frac{1}{2}}$ (o) $(\frac{25}{64})^{\frac{3}{2}}$
(p) $\dfrac{64^{\frac{2}{3}}}{216^{-\frac{1}{3}}}$ (q) $(0.16)^{\frac{1}{2}}(0.008)^{\frac{1}{3}}$ (r) $3^{\frac{1}{2}}\times9^{\frac{1}{4}}$
(s) $256^{0.375}$ (t) $0^{1.356}$ (u) $[(\sqrt{343})^{\frac{1}{9}}]^6$
(v) $\dfrac{(0.09)^{-\frac{1}{2}}}{(0.125)^{-\frac{2}{3}}}$ (w) $(81^{-1})^{-\frac{1}{4}}$ (x) $\dfrac{(0.81)^{\frac{1}{2}}\times6^{-3}}{(0.027)^{\frac{2}{3}}}$

5. Simplify.
(a) $2^{\frac{1}{2}}\times2^{\frac{1}{3}}$ (b) $3^{\frac{2}{9}}\times9^{\frac{1}{3}}$ (c) $(x^{\frac{2}{3}}y^{\frac{1}{6}})^3$
(d) $(a^{\frac{1}{4}}b^{\frac{1}{3}})^{12}$ (e) $(a^3b^6c^9)^{\frac{1}{3}}$ (f) $(x^{\frac{2}{3}}+3x^{\frac{1}{3}})x^{\frac{1}{3}}$
(g) $(16x^8y^2)^{\frac{1}{4}}$ (h) $(64x^9y^{-3})^{\frac{2}{3}}$ (i) $(20x^2y^3z^{-1})^{\frac{3}{2}}$
(j) $\left(\dfrac{a^3b^{-4}}{x^{-1}y^2}\right)^2\times\dfrac{x^{-1}b^{-1}}{a^{\frac{3}{2}}y^{\frac{4}{5}}}$ (k) $\sqrt[4]{\dfrac{y^{\frac{1}{2}}\sqrt{xy}}{x^{\frac{2}{3}}}}$ (l) $\sqrt[4]{a^{2n+1}}\times\sqrt[4]{a^{-1}}$

C **6.** Determine which is the larger of each of the following pairs of numbers.
(a) $5^{\frac{1}{3}},3^{\frac{1}{2}}$ (b) $7^{\frac{1}{4}},4^{\frac{1}{3}}$
(c) $3^{\frac{3}{2}},9^{\frac{2}{3}}$ (d) $6^{-\frac{1}{2}},14^{-\frac{1}{3}}$

5.5 EXPONENTIAL FUNCTIONS

We have now defined a^x if $a>0$ and $x\in Q$ but we have not yet defined irrational powers. For instance, what is meant by $2^{\sqrt{3}}$ or 6^{π}?

To help us answer this question we first look at the graph of the function $y=2^x$, $x\in I$.

x	2^x
-3	$\frac{1}{8}$
-2	$\frac{1}{4}$
-1	$\frac{1}{2}$
0	1
1	2
2	4
3	8

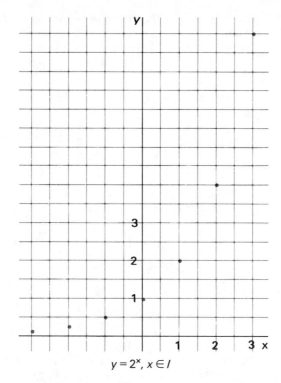

$y = 2^x, x \in I$

Now let us enlarge the domain of $y = 2^x$ to include the rational numbers. Approximate values of 2^x are given for some rational values of x.

x	2^x		x	2^x		x	2^x
-3.0	0.13		-1.0	0.50		1.0	2.00
-2.8	0.14		-0.8	0.57		1.2	2.30
-2.6	0.16		-0.6	0.66		1.4	2.64
-2.4	0.19		-0.4	0.76		1.6	3.03
-2.2	0.22		-0.2	0.87		1.8	3.48
-2.0	0.25		0.0	1.00		2.0	4.00
-1.8	0.29		0.2	1.15		2.2	4.59
-1.6	0.33		0.4	1.32		2.4	5.28
-1.4	0.38		0.6	1.52		2.6	6.06
-1.2	0.44		0.8	1.74		2.8	6.96

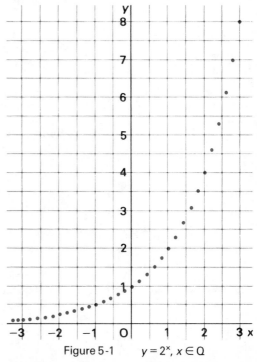

Figure 5-1 $y = 2^x, x \in Q$

exponential and logarithmic functions   149

We want to further enlarge the domain of $y = 2^x$ to include both rational and irrational numbers. There are holes in the graph shown in Figure 5-1. We want to fill in the holes by defining $f(x) = 2^x$, $x \in R$, in such a way that f is a continuous increasing function.

In particular, since

$$1.7 < \sqrt{3} < 1.8$$

we must have

$$2^{1.7} < 2^{\sqrt{3}} < 2^{1.8}$$

Similarly, using better approximations for $\sqrt{3}$, we obtain better approximations for $2^{\sqrt{3}}$.

$$1.73 < \sqrt{3} < 1.74 \qquad \therefore \quad 2^{1.73} < 2^{\sqrt{3}} < 2^{1.74}$$

$$1.732 < \sqrt{3} < 1.733 \qquad \therefore \quad 2^{1.732} < 2^{\sqrt{3}} < 2^{1.732}$$

$$1.7320 < \sqrt{3} < 1.7321 \qquad \therefore \quad 2^{1.7320} < 2^{\sqrt{3}} < 2^{1.7321}$$

$$1.732\ 05 < \sqrt{3} < 1.732\ 06 \qquad \therefore \quad 2^{1.732\ 05} < 2^{\sqrt{3}} < 2^{1.732\ 06}$$

Using advanced mathematics it can be shown that there is exactly one number which is greater than all of the numbers

$$2^{1.7}, 2^{1.73}, 2^{1.732}, 2^{1.7320}, 2^{1.732\ 05}, \ldots$$

and less than all of the numbers

$$2^{1.8}, 2^{1.74}, 2^{1.733}, 2^{1.7321}, 2^{1.732\ 06}, \ldots$$

We define $2^{\sqrt{3}}$ to be this number. Using the above approximation process we can compute that, correct to 7 decimal places,

$$2^{\sqrt{3}} \doteq 3.321\ 997\ 1$$

Similarly we can define 2^x (or a^x, if $a > 0$) where x is any irrational number. It turns out that the laws of exponents are still true for irrational exponents.

The graph of $y = 2^x$, $x \in R$, is shown in Figure 5-2.

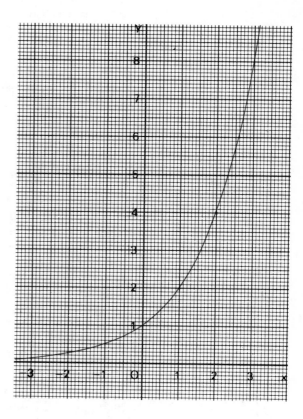

You can see that $f(x) = 2^x$ is an increasing, continuous, one-to-one function whose domain is R and whose range is the set of all positive real numbers.

If $a > 0$, the function $f(x) = a^x$ is called the exponential function with base a. Figure 5-3 shows the graphs of $y = a^x$ for several values of the base a. Notice that all of the exponential functions $y = a^x$ pass through the same point $(0, 1)$ because $a^0 = 1$ for any $a \neq 0$.

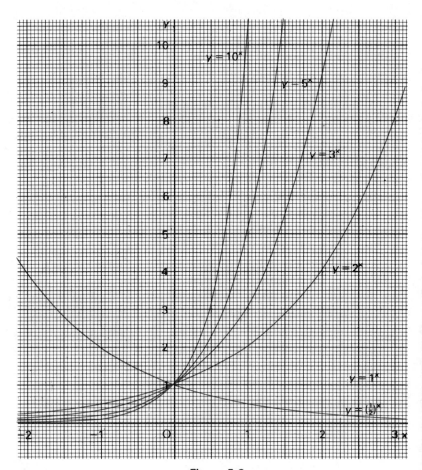

Figure 5-3

EXAMPLE 1. *Use the graph of $y = 2^x$ given in Figure 5-2 to find the values of x or y in the following equations to one decimal place.*

$$\text{(a) } y = 2^{2.3} \qquad \text{(b) } 2^x = 5.7$$

$$\text{(c) } y = 2^{6.7} \qquad \text{(d) } 2^x = 28$$

Solution

(a) From the graph $y \doteq 4.9$ (b) From the graph $x \doteq 2.5$

(c) $2^{6.7} = 2^4 \times 2^{2.7}$ (d) $2^x = 4 \times 7$

$\qquad = 16 \times 2^{2.7}$ $\qquad\qquad\qquad = 2^2 \times 7$

$\qquad \doteq 16(6.5)$ $\qquad\qquad\qquad\quad \doteq 2^2 \times 2^{2.8}$

$\qquad = 104.0$ $\qquad\qquad\qquad\quad = 2^{4.8}$

$\qquad\qquad\qquad\qquad\qquad\qquad \therefore \quad x = 4.8$

EXERCISE 5-5

1. Use the graphs in Figure 5-3 to find approximate values of the following numbers.

(a) $2^{1.7}$ (b) $2^{2.2}$ (c) $3^{1.9}$ (d) $5^{1.3}$

(e) $10^{0.7}$ (f) $2^{-0.6}$ (g) $5^{0.2}$ (h) $3^{-1.4}$

(i) $\sqrt{10}$ (j) $3^{1.5}$ (k) $10^{-0.4}$ (l) $2^{3.1}$

2. Use the graphs in Figure 5-3 to find an approximate value of x satisfying the following equations.

(a) $2^x = 6$ (b) $2^x = 1.8$ (c) $2^x = 0.5$ (d) $3^x = 10$

(e) $3^x = 2$ (f) $5^x = 8$ (g) $5^x = 0.8$ (h) $10^x = 3$

(i) $10^x = 7$ (j) $10^x = 0.1$ (k) $3^x = 1.5$ (l) $5^x = 3$

3. Use the graph of $y = 2^x$ in Figure 5-2 to find approximate values of x and y in the following equations.

(a) $y = 2^{1.9}$ (b) $y = 2^{5.8}$ (c) $y = 2^{\sqrt{2}}$ (d) $y = 2^{9.7}$

(e) $2^x = 0.8$ (f) $2^x = 24$ (g) $2^x = 30$ (h) $2^x = 96$

4. Use the graphs in Figure 5-3 to find approximate values of x and y in the following equations.

(a) $y = 3^{1.8}$ (b) $y = 3^{5.6}$ (c) $y = 5^{3.1}$ (d) $y = 10^{2.8}$

(e) $5^x = 7$ (f) $5^x = 50$ (g) $3^x = 36$ (h) $10^x = 90$

5. Draw the graph of $y = (\frac{1}{3})^x$ with the same axes as $y = 3^x$. Use the fact that $\left(\dfrac{1}{3}\right)^x = \dfrac{1}{3^x}$

State the domain and range of $y = \left(\dfrac{1}{3}\right)^x$

6. Graph $y = 2^{|x|}$

5.6 APPLICATIONS: EXPONENTIAL GROWTH AND DECAY

The exponential function occurs frequently in nature and society. For example, it can be used in problems of population growth, compound interest, investment growth, depreciation, inflation rates, bacterial growth, and radioactive decay.

EXAMPLE 1. *Bacteria of a certain type are known to divide every hour, thus producing two bacteria for every previously existing bacterium. Suppose that 100 of these bacteria are breathed into Paul's lung.*

  (a) *How many bacteria will live in his lung after 5 h?*

  (b) *How many after t hours?*

Solution

Let $N = N(t)$ be the number of bacteria after t hours.

If $t = 0$, $N = 100$

$t = 1$, $N = 2 \times 100$

$t = 2$, $N = 2 \times (2 \times 100) = 2^2 \times 100$

$t = 3$, $N = 2 \times (2^2 \times 100) = 2^3 \times 100$

$t = 4$, $N = 2 \times (2^3 \times 100) = 2^4 \times 100$

$t = 5$, $N = 2 \times (2^4 \times 100) = 2^5 \times 100$

$\vdots$

(a) After 5 h the number of bacteria is

$$N(5) = 2^5 \times 100 = 3200$$

(b) After t hours the number of bacteria is

$$N(t) = 2^t \times 100$$

More generally

$$\boxed{N(t) = c \times 2^{\frac{t}{d}}}$$

where $N(t)$ is the number of bacteria present after t hours, c is the number of bacteria at the beginning, and d is the doubling period, i.e., the number of hours required for a given quantity to be doubled.

EXAMPLE 2. *A biologist makes a sample count of bacteria in a culture and finds that it doubles every 3 h. The estimated count after 6 h was 10 000.*
   (a) *What was the initial size of the culture at time $t = 0$?*
   (b) *What was the estimated count after 1 d?*
   (c) *What was it after 1.5 h?*

Solution
   (a) The doubling period is $d = 3$ h.

$$N(t) = c \times 2^{\frac{t}{3}}$$

where c is the initial size.

We are given $N(6) = 10\ 000$

But $N(6) = c \times 2^{\frac{6}{3}}$

$\qquad\qquad = c \times 2^2 = 4c$

$\therefore\quad 4c = 10\ 000$

$\qquad c = 2500$

The initial count was 2500 bacteria.

(b) From part (a) we have $N(t) = 2500 \times 2^{\frac{t}{3}}$

$$\therefore \quad N(24) = 2500 \times 2^{\frac{24}{3}}$$
$$= 2500 \times 2^8$$
$$= 2500 \times 256$$
$$= 640\ 000$$

The estimated count after one day was 640 000 bacteria.

(c)
$$N(1.5) = 2500 \times 2^{\frac{1.5}{3}}$$
$$= 2500 \times 2^{\frac{1}{2}}$$
$$= 2500\sqrt{2}$$
$$\doteq 2500 \times 1.414$$
$$\doteq 3535$$

After 1.5 h the estimated count was 3535

EXAMPLE 3. *Half-life is the period of time during which a given amount of radioactive material decays until one half of it is left. An isotope of strontium, Sr^{90}, has a half-life of 25 years.*

(a) *Find the mass of Sr^{90} remaining from a sample of 18 mg after 125 years.*

(b) *after t years.*

Solution

Let $m(t)$ be the mass, in grams, remaining after t years. We are given that $m(0) = 18$

$$m(25) = \tfrac{1}{2} \times 18$$

$$m(50) = \tfrac{1}{2} \times (\tfrac{1}{2} \times 18) = \frac{1}{2^2} \times 18$$

$$m(75) = \tfrac{1}{2} \times \left(\frac{1}{2^2} \times 18\right) = \frac{1}{2^3} \times 18$$

$$m(100) = \tfrac{1}{2} \times \left(\frac{1}{2^3} \times 18\right) = \frac{1}{2^4} \times 18$$

$$m(125) = \tfrac{1}{2} \times \left(\frac{1}{2^4} \times 18\right) = \frac{1}{2^5} \times 18$$

(a) The mass of Sr^{90} after 125 years is $\frac{1}{2^5} \times 18 = \frac{9}{16}$ g.

(b) The mass of Sr^{90} after t years is

$$m(t) = \frac{1}{2^{\frac{t}{25}}} 18 = 18 \times 2^{-\frac{t}{25}}$$

More generally

$$m(t) = c\left(\tfrac{1}{2}\right)^{\frac{t}{h}} = c \times 2^{-\frac{t}{h}}$$

where $m(t)$ is the mass remaining after time t, c is the initial mass, and h is the half-life (measured in the same unit of time as t). Some radioactive substances decay very slowly, having half-lives of thousands of years. Other substances decay very quickly, having half-lives of less than a second.

EXAMPLE 4. *In eight days a certain amount of Vandium-48, V^{48}, decays to $\dfrac{1}{\sqrt{2}}$ of its original amount. What is the half-life of V^{48}?*

Solution

$$m(t) = c \times 2^{-\frac{t}{h}}$$

where c is the original amount.

We are given that $m(8) = \dfrac{1}{\sqrt{2}} c$

But $\quad m(8) = c \times 2^{-\frac{8}{h}}$

$$\therefore \quad \frac{1}{\sqrt{2}} c = c \times 2^{-\frac{8}{h}}$$

$$\frac{1}{\sqrt{2}} = 2^{-\frac{8}{h}}$$

$$2^{-\frac{1}{2}} = 2^{-\frac{8}{h}}$$

$$\tfrac{1}{2} = \frac{8}{h}$$

$$h = 16$$

The half-life of V^{48} is 16 d.

EXERCISE 5-6

A **1.** Strontium-90 has a half-life of 25 years. How long would it take 4 mg of it to decay to
(a) 2 mg?   (b) 1 mg?   (c) 0.25 mg?   (d) $\frac{1}{2}$ mg?

2. Radium-221 has a half-life of 30 s. What fraction of a sample would remain after the following time?
(a) 30 s   (b) 1 min   (c) 2 min   (d) 3 min

3. The doubling period of a bacteria culture is 15 min and it starts with 5000 bacteria. How many bacteria will there be after
(a) 15 min?   (b) 45 min?   (c) 1 h?   (d) 1.5 h?

4. A bacteria culture grows according to the formula

$$N(t) = 12\,000 \times 2^{\frac{t}{4}}$$

where the time t is given in hours. How many bacteria are there
(a) at the beginning of the experiment?
(b) after 4 h?   (c) after 8 h?   (d) after 12 h?
5. Five million bacteria live in an organism. The doubling period is
1.5 h. How many will there be after

(a) t hours?   (b) 9 h?   (c) 1 d?   (d) 2 h?

6. A bacteria culture doubles every $\frac{1}{4}$ h. At time $1\frac{1}{4}$ h an estimate of
40 000 is taken.
(a) What was the initial size of the culture?
(b) What is it after 2 h?   (c) after 3 h?
7. A bacteria culture starts with 3000 bacteria. After 3 h the estimated
count is 48 000. What is the doubling period?
8. A bacteria culture starts with 6000 bacteria. After half an hour the
bacteria count is 33 600. Estimate the number of minutes it takes for
the culture to double. [Use the graph of $y = 2^x$ in Figure 5-2.]

9. A bacteria culture *triples* every 4 h and starts with 10 000 bacteria.
Find the number of bacteria in the culture
(a) after 24 h,   (b) after t hours.

10. The world population is doubling about every 35 years. In 1980
the total population was about 4.5 billion. If the doubling period
remains at 35, find the projected world population for the year 2120.

11. An isotype of sodium, Na^{24}, has a half-life of 15 h.
(a) Find the amount remaining from a 4 g sample after
(i) 30 h   (ii) t hours   (iii) 5 d   (iv) 7.5 h
(b) How many hours will it take to decay to 2^{-4} g?
(c) to 1.6 g?   [For (c) use Figure 5-2.]

Determine the pattern.
Find the missing number.

12. The half-life of Palladium-100, Pd^{100}, is 4 d. After 16 d a sample
of Pd^{100} has been reduced to a mass of 0.75 g.
(a) What was the initial mass of the sample?
(b) What is the mass after 2 d?   (c) 2 weeks?

4	7	8	5
3	▨	3	4
2	5	7	3
2	3	5	2

13. After 30 h a sample of Plutonium-243, Pu^{243}, has decayed to $\frac{1}{64}$ of
its original mass. Find the half-life of Pu^{243}.
14. After 90 d a sample of Silver-110, Ag^{110}, has decayed to about 80%
of its original amount. What is the approximate half-life of Ag^{110}? [Use
Figure 5-2.]

15. Scientists can determine the age of certain objects by a method
called radiocarbon dating. The bombardment of the upper atmos-
phere by cosmic rays converts nitrogen to radioactive carbon-14 with
a half-life of 5760 years. This C^{14} is assimilated by all plants and
animals. When the plant or animal dies it cannot assimilate new C^{14},
and the amount present at death decreases by radioactivity as time
passes. A small sample of a bone was burned and the resulting
carbon dioxide was tested with a Geiger counter. It was found that the
amount of C^{14} had decayed to $\frac{1}{8}$ of its original amount. How old was
the bone?

5.7 LOGARITHMIC FUNCTIONS

Recall that if $a > 0$ and $a \neq 1$, then the function $y = a^x$ is a 1-1 function with domain R and range $\{y \in R \mid y > 0\}$. It is increasing if $a > 1$ and decreasing if $0 < a < 1$

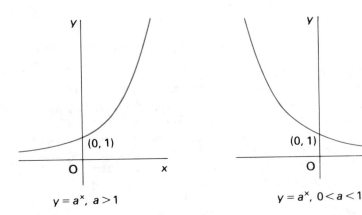

$y = a^x, \ a > 1$

$y = a^x, \ 0 < a < 1$

Therefore $f(x) = a^x$ has an inverse function if $a > 0$ and $a \neq 1$. The inverse function f^{-1} of $f(x) = a^x$ is called a logarithmic function and is denoted by $f^{-1} = \log_a$

> The logarithmic function $y = \log_a x$, $a > 0$, $a \neq 1$, is the inverse of the function $y = a^x$

We read "$\log_a x$" as "the logarithm of x to the base a" or as "log x to the base a."

We know that the graph of f^{-1} is the reflection of the graph of f in the line $y = x$. Therefore to draw the graph of $y = \log_a x$, we need only reflect the graph of $y = a^x$ in the line $y = x$.

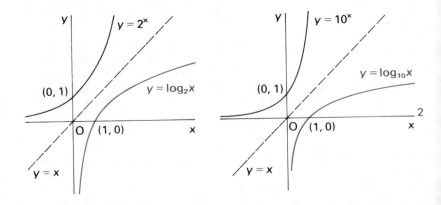

The domain of $\log_a$ is $\{x \in R \mid x > 0\}$ and its range is R.
By the definition of an inverse function

$$f^{-1}(y) = x \Leftrightarrow f(x) = y$$

or, interchanging x and y,

$$f^{-1}(x) = y \Leftrightarrow f(y) = x$$

Therefore

$$\boxed{\log_a x = y \quad \Leftrightarrow \quad a^y = x}$$

Notice that $\log_a x$ is the exponent to which the base a must be raised to give x.

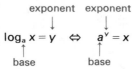

In particular

$$\log_2 x = y \quad \Leftrightarrow \quad 2^y = x$$

Thus the curve in Figure 5-4 can be labelled $y = \log_2 x$ if you think of y as a function of x, or it can also be labelled $x = 2^y$ if you think of x as a function of y.

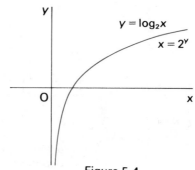

Figure 5-4

EXAMPLE 1. *Express in logarithmic form.*
   (a) $x = 5^y$ (b) $1000 = 10^3$ (c) $2^{-3} = \frac{1}{8}$

Solution

   (a) $x = 5^y$ (b) $1000 = 10^3$ (c) $2^{-3} = \frac{1}{8}$
   $\therefore \ \log_5 x = y$ $\therefore \ \log_{10} 1000 = 3$ $\therefore \ \log_2 \left(\frac{1}{8}\right) = -3$

EXAMPLE 2. *Express in exponential form.*
   (a) $\log_a s = r$ (b) $\log_{10} 10\,000 = 4$ (c) $\log_4 \left(\frac{1}{4}\right) = -1$

Solution

   (a) $\log_a s = r$ (b) $\log_{10} 10\,000 = 4$ (c) $\log_4 \left(\frac{1}{4}\right) = -1$
       $\therefore \ \ a^r = s$ $\therefore \ \ 10^4 = 10\,000$ $\therefore \ \ 4^{-1} = \frac{1}{4}$

EXAMPLE 3. *Evaluate.*

(a) $\log_3 81$ (b) $\log_{10} 0.001$ (c) $\log_8 1$

(d) $\log_2 2^x$ (e) $5^{\log_5 x}$

Solution

(a) Let $\log_3 81 = y$

$\therefore\ 3^y = 81$

But $81 = 3^4$

$\therefore\ 3^y = 3^4$

$\therefore\ y = 4$

$\log_3 81 = 4$

(b) Let $\log_{10} 0.001 = y$

$\therefore\ 10^y = 0.001$

$10^y = 10^{-3}$

$\therefore\ y = -3$

(c) Let $\log_8 1 = y$

$\therefore\ 8^y = 1$

$8^y = 8^0$

$\therefore\ y = 0$

$\log_8 1 = 0$

(d) Let $\log_2 2^x = y$

$2^y = 2^x$

$\therefore\ y = x$

$\log_2 2^x = x$

(e) Let $5^{\log_5 x} = a$

$\therefore\ \log_5 a = \log_5 x$

$\therefore\ a = x$ (since $\log_5$ is 1-1)

$5^{\log_5 x} = x$

The first three parts of Example 3 could be done mentally by remembering that $\log_a x$ is the exponent to which you need to raise a to get x.

Parts (c), (d), and (e) of Example 3 illustrate some general properties of logarithms:

> If $a > 0$ and $a \neq 1$, then
>
> (i) $\log_a 1 = 0$
>
> (ii) $\log_a a^x = x$
>
> (iii) $a^{\log_a a^x} = x$

Property (i) is true because $a^0 = 1$. Properties (ii) and (iii) are proved as in Example 3 or by observing that for any pair of inverse functions f and f^{-1}, $f(f^{-1}(x)) = x$ and $f^{-1}(f(x)) = x$

EXERCISE 5-7

A   **1.** Express in logarithmic form.

(a) $3^2 = 9$ (b) $2^4 = 16$ (c) $6^3 = 216$ (d) $9^{-1} = \frac{1}{9}$

(e) $a^b = c$ (f) $8^0 = 1$ (g) $4^5 = 1024$ (h) $49^{\frac{1}{2}} = 7$

(i) $8^{\frac{2}{3}} = 4$ (j) $5^{-2} = \frac{1}{25}$ (k) $10^4 = 10\,000$ (l) $4^{-\frac{3}{2}} = 0.125$

2. Express in exponential form.

(a) $\log_7 49 = 2$

(b) $\log_3 729 = 6$

(c) $\log_4 512 = 4.5$

(d) $\log_{10} 0.1 = -1$

(e) $\log_2 (\frac{1}{16}) = -4$

(f) $\log_a b = c$

(g) $\log_{12} 1728 = 3$

(h) $\log_{10} 1 = 0$

(i) $\log_5 5 = 1$

(j) $\log_{16} 4 = 0.5$

(k) $\log_8 4 = \frac{2}{3}$

(l) $\log_2 4096 = 12$

3. Evaluate.

(a) $\log_2 4$

(b) $\log_2 32$

(c) $\log_{10} 1000$

(d) $\log_3 27$

(e) $\log_5 (\frac{1}{5})$

(f) $\log_9 1$

(g) $\log_6 (\frac{1}{36})$

(h) $\log_7 7$

(i) $\log_5 125$

(j) $\log_2 2^9$

(k) $\log_3 3^{87}$

(l) $\log_5 5^{\sqrt{3}}$

(m) $\log_a a$

(n) $10^{\log_{10} 19}$

(o) $a^{\log_a 4379}$

4. Evaluate.

(a) $\log_2 128$

(b) $\log_3 81$

(c) $\log_5 (\frac{1}{625})$

(d) $\log_6 (\frac{1}{216})$

(e) $\log_4 256$

(f) $\log_2 0.25$

(g) $\log_5 0.04$

(h) $\log_{10} 0.000\,01$

(i) $\log_6 \sqrt{6}$

(j) $\log_2 8\sqrt{2}$

(k) $\log_4 \sqrt{2}$

(l) $\log_4 0.125$

5. (a) Use the graph of $y = 2^x$ in Figure 5-2 to find approximate values of $\log_2 0.5$, $\log_2 1.0$, $\log_2 1.5$, $\log_2 2.0$, $\log_2 2.5$, ..., $\log_2 7.0$. Use these values to sketch the graph of the function $y = \log_2 x$

(b) Using the same method and Figure 5-3, sketch the graph of $y = \log_{10} x$

$\log_2 3 = x$
where
$2^x = 3$

6. Solve the following equations for x

(a) $\log_{10} x = 6$

(b) $\log_2 x = 8$

(c) $\log_x 25 = 2$

(d) $\log_x \frac{1}{5} = -1$

(e) $\log_x 4 = \frac{1}{2}$

(f) $\log_2 \sqrt[3]{2} = x$

(g) $\log_{\frac{1}{2}} 2 = x$

(h) $\log_{\frac{1}{3}} 9 = x$

(i) $\log_4 x = -2$

(j) $\log_x 16 = \frac{4}{3}$

(k) $\log_x 81 = \frac{4}{5}$

(l) $\log_9 3\sqrt{3} = x$

7. Draw the graph of $y = \log_{\frac{1}{2}} x$ by reflecting the graph of $y = (\frac{1}{2})^x$ in the line $y = x$.

8. Draw the graph of $y = |\log_2 x|$

9. Draw the graph of $y = \log_2 |x|$, $x \in R$, $x \neq 0$.

10. Evaluate.

(a) $10^{(\log_{10} 7 + \log_{10} 5)}$

(b) $3^{(\log_3 7 - \log_3 5)}$

(c) $8^{\log_2 7}$

(d) $2^{\log_4 9}$

11. If $\log_a x = L$, find $\log_a x^2$

12. If $\log_a x = M$ and $\log_a y = N$, find $\log_a xy$

13. Show that $\log_a c = \dfrac{\log_b c}{\log_b a}$

5.8 LAWS OF LOGARITHMS

Because logarithms are exponents, the laws of exponents give rise to corresponding laws of logarithms. These properties give the logarithmic functions a wide range of application.

1. The logarithm of a product is equal to the sum of the logarithms of the factors.

Let $\qquad \log_a M = b \qquad$ and $\quad \log_a N = c$

Then $\qquad\qquad a^b = M \qquad$ and $\qquad a^c = N$

$$\therefore \quad \log_a (MN) = \log_a (a^b \times a^c)$$
$$= \log_a (a^{b+c})$$
$$= b + c$$
$$= \log_a M + \log_a N$$

$$\boxed{\log_a (MN) = \log_a M + \log_a N}$$

For example,

  (a) $\log_{10} (65.2 \times 35.7) = \log_{10} 65.2 + \log_{10} 35.7$
  (b) $\log_2 12 + \log_2 7 = \log_2 (12 \times 7)$
  $$= \log_2 84$$

2. The logarithm of a quotient is equal to the logarithm of the numerator minus the logarithm of the denominator.

Let $\qquad \log_a M = b \qquad$ and $\quad \log_a N = c$

Then $\qquad\qquad a^b = M \qquad$ and $\qquad a^c = N$

$$\therefore \quad \log_a \left(\frac{M}{N}\right) = \log_a \frac{a^b}{a^c}$$
$$= \log_a a^{b-c}$$
$$= b - c$$
$$= \log_a M - \log_a N$$

$$\boxed{\log_a \left(\frac{M}{N}\right) = \log_a M - \log_a N}$$

For example,

  (a) $\log_5(\frac{97}{62}) = \log_5 97 - \log_5 62$
  (b) $\log_2 15 - \log_2 3 = \log_2(\frac{15}{3})$
  $$= \log_2 5$$
  (c) $\log_{10}(\frac{1}{9}) = \log_{10} 1 - \log_{10} 9$
  $$= 0 - \log_{10} 9$$
  $$= -\log_{10} 9$$

3. The logarithm of a power of a number is equal to the exponent multiplied by the logarithm of the number.

Let $\qquad \log_a M = b$

Then $\qquad a^b = M$

$$\therefore \quad \log_a M^n = \log_a (a^b)^n$$

$$= \log_a a^{nb}$$

$$= nb$$

$$= n \log_a M$$

$$\boxed{\log_a M^n = n \log_a M} \qquad \text{(The Power Law)}$$

For example,
  (a) $\log_{10} 8^9 = 9 \log_{10} 8$
  (b) $2 \log_3 5 = \log_3 5^2$
      $\qquad\quad = \log_3 25$
  (c) $\log_5 \sqrt{125} = \log_5 (125)^{\frac{1}{2}}$
      $\qquad\qquad = \frac{1}{2} \log_5 125$
      $\qquad\qquad = \frac{1}{2} \times 3$
      $\qquad\qquad = 1.5$

Laws of Logarithms
If $a > 0$, $M > 0$, $N > 0$, $n \in R$, then
1. $\log_a (MN) = \log_a M + \log_a N$
2. $\log_a \left(\dfrac{M}{N}\right) = \log_a M - \log_a N$
2'. $\log_a \left(\dfrac{1}{N}\right) = -\log_a N$
3. $\log_a M^n = n \log_a M$
3'. $\log_a \sqrt[n]{M} = \dfrac{1}{n} \log_a M$

EXAMPLE 1. *Solve the equation*

$$\log_{10} (x + 2) + \log_{10} (x - 1) = 1$$

Find a number equal to the cube of the sum of its digits.

Solution

$$\log_{10} (x + 2) + \log_{10} (x - 1) = 1$$

$$\log_{10} (x + 2)(x - 1) = \log_{10} 10$$

$$\therefore \quad (x + 2)(x - 1) = 10$$

$$x^2 + x - 2 = 10$$

$$x^2 + x - 12 = 0$$

$$(x + 4)(x - 3) = 0$$

$$x = -4 \quad \text{or} \quad x = 3$$

If $x = -4$, then $\log (x + 2) = \log (-4 + 2) = \log (-2)$ is not defined.
Hence the root $x = -4$ is inadmissible.
$\therefore$ The only root is $x = 3$

EXERCISE 5-8

A **1.** Express as sums or differences of logarithms.

(a) $\log_{10}(8 \times 13)$ (b) $\log_2(9.1 \times 6.3)$ (c) $\log_5(14 \times 8.1)$

(d) $\log_5\left(\frac{11}{37}\right)$ (e) $\log_8\left(\frac{104}{97.2}\right)$ (f) $\log_{10}\left(\frac{2}{\pi}\right)$

(g) $\log_3 2\pi$ (h) $\log_2(19 \times 97)$ (i) $\log_{12}(16 \div 65)$

(j) $\log_{10} xy$ (k) $\log_{10}\dfrac{x}{y}$ (l) $\log_x(AB)$

2. Express as logarithms of products or quotients.

(a) $\log_{10} 89 + \log_{10} 14$ (b) $\log_5 12.2 + \log_5 2.79$

(c) $\log_2 75 - \log_2 36$ (d) $\log_3 634 - \log_3 149$

(e) $\log_6 2 + \log_6 9$ (f) $\log_7 54 - \log_7 9$

(g) $\log_{10} x + \log_{10} y$ (h) $\log_2 x - \log_2 y$

(i) $\log_{10} 36 - \log_{10} 4$ (j) $\log_9 12 + \log_9 5$

3. Apply the Power Law to the following.

(a) $\log_{10} 68^2$ (b) $\log_2 3.9^5$ (c) $\log_5 \pi^{10}$

(d) $\log_{10} 7^{\frac{3}{4}}$ (e) $\log_3 5^{\frac{1}{2}}$ (f) $\log_5 \sqrt{3}$

(g) $\log_{10} 8^{-1}$ (h) $\log_{10}\left(\frac{1}{12}\right)$ (i) $\log_{10} x^9$

(j) $2\log_{10} 37$ (k) $8\log_2 21$ (l) $3\log_5 2$

(m) $\frac{1}{3}\log_5 97$ (n) $\frac{1}{2}\log_{10} 9$ (o) $-\log_{10} 5$

(p) $-\frac{1}{2}\log_{10} 16$ (q) $\log_2 x^y$ (r) $m\log_6 A$

4. Apply the Laws of Logarithms to the following.

(a) $\log_{12}(82 \times 28)$ (b) $\log_2(9 \times 13 \times 14)$ (c) $\log_5 9^{20}$

(d) $\log_3(79 \div 53)$ (e) $2\log_{10} 6$ (f) $\log_2(LMN)$

(g) $\frac{1}{2}\log_{10} 49$ (h) $\log_2\left(\frac{937}{1005}\right)$ (i) $\log_{10}\left(\frac{1}{67}\right)$

(j) $\log_5 \sqrt{83}$ (k) $\log_a(5x)$ (l) $-\log_3 8$

(m) $\log_2 6 + \log_2 7$ (n) $\log_{10} 28 - \log_{10} 4$

B **5.** Given the approximate values $\log_{10} 2 = 0.3010$, $\log_{10} 3 = 0.4771$, and $\log_{10} 5 = 0.6990$, evaluate the following.

(a) $\log_{10} 6$ (b) $\log_{10} 15$ (c) $\log_{10} 4$

(d) $\log_{10} 18$ (e) $\log_{10} 125$ (f) $\log_{10}\left(\frac{5}{2}\right)$

(g) $\log_{10} 1.5$ (h) $\log_{10}\left(\frac{3}{5}\right)$ (i) $\log_{10} 7.5$

(j) $\log_{10} \sqrt{5}$ (k) $\log_{10} \sqrt[4]{3}$ (l) $\log_{10}\frac{1}{2}$

(m) $\log_{10} 200$ (n) $\log_{10} 50\,000$ (o) $\log_{10} 0.003$

6. Use the Laws of Logarithms to evaluate the following.

(a) $\log_4 2 + \log_4 32$ (b) $\log_{10} 1.25 + \log_{10} 80$

(c) $\log_3 108 - \log_3 4$ (d) $\log_2 80 - \log_2 5$

(e) $\log_{12} 16 + \log_{12} 9$ (f) $\log_8 6 - \log_8 3 + \log_8 2$

(g) $\log_3 \sqrt[3]{9}$ (h) $\log_2 8^{27}$

(i) $\log_{10} \sqrt{0.1}$ (j) $\log_5 5\sqrt{5}$

7. Solve for x.

(a) $\log_2 x = \log_2 5 + \log_2 3$ (b) $\log_2 x = \log_2 18 - \log_2 6$

(c) $\log_{10} x + \log_{10} 12 = \log_{10} 8$ (d) $\log_{10} x = 1 + \log_{10} 2$

(e) $\log_3 x + \log_3(x-1) = \log_3(2x)$ (f) $\log_9(x-5) + \log_9(x+3) = 1$

(g) $\log_2(x+1) - \log_2(x-1) = 1$ (h) $3\log_2 x = \log_2 8$

(i) $\log_{10} x = 3\log_{10} 7$ (j) $4\log_6 x = \log_6 625$

8. Solve for x.

(a) $\log_2 (3x + 2) - \log_2 (x - 2) = 3$ (b) $\log_2 (3x + 2) + \log_2 (x - 2) = 3$

9. Express as a single logarithm.

(a) $\log_2 a + \log_2 b - \log_2 c$

(b) $\log_{10} a + \frac{1}{2} \log_{10} b - 2 \log_{10} c$

(c) $\frac{1}{2}[\log_{10} x + \log_{10} y] - 2 \log_{10} c$

(d) $\frac{1}{2}[(\log_5 a + 2 \log_5 b) - 3 \log_5 c]$

(e) $\log_2 (a + b) + \log_2 (a - b) - 2 \log_2 a$

(f) $\log_2 a + b \log_2 c - d \log_2 e$

10. Find the error.

$$\log_3 0.1 < 2 \log_3 0.1$$
$$= \log_3 (0.1)^2$$
$$= \log_3 0.01$$
$$\log_3 0.1 < \log_3 0.01$$
$$\therefore \quad 0.1 < 0.01$$

WORD LADDER

Start with the word "wood" and change one letter at a time to form a new word until you reach "fire". The best solution has the fewest steps.

w o o d
_ _ _ _
_ _ _ _
_ _ _ _
_ _ _ _
f i r e

5.9 APPLICATIONS OF LOGARITHMS

Logarithms were originally invented in about 1600 for the purpose of eliminating the tedious calculations involved in multiplying, dividing, and taking roots of the large numbers which occur in astronomy and other sciences. With the advent of computers and hand calculators which can quickly perform such calculations, logarithms are no longer important for such computations. However it has been discovered that logarithms are useful for other reasons.

In this section we shall discuss three kinds of applications of logarithms.

(i) *Computation*. We shall see why the laws of logarithms made them a useful tool in computation for three and a half centuries.

(ii) *Applications in biology, chemistry, and physics*. The logarithmic functions occur in these sciences mainly because they are the inverse functions of the exponential functions.

(iii) *Logarithmic scales*. Quantities which vary over immense ranges, e.g., intensity of light, sound, and earthquakes, are conveniently represented by logarithmic scales.

COMPUTATION

In 1614 John Napier, a Scottish nobleman, published the first table of logarithms. He had been working on his invention for twenty years and his logarithms were slightly different from those we use today. Henry Briggs, a professor of mathematics at Oxford, visited Napier and suggested a change to the present system. Napier agreed and in 1617 Briggs published a table of logarithms (with base 10) of numbers from 1 to 1000, each logarithm being given to 14 decimal places. At about the same time Jobst Bürgi published a similar table in Switzerland.

Napier, Briggs, and Bürgi observed that addition and subtraction are much easier than multiplication and division. They also observed that the first two laws of logarithms

$$\log_{10}(MN) = \log_{10} M + \log_{10} N$$

$$\log_{10}\left(\frac{M}{N}\right) = \log_{10} M - \log_{10} N$$

could be used to convert multiplication into addition and division into subtraction.

EXAMPLE 1. *Evaluate*

(a) 5640×0.638 (b) $5640 \div 0.638$ (c) $\sqrt[8]{0.638}$

using Table 5-1 of values of $\log_{10} x$ and Table 5-2 of values of 10^x

Solution

(a) Let $x = 5640 \times 0.638$

$\therefore \quad \log_{10} x = \log_{10} 5640 + \log_{10} 0.638$

$\qquad\qquad = \log_{10}(5.640 \times 10^3) + \log_{10}(6.38 \times 10^{-1})$

$\qquad\qquad = \log_{10} 5.640 + \log_{10} 10^3 + \log_{10} 6.38 + \log_{10} 10^{-1}$

$\qquad\qquad \doteq 0.7513 + 3 + 0.8048 + (-1)$

$\qquad\qquad = 3.5561$

$\qquad \therefore \quad x = 10^{\log_{10} x}$

$\qquad\qquad \doteq 10^{3.5561}$

$\qquad\qquad = 10^{3 + 0.5561}$

$\qquad\qquad = 10^3 \times 10^{0.5561}$

$\qquad\qquad \doteq 1000 \times 3.598$

$\qquad\qquad = 3598$

$\therefore \quad 5640 \times 0.638 \doteq 3598$

$10^{0.556} = 3.597$

Difference for $1 = \dfrac{1}{3.598}$

(b) Let $x = 5640 \div 0.638$

$\therefore \quad \log_{10} x = \log_{10}(5.64 \times 10^3) - \log_{10}(6.38 \times 10^{-1})$

$\qquad\qquad = \log_{10} 5.640 + 3 - [\log_{10} 6.38 - 1]$

$\qquad\qquad \doteq 0.7513 + 3 - 0.8048 + 1$

$\qquad\qquad = 3.9465$

$\qquad \therefore \quad x = 10^{\log_{10} x}$

$\qquad\qquad \doteq 10^{3.9465}$

$\qquad\qquad = 10^3 \times 10^{0.9465}$

$\qquad\qquad \doteq 1000 \times 8.841$

$\qquad\qquad = 8841$

$\therefore \quad 5640 \div 0.638 \doteq 8841$

Logarithms

	0	1	2	3	4	5	6	7	8	9	1	2	3	4	5	6	7	8	9
														Differences					
5.5	0.7404	0.7412	0.7419	0.7427	0.7435	0.7443	0.7451	0.7459	0.7466	0.7474	1	2	2	3	4	5	5	6	7
5.6	0.7482	0.7490	0.7497	0.7505	0.7513	0.7520	0.7528	0.7536	0.7543	0.7551	1	2	2	3	4	5	5	6	7
5.7	0.7559	0.7566	0.7574	0.7582	0.7589	0.7597	0.7604	0.7612	0.7619	0.7627	1	2	2	3	4	5	5	6	7
5.8	0.7634	0.7642	0.7649	0.7657	0.7664	0.7672	0.7679	0.7686	0.7694	0.7701	1	1	2	3	4	4	5	6	7
5.9	0.7709	0.7716	0.7723	0.7731	0.7738	0.7745	0.7752	0.7760	0.7767	0.7774	1	1	2	3	4	4	5	6	7
6.0	0.7782	0.7789	0.7796	0.7803	0.7810	0.7818	0.7825	0.7832	0.7839	0.7846	1	1	2	3	4	4	5	6	6
6.1	0.7853	0.7860	0.7868	0.7875	0.7882	0.7889	0.7896	0.7903	0.7910	0.7917	1	1	2	3	4	4	5	6	6
6.2	0.7924	0.7931	0.7938	0.7945	0.7952	0.7959	0.7966	0.7973	0.7980	0.7987	1	1	2	3	4	4	5	6	6
6.3	0.7993	0.8000	0.8007	0.8014	0.8021	0.8028	0.8035	0.8041	0.8048	0.8055	1	1	2	3	3	4	5	6	6
6.4	0.8062	0.8069	0.8075	0.8082	0.8089	0.8096	0.8102	0.8109	0.8116	0.8122	1	1	2	3	3	4	5	5	6

Table 5-1

VALUES OF THE EXPONENTIAL FUNCTION $y = 10^x$

	0	1	2	3	4	5	6	7	8	9	1	2	3	4	5	6	7	8	9
														Differences					
0.50	3.162	3.170	3.177	3.184	3.192	3.199	3.206	3.214	3.221	3.228	1	2	3	3	4	4	5	6	7
0.51	3.236	3.243	3.251	3.258	3.266	3.273	3.281	3.289	3.296	3.304	1	2	2	3	4	5	5	6	7
0.52	3.311	3.319	3.327	3.334	3.342	3.350	3.357	3.365	3.373	3.381	1	2	2	3	4	5	5	6	7
0.53	3.388	3.396	3.404	3.412	3.420	3.428	3.436	3.443	3.451	3.459	1	2	2	3	4	5	5	6	7
0.54	3.467	3.475	3.483	3.491	3.499	3.508	3.516	3.524	3.532	3.540	1	2	2	3	4	5	6	6	7
0.55	3.548	3.556	3.565	3.573	3.581	3.589	3.597	3.606	3.614	3.622	1	2	2	3	4	5	6	7	7
0.56	3.631	3.639	3.648	3.656	3.664	3.673	3.681	3.690	3.698	3.707	1	2	3	3	4	5	6	7	8
0.57	3.715	3.724	3.733	3.741	3.750	3.758	3.767	3.776	3.784	3.793	1	2	3	3	4	5	6	7	8
0.58	3.802	3.811	3.819	3.828	3.837	3.846	3.855	3.864	3.873	3.882	1	2	3	3	4	5	6	7	8
0.59	3.890	3.899	3.908	3.917	3.926	3.936	3.945	3.954	3.963	3.972	1	2	3	4	5	5	6	7	8
0.60	3.981	3.990	3.999	4.009	4.018	4.027	4.036	4.046	4.055	4.064	1	2	3	4	5	6	6	7	8
0.90	7.943	7.962	7.980	7.998	8.017	8.035	8.054	8.072	8.091	8.110	2	4	6	7	9	11	13	15	17
0.91	8.128	8.147	8.166	8.185	8.204	8.222	8.241	8.260	8.279	8.299	2	4	6	8	9	11	13	15	17
0.92	8.318	8.337	8.356	8.375	8.395	8.414	8.433	8.453	8.472	8.492	2	4	6	8	10	12	14	15	17
0.93	8.511	8.531	8.551	8.570	8.590	8.610	8.630	8.650	8.670	8.690	2	4	6	8	10	12	14	16	18
0.94	8.710	8.730	8.750	8.770	8.790	8.810	8.831	8.851	8.872	8.892	2	4	6	8	10	12	14	16	18
0.95	8.913	8.933	8.954	8.974	8.995	9.016	9.036	9.057	9.078	9.099	2	4	6	8	10	12	15	17	19
0.96	9.120	9.141	9.162	9.183	9.204	9.226	9.247	9.268	9.290	9.311	2	4	6	8	11	13	15	17	19
0.97	9.333	9.354	9.376	9.397	9.419	9.441	9.462	9.484	9.506	9.528	2	4	7	9	11	13	15	17	20
0.98	9.550	9.572	9.594	9.616	9.638	9.661	9.683	9.705	9.727	9.750	2	4	7	9	11	13	15	17	20
0.99	9.772	9.795	9.817	9.840	9.863	9.886	9.908	9.931	9.954	9.977	2	5	7	9	11	14	16	18	20

Table 5-2

(c) Let $x = \sqrt[8]{0.638}$

$$x = (0.638)^{\frac{1}{8}}$$

$\therefore \quad \log_{10} x = \frac{1}{8} \log_{10} 0.638$

$$= \frac{1}{8} \log_{10} (6.38 \times 10^{-1})$$

$$= \frac{1}{8} (\log_{10} 6.38 + \log_{10} 10^{-1})$$

$$\doteq \frac{1}{8}(0.8048 - 1)$$

$$= \frac{1}{8}(-0.1952)$$

$$= -0.0244$$

$$= -1 + 1 - 0.0244$$

$$= -1 + 0.9756 \qquad \text{[so that we can use tables of } 10^x \\ \text{where } 0 < x < 1]$$

$\therefore \quad x = 10^{\log_{10} x}$

$$\doteq 10^{-1+0.9756}$$

$$= 10^{-1} \times 10^{0.9756}$$

$$\doteq 0.1 \times 9.454$$

$$= 0.9454$$

$\therefore \quad \sqrt[8]{0.638} \doteq 0.9454$

From Example 1 you can see how it is possible to perform multiplication and division and take powers and roots using addition and subtraction and tables of $\log_{10} x$ and 10^x. This is how scientists often made calculations from 1614 until recently. It is worthwhile for you to do a few exercises of this nature for two reasons. First, they give practice in the use of the laws of logarithms and exponents. Secondly, you will gain some historical insight into the way computations were made for centuries and you will thereby have a greater appreciation of the labour which is saved in using computers and hand calculators today.

APPLICATIONS TO NATURAL SCIENCES

Logarithmic functions occur in the description of many situations in science. For instance the equation

$$t = c \log_2 \frac{b(a-x)}{a(b-x)}$$

occurs in the study of certain chemical reactions, where x is the concentration of a substance at time t and a, b, c are constants.

Often the function $y = \log_a x$ arises in science because it is the inverse of the exponential function $y = a^x$. Thus logarithms occur frequently in solving the equations of exponential growth and decay that were given in §5.6.

EXAMPLE 2. *The half-life of radium-226, Ra^{226}, is 1620 years. Starting with a sample of 120 mg, after how many years is only 40 mg left?*

Solution

Using the equation

$$m(t) = c \times 2^{\frac{t}{h}}$$

with

$$c = 120$$

$$h = 1620$$

we have that the mass remaining after t years is

$$m(t) = 120 \times 2^{-\frac{t}{1620}}$$

We are required to find the value of t such that $m(t) = 40$.

$$\therefore \quad 120 \times 2^{-\frac{t}{1620}} = 40$$

$$2^{-\frac{t}{1620}} = \frac{1}{3}$$

To solve this equation for t we take logarithms of both sides.

$$\log_2 (2^{-\frac{t}{1620}}) = \log_2 (\tfrac{1}{3})$$

$$-\frac{t}{1620} = -\log_2 3$$

$$\therefore \quad t = 1620 \log_2 3$$

$\therefore$ the sample is reduced to 40 mg after $1620 \log_2 3$ years.

From tables, or a calculator, we find that

$$1620 \log_2 3 = 1620 \frac{\log_{10} 3}{\log_{10} 2} \qquad \text{(Exercise 5-7, \#13)}$$

$$\doteq 1620 \frac{0.4771}{0.3010}$$

$$\doteq 2568$$

The answer can therefore be expressed as 2568 years.

LOGARITHMIC SCALES

When quantities can vary over very large ranges it is sometimes convenient to take their logarithms in order to get a more manageable set of numbers. For instance this is done in the Richter scale which measures the intensity of earthquakes.

In 1935 C. F. Richter defined a logarithmic scale in which the magnitude of an earthquake is

$$\log_{10} \frac{I}{S}$$

where I is the intensity of a given earthquake (measured by the amplitude of a seismograph 100 km from the earthquake) and S is the intensity of a "standard" earthquake (where the amplitude is only $1 \, \mu m = 10^{-4}$ cm.) Notice that the magnitude of the standard earthquake is

$$\log_{10}\frac{S}{S} = \log_{10} 1 = 0$$

Of all the earthquakes studied by Richter from 1900 to 1950 the largest had magnitude 8.9 on the Richter scale and the smallest had magnitude 0. This corresponds to a ratio of intensities of 800 000 000. Thus the Richter scale gives more manageable numbers to work with. For example an earthquake of magnitude 7 is 10 times as strong as an earthquake of magnitude 6.

In general if two earthquakes have intensities I_1 and I_2, then

$$\log_{10}\frac{I_1}{I_2} = \log_{10}\frac{\dfrac{I_1}{S}}{\dfrac{I_2}{S}}$$

$$= \underbrace{\log_{10}\frac{I_1}{S} - \log_{10}\frac{I_2}{S}}_{\text{difference in magnitudes on Richter scale}}$$

EXAMPLE 3. *The Alaska earthquake of 1964 had a magnitude of 8.5 on the Richter scale. How many times more intense was the Alaska earthquake than a moderately destructive earthquake which has a magnitude of 6.0?*

Solution

Let

$$I_1 = \text{intensity of the Alaska earthquake}$$

$$I_2 = \text{intensity of a moderate earthquake}$$

Then

$$\log_{10}\frac{I_1}{I_2} = \log_{10}\frac{I_1}{S} - \log_{10}\frac{I_2}{S}$$

$$= 8.5 - 6.0$$

$$\log_{10}\frac{I_1}{I_2} = 2.5$$

$$\therefore \quad \frac{I_1}{I_2} = 10^{2.5}$$

$$= 10^{2+0.5}$$

$$= 10^2 \times 10^{0.5}$$

$$= 100\sqrt{10}$$

$$\doteq 100(3.16)$$

$$= 316$$

∴ the Alaska earthquake was 316 times as strong as a moderate earthquake.

A similar scheme is used in the decibel scale which measures the loudness of sounds. A threshold value of 1 unit is used for a sound so faint that it can just be detected. The loudest sound has an intensity of about 10^{14} units.

type of noise	units	decibels (dB)
jet plane (20 m away)	100 000 000 000 000	140
	10 000 000 000 000	130
rock music with amplifiers	1 000 000 000 000	120
pneumatic drill	100 000 000 000	110
	10 000 000 000	100
heavy traffic	1 000 000 000	90
	100 000 000	80
ordinary traffic	10 000 000	70
	1 000 000	60
ordinary conversation	100 000	50
	10 000	40
quiet conversation	1 000	30
whisper	100	20
rustle of leaves	10	10
barely audible	1	0

Table 5-3   Intensity of Sound

Notice that the number of decibels of a sound is

$$10 \log_{10} L$$

where L is the loudness of the sound (i.e., it is L times as intense as a barely audible sound.) Thus a sound measured at 30 dB is ten times as loud as a sound measured at 20 dB.

Other quantities which are commonly measured on logarithmic scales are light intensity, information capacity, and radiation.

EXERCISE   5-9

A   1. Three earthquakes occurred in locations A, B, and C with magnitudes 3, 4, and 5 respectively on the Richter scale. How many times stronger was the earthquake
(a) at B than the earthquake at A?
(b) at C than the earthquake at B?
(c) at C than the earthquake at A?

2. According to Table 5-3, amplified rock music has a loudness of 120 dB, ordinary conversation has a loudness of 50 dB, and whispering has a loudness of 20 dB. How many times louder is
(a) ordinary conversation than whispering?
(b) rock music than ordinary conversation?
(c) rock music than whispers?

B **3.** Evaluate the following using Tables 5-1 and 5-2.

(a) 555×621

(b) $555 \div 621$

(c) 0.0607×0.648

(d) $0.0607 \div 0.648$

(e) $(5.55)^4$

(f) $\sqrt[3]{596}$

(g) 6351×5678

(h) $(5.71)^{10}$

(i) $(6.24)^{\frac{8}{5}}$

(j) $\dfrac{601^4 \times 599^2}{583}$

In questions 4–10 leave your answer in terms of logarithms.

4. Strontium-90 has a half-life of 25 years. How many years does it take for a 20 mg sample to decay to a mass of 2 mg?

5. Radium-221 has a half-life of 30 s. How long will it take for 95% of it to decompose?

6. If 25 mg of a radioactive element decays to 20 mg in 48 h, find the half-life of the element.

7. A sample of Radon-211 decays to 30% of its original mass in 29 h. What is the half-life of Rn^{211}?

8. If, under certain conditions, the number of bacteria in a jug of milk doubles in one hour, in how many hours will it be 100 times the original number?

9. A bacteria culture starts with 100 000 bacteria and the doubling period is 40 min. After how many minutes will there be 600 000 bacteria?

Write 1 using all the 10 digits exactly once.

10. A bacteria culture starts with 50 000 bacteria. After 60 min the count is 125 000. What is the doubling period?

11. The 1906 earthquake in San Francisco had a magnitude of 8.3 on the Richter scale. At the same time in Japan there was an earthquake of magnitude 4.8 which caused only minor damage. How many times more intense was the San Francisco earthquake than the Japan earthquake?

12. The strongest earthquake ever recorded occurred on the Colombia-Ecuador border in the same year as the San Francisco earthquake (see question 11) but was four times as intense. What was the magnitude of the Colombia-Ecuador earthquake on the Richter scale? [Use $\log_{10} 2 \doteq 0.3$.]

13. A power mower makes a noise which is measured at 106 dB. Ordinary traffic registers about 70 dB. How many times louder is the mower than the traffic? [Use Table 5-2.]

C **14.** In chemistry the equation

$$t = c \log_2 \frac{b(a-x)}{a(b-x)}$$

is used where x is the concentration of a substance at time t and a, b, c are constants. Solve this equation to express x as a function of t.

REVIEW EXERCISE

A **1.** State the following numbers as powers of 2.

(a) 32   (b) $(2^3)^5$ (c) $2^3 \times 2^5$ (d) $\frac{1}{2}$

(e) $\sqrt{2}$ (f) $2\sqrt{2}$ (g) 1   (h) $2^8 \times 2^4$

(i) $\dfrac{2^9}{2^4}$ (j) $\frac{1}{8}$ (k) $\dfrac{2^{1.5}}{2^{2.5}}$ (l) $(2^{12})^{\frac{1}{2}}$

2. Evaluate.

(a) 9^0 (b) 3^{-1} (c) 6^{-2} (d) $9^{\frac{1}{2}}$

(e) $8^{\frac{1}{3}}$ (f) $\dfrac{1}{7^{-1}}$ (g) $9^{\frac{3}{2}}$ (h) $16^{-\frac{1}{2}}$

(i) 4^{-3} (j) $(-6.5)^0$ (k) $8^{-\frac{2}{3}}$ (l) $25^{1.5}$

3. Use the Laws of Exponents to express the following in another form.

(a) $(8 \times 17)^9$ (b) $5^6 \times 9^6$ (c) $4^{\frac{1}{2}}$ (d) $7^{\frac{3}{4}}$

(e) $(\frac{3}{17})^8$ (f) $\dfrac{12^6}{3^6}$ (g) $\sqrt[3]{x^2}$ (h) $\dfrac{\pi^{10}}{\pi^2}$

(i) $5^9 \times 5^4$ (j) $3^4\sqrt{3}$ (k) $(2x^2)^4$ (l) $\dfrac{1}{(\sqrt[3]{5})^2}$

(m) $(x^5)^n$ (n) $x^5 \times x^n$ (o) $\left(\dfrac{x}{2}\right)^4$ (p) $\dfrac{3^8}{3^{6.5}}$

(q) $5^3 \times 5^{-1} \times 5^{\frac{1}{2}}$ (r) $x^a \times x^b \times x^c$ (s) $\dfrac{6^{12}}{6^4 \times 6^5}$ (t) $\dfrac{(x^2)^n \times x^3}{x^n}$

4. Express in scientific notation.

(a) 234   (b) 18 000   (c) 0.016   (d) 0.000 062

(e) 1 250 000   (f) 193.8   (g) 634 000   (h) 0.71

5. Evaluate

(a) $\log_3 9$ (b) $\log_2 16$ (c) $\log_{10} 1000$ (d) $\log_5 125$

(e) $\log_6 1$ (f) $\log_2 \left(\frac{1}{2}\right)$ (g) $\log_3 \sqrt{3}$ (h) $\log_a a^7$

6. Apply the Laws of Logarithms to the following.

(a) $\log_{10}(14 \times 29)$ (b) $\log_2(11 \times 13 \times 15)$ (c) $\log_3 2^{10}$

(d) $\log_{10}\left(\frac{61}{43}\right)$ (e) $\log_5 \sqrt{37}$ (f) $\log_{10}\left(\frac{1}{6}\right)$

(g) $\log_2(3\pi)$ (h) $\frac{1}{2}\log_3 25$ (i) $\log_2 24 - \log_2 4$

7. Simplify the following.

(a) $\dfrac{5^9 \times 5^{11} \times 5^6}{(5^2)^{12}}$ (b) $\dfrac{x^3 \times x^5 \times x^7}{x^4 \times x^6}$ (c) $\dfrac{216^{10}}{6^{32}}$

(d) $\dfrac{a^{n+2} \times a^{n-2}}{(a^n)^{n-2}}$ (e) $(-3x^2)^3(x^4y)^2$ (f) $(x^2y^3)^4(xy^4)^{-2}$

(g) $\dfrac{(xy^2z^3)^3}{(x^3y^2z)^2}$ (h) $\dfrac{a^4b^3}{ab^2} \times \left(\dfrac{b^2}{a^3}\right)^2$ (i) $\dfrac{a^{10} + a^9}{a^2 + a}$

8. Evaluate.

(a) $(2^4 \times 3^{-3})^{-1}$ (b) $(3^6 \times 9^{-4})^{-3}$ (c) $81^{\frac{3}{4}}$

(d) $64^{\frac{5}{6}}$ (e) $343^{-\frac{1}{3}}$ (f) $3^{\frac{1}{2}} \times 27^{\frac{1}{2}}$

(g) $1\,000\,000^{1.5}$ (h) $(256^{-\frac{1}{4}})^{-\frac{1}{2}}$ (i) $3^{\frac{1}{3}} \times 9^{\frac{1}{6}} \times 27^{\frac{1}{9}}$

(j) $\left(\frac{25}{121}\right)^{-\frac{1}{2}}$ (k) $\dfrac{5^{-10} + 5^{-11}}{5^{-10} - 5^{-11}}$ (l) $\left(\frac{27}{64}\right)^{\frac{2}{3}}$

(m) $[(1 + 2^{-1})^{-1} + 2^{-1}]^{-1}$ (n) $\dfrac{(0.09)^{\frac{3}{2}}}{10^{-2}}$ (o) $\{[(-2)^{-2}]^{-2}\}^{-2}$

9. Rewrite the following using only positive exponents. Simplify where possible.

(a) $5x^{-2}y^{-3}$

(b) $(2x^{-\frac{1}{2}})^6$

(c) $\dfrac{3x^{-2}}{4y^{-1}}$

(d) $\dfrac{a^3b^{-2}}{a^4b^{-6}}$

(e) $(3a^{-1}b^2c^{-4})^4$

(f) $x^5(x^2+1+x^{-2})$

(g) $(1+a^2)(1-a^{-2})$

(h) $\dfrac{(a+b)^{-1}}{a^{-1}-b^{-1}}$

10. Solve the following equations for x.

(a) $2^{3x}=\frac{1}{2}$

(b) $2\times 5^{2x-9}=250$

(c) $16\times 8^{1-x}=1$

11. Express the following numbers in scientific notation.

(a) 0.000 000 000 186

(b) 26 850 000 000 000 000

(c) $(9\times 10^6)(3.4\times 10^8)$

(d) $120(7\times 10^{-15})$

(e) $\dfrac{420\,000}{0.000\,06}$

(f) $\dfrac{5.6\times 10^{-8}}{7\times 10^4}$

12. Find an approximate value for $\dfrac{(0.000\,000\,001\,528)(1135)}{(168\,000\,000)(0.000\,046\,8)}$

13. (a) Draw the graph of $y=4^x,\ -2\leqslant x\leqslant 2$.

(b) Draw the graph of $y=(\frac{1}{4})^x,\ -2\leqslant x\leqslant 2$.

(c) Use (a) to draw the graph of $y=\log_4 x,\ 0<x\leqslant 16$.

14. Evaluate.

(a) $\log_{10} 0.000\,01$

(b) $\log_4 64$

(c) $\log_2 \frac{1}{128}$

(d) $\log_2 \sqrt{2}$

(e) $\log_7 343$

(f) $\log_3 9\sqrt{3}$

(g) $\log_{10} 10^{3.7}$

(h) $10^{\log_{10} 97}$

(i) $\log_8 4+\log_8 16$

(j) $\log_5 250-\log_5 2$

15. Solve the following equations for x.

(a) $\log_8 x=5$

(b) $\log_x 216=3$

(c) $\log_{10} \sqrt[5]{10}=x$

(d) $\log_5 x=-4$

(e) $4\log_{10} x=\log_{10} 81$

(f) $\log_6 x-\log_6 4=\log_6 8$

(g) $\log_8 (x+5)-\log_8 (x-2)=1$

(h) $\log_8 (x+5)+\log_8 (x-2)=1$

16. Express as a single logarithm.

(a) $\log_{10} x-2\log_{10} y$

(b) $3\log_2 x+6\log_2 y$

(c) $\log_3 M+\log_3 N+\frac{1}{2}\log_3 P$

(d) $4\log_5 A-\frac{1}{2}\log_5 B$

17. Evaluate the following using Tables 5-1 and 5-2.

(a) 5.71×606

(b) $5.71\div 606$

(c) $\sqrt[3]{589}$

18. A bacteria culture doubles every 20 min. After an hour there are 32 000 bacteria.

(a) What is the initial size of the culture?

(b) What is the size after t minutes?

(c) after $\frac{1}{2}$ h?

(d) after 6 h?

19. A bacteria culture starts with 10 000 bacteria. After 40 min the count is 30 000. What is the doubling period? [Leave your answer in terms of logarithms.]

20. The half-life of V^{48} is 16 d.

(a) Find the amount remaining from a 120 mg sample after

(i) t days

(ii) 256 d

(iii) 40 d

(b) How many days will it take to decay to 1 mg? [Leave your answer to (b) in terms of logarithms.]

21. How many times more intense is an earthquake with a magnitude of 8.1 on the Richter scale than an earthquake with magnitude 3.6?

REVIEW AND PREVIEW TO CHAPTER 6

EXERCISE 1. TRIGONOMETRIC RATIOS OF ANY ANGLE

$$\sin \theta = \frac{y}{r}$$

$$\cos \theta = \frac{x}{r}$$

$$\tan \theta = \frac{y}{x}$$

$$\csc \theta = \frac{r}{y}$$

$$\sec \theta = \frac{r}{x}$$

$$\cot \theta = \frac{x}{y}$$

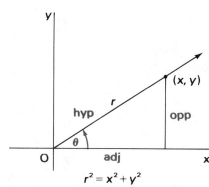

$$r^2 = x^2 + y^2$$

1. Find the six trigonometric ratios of the indicated angle in standard position if the given point lies on the terminal arm.

(a)

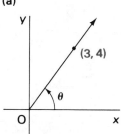

(b)

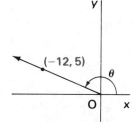

(c)

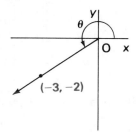

2. Find the six trigonometric ratios for each indicated angle.

(a)

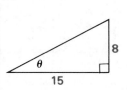

(b)

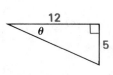

(c)

3. Find the other five trigonometric ratios, given
(a) $\sin \theta = \frac{3}{5}$ and θ is a first quadrant angle.
(b) $\cos \theta = -\frac{5}{15}$ and θ is a second quadrant angle.
(c) $\tan \theta = -1$ and θ is a fourth quadrant angle.
(d) $\cot \theta = 1$ and θ is a third quadrant angle.

4. Use the given triangles to find the following.

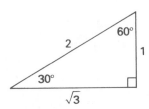

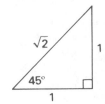

(a) $\sin 45°$ (b) $\cos 30°$ (c) $\tan 60°$
(d) $\cos 135°$ (e) $\tan 225°$ (f) $\sin 330°$
(g) $\sin^2 45° + \cos^2 45°$ (h) $2 \sin 135° \cos 135°$
(i) $\cos 315° + \tan 225°$ (j) $\sin 240° - \cos 240°$

5. Find the six trigonometric ratios of
(a) $0°$ (b) $90°$ (c) $180°$ (d) $270°$
(e) $360°$ (f) $-90°$ (g) $-180°$

6. Use the definitions of the trigonometric ratios to show that:
(a) $\sin^2 \theta + \cos^2 \theta = 1$ (b) $\sin \theta \times \csc \theta = 1$
(c) $\cos \theta \times \sec \theta = 1$ (d) $\tan \theta \times \cot \theta = 1$
(e) $\dfrac{\sin \theta}{\cos \theta} = \tan \theta$ (f) $\dfrac{\cos \theta}{\sin \theta} = \cot \theta$
(g) $1 + \tan^2 \theta = \sec^2 \theta$ (h) $1 + \cot^2 \theta = \csc^2 \theta$

EXERCISE 2 SOLVING RIGHT TRIANGLES

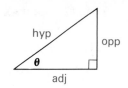

1. Find the length of the side labelled *x*.

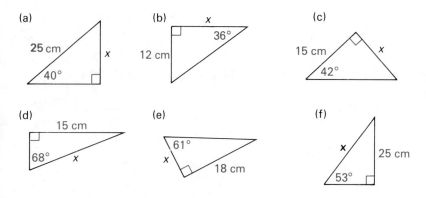

(a)

25 cm   40°   *x*

(b)

x   36°   12 cm

(c)

15 cm   42°   *x*

(d)

15 cm   68°   *x*

(e)

61°   *x*   18 cm

(f)

x   53°   25 cm

2. Find *θ* to the nearest degree in each of the following.

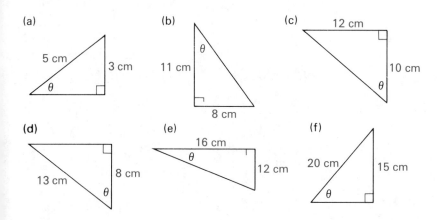

(a)

5 cm   3 cm   *θ*

(b)

θ   11 cm   8 cm

(c)

12 cm   10 cm   *θ*

(d)

13 cm   8 cm   *θ*

(e)

16 cm   *θ*   12 cm

(f)

20 cm   15 cm   *θ*

3. Solve the following triangles:

(a) 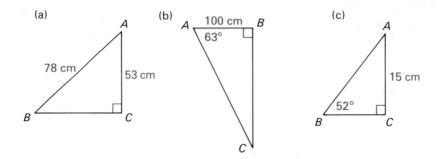 (b)

(c)

4. A tree casts a shadow 12 m long when the angle of elevation of the sun is 31°. Find the height of the tree.

5. Find *x* in each of the following.

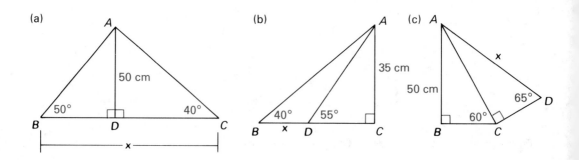

(a)

(b)

(c)

ADDITION

```
    ONE
   FOUR
  THREE
  THREE
  ─────
 ELEVEN
```

Applied Trigonometry

The mathematician, carried along on his flood of symbols, dealing apparently with purely formal truths, may still reach results of endless importance for our description of the physical universe.

Karl Pearson

Heron of Alexandria

Heron (Hero) of Alexandria, a Greek mathematician who flourished about 62 AD, is best remembered for his formula of the area of a triangle

$$s(s - a)(s - b)(s - c).$$

Hero's ingenuity was also displayed in such inventions as the aeolipile, the first steam powered engine. His device consisted of a spherical boiler with two canted nozzles mounted on an axle to produce a rotary motion from the escaping steam. One of his mechanical works, Pneumatica, describes many interesting machines such as siphons, the aeolipile, coin-operated machines, a fire engine, a water organ, ''Hero's fountain'' — a device similar to a lawn sprinkler, and various arrangements for employing the force of steam to do work.

Hero also described a graphical method for finding the distance between Alexandria and Rome from the difference of local times at which a lunar eclipse would occur at each city.

Trigonometry relates algebra and geometry in a way that makes it possible to solve practical problems. It relates the lengths of sides of triangles to the measures of the angles.

6.1 THE TRIGONOMETRIC FUNCTIONS

The measure of an angle is the amount of rotation of a ray about a fixed point called the vertex Angles are measured in degrees where

1 complete rotation $= 360°$
$1° = 60'$:   (minutes)
$1' = 60''$:   (seconds)

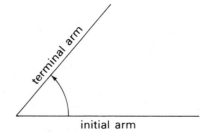

EXAMPLE 1. *Express*

$$\text{(a)} \ 63°12'24'' \qquad \text{(b)} \ 15°54'36''$$

in degrees correct to five significant figures.

Solution

(a)
$$24'' = \left(\frac{24}{60}\right)' = 0.4'$$

$$12.4' = \left(\frac{12.4}{60}\right)° \doteq 0.2067°$$

$$63°12'24'' \doteq 63.207°$$

(b)
$$36'' = \left(\frac{36}{60}\right)' = 0.6'$$

$$54.6' = \left(\frac{54.6}{60}\right)° = 0.91°$$

$$15°54'36'' = 15.910°$$

In our previous work, we defined the trigonometric functions as follows:

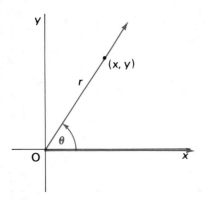

$$\text{sine } \theta = \sin \theta = \frac{y}{r} \qquad\qquad \text{cosecant } \theta = \csc \theta = \frac{r}{y}$$

$$\text{cosine } \theta = \cos \theta = \frac{x}{r} \qquad\qquad \text{secant } \theta = \sec \theta = \frac{r}{x}$$

$$\text{tangent } \theta = \tan \theta = \frac{y}{x} \qquad\qquad \text{cotangent } \theta = \cot \theta = \frac{x}{y}$$

These definitions are used to prove some identities which will be used in the following sections.

EXAMPLE 2. *Show that*

$$\text{(i)} \quad \sin (180° - \theta) = \sin \theta$$

$$\text{(ii)} \quad \cos (180° - \theta) = -\cos \theta$$

$$\text{(iii)} \quad \tan (180° - \theta) = -\tan \theta$$

Solution

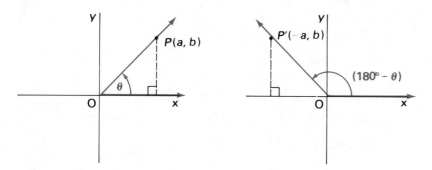

If $P(a, b)$ lies on the terminal arm of θ in standard position, then $P'(-a, b)$ lies on the terminal arm of $(180° - \theta)$ following a reflection in the y-axis. If $P(a, b)$ and $P'(-a, b)$ lie on the terminal arms of θ and $(180° - \theta)$, then $r = \sqrt{a^2 + b^2}$ and

(i) $\sin(180° - \theta) = \dfrac{b}{\sqrt{a^2 + b^2}}$, $\quad \sin\theta = \dfrac{b}{\sqrt{a^2 + b^2}}$

$$\therefore \quad \sin(180° - \theta) = \sin\theta$$

(ii) $\cos(180° - \theta) = \dfrac{-a}{\sqrt{a^2 + b^2}}$, $\quad \cos\theta = \dfrac{a}{\sqrt{a^2 + b^2}}$

$$\therefore \quad \cos(180° - \theta) = -\cos\theta$$

(iii) $\tan(180° - \theta) = \dfrac{b}{-a}$ $\quad \tan\theta = \dfrac{b}{a}$

$$= -\dfrac{b}{a}$$

$$\therefore \quad \tan(180° - \theta) = -\tan\theta$$

The results of Example 2 are summarized in the following table.

$\sin(180° - \theta) = \sin\theta$
$\cos(180° - \theta) = -\cos\theta$
$\tan(180° - \theta) = -\tan\theta$

Since $6' = 0.1°$, four place tables accurate to the nearest $6'$ are provided in the appendix. This enables us to make consistent calculations with or without a scientific calculator.

EXAMPLE 3. *Find*

(a) $\sin 37°24'$ (b) $\tan 83°12'$

(c) $\cos 124°36'$ (d) $\sin 110°12'$ (e) $\tan 156°48'$

Solution

(a) $\sin 37°24' = 0.6074$

(b) $\tan 83°12' = 8.3863$

(c) $\cos 124°36' = -\cos (180° - 124°36')$
$= -\cos 55°24' = -0.5678$

(d) $\sin 110°12' = \sin (180° - 110°12')$
$= \sin 69°48' = 0.9385$

(e) $\tan 156°48' = -\tan (180° - 156°48')$
$= -\tan 23°12' = -0.4286$

EXAMPLE 4. *Find θ in the following to the nearest 6', $0° \leqslant \theta \leqslant 180°$.*

(a) $\cos \theta = -0.2557$ (b) $\tan \theta = 1.3512$ (c) $\sin \theta = 0.3791$

Solution

(a) From tables,

$$\cos 75°12' = 0.2554 \quad \text{and} \quad \cos 75°18' = 0.2538$$

$$\therefore \quad \theta = 180° - 75°12'$$

$$= 104°48'$$

(b) From tables,

$$\tan 53°24' = 1.3465 \quad \text{and} \quad \tan 53°30' = 1.3514$$

$$\therefore \quad \theta = 53°30'$$

Write 25 using five 8's.

(c) From tables,

$$\sin 22°12' = 0.3778 \quad \text{and} \quad \sin 22°18' = 0.3795$$

$$\therefore \quad \theta = 22°18'$$

or

$$\theta = 180° - 22°18'$$

$$= 157°42'$$

EXERCISE 6-1

B   **1.** Express the following angle measures in degrees correct to five significant figures.

(a) $25°36'$ (b) $54°54'$ (c) $33°42'$ (d) $40°18'$

(e) $50°25'15''$ (f) $27°25'30''$ (g) $47°29'30''$ (h) $17°36'45''$

2. Express the following angle measures in degrees, minutes, and seconds.

(a) $35.3°$ (b) $47.6°$ (c) $53.8°$ (d) $72.1°$

(e) $53.143°$ (f) $25.371°$ (g) $48.216°$ (h) $83.914°$

3. Perform the indicated operation.

(a) $35°12' + 18°24'$ (b) $63°55' - 21°34'$

(c) $22°48' + 17°36'$ (d) $49°18' - 12°42'$

(e) $25°18'22'' + 34°12'48''$ (f) $7°38'24'' - 2°45'30''$

(g) $3(25°12'8'')$ (h) $4(18°24'30'')$

(i) $2(35°18'35'')$

4. Prove the following using the methods of Example 2.

(a) $\sin(180° + \theta) = -\sin\theta$
$\cos(180° + \theta) = -\cos\theta$
$\tan(180° + \theta) = \tan\theta$

(b) $\sin(360° - \theta) = -\sin\theta$
$\cos(360° - \theta) = \cos\theta$
$\tan(360° - \theta) = -\tan\theta$

5. Use trigonometric tables to evaluate:

(a) $\sin 62°$
(b) $\tan 135°$
(c) $\cos 100°$
(d) $\sin 138°$
(e) $\tan 104°30'$
(f) $\sin 152°48'$
(g) $\cos 137°54'$
(h) $\tan 148°24'$
(i) $\sin 102°6'$
(j) $\cos 161°18'$
(k) $\tan 124°42'$

 sine is positive

 all ratios positive

tangent is positive

cosine is positive

6. Find the angle θ to the nearest 6', $0° \le \theta \le 180°$.

(a) $\cos\theta = 0.2157$
(b) $\sin\theta = 0.8140$
(c) $\tan\theta = -0.7147$
(d) $\sin\theta = 0.7843$
(e) $\tan\theta = 0.6141$
(f) $\cos\theta = -0.7581$
(g) $\sin\theta = 0.2155$
(h) $\cos\theta = -0.2175$

7. Prove the following.

(a) $\csc(180° - \theta) = \csc\theta$
$\sec(180° - \theta) = -\sec\theta$
$\cot(180° - \theta) = -\cot\theta$

(b) $\csc(180° + \theta) = -\csc\theta$
$\sec(180° + \theta) = -\sec\theta$
$\cot(180° + \theta) = \cot\theta$

8. Prove the following.

(a) $\sin(90° - \theta) = \cos\theta$
$\cos(90° - \theta) = \sin\theta$
$\tan(90° - \theta) = \cot\theta$

(b) $\csc(90° - \theta) = \sec\theta$
$\sec(90° - \theta) = \csc\theta$
$\cot(90° - \theta) = \tan\theta$

9. Prove the following.

(a) $\sin(90° + \theta) = \cos\theta$
$\cos(90° + \theta) = -\sin\theta$
$\tan(90° + \theta) = -\tan\theta$

(b) $\sin(360° + \theta) = \sin\theta$
$\cos(360° + \theta) = \cos\theta$
$\tan(360° + \theta) = \tan\theta$

10. Use trigonometric tables to evaluate.

(a) $\sin 225°12'$
(b) $\cos 320°42'$
(c) $\tan 250°18'$
(d) $\sin 118°30'$
(e) $\tan 212°18'$
(f) $\cos 202°42'$
(g) $\sin 320°36'$
(h) $\cos 260°18'$
(i) $\sin 124°48'$
(j) $\sec 125°54'$
(k) $\csc 170°6'$
(l) $\cot 305°30'$

6.2 THE LAW OF COSINES

Triangles that do not contain a right angle are called *oblique* triangles. In solving right triangles, if one side and two other parts (sides and angles) are given, then the remaining three parts can be found using the trigonometric ratios. In this section we shall begin solving oblique triangles using a general formula—the law of cosines. The derivation of the law of cosines follows.

In $\triangle ABC$, we draw AD perpendicular to BC, or BC extended, representing an altitude of $\triangle ABC$.

$\cos(180° - \theta) = -\cos\theta$

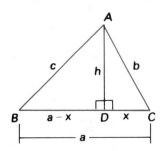

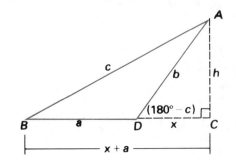

Side a is opposite vertex A

(i) $\triangle ABC$ is acute

In $\triangle ADC$, $\dfrac{x}{b} = \cos C$

$\qquad x = b\cos C$

and $\qquad b^2 = h^2 + x^2$

In $\triangle ABD$, $c^2 = h^2 + (a-x)^2$

$\qquad\qquad = h^2 + a^2 - 2ax + x^2$

$\qquad\qquad = a^2 + (h^2 + x^2) - 2ax$

$\qquad c^2 = a^2 + b^2 - 2ab\cos C$

(ii) $\triangle ABC$ is obtuse

In $\triangle ABC$, $\dfrac{x}{b} = \cos(180° - C)$

$\qquad x = b\cos(180° - C)$

$\qquad\quad = -b\cos C$

and $\qquad b^2 = h^2 + x^2$

In $\triangle ABD$, $c^2 = h^2 + (a + x^2)$

$\qquad\qquad = h^2 + a^2 + 2ax + x^2$

$\qquad\qquad = a^2 + (h^2 + x^2) + 2ax$

$\qquad\qquad = a^2 + b^2 + 2a(-b\cos C)$

$\qquad c^2 = a^2 + b^2 - 2ab\cos C$

The three forms of the law of cosines are

$$
\begin{array}{l}
a^2 = b^2 + c^2 - 2bc\cos A \\
b^2 = a^2 + c^2 - 2ac\cos B \\
c^2 = a^2 + b^2 - 2ab\cos C
\end{array}
$$

We shall now apply the law of cosines to the solution of triangles.

EXAMPLE 1. In $\triangle ABC$, $a = 51$ cm, $\angle B = 39°$ and $c = 42$ cm. Find b, assuming the data to be exact.

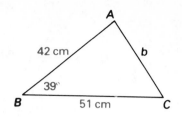

Solution

(i) Using tables

$b^2 = a^2 + c^2 - 2ac \cos B$

$b^2 = (51)^2 + (42)^2 - 2(51)(42) \cos 39°$

$\doteq 2601 + 1764 - 4284(0.7771)$

$\doteq 2601 + 1764 - 3329$

$\doteq 1036$

$b \doteq 32.19$

(ii) Using a calculator

$b^2 = a^2 + c^2 - 2ac \cos B$

$b^2 = (51)^2 + (42)^2 - 2(51)(42) \cos 39°$

$\doteq 2601 + 1764 - 3329.2933$

$\doteq 1035.7067$

$b \doteq 32.18$

∴ the length of b is approximately 32.2 cm.

Since most of the values in a trigonometric table are approximations, lengths computed using these values should generally be given to at most four significant figures. In the work that follows, we shall assume the given data to be exact.

EXAMPLE 2. *SAS* In $\triangle ABC$, $a = 32$ cm, $\angle C = 121°24'$, and $b = 27$ cm. Find c.

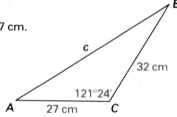

Solution

$$\cos 121°24' = -\cos (180° - 121°24')$$
$$= -\cos 58°36'$$

(i) Using tables

$c^2 = a^2 + b^2 - 2ab \cos C$

$c^2 = (32)^2 + (27)^2 - 2(32)(27) \cos 121°24'$

$= 1024 + 729 - 1728(-0.5210)$

$= 1753 + 900.3$

$= 2653$

$c = 51.51$

(ii) Using a calculator

$c^2 = a^2 + b^2 - 2ab \cos C$

$c^2 = (32)^2 + (27)^2 - 2(32)(27) \cos 121°24'$

$= 1024 + 729 + 2(32)(27) \cos 121.4°$

$= 2653.3046$

$c = 51.51$

∴ the length of c is approximately 51.5 cm.

The Law of Cosines can also be used to find the measure of an angle of a triangle when the lengths of the three sides are known. To do this we solve the formula for the cosine value:

$$a^2 = b^2 + c^2 - 2bc \cos A$$

$$2bc \cos A = b^2 + c^2 - a^2$$

$$\cos A = \frac{b^2 + c^2 - a^2}{2bc}$$

Similarly

$$\cos B = \frac{a^2 + c^2 - b^2}{2ac}$$

and

$$\cos C = \frac{a^2 + b^2 - c^2}{2ab}$$

We use this form of the formula to find angles as in the following example.

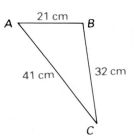

EXAMPLE 3. *SSS   In △ABC, a = 32 cm, b = 41 cm, and c = 21 cm. Find the measure of the largest angle.*

Solution
    The largest angle is opposite the longest side.

(i) Using tables

$$\cos B = \frac{a^2 + c^2 - b^2}{2ac}$$

$$\cos B = \frac{32^2 + 21^2 - 41^2}{2(32)(21)}$$

$$= \frac{1024 + 441 - 1681}{1344}$$

$$= -0.1607$$

$\cos 80°42' = 0.1616$ and
$\cos 80°48' = 0.1599$

$$\angle B \doteq 180° - 80°48'$$

$$\doteq 99°12'$$

(ii) Using a calculator

$$\cos B = \frac{a^2 + c^2 - b^2}{2ac}$$

$$\cos B = \frac{32^2 + 21^2 - 41^2}{2(32)(21)}$$

$$= \frac{-216}{1344}$$

$$\doteq -0.1607$$

$$\angle B \doteq 99.2484°$$

$$\doteq 99°12'$$

∴   the largest angle is ∠B = 99°12'.

EXERCISE 6-2

1. Find the indicated side in the following.

(a)

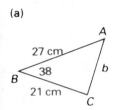

(b)

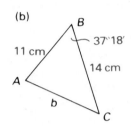

(c)

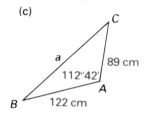

2. Find the indicated angle in the following.

(a)

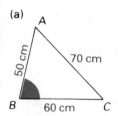

(b)

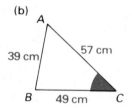

(c)

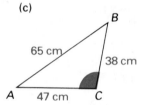

3. For each of the following, make a reasonably accurate diagram and use the law of cosines to find the required value.
(a) In $\triangle ABC$, $a = 59$ cm, $\angle B = 48°$, $c = 48$ cm. Find b.
(b) In $\triangle ABC$, $b = 91$ cm, $\angle C = 52°24'$, $a = 69$ cm. Find c.
(c) In $\triangle ABC$, $a = 37$ cm, $b = 51$ cm, $c = 41$ cm. Find $\angle C$.
(d) In $\triangle ABC$, $a = 82$ cm, $b = 50$ cm, $c = 61$ cm. Find $\angle A$.
(e) In $\triangle ABC$, $\angle A = 132°54'$, $b = 25$ cm, $c = 19$ cm. Find a.

WORD LADDER

Start with the word "slow" and change one letter at a time to form a new word until you reach "fast". The best solution has the fewest steps.

s l o w

_ _ _ _

_ _ _ _

_ _ _ _

_ _ _ _

_ _ _ _

f a s t

6.3 THE LAW OF SINES

When an oblique triangle has two angles and a side given (*ASA*), we can find the remaining sides using the law of sines.

In $\triangle ABC$, we draw AD perpendicular to BC, or BC extended, representing an altitude of $\triangle ABC$.

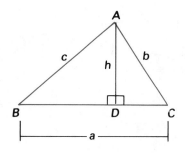

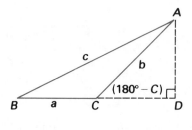

$$\sin(180° - \theta) = \sin\theta$$

(i) Acute Triangle

(ii) Obtuse Triangle

In $\triangle ACD$, $\dfrac{h}{b} = \sin C$

$$h = b\sin C$$

In $\triangle ABD$, $\dfrac{h}{c} = \sin B$

$$h = c\sin B$$

In $\triangle ACD$, $\dfrac{h}{b} = \sin(180° - C)$

$$= \sin C$$

$$h = b\sin C$$

In $\triangle ABD$, $\dfrac{h}{c} = \sin B$

$$h = c\sin B$$

From both the acute and obtuse triangles

$$b\sin C = c\sin B$$

Dividing both sides by bc,

$$\frac{b\sin C}{bc} = \frac{c\sin B}{bc}$$

$$\frac{\sin B}{b} = \frac{\sin C}{c}$$

By drawing the altitude from C, we have

$$\frac{\sin A}{a} = \frac{\sin B}{b}$$

We combine these results to give two forms of the Law of Sines.

$$\frac{\sin A}{a} = \frac{\sin B}{b} = \frac{\sin C}{c} \quad \text{or} \quad \frac{a}{\sin A} = \frac{b}{\sin B} = \frac{c}{\sin C}$$

EXAMPLE 1. *AAS* *In △ABC, ∠A = 71°12′, ∠B = 63°42′, a = 75 cm.*
Find c.

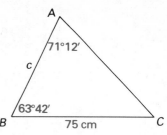

Solution

$$\angle C = 180° - (71°12' + 63°42')$$
$$= 55°6'$$

(i) Using tables

$$\frac{c}{\sin C} = \frac{a}{\sin A}$$

$$c = \frac{a \sin C}{\sin A}$$

$$c = \frac{75 \times 0.8202}{0.9466}$$

$$= 65.00$$

(ii) Using a calculator

$$\frac{c}{\sin C} = \frac{a}{\sin A}$$

$$c = \frac{a \sin C}{\sin A}$$

$$c \doteq \frac{75 \times \sin 55.1°}{\sin 71.2°}$$

$$\doteq 64.9780$$

∴ The length of c is approximately 65.0 cm.

EXAMPLE 2. *ASA* *In △ABC, ∠A = 32°30′, ∠B = 110°54′, c = 88 cm.*
Solve the triangle.

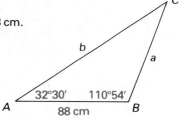

Solution

$$\angle C = 180° - (32°30' + 110°54')$$
$$= 36°36'$$

(i) Using tables

$$\frac{a}{\sin A} = \frac{c}{\sin C}$$

$$a = \frac{c \sin A}{\sin C}$$

$$a \doteq \frac{88 \times 0.5373}{0.5962}$$

$$\doteq 79.31$$

$$\frac{b}{\sin B} = \frac{c}{\sin C}$$

$$b = \frac{c \sin B}{\sin C}$$

$$b \doteq \frac{88 \times 0.9342}{0.5962} \qquad \sin 110°54' = \sin 69°6'$$

$$\doteq 137.9$$

(ii) Using a calculator

$$\frac{a}{\sin A} = \frac{c}{\sin C}$$

$$a = \frac{c \sin A}{\sin C}$$

$$a = \frac{88 \times \sin 32.5°}{\sin 36.6°}$$

$$\doteq 79.3029$$

$$\frac{b}{\sin B} = \frac{c}{\sin C}$$

$$b = \frac{c \sin B}{\sin C}$$

$$b = \frac{88 \times \sin 110.9°}{\sin 36.6°}$$

$$\doteq 137.8842$$

A triangle is solved when you can state the three angles and the three sides.

∴ in △ABC, a = 79.3 cm, b = 138 cm, and ∠C = 36°6′.

EXAMPLE 3. *SSA* *In △ABC, a = 63 cm, c = 47 cm, ∠C = 38°24′. Find ∠A given that △ABC is acute.*

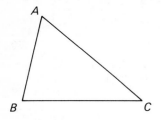

Solution

(i) Using tables

$$\frac{\sin A}{a} = \frac{\sin C}{c}$$

$$\sin A = \frac{a \sin C}{c}$$

from tables:

sin 56°18′ = 0.8320

sin 56°24′ = 0.8329

$$\sin A \doteq \frac{63 \times 0.6211}{47}$$

$$\doteq 0.8325$$

∠A = 56°24′   or   ∠A = 180° − 56°24′

= 123°36′

(ii) Using a calculator

$$\frac{\sin A}{a} = \frac{\sin C}{c}$$

$$\sin A = \frac{a \sin C}{c}$$

$$\sin A = \frac{63 \times \sin 38.4°}{47}$$

$$\doteq 0.8326$$

∠A ≐ 56.367

≐ 56°24′

The value ∠A = 123°36′ comes from the relationship sin (180° − θ) = sin θ. Since it was stated that △ABC is acute, the value ∠A = 123°26′ is inadmissible so the solution is ∠A = 56°24′.

EXERCISES 6-3

B   **1.** Find the indicated side in each of the following.

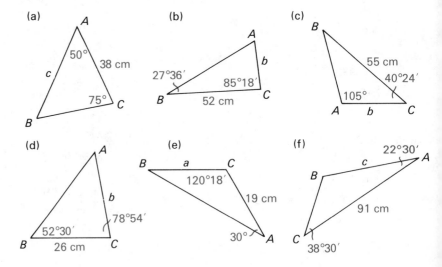

(a)

(b)

(c)

(d)

(e)

(f)

2. Find the indicated quantity.
(a) In $\triangle ABC$, $\angle A = 30°$, $\angle C = 75°$, $a = 26$ cm. Find b.
(b) In $\triangle ABC$, $\angle B = 28°18'$, $\angle C = 72°36'$, $b = 83$ cm. Find a.
(c) In $\triangle ABC$, $\angle A = 118°24'$, $\angle B = 31°$, $a = 71$ cm. Find b.
(d) In $\triangle ABC$, $\angle A = 43°24'$, $\angle B = 27°12'$, $c = 9.5$ cm. Find a and b.

3. Solve the following triangles.

(a)
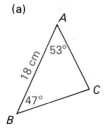

(b)
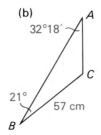

(c)
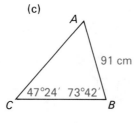

(d) $\triangle ABC$, $a = 13$ cm, $\angle B = 49°54'$, $\angle C = 67°18'$.
(e) $\triangle ABC$, $\angle A = 112°42'$, $b = 12$ cm, $\angle C = 26°30'$.

4. Solve the following triangles.

(a)
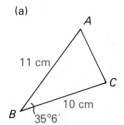

(b)
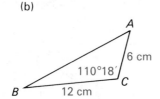

(c)
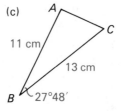

(d) $\triangle ABC$, $a = 26$ cm, $\angle B = 53°30'$, $c = 19$ cm.
(e) $\triangle ABC$, $\angle A = 124°12'$, $b = 83$ cm, $c = 61$ cm.

6.4 SSA THE AMBIGUOUS CASE

When two sides and a *non-included* angle are given the triangle may not be uniquely determined. The four possibilities when given *SSA* are illustrated in the following examples.

We shall consider $\triangle ABC$, where $b = 2.0$, $\angle A = 30°$, and we shall let a take the values 2.3, 1.5, 1.0, and 0.8, then proceed to construct the triangle.

Case 1	Case 2	Case 3	Case 4
$a = 2.5$	$a = 1.5$	$a = 1.0$	$a = 0.8$
$b = 2.0$	$b = 2.0$	$b = 2.0$	$b = 2.0$
$\angle A = 30°$	$\angle A = 30°$	$\angle A = 30°$	$\angle A = 30°$

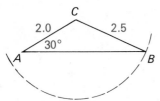 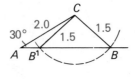 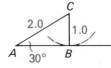 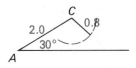

Point B has one position	Point B has two positions	Point B has one position and $\angle B = 90°$	Point B has no position

The results of these four cases suggest the following general conclusions:

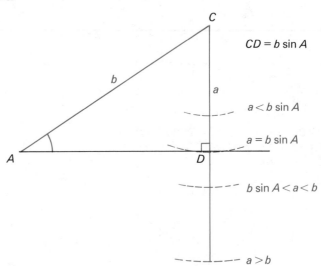

$CD = b \sin A$

$a < b \sin A$

$a = b \sin A$

$b \sin A < a < b$

$a > b$

If $a > b$, it is clear that there is only one solution.
If $a < b$ then there are three possibilities:

      I $a < b \sin A$ _____ no solution
     II $a = b \sin A$ _____ one solution
    III $a > b \sin A$ _____ two solutions

where $b \sin A$ is the altitude to AB from C

When $\angle A$ is obtuse, we have the following additional cases.

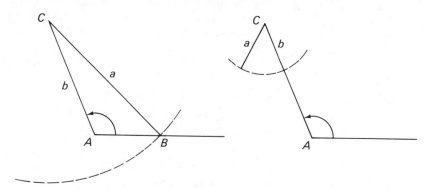

Point B has one position:
one solution

Point B has no position:
no solution

Since when given *SSA* there may be no solution, one solution or two solutions, the *SSA* case is called the ambiguous case.

EXAMPLE 1. *In* $\triangle ABC$, $\angle A = 42°$, $a = 10.2$ cm, *and* $b = 8.5$ cm. *Find* $\angle B$ *and* $\angle C$.

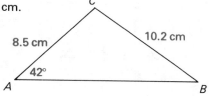

Solution
Since $\angle A$ is given and $a > b$ there is only one solution.

(i) Using tables

$$\frac{\sin B}{b} = \frac{\sin A}{a}$$

$$\sin B = \frac{b \sin A}{a}$$

$$\sin B \doteq \frac{8.5 \times 0.6691}{10.2}$$

$$\doteq 0.5576$$

$\angle B \doteq 33°54'$ and $\angle C \doteq 180° - (42° + 33°54')$

$$\doteq 104°6'$$

(ii) Using a calculator

$$\frac{\sin B}{b} = \frac{\sin A}{a}$$

$$\sin B = \frac{b \sin A}{a}$$

$$\sin B = \frac{8.5 \times \sin 42°}{10.2}$$

$$\doteq 0.5576$$

$$\angle B \doteq 33.8906°$$

$$\doteq 33°54'$$

$$\angle C \doteq 180° - (42° + 33°54')$$

$$\doteq 104°6'$$

$\angle B \doteq 33°54'$ and $\angle C \doteq 104°6'$

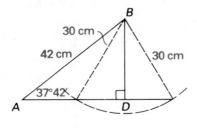

EXAMPLE 2. *Solve* $\triangle ABC$ *if* $\angle A = 37°42'$, $a = 30$ cm, $c = 42$ cm.

Solution
From the diagram,

$$BD = c \sin A$$
$$= 42 \sin 37°42'$$
$$\doteq 42(0.6115)$$
$$\doteq 25.68$$

Since $c \sin A < a < c$, there are two solutions.
$(25.68 < 30 < 42)$

$$\frac{\sin C}{c} = \frac{\sin A}{a}$$

$$\sin C = \frac{c \sin A}{a}$$

$$\sin C = \frac{42 \sin 37°42'}{30}$$

$$\doteq \frac{42(0.6115)}{30}$$

$$\doteq 0.8561$$

$$\therefore \quad \angle C \doteq 58°54' \quad \text{or} \quad \angle C \doteq 180° - 58°54' \doteq 121°6'$$

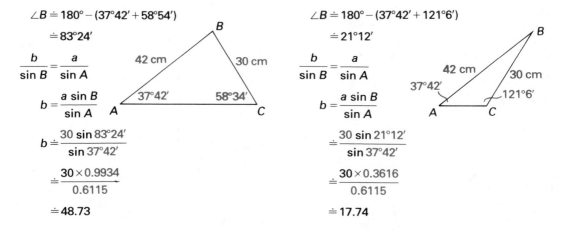

$$\angle B \doteq 180° - (37°42' + 58°54')$$
$$\doteq 83°24'$$
$$\frac{b}{\sin B} = \frac{a}{\sin A}$$
$$b = \frac{a \sin B}{\sin A}$$
$$b \doteq \frac{30 \sin 83°24'}{\sin 37°42'}$$
$$\doteq \frac{30 \times 0.9934}{0.6115}$$
$$\doteq 48.73$$

$$\angle B \doteq 180° - (37°42' + 121°6')$$
$$\doteq 21°12'$$
$$\frac{b}{\sin B} = \frac{a}{\sin A}$$
$$b = \frac{a \sin B}{\sin A}$$
$$\doteq \frac{30 \sin 21°12'}{\sin 37°42'}$$
$$\doteq \frac{30 \times 0.3616}{0.6115}$$
$$\doteq 17.74$$

The two solutions are
1. $\angle B = 83°24'$, $\angle C = 58°54'$ and $b = 48.8$ cm.
2. $\angle B = 21°12'$, $\angle C = 121°6'$ and $b = 17.7$ cm.
In this example the results using a calculator are identical.

EXERCISE 6-4

B **1.** Determine the number of solutions (0, 1, 2)
(a) $\triangle ABC$ where $\angle A = 42°$, $a = 30$ cm and $b = 25$ cm
(b) $\triangle ABC$ where $\angle B = 27°$, $b = 25$ cm and $c = 30$ cm
(c) $\triangle ABC$ where $\angle C = 37°18'$, $c = 85$ cm and $b = 90$ cm
(d) $\triangle ABC$ where $\angle A = 30°$, $a = 50$ cm and $b = 25$ cm
(e) $\triangle ABC$ where $\angle C = 38°42'$, $c = 10$ cm and $b = 25$ cm.

2. In $\triangle ABC$, $\angle A = 30°$ and $b = 100$ cm. Find the range of values of a for which there are two solutions.

3. In $\triangle ABC$, $\angle B = 41°24'$ and $c = 18$ cm. Find the set of values of b for which there is no solution.

4. In $\triangle ABC$, $\angle C = 28°54'$ and $a = 125$ cm. Find the set of values of c for which there is exactly one solution.

Solve the following triangles.

C **5.** $\triangle ABC$, where $\angle A = 45°$, $a = 30$ cm, $b = 24$ cm.

6. $\triangle ABC$, where $\angle B = 32°42'$, $b = 54$ cm, $a = 25$ cm.

7. $\triangle ABC$, where $\angle C = 40°18'$, $c = 35$ cm, $b = 40$ cm.

Determine the pattern.
Find the missing number.

21	19	16	28
35	33	41	31
46	28	22	35
10	24		24

6.5 PROBLEMS INVOLVING OBLIQUE TRIANGLES

Since there is no right angle in an oblique triangle, the six trigonometric ratios cannot be applied directly. The uses of the law of sines and law of cosines are summarized in the following table.

Given	Formula	You can calculate
ASA	$\dfrac{a}{\sin A} = \dfrac{b}{\sin B} = \dfrac{c}{\sin C}$	side
SAS	$a^2 = b^2 + c^2 - 2bc \cos A$ $b^2 = a^2 + c^2 - 2ac \cos B$ $c^2 = a^2 + b^2 - 2ab \cos C$	side
SSS	$\cos A = \dfrac{b^2 + c^2 - a^2}{2bc}$ $\cos B = \dfrac{a^2 + c^2 - b^2}{2ac}$ $\cos C = \dfrac{a^2 + b^2 - c^2}{2ab}$	angle
SSA	$\dfrac{\sin A}{a} = \dfrac{\sin B}{b} = \dfrac{\sin C}{c}$	angle *

* In the SSA case, the number of solutions must be determined first as in section 6.4 Example 2.

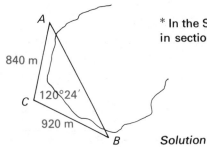

EXAMPLE 1. *In order to find the distance, AB, across a small inlet, point C is located and the following measurements were re-corded:* $\angle C = 102°24'$, $a = 920$ m, *and* $b = 840$ m. *Find c.*

Solution

(i) Using tables

$c^2 = a^2 + b^2 - 2ab \cos C$

$c^2 = 920^2 + 840^2 - 2(920)(840) \cos 102°24'$

$\doteq 846\,400 + 705\,600 - 1\,546\,000(-0.2147)$

$\doteq 1\,884\,000$

$c \doteq 1373$

(ii) Using a calculator

$c^2 = a^2 + b^2 - 2ab \cos C$

$= 920^2 + 840^2 - 2(920)(840) \cos 102.4°$

$\doteq 1\,883\,894.9$

$c \doteq 1372.5505$

∴ the distance across is approximately 1373 m.

EXERCISE 6-5

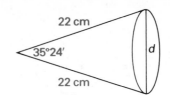

1. The angle of a cone is 35°24′. Find the diameter of the cone at a point on the face 22 cm from the vertex.

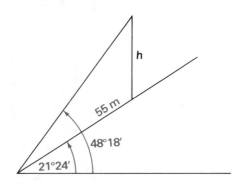

2. A light pole on a hillside casts a shadow of 55 m down the hill. If the angle of elevation of the sun is 48°18′ and the angle of inclination of the hill is 21°24′, find the height of the pole.

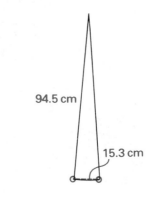

3. A grandfather clock has a pendulum 94.5 cm long. From one end of the swing to the other, the straight line separation is 15.3 cm. Find the angle through which the pendulum swings.

4. Two ships leave a position at the same time. One ship sails 300 km in a north west direction, the other 250 km east. How far apart are the ships?

5. Two aircraft have radio equipment with a range of 350 km. The distances and bearings from a radio beacon are 245 km on a bearing 228° for one aircraft, and 200 km on a bearing 140° for the other. Can the two aircraft make radio contact?

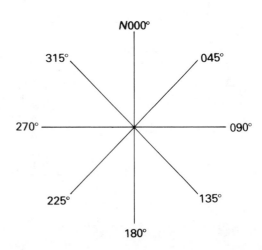

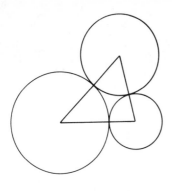

6. Three circles with radii 35 cm, 50 cm, and 65 cm respectively are tangent to each other externally. Find the angles of the triangle formed by joining the centres of the circles.

7. Two aircraft leave Mirabel airport at approximately the same time flying at 750 km/h and 850 km/h. After 2.5 h, they are 1900 km apart. Find the angle between their flight paths.

8. Find the perimeter of an isosceles triangle with base 85 cm and vertical angle 30°.

9. A transmission tower 200 m tall stands on the top of a hill. From a point 175 m down the hill, the tower subtends an angle of 48°36′. Find the length of the wire from this point to the top of the tower.

10. Two streets intersect making an angle of 63°18′. A triangular corner lot has lot lines 53 m along one street and 48 m along the other. What is the length of the third side?

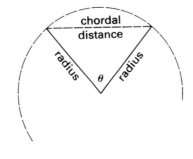

11. (a) Find the chordal distance between equally spaced points on a circle with radius 1 m if there are to be (i) 4 points (ii) 5 points (iii) 6 points
(b) Develop a formula for chordal distance having n points equally spaced on a circle with radius r.

12. Two tracking stations 20 km apart measure the angles of elevation of a rocket to be 42°24′ and 78°6′. Find the height of the rocket, ignoring the curvature of the earth.

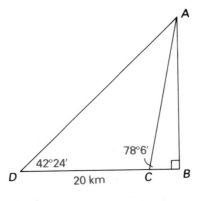

13. In order to measure the height of an inaccessible cliff, *AB*, a surveyor lays off a baseline *CD* and records the following data: $\angle BCD = 68°12'$, $\angle BDC = 52°48'$, $CD = 210$ m, and $\angle ACB = 32°$. Find the height of the cliff *AB*.

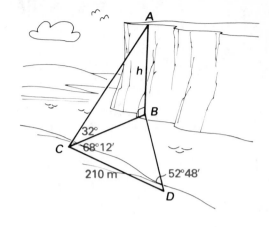

14. A set up for tracking model rockets is shown in the accompanying diagram. The rocket is launched from position *C* and reaches an altitude *CD*. Observers at *A* and *B* measure the angles of elevation, $\angle DAC$ and $\angle DBC$.
(a) Find the height of the rocket if $AB = 300$ m, $\angle CAB = 42°36'$, $\angle CBA = 25°12'$, $\angle DAC = 41°$ and $\angle DBC = 15°$.
(b) The height of the rocket in (a) can be calculated using either angle of elevation, $\angle DAC$ or $\angle DBC$. Find the height using the other angle of elevation and determine if the two results are within 10%.

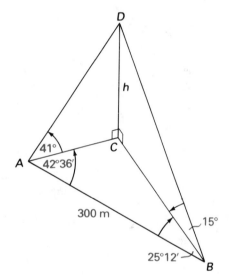

15. A satellite travels in a circular orbit 1600 km above Earth and it will pass over a tracking station at noon. If it takes 2 h to complete an orbit, and the radius of the earth is 6400 km, find the time that the satellite will be picked up by an antenna aimed 30° above the horizon.

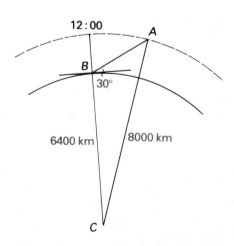

6.6 AREA OF A TRIANGLE

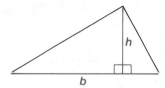

The area of a triangle has been calculated using the base and altitude (height) of the figure as

$$\triangle = \tfrac{1}{2}bh$$

We cannot find the area of $\triangle ABC$ in Figure 6-1 since the altitude is not known. The altitude, h, can be found using trigonometry.

$$\frac{h}{25} = \sin 48°42'$$

$$h = 25 \sin 48°42'$$

$$\doteq 25 \times 0.7513$$

$$\doteq 18.78$$

Using the formula $\triangle = \tfrac{1}{2}bh$, the area is

$$\triangle \doteq \tfrac{1}{2}(30)(18.78)$$

$$\doteq 281.7$$

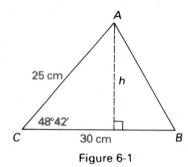

Figure 6-1

Hence the area of $\triangle ABC$ is approximately 281.7 cm².

Using trigonometry, we can develop formulas to find the area of a triangle where the altitude is not known.

SAS (two sides and the included angle are known).

In $\triangle ABC$, BC, AC and $\angle ACB$ are given. We draw AD perpendicular to BC, or BC extended, representing an altitude of $\triangle ABC$

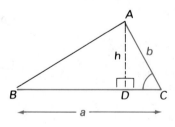

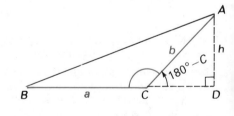

In $\triangle ACD$,

$$\frac{h}{b} = \sin C \qquad\qquad \frac{h}{b} = \sin (180° - C)$$

$$h = b \sin C \qquad\qquad h = b \sin (180° - C)$$

$$\qquad\qquad\qquad\qquad = b \sin C$$

In $\triangle ABC$,

$$\triangle = \tfrac{1}{2}(\text{base})(\text{height})$$

$$\triangle = \tfrac{1}{2}ah$$

$$= \tfrac{1}{2}ab \sin C$$

We generalize this result as follows.

$$\triangle = \tfrac{1}{2}bc \sin A \qquad \triangle = \tfrac{1}{2}ac \sin B \qquad \triangle = \tfrac{1}{2}ab \sin C$$

EXAMPLE 1. *Find the area of* $\triangle ABC$, *given* $\angle A = 37°$, $b = 2.5\,\text{cm}$ *and* $c = 4.3\,\text{cm}$.

Solution

$$\triangle ABC = \tfrac{1}{2}bc \sin A$$

$$\triangle ABC = \tfrac{1}{2}(2.5)(4.3) \sin 37°$$

$$\doteq \tfrac{1}{2}(2.5)(4.3)(0.6018)$$

$$\doteq 3.2348$$

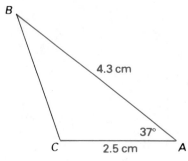

$\therefore$ the area of the triangle is approximately $3.23\,\text{cm}^2$.

AAS (one side and any two angles are known).

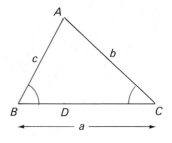 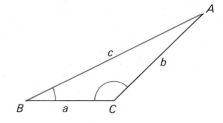

From the Law of Sines

$$\frac{b}{\sin B} = \frac{c}{\sin C}$$

$$b \sin C = c \sin B$$

$$b = \frac{c \sin B}{\sin C}$$

Using one of the *SAS* formulas,

$$\triangle ABC = \tfrac{1}{2}bc \sin A$$

$$= \frac{1}{2}\left(\frac{c \sin B}{\sin C}\right) c \sin A$$

$$= \frac{c^2 \sin A \sin B}{2 \sin C}$$

The three forms of this formula are:

$$\triangle = \frac{c^2 \sin A \sin B}{2 \sin C} \qquad \triangle = \frac{b^2 \sin A \sin C}{2 \sin B} \qquad \triangle = \frac{a^2 \sin B \sin C}{2 \sin A}$$

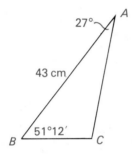

EXAMPLE 2. *Find the area of $\triangle ABC$, given that $\angle A = 27°$, $\angle B = 51°12'$, and $c = 43$ cm.*

Solution

$$\angle C = 180° - (\angle A + \angle B)$$

$$= 180° - (27° + 51°12')$$

$$= 101°48'$$

(i) Using tables

$$\triangle = \frac{c^2 \sin A \sin B}{2 \sin C}$$

$$= \frac{43^2 \sin 27° \sin 51°12'}{2 \sin 101°48'}$$

sin 101°48'
= sin (180° − 101°48')
= sin 78°12'
= 0.9789

$$\doteq \frac{43^2 \times 0.4540 \times 0.7793}{2 \times 0.9789}$$

$$\doteq 334.1$$

(ii) Using a calculator

$$\triangle = \frac{c^2 \sin A \sin B}{2 \sin C}$$

$$= \frac{43^2 \sin 27° \sin 51.2°}{2 \sin 101.8°}$$

$$\doteq 334.1609$$

∴   the area of $\triangle ABC$ is approximately 334 cm².

SSS   (three sides are known)

The area of a triangle whose three sides are known can be found using Heron's Formula.

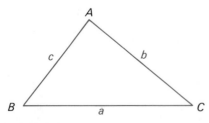

$$\triangle = \sqrt{s(s-a)(s-b)(s-c)}$$

$$\text{where } s = \frac{a+b+c}{2}$$

Proof:

From the law of cosines,

$$\cos A = \frac{b^2 + c^2 - a^2}{2bc}$$

$$\sin A = \sqrt{1 - \cos^2 A} = \frac{\sqrt{-a^4 - b^4 - c^4 + 2b^2c^2 + 2c^2a^2 + 2a^2b^2}}{2bc}$$

$$\triangle = \tfrac{1}{2}bc \sin A$$

$$= \tfrac{1}{4}\sqrt{-a^4 - b^4 - c^4 + 2b^2c^2 + 2c^2a^2 + 2a^2b^2}$$

$$= \tfrac{1}{4}\sqrt{(a+b+c)(-a+b+c)(a-b+c)(a+b-c)}$$

$$= \sqrt{s(s-a)(s-b)(s-c)} \quad \text{where} \quad s = \frac{a+b+c}{2}$$

The intermediate steps are left to the student.

EXAMPLE 3. *Find the area of a triangle with sides 9, 10, and 11 cm.*

Solution

$$a = 9 \qquad\qquad \triangle = \sqrt{s(s-a)(s-b)(s-c)}$$

$$b = 10 \qquad\qquad \triangle = \sqrt{15(15-9)(15-10)(15-11)}$$

$$c = 11 \qquad\qquad\quad = \sqrt{15 \times 6 \times 5 \times 4}$$

$$s = \frac{a+b+c}{2} \qquad\quad = \sqrt{1800}$$

$$\qquad\qquad\qquad\quad \doteq 42.43$$

$$= \tfrac{30}{2} = 15$$

∴ the area of the triangle is approximately 42.43 cm².

EXERCISE 6-6

B Find the area of each of the following.

1. (a) 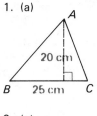   (b) 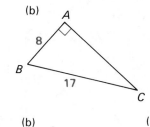   (c)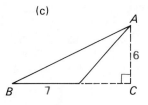

2. (a) 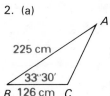   (b) 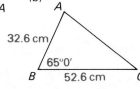   (c)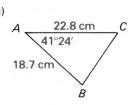

(d) △ABC, ∠A = 84°18′, b = 18.2 cm, c = 14.8 cm
(e) △ABC, ∠B = 108°24′, a = 21.5 cm, c = 47.2 cm

3. (a)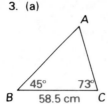

(b)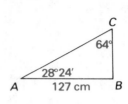

(c)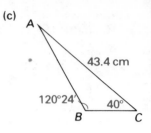

(d) △ABC, ∠A = 35°, ∠B = 75°18′, a = 41.2 cm
(e) △ABC, a = 257 cm, ∠B = 48°, ∠C = 78°30′

4. (a)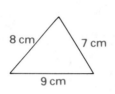

(b)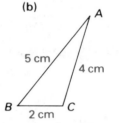

(c)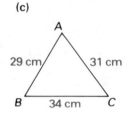

(d) △ABC, a = 15 cm, b = 17 cm, c = 19 cm
(e) △ABC, a = 41 cm, b = 38 cm, c = 52 cm

5. Find the area of a parallelogram with sides 9.5 cm and 8.2 cm. The angle between these sides is 81°24′.

C 6. Given △ABC, a = 4.5 cm, b = 3 cm, and c = 4 cm,
(a) find the area of △ABC
(b) find the length of CD so that △BCD = △ABC when CD ⊥ BC.

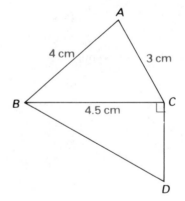

Find a four digit perfect square whose first two digits and last two digits each represent perfect squares.

REVIEW EXERCISE

1. Find the indicated quantity in each of the following.
(a) In $\triangle ABC$, $a = 43$ cm, $b = 68$ cm, $c = 35$ cm. Find the largest angle.
(b) In $\triangle ABC$, $a = 25$ cm, $\angle B = 35°30'$, $c = 18$ cm, Find b.
(c) In $\triangle ABC$, $\angle A = 33°12'$, $b = 82$ cm, $\angle C = 81°42'$. Find a.
(d) In $\triangle ABC$, $a = 58$ cm, $\angle B = 12°$, $\angle C = 109°24'$. Find c.

2. Solve the following triangles.

(a)

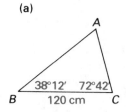

(b)

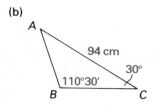

(c)

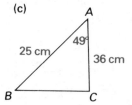

(d) $\triangle ABC$, $\angle A = 47°48'$, $b = 76$ cm, $\angle C = 21°30'$.
(e) $\triangle ABC$, $a = 48$ cm, $b = 63$ cm, $c = 95$ cm.

3. Solve the following triangles.
(a) $\triangle ABC$, $a = 32$ cm, $b = 44$ cm, $\angle B = 32°48'$.
(b) $\triangle ABC$, $\angle A = 112°18'$, $a = 53$ cm, $c = 41$ cm.
(c) $\triangle ABC$, $b = 80$ cm, $c = 65$ cm, $\angle C = 52°24'$.
(d) $\triangle ABC$, $\angle A = 32°18'$, $\angle B = 74°12'$, $c = 21.5$ cm.
(e) $\triangle ABC$, $a = 35.4$ cm, $\angle B = 121°48'$, $c = 41.8$ cm

4. Find the area of each of the following

(a)

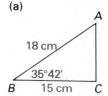

(b)

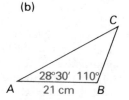

(c)

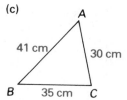

(d) $\triangle ABC$, $\angle A = 39°30'$, $b = 46$ cm, $\angle C = 53°48'$.
(e) $\triangle ABC$, $a = 39$ cm, $b = 46$ cm, $c = 53$ cm.
(f) $\triangle ABC$, $a = 85$ cm, $b = 63$ cm, $c = 34$ cm.

5. A hockey net is 1.83 m wide. A player shoots from a point where the puck is 12 m from one goal post and 10.8 m from the other. Within what angle must he shoot?

6. Parallelogram $ABCD$ has $\angle C = 115°30'$, $AD = 35$ cm, $CD = 27$ cm, as shown. Find the lengths of the diagonals AC and BD.

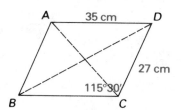

7. Two highways diverge at $53°12'$. If two bike riders take separate routes at 17 km/h and 24 km/h, find how far apart they are after 2 h.

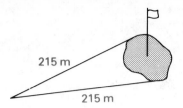

8. A golf green is 18 m wide. Within what angle must a player hit the ball in order to land on the green from a position 215 m from the green?

9. Find the dimensions indicated.

(a)

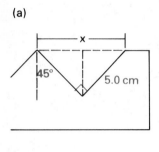

(b)

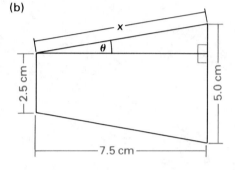

(c)

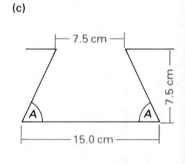

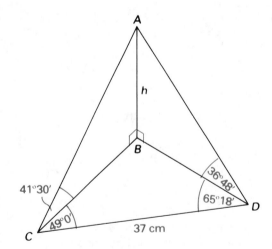

10. A rocket launched vertically from *B* is tracked by stations at *C* and *D* and data were recorded as in the diagram.
(a) What was the height of the rocket?
(b) Determine whether it was a good track within 10% by finding the height using the other station's angle of elevation.

REVIEW AND PREVIEW TO CHAPTER 7

EXERCISE 1.   TRIGONOMETRIC FUNCTIONS

$\sin \theta = \dfrac{y}{r}$ $\cos \theta = \dfrac{x}{r}$ $\tan \theta = \dfrac{y}{x}$

$\csc \theta = \dfrac{r}{y}$ $\sec \theta = \dfrac{r}{x}$ $\cot \theta = \dfrac{x}{y}$

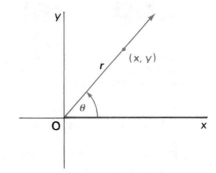

1. Find the six trigonometric ratios of the angles in standard position if a point on the terminal arm is:
(a) $(3, 4)$ (b) $(-6, 8)$ (c) $(-5, -13)$ (d) $(5, -2)$
(e) $(-5, 0)$ (f) $(0, -3)$ (g) $(-2, -5)$ (h) $(3, -3)$

2. Find the other five trigonometric ratios if
(a) $\sin \theta = \frac{3}{5}$ (b) $\cos \theta = 0.5$ (c) $\tan \theta = 1$
(d) $\sec \theta = \frac{5}{3}$ (e) $\csc \theta = \frac{13}{5}$ (f) $\cot \theta = \sqrt{2}$
(g) $\sin \theta = -\frac{5}{13}$ (h) $\tan \theta = -\frac{3}{4}$ (i) $\sin \theta = 0$
(j) $\cos \theta = \dfrac{-3}{5}$ (k) $\tan \theta = \dfrac{-5}{12}$ (l) $\sin \theta = -0.75$

EXERCISE 2.   EQUATIONS AND GRAPHS

1. Sketch the graph of each of the following for $x \in R$.
(a) $y = 3x - 2$ (b) $y = \frac{1}{2}x + 3$ (c) $2x - 3y = 2$
(d) $y = x^2 - 2$ (e) $y = 2(x - 3)^2 - 1$ (f) $y = -(x + 2)^2 + 3$

(g) $y = \dfrac{1}{x^2}$ (h) $y = \dfrac{1}{x^2 + 1}$ (i) $y = \dfrac{1}{x^2 - 1}$

2. Solve the following equations.

(a) $3(x - 2) + 5 = x$ (b) $\dfrac{x^1 - 1}{2} + \dfrac{x - 3}{4} = \dfrac{x - 5}{6}$

(c) $x^2 - x - 6 = 0$ (d) $5x^2 - 6x + 1 = 0$
(e) $3x^2 + 7x + 2 = 0$ (f) $x^2 + x + 1 = 0$

(g) $\dfrac{1}{x} + \dfrac{2}{x + 3} = \dfrac{9}{10}$ (h) $|x - 1| = 5$

CHAPTER 7

Trigonometric Functions and Their Graphs

Mathematics compares the most diverse phenomena and discovers the secret analogies which unite them.

Joseph Fourier

Trigonometry began with the measure of triangles. Today, this branch of mathematics continues to grow in importance not only in the space program but also in the routine work of engineers and technologists. Trigonometry is now finding new applications in the study of cycles such as tides, harmonic motion, and some economic data.

7.1 RADIAN MEASURE

We can measure angles in degrees, minutes and seconds, where

$$1 \text{ revolution} = 360°$$
$$1° = 60'$$
$$1' = 60''$$

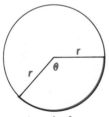

The measure of an angle can also be stated in terms of the length of arc that subtends the angle at the centre of a circle, as in Figure 7-1. In this manner the measure of an angle is associated with a real number.

length of arc

Figure 7-1

An angle subtended at the centre of a circle by an arc equal in length to the radius has a measure of one radian.

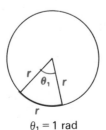

$\theta_1 = 1$ rad

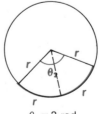

$\theta_2 = 2$ rad

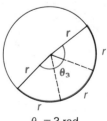

$\theta_3 = 3$ rad

These diagrams suggest that the arc lengths are r, $2r$, and $3r$.

$$\therefore \qquad 1 = \theta_1 = \frac{r}{r}, \qquad 2 = \theta_2 = \frac{2r}{r}, \qquad 3 = \theta_3 = \frac{3r}{r}.$$

This leads to the generalization

$$\theta = \frac{a}{r} \quad \text{or} \quad \text{Number of radians} = \frac{\text{arc length}}{\text{radius}}$$

Since $\theta = \frac{a}{r}$, it follows that

$$a = r\theta, \qquad \theta > 0$$

where a is the arc length, r the radius and θ, the radian measure of the angle.

EXAMPLE 1. Find the indicated quantity in each of the following.

(a)

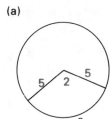

(b)

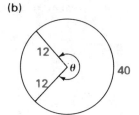

(c)

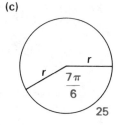

Solution

(a) $a = r\theta$

$a = 5 \times 2$

$= 10$

(b) $\theta = \frac{a}{r}$

$= \frac{40}{12}$

$= 3\frac{1}{3}$

(c) $r = \frac{a}{\theta}$

$r = \frac{25}{\dfrac{7\pi}{6}}$

$= \frac{150}{7\pi}$

$\doteq 6.820\,93$

In order to convert from degree measure to radian measure, we now establish the relationship between degrees and radians. In degree measure, one revolution is 360°. In radian measure, one revolution is $\frac{2\pi r}{r} = 2\pi$ rad. The relationship between degrees and radians is given by:

$$2\pi \text{ rad} = 360°$$

which simplifies to

$$\pi \text{ rad} = 180°$$

EXAMPLE 2. *Calculate the degree measure of the angles whose radian measures are*

$$\text{(a) } \frac{\pi}{3} \quad \text{(b) } \frac{\pi}{2} \quad \text{(c) } \frac{5\pi}{4} \quad \text{(d) } -3\pi \quad \text{(e) } 1$$

Solution

(a) $\frac{\pi}{3}$ rad $= (\frac{180}{3})° = 60°$

(b) $\frac{\pi}{2}$ rad $= (\frac{180}{2})° = 90°$

(c) $\frac{5\pi}{4}$ rad $= \left(\frac{5 \times 180}{4}\right)° = 225°$

(d) -3π rad $= (-3 \times 180)° = -540°$

(e) 1 rad $= \left(\frac{180}{\pi}\right)°$

$$\doteq \left(\frac{180}{3.141\ 592\ 7}\right)°$$

$$\doteq 57.295\ 780°$$

$$\doteq 57°17'45''$$

EXAMPLE 3. *Calculate the radian measure of the angles whose measures are*

$$\text{(a) } 30° \quad \text{(b) } 225° \quad \text{(c) } 1° \quad \text{(d) } -135°24'$$

Solution

$$180° = \pi \text{ rad and } 1° = \frac{\pi}{180} \text{ rad.}$$

(a) $30° = 30\left(\frac{\pi}{180}\right) = \frac{\pi}{6}$ rad

(b) $225° = 225\left(\frac{\pi}{180}\right) = \frac{5\pi}{4}$ rad

(c) $1° = \frac{\pi}{180} \doteq 0.017\ 453\ 293$ rad

(d) $-135°24' = -135.4°$

$$= -135.4\left(\frac{\pi}{180}\right)$$

$$\doteq -2.363\ 175\ 8 \text{ rad}$$

EXAMPLE 4. *A small electrical motor turns at* 2200 r/min.
(a) *Express this angular velocity in radians per second.*
(b) *Find the distance a point* 0.8 cm *from the centre of rotation travels in* 0.008 s.

Solution
(a) 2200 r/min $= 2200 \times 2\pi$ rad/min

$$= \frac{2200 \times 2\pi}{60} \text{ rad/s}$$

$$= \frac{220\pi}{3}$$

$$\doteq 230.383\ 46 \text{ rad/s}$$

∴ 2200 r/min is approximately 230 rad/s.

(b) In 0.008 s, the point travels along an arc with central angle

$$0.008 \times 230.383\,46 \doteq 1.843\,067\,7 \text{ rad}$$

$$a = r\theta$$

$$a \doteq 0.8 \times 1.843\,067\,7$$

$$\doteq 1.474\,454\,2$$

∴ in 0.008 s the point travels approximately 1.474 cm.

EXERCISE 7-1

A 1. Find the exact number of degrees in the angles whose radian measures are:

(a) $\dfrac{\pi}{4}$ (b) 2π (c) $\dfrac{3\pi}{4}$ (d) $\dfrac{3\pi}{2}$ (e) $\dfrac{\pi}{6}$

(f) $\dfrac{5\pi}{6}$ (g) $\dfrac{\pi}{3}$ (h) $\dfrac{-3\pi}{2}$ (i) $-\dfrac{7\pi}{6}$ (j) $\dfrac{2\pi}{3}$ Write 5 using four 4's.

2. Find the exact radian measure in terms of π for each of the following.

(a) 120°   (b) 225°   (c) 315°   (d) −270°   (e) 330°
(f) 240°   (g) −210°   (h) 540°   (i) −180°   (j) 135°

B 3. Find the measure to the nearest 6' of the angles whose radian measures are

(a) 0.35   (b) 1.25   (c) 0.63   (d) 0.5   (e) 2.5
(f) 6.25   (g) 1.75   (h) −0.75   (i) 3.14   (j) −1.21

4. Find the approximate number of radians to two decimal places in the angles whose degree measures are

(a) 40°   (b) 83°   (c) 145°   (d) 230°   (e) 325°
(f) 35°18′   (g) 52°48′   (h) 128°30′   (i) 255°24′   (j) 310°54′

5. Find the indicated quantity in each of the following.

(a)

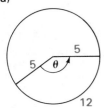

(b)

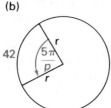

(c)

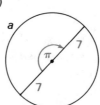

(d)

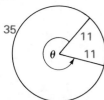

(e)

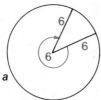

(f)

6. A wheel turns at 150 r/min.
(a) Find the angular velocity in radians per second.
(b) How far does a point 45 cm from the point of rotation travel in 5 s?

7. A ferris wheel with radius 31 m makes 2 rotations in one minute.
(a) Find the angular velocity in radians per second.
(b) How far has a rider travelled if the ride is 10 min long?

8. A wheel turns with an angular velocity of 10 rad/s.
(a) What is the rotational frequency in revolutions per minute of this wheel?
(b) How far will the wheel roll in 8 s if the radius of the wheel is 12 cm?

9. A satellite with a circular orbit has an angular velocity of 0.002 rad/s.
(a) How long will it take for the satellite to make one orbit?
(b) What is the speed of the satellite if it is orbiting 800 km above the surface of the earth? (The radius of the earth is 6400 km.)

10. An automobile travels at 100 km/h.
(a) Find the angular velocity of a tire with radius 36 cm.
(b) Through what angle will the tire turn in 30 s at this speed?

7.2 GRAPHS OF TRIGONOMETRIC FUNCTIONS

In this section we shall use the ratios of special angles to draw the graphs of the six trigonometric functions.

EXAMPLE 1. *Find*

$$(a)\ \sin 0° \qquad (b)\ \cos \frac{\pi}{2} \qquad (c)\ \cos \pi$$

$$(d)\ \tan 270° \qquad (e)\ \sin 2\pi$$

Solution
When we write sin 10° we mean the measure of the angle is 10°, while when we write sin 10 we mean the measure of the angle is 10 rad.

(a)   (b)   (c)

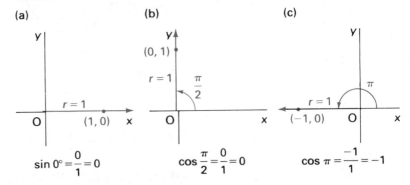

$$\sin 0° = \frac{0}{1} = 0 \qquad \cos \frac{\pi}{2} = \frac{0}{1} = 0 \qquad \cos \pi = \frac{-1}{1} = -1$$

(d)

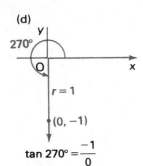

$$\tan 270° = \frac{-1}{0}$$
which is undefined.

(e)

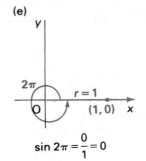

$$\sin 2\pi = \frac{0}{1} = 0$$

EXAMPLE 2. *Find*

(a) $\sin \dfrac{\pi}{4}$ (b) $\cos \dfrac{2\pi}{3}$ (c) $\tan \dfrac{11\pi}{6}$

Solution

We use the special triangles to find the values of these trigonometric ratios.

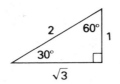

(a)

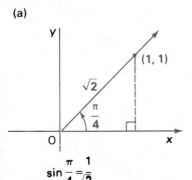

$$\sin \frac{\pi}{4} = \frac{1}{\sqrt{2}}$$

(b)

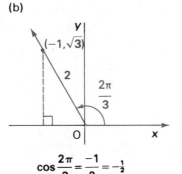

$$\cos \frac{2\pi}{3} = \frac{-1}{2} = -\tfrac{1}{2}$$

(c)

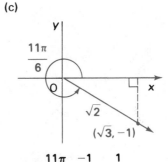

$$\tan \frac{11\pi}{6} = \frac{-1}{\sqrt{3}} = -\frac{1}{\sqrt{3}}$$

The graph of the sine and cosine functions can be plotted by preparing a table of values using the methods of Example 2.

θ	0	$\dfrac{\pi}{6}$	$\dfrac{\pi}{3}$	$\dfrac{\pi}{2}$	$\dfrac{2\pi}{3}$	$\dfrac{5\pi}{6}$	π	$\dfrac{7\pi}{6}$	$\dfrac{4\pi}{3}$	$\dfrac{3\pi}{2}$	$\dfrac{5\pi}{3}$	$\dfrac{11\pi}{6}$	2π
$y = \sin \theta$	0	$\tfrac{1}{2}$	$\dfrac{\sqrt{3}}{2}$	1	$\dfrac{\sqrt{3}}{2}$	$\tfrac{1}{2}$	0	$-\tfrac{1}{2}$	$-\dfrac{\sqrt{3}}{2}$	-1	$-\dfrac{\sqrt{3}}{2}$	$-\tfrac{1}{2}$	0
$y = \cos \theta$	1	$\dfrac{\sqrt{3}}{2}$	$\tfrac{1}{2}$	0	$-\tfrac{1}{2}$	$-\dfrac{\sqrt{3}}{2}$	-1	$-\dfrac{\sqrt{3}}{2}$	$-\tfrac{1}{2}$	0	$\tfrac{1}{2}$	$\dfrac{\sqrt{3}}{2}$	1

$$\frac{\sqrt{3}}{2} \doteq 0.87$$

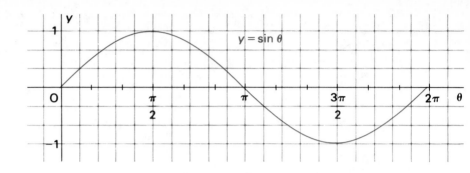

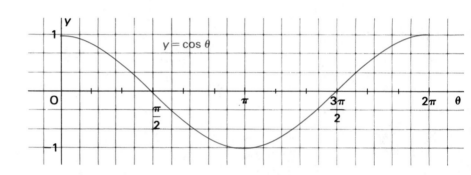

If we continue this process for negative values of θ, or for values $\theta > 2\pi$, we see that the sine and cosine functions are continuous.

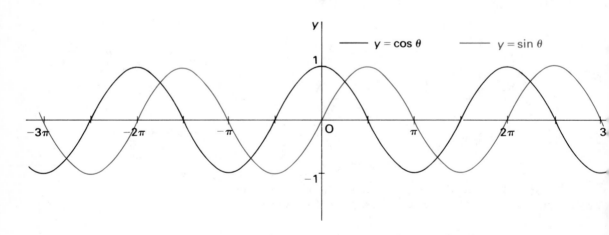

Using function notation, $f(x) = \sin x$, $x \in R$, is a function whose value at x is the sine of the angle whose radian measure is x. These graphs demonstrate a periodic nature where the function takes on all possible values from -1 to $+1$ in the interval $0 \leqslant \theta \leqslant 2\pi$ and then the pattern repeats. Hence the functions $y = \sin \theta$ and $y = \cos \theta$ are periodic, with period 2π, that is

$$\sin(\theta + 2\pi) = \sin\theta$$

$$\cos(\theta + 2\pi) = \cos\theta$$

Further examination of these graphs, shows that for all real numbers,

$$\sin(-\theta) = -\sin\theta,$$

and

$$\cos(-\theta) = \cos\theta.$$

Hence according to our definition in Chapter 1, the sine function is an odd function and the cosine function is an even function.

Since $\sin\theta = \dfrac{y}{r}$, and $\cos\theta = \dfrac{x}{r}$, we have

ODD
$$f(-x) = -f(x)$$

EVEN
$$f(-x) = f(x)$$

$$\frac{\sin\theta}{\cos\theta} = \frac{\dfrac{y}{r}}{\dfrac{x}{r}} = \frac{y}{x} = \tan\theta$$

We can now use $\tan\theta = \dfrac{\sin\theta}{\cos\theta}$ and the preceding tables to find the values to graph the tangent function. Since $\frac{1}{0}$ is not defined and $\cos\dfrac{\pi}{2} = 0$, we conclude that $\tan\dfrac{\pi}{2}$ does not exist. Following is the graph of the tangent function—the table of values is left to the student.

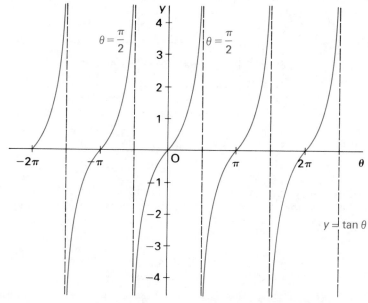

The tangent function takes on all possible values as θ increases from $-\dfrac{\pi}{2}$ to $\dfrac{\pi}{2}$. The tangent function is periodic and the period is π. The lines $\theta = -\dfrac{\pi}{2}, \dfrac{\pi}{2}$, and so on are vertical asymptotes.

trigonometric functions and their graphs   215

The tables and graphs of the sine, cosine, and tangent functions can be used to produce the graphs of the reciprocal functions—cosecant, secant, cotangent.

In order to graph $y = \csc \theta$, we use the relationship $\csc \theta = \dfrac{1}{\sin \theta}$ and show the analysis in the following table.

θ	$\sin \theta$	$\csc \theta$
0	0	undefined
$0 < \theta < \dfrac{\pi}{2}$	increasing	decreasing
$\dfrac{\pi}{2}$	1	1
$\dfrac{\pi}{2} < \theta < \pi$	decreasing	increasing
π	0	undefined
$\pi < \theta < \dfrac{3\pi}{2}$	decreasing	increasing
$\dfrac{3\pi}{2}$	-1	-1
$\dfrac{3\pi}{2} < \theta < 2\pi$	increasing	decreasing
2π	0	undefined

The graphs of both $y = \sin \theta$, and $y = \csc \theta$ are shown below. Note that for $\theta \in R$, the range of $y = \sin \theta$ is $\{y \mid -1 \leqslant y \leqslant 1\}$ and the range of $y = \csc \theta$ is $\{y \mid y \leqslant -1 \text{ or } y \geqslant 1\}$.

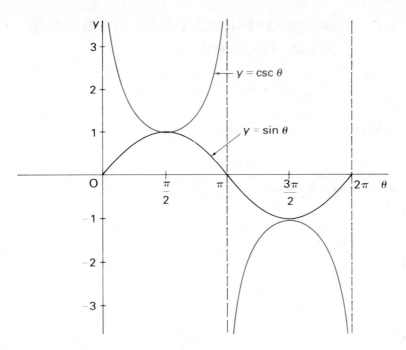

EXERCISE 7-2

1. Find the six trigonometric ratios of each of the following.

(a) $\dfrac{4\pi}{3}$ (b) $\dfrac{5\pi}{4}$ (c) $\dfrac{7\pi}{6}$

2. For the function $y = \sec \theta$,
(a) draw the graph.
(b) state the range.
(c) For what values of θ is $\sec \theta$ not defined?
(d) What is the period of the function $y = \sec \theta$
(e) For what values of θ is $y = \sec \theta$
   (i) increasing? (ii) decreasing?
(f) Is $y = \sec \theta$ an odd or even function?

3. For the function $y = \cot \theta$,
(a) draw the graph.
(b) state the range.
(c) For what values of θ is $\cot \theta$ not defined?
(d) What is the period of the function $y = \cot \theta$?
(e) For what values of θ is $y = \cot \theta$?
   (i) increasing? (ii) decreasing?
(f) Is $y = \cot \theta$ an odd or even function?

SUBTRACTION

READ
TH IS
———
PAGE

7.3 TRANSFORMATIONS OF SINE AND COSINE GRAPHS

From the work in section 1.5 we know that the graph of $y = af(x)$ is the image of $y = f(x)$ under a transformation that causes a vertical stretch.

EXAMPLE 1. *Sketch the graph of $y = 2 \sin \theta$, $-\pi \leqslant \theta \leqslant 3\pi$.*

Solution

We begin with the graph of $y = \sin \theta$, $-\pi \leqslant \theta \leqslant 3\pi$, then apply the required transformation.

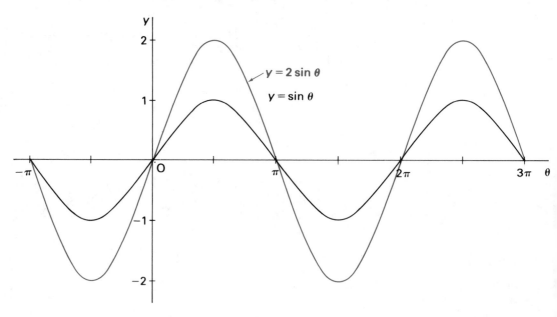

Note that the zeros of $y = 2 \sin \theta$ are the same as the zeros of $y = \sin \theta$. The maximum and minimum values of $y = 2 \sin \theta$ occur for the same values of θ and have a magnification of 2. This magnification is caused by the factor 2 in the equation $y = 2 \sin \theta$ and we say that the amplitude is 2.

AMPLITUDE

The amplitude of the functions $y = a \sin \theta$ and $y = a \cos \theta$ is $|a|$.

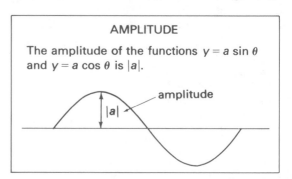

Note that $|a| = \dfrac{M - m}{2}$ where M is the maximum value and m is the minimum value of the function.

The graph of $y = f(kx)$ is the image of $y = f(x)$ under a transformation that causes a horizontal stretch.

EXAMPLE 2. *Sketch the graph of $y = \sin 2\theta$, $-\pi \leqslant \theta \leqslant 2\pi$.*

Solution

As θ varies from 0 to π, 2θ varies from 0 to 2π. Hence the function $y = \sin 2\theta$ completes one period from 0 to π so that its period is π instead of 2π.

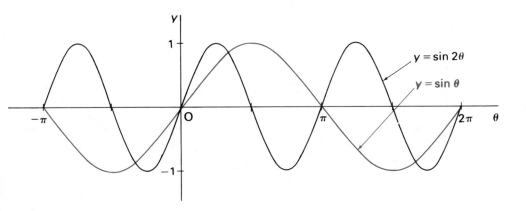

$$\boxed{\begin{array}{c} \text{PERIOD} \\[4pt] \text{The period of the functions } y = \sin k\theta \\[4pt] \text{and } y = \cos k\theta \text{ is } \dfrac{2\pi}{k} ,\ k > 0. \end{array}}$$

We can obtain the graph of $y = \cos \theta$ by shifting the graph of $y = \sin \theta$ either to the left $\dfrac{\pi}{2}$ units or to the right $\dfrac{3\pi}{2}$ units.

$$\sin \left(\theta + \frac{\pi}{2} \right) = \cos \theta$$

$$\sin \left(\theta - \frac{3\pi}{2} \right) = \cos \theta$$

Recall from Chapter 1 that the graph of $y = f(x + c)$ is the image of $y = f(x)$ under a translation that shifts the function to the right if c is negative and to the left if c is positive.

EXAMPLE 3. *Sketch the graph of $y = \sin\left(\theta + \dfrac{\pi}{3}\right)$, $-2\pi \leqslant \theta \leqslant 2\pi$.*

Solution

We first sketch the graph of $y = \sin\theta$, then apply the appropriate transformation—a horizontal shift $\dfrac{\pi}{3}$ units to the left. In trigonometry this shifting is called the phase shift of the function.

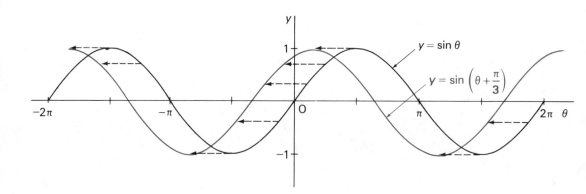

PHASE ANGLE

The phase angle for $y = \sin(\theta + c)$ and $y = \cos(\theta + c)$ is the constant angle c.
The phase shift is c units to the right if c is negative and c units to the left if c is positive.

The graph of $y = f(x) + d$ is the image of the graph of $y = f(x)$ under a vertical translation, d units upwards if d is positive and downwards if d is negative.

EXAMPLE 4. *Sketch the graph of $y = \sin\theta + 1.5$, $-2\pi \leqslant \theta \leqslant 2\pi$.*

Solution

We first sketch the graph of $y = \sin \theta$, then we apply the required translation causing a vertical shift up 1.5 units.

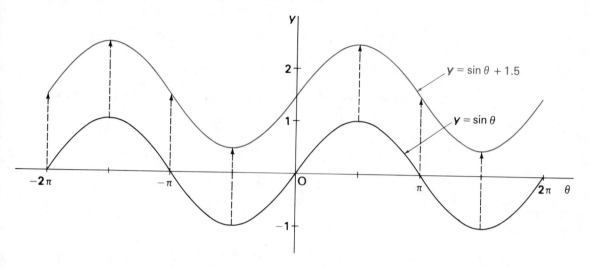

VERTICAL TRANSLATION

The vertical translation for $y = \sin \theta + d$, and $y = \cos \theta + d$ is d units upwards if d is positive and downwards if d is negative.

The general equations of the sine function and cosine function are

$$y = a \sin k(\theta + c) + d$$
$$y = a \cos k(\theta + c) + d$$

We can summarize the results of the examples of this section in the following chart.

	$y = \sin \theta$ $y = \cos \theta$	$y = a \sin k(\theta + c) + d$ $y = a \cos k(\theta + c) + d$
Domain	R	R
Range	$-1 \leqslant y \leqslant 1$	$-|a| + d \leqslant y \leqslant |a| + d$
Amplitude	1	$|a|$
Period	2π	$\dfrac{2\pi}{k}$
Phase Shift	none	$c \begin{cases} \text{left} & c > 0 \\ \text{right} & c < 0 \end{cases}$
Vertical Translation	none	$d \begin{cases} \text{up} & d > 0 \\ \text{down} & d < 0 \end{cases}$

EXAMPLE 5. *Sketch the graph of*

(a) $y = 3 \sin 2\left(\theta - \dfrac{\pi}{4}\right)$, $-\pi \leqslant \theta \leqslant 2\pi$

(b) $y = \cos 3\left(\theta + \dfrac{\pi}{6}\right) + 1$, $-\pi \leqslant \theta \leqslant \pi$

Solution

(a) We compare $y = 3 \sin 2\left(\theta - \dfrac{\pi}{4}\right)$ to the general equation $y = a \sin k(\theta + c) + d$ so that we have

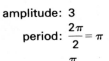

amplitude: 3

period: $\dfrac{2\pi}{2} = \pi$

phase shift: $\dfrac{\pi}{4}$ right

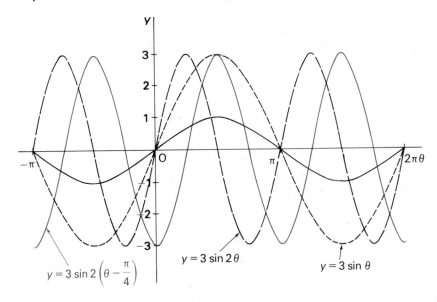

(b) We compare $y = \cos 3\left(\theta + \dfrac{\pi}{6}\right) + 1$ to the general equation $y = a \cos k(\theta + c) + d$ so that we have

amplitude: 1

period: $\dfrac{2\pi}{3}$

phase shift: $\dfrac{\pi}{6}$ left

vertical
translation: 1 up

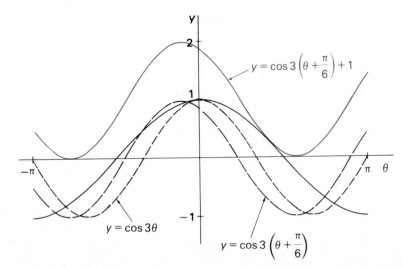

EXAMPLE 6. *Sketch the graph of*

$$f(x) = \sin(2x + \pi), \qquad -\pi \leqslant x \leqslant 2\pi$$

Solution

We first factor the 2 in the equation to get the equation in the general form:

$$f(x) = \sin 2\left(x + \frac{\pi}{2}\right), \qquad -\pi \leqslant x \leqslant 2\pi$$

amplitude: 1

period: $\dfrac{2\pi}{2} = \pi$

phase shift: $\dfrac{\pi}{2}$ left

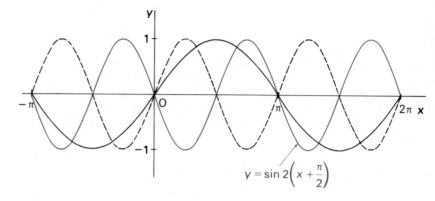

$$y = \sin 2\left(x + \frac{\pi}{2}\right)$$

EXERCISE 7-3

A 1. State the amplitude of the following functions.

(a) $y = \cos\theta$ (b) $y = 3\sin\theta$ (c) $y = \frac{1}{2}\cos\theta$

(d) $y = -\sin\theta$ (e) $y = -2\cos\theta$ (f) $f(x) = \frac{2}{3}\sin x$

(g) $y = 0.5\sin\theta$ (h) $y = 1.5\sin\theta$ (i) $f(x) = -3\sin x$

2. State the period of the following functions.

(a) $y = \sin 3\theta$ (b) $y = \cos 2x$ (c) $y = \sin\frac{1}{2}t$

(d) $y = \sin\dfrac{\theta}{3}$ (e) $y = \sin(-\theta)$ (f) $y = \cos k\theta$

(g) $f(\theta) = \sin(-3\theta)$ (h) $y = \cos\theta$ (i) $f(x) = 2\sin 4x$

(j) $y = \cos\dfrac{2t}{3}$

3. State the phase shift of the following functions.

(a) $y = \cos(\theta - \pi)$ (b) $y = \sin\left(\theta + \dfrac{\pi}{2}\right)$ (c) $f(x) = \sin\left(x - \dfrac{\pi}{3}\right)$

(d) $y = -\cos\left(x + \dfrac{\pi}{6}\right)$ (e) $f(\theta) = \sin\left(\theta - \dfrac{\pi}{4}\right)$ (f) $y = \cos\left(2\theta + \dfrac{\pi}{2}\right)$

(g) $y = \sin 2(\theta - \pi)$ (h) $y = \sin(3\theta + 2\pi)$ (i) $y = -\cos(3\theta + \pi)$

(j) $y = -\sin(2\theta - \pi)$ (k) $f(t) = \sin(2t - \pi)$ (l) $y = -\sin(3x - \pi)$

4. State the amplitude, period, phase shift, and vertical translation for the following functions.

(a) $y = 2\sin\theta$ (b) $y = \sin 2\theta + 3$ (c) $y = \sin\left(\theta + \dfrac{\pi}{2}\right)$

(d) $y = \sin\dfrac{\theta}{2}$ (e) $y = 3\sin 2x + 2$ (f) $y = 2\sin\left(t + \dfrac{\pi}{3}\right)$

(g) $f(\theta) = 2\cos 3\theta$ (h) $y = \sin\left(\theta - \dfrac{\pi}{6}\right)$ (i) $y = \cos\left(2\theta - \dfrac{\pi}{2}\right)$

trigonometric functions and their graphs   223

(j) $y = \frac{1}{2}\sin\theta - 5$ (k) $y = |\sin x|$ (l) $f(\theta) = 2\cos(\theta + \pi)$

B 5. Sketch the graphs of the following functions.

(a) $y = 2\sin 3\theta - 2, \; -\pi \leqslant \theta \leqslant 2\pi$

(b) $y = 3\cos\left(\theta + \dfrac{\pi}{2}\right), \; 0 \leqslant \theta \leqslant 2\pi$

(c) $f(x) = \frac{1}{2}\sin\left(x - \dfrac{\pi}{2}\right), \; 0 \leqslant x \leqslant 4\pi$

(d) $y = -\sin 2\theta + 1, \; \theta \in R$

(e) $y = 2\sin\left(\theta + \dfrac{\pi}{4}\right), \; -2\pi \leqslant \theta \leqslant \pi$

(f) $y = \cos 2\left(x - \dfrac{\pi}{6}\right), \; -\pi \leqslant x \leqslant \pi$

(g) $y = |\sin\theta|, \; -2\pi \leqslant \theta \leqslant 2\pi$

(h) $y = |\cos\theta|, \; -2\pi \leqslant \theta \leqslant 2\pi$

6. Write an equation and sketch the graphs of the sine functions having the following properties.

(a) amplitude 2, period π, no phase shift

(b) amplitude 1, period π, phase shift $\dfrac{\pi}{2}$ left

(c) amplitude 3, period 2π

(d) amplitude 2, period $\dfrac{2\pi}{3}$, phase shift $\dfrac{\pi}{3}$ right

7. Sketch the graphs of the following functions.

(a) $y = \sin(2\theta + \pi), \; -\dfrac{\pi}{2} \leqslant \theta \leqslant \dfrac{3\pi}{2}$

(b) $y = 2\cos\dfrac{x}{2}, \; 0 \leqslant x \leqslant 4\pi$

(c) $f(\theta) = \sin(2\theta - \pi), \; -2\pi \leqslant \theta \leqslant 0$

(d) $y = \sin\frac{1}{2}\left(t + \dfrac{\pi}{4}\right), \; t \in R$

8. Sketch the graphs of the following functions.

(a) $y = 2\sin\theta + 2, \; 0 \leqslant \theta \leqslant 3\pi$

(b) $y = \sin 3\theta + 2, \; -2\pi \leqslant \theta \leqslant \pi$

(c) $y = \cos x - 1, \; 0 \leqslant x \leqslant 4\pi$

(d) $f(t) = \sin\left(t - \dfrac{\pi}{2}\right) + 1, \; 0 \leqslant t \leqslant 3\pi$

C 9. Sketch the graphs of the following functions,

(a) $y = \sin\left(\dfrac{t}{2} + \dfrac{\pi}{2}\right)$

(b) $y = |2\sin\theta + 1|$

(c) $y = \pi\cos(2x - \pi)$

(d) $y = \sin\left(\dfrac{\pi}{2} - \theta\right)$

10. Sketch the graph of each function for $\theta, x \in R$

(a) $y = 2\sin 2(\theta + 1)$ (b) $y = -2\cos(2\theta + 4)$

(c) $y = -\frac{1}{2}\sin(x - 1)$ (d) $f(\theta) = \frac{1}{2}\cos(2\theta + 3)$

7.4 APPLICATIONS OF TRIGONOMETRIC GRAPHS

With the linear function $f(x) = mx + b$ we can model various simple situations. With the quadratic function $f(x) = ax^2 + bx + c$ we were able to model trajectories. Growth in nature and decay of radioactive materials were described using the exponential function $f(x) = a^x$. In this section we shall use the sine and cosine functions as models for various physical situations that fluctuate and display cyclical patterns.

EXAMPLE 1. *A carnival ferris wheel with a radius of 7 m makes one complete revolution every 16 s. The bottom of the wheel is 1.5 m above the ground.*
(a) Draw a graph to show how a person's height above the ground varies with time.
(b) Find an equation of the graph in (a).

Solution

(a)

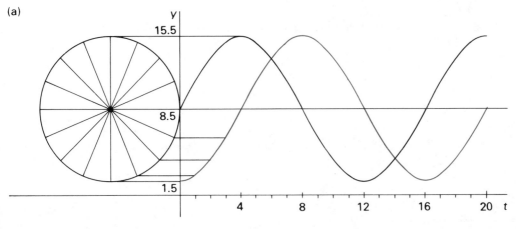

(b) We relate our graph to the general sine function

$$y = a \sin k(t+c) + d$$

where

amplitude: $a = 7$

period: $16 = \dfrac{2\pi}{k}$, $\quad \therefore\ k = \dfrac{\pi}{8}$

phase shift: **4 right,** $\quad \therefore\ c = -4$

vertical translation: $d = 1.5 + 7 = 8.5$

$\therefore$ an equation of the graph is

$$y = 7 \sin \frac{\pi}{8}(t-4) + 8.5$$

Assuming that the wheel keeps turning, the height function would be repeated with the same pattern every 16 s.
Example 1 suggests the following approach:
1. Sketch a graph using the available information.
2. Relate the graph to the general sine function

$$y = a \sin k(\theta + c) + d$$

3. Write an equation.

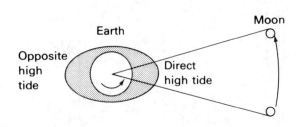

Earth — Moon — Opposite high tide — Direct high tide

EXAMPLE 2. *The alternating half-daily cycles of the rise and fall of oceans are called tides. Tides in one section of the Bay of Fundy caused the water level to rise 6.5 m above mean sea-level and to drop 6.5 m below. The tide completes one cycle every 12 h. Assuming the height of water with respect to mean sea-level to be modelled a by a sine function,*
(a) draw a graph for a 24 h period.
(b) find an equation of the graph in (a).

Solution
We take mean sea-level as our reference point.

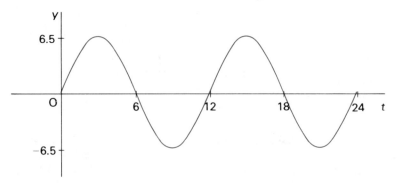

(b) Relating the graph to the general sine function

$$y = a \sin k(t+c)+d$$

we have

> amplitude: 6.5
>
> period: $12 = \dfrac{2\pi}{k}$, $\quad k = \dfrac{\pi}{6}$
>
> phase shift: none
>
> vertical translation: none

∴ the equation is

$$y = 6.5 \sin \frac{\pi}{6} t$$

EXAMPLE 3. *Normal* 110 V *household alternating current varies from* −155 V *to* +155 V *with a frequency of* 60 Hz.
(a) *Draw a graph showing at least 2 cycles.*
(b) *Find an equation that describes alternating current.*

One hertz (Hz) is one cycle per second $\left(\dfrac{1}{s}\right)$.

Solution

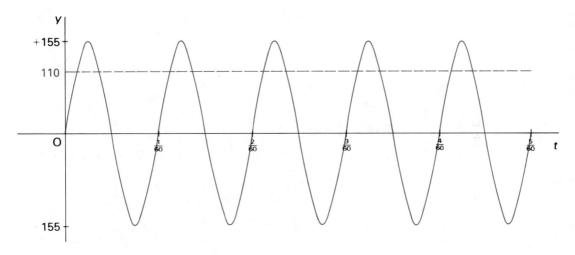

(b) Relating the graph to the general sine function

$$y = a \sin k(\theta + c)+d,$$

we have

> amplitude: 155
>
> period: $\dfrac{1}{60} = \dfrac{2\pi}{k}$, $\quad$ ∴ $\quad k = 120\,\pi$
>
> phase shift: none
>
> vertical translation: none

∴ the equation is

$$y = 155 \sin 120\, \pi t$$

Why do we say household current is 110 V if the amplitude is 155 V?

The instantaneous value of electrical voltage varies continuously from a maximum of 155 V in one direction through 0 to 155 V in the opposite direction and so on. Due to the symmetry of the sine function, the value of $y = 155 \sin 120\pi t$ averages 0 over each cycle. In order to avoid the zero value, electrical engineers have found it more convenient to describe alternating voltages in terms of an effective value called the root-mean-square (RMS) rather than in terms of the maximum values. It can be shown that the RMS value is $\dfrac{1}{\sqrt{2}}$ times the maximum value.

$$155 \times \frac{1}{\sqrt{2}} = \frac{155}{\sqrt{2}} \doteq 110$$

In general, for $y = a \sin k\theta$,

the root-mean-square (RMS) value is $\dfrac{|a|}{\sqrt{2}}$

EXERCISE 7-4

B **1.** State a defining equation for each of the following graphs.

(a)

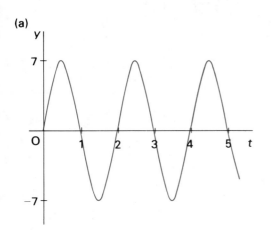

(b)

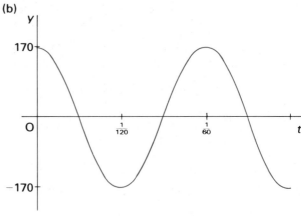

(c)

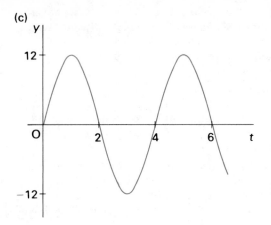

(d)

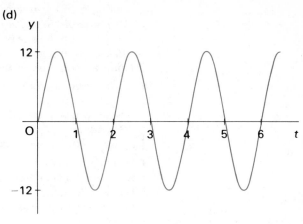

(e)

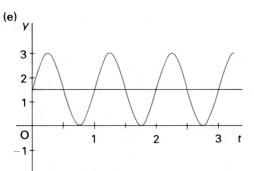

(f)

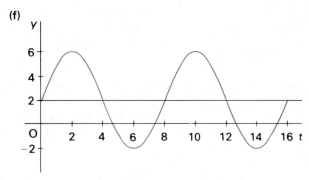

2. Temperature readings were recorded every 2 h over a 24 h period on an early summer day as in the following table.

time	temp °C
13:00	27.3
15:00	28.9
17:00	27.8
19:00	26.0
21:00	22.0
23:00	18.1
01:00	16.0
03:00	15.1
05:00	16.1
07:00	18.2
09:00	22.1
11:00	25.5
13:00	27.4

(a) Plot the data on a graph and draw a smooth curve through the points.
(b) Relate the graph to the general sine function

$$y = a \sin k(\theta + c) + d.$$

(c) Write the equation of the graph.
(d) Use the equation to find the temperature at (i) 04:00 (ii) 16:00 (iii) 20:30.

3. A ferris wheel has a diameter of 40 m and rotates once every 24 s.
(a) Draw a graph to show a person's height above or below the centre of rotation starting at the lowest position.
(b) Find an equation of the graph in (a).

4. During a spring tide on the Petitcodiac River, readings were taken and a range of 15 m was reported. Assuming the height of water with respect to mean sea-level is a sine function,
(a) draw a graph of the height of water over a 24 h period.
(b) find an equation of the graph in (a).

5. A small generator produces 17 V peak power at 25 Hz.
(a) Find the root-mean-square (RMS) voltage.
(b) Draw a graph showing 1 cycle, and also a horizontal line at the RMS reading.
(c) Find an equation of the graph.

6. A mass is suspended from a spring and allowed to bounce up and down. The distance from the high point to the low point is 20 cm and it takes 4 s to complete 5 cycles. The distance from the position of rest with respect to time is modelled by a sine function for the first few cycles.
(a) Draw a graph of this sine function.
(b) Write the equation that describes distance from the position of rest with respect to time.

7. A water wheel with radius 2 m has 0.2 m submerged and rotates at 5 r/min.
(a) Draw a graph showing two complete rotations taking the surface of the water at the horizontal axis.
(b) Write the equation of the sine function describing the height above the water taking the point at which the wheel touches the water at $t = 0$.

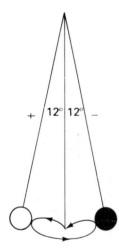

8. A grandfather clock pendulum swings making one period every 2 s, and an angle of 12° from the position of rest.
(a) Express the angle between the arm and the position of rest as a function of time, assuming the relationship is a sine function.
(b) Draw the graph of the above function for $0 \leqslant t \leqslant 6$, starting from the middle position.

9. A dual-voltage generator can generate electrical power at 220 V (RMS) and 60 Hz.
(a) Find the amplitude of the sine function that describes the voltage.
(b) Draw a graph showing 3 cycles.
(c) Find an equation of the graph.

10. During high tide, the water depth in a harbour is 22 m, and during low tide it is 10 m. (Assume a 12 h cycle.)
(a) Find an expression for water depth t hours after low tide.
(b) Draw a graph of the function for a 48 h period.
(c) State the times at which water level is at (i) maximum (ii) minimum (iii) mean sea-level.

11. A ferris wheel has a radius of 8 m and rotates once every 12 s. The bottom of the wheel is 1 m above the ground.
(a) Draw a graph to show a person's height above the ground starting at a position level with the centre.
(b) Find an equation of the graph in (a).

12. A small generator produces electricity at 110 V (RMS) and 60 Hz.
(a) Find the peak power generated.
(b) Draw a graph showing 4 cycles.
(c) Find an equation of the graph.

13. On a certain day, the depth of water off a pier at high-tide was 6 m. After 12 h the depth of the water was found to be 3 m.
(a) Find an equation expressing depth of water with respect to mean sea-level in terms of t hours since high-tide.
(b) Draw a graph for a 48 h period.
(c) Predict the depth of water at $t = 6, 15, 20, 30$.

14. A ferris wheel has a radius of 10 m and makes one revolution every 12 s. Draw a graph and find an equation to show a person's height above or below the centre of rotation starting at (a) A (b) B (c) C.

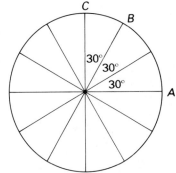

7.5   TRIGONOMETRIC IDENTITIES

An algebraic statement such as $3x + 2x = 5x$ is true for all values of x and is called an identity. It is not always obvious that both sides of an equation are identical and so a proof is required.

Reciprocal Formulas

$$1. \;\; \csc \theta = \frac{1}{\sin \theta} \qquad \frac{1}{\sin \theta} = \frac{1}{\frac{y}{r}} = \frac{r}{y} = \csc \theta$$

$$2. \;\; \sec \theta = \frac{1}{\cos \theta} \qquad \frac{1}{\cos \theta} = \frac{1}{\frac{x}{r}} = \frac{r}{x} = \sec \theta$$

$$3. \;\; \cot \theta = \frac{1}{\tan \theta} \qquad \frac{1}{\tan \theta} = \frac{1}{\frac{y}{x}} = \frac{x}{y} = \cot \theta$$

Quotient Formulas

$$4. \;\; \tan \theta = \frac{\sin \theta}{\cos \theta} \qquad \frac{\sin \theta}{\cos \theta} = \frac{\frac{y}{r}}{\frac{x}{r}} = \frac{y}{x} = \tan \theta$$

$$5. \;\; \cot \theta = \frac{\cos \theta}{\sin \theta} \qquad \frac{\cos \theta}{\sin \theta} = \frac{\frac{x}{r}}{\frac{y}{r}} = \frac{x}{y} = \cot \theta$$

Pythagorean Formulas

6. $\sin^2 \theta + \cos^2 \theta = 1$ $\qquad \sin^2 \theta + \cos^2 \theta = \dfrac{y^2}{r^2} + \dfrac{x^2}{r^2}$

$$= \dfrac{y^2 + x^2}{r^2}$$

$$= \dfrac{r^2}{r^2}$$

$$= 1$$

7. $1 + \tan^2 \theta = \sec^2 \theta$ $\qquad 1 + \tan^2 \theta = 1 + \dfrac{y^2}{x^2}$

$$= \dfrac{x^2 + y^2}{x^2}$$

$$= \dfrac{r^2}{x^2}$$

$$= \sec^2 \theta$$

8. $1 + \cot^2 \theta = \csc^2 \theta$ $\qquad 1 + \cot^2 \theta = 1 + \dfrac{x^2}{y^2}$

$$= \dfrac{y^2 + x^2}{y^2}$$

$$= \dfrac{r^2}{y^2}$$

$$= \csc^2 \theta$$

EXAMPLE 1. *Prove:* $\dfrac{1 + \cot \theta}{\csc \theta} = \sin \theta + \cos \theta$

Solution

$$\text{L.S.} = \dfrac{1 + \cot \theta}{\csc \theta} \qquad\qquad\qquad \text{R.S.} = \sin \theta + \cos \theta$$

$$= \dfrac{1 + \dfrac{\cos \theta}{\sin \theta}}{\dfrac{1}{\sin \theta}}$$

$$= \dfrac{\sin \theta}{1} \times \left(\dfrac{\sin \theta + \cos \theta}{\sin \theta} \right)$$

$$= \sin \theta + \cos \theta, \qquad \sin \theta \neq 0$$

$$\text{L.S.} = \text{R.S. and } \dfrac{1 + \cot \theta}{\csc \theta} = \sin \theta + \cos \theta$$

EXAMPLE 2. *Prove that* $\dfrac{\cos \theta - 1}{1 - \sec \theta} = \dfrac{\cos \theta + 1}{1 + \sec \theta}$

Solution

$$\text{L.S.} = \frac{\cos\theta - 1}{1 - \sec\theta} \qquad\qquad \text{R.S.} = \frac{\cos\theta + 1}{1 + \sec\theta}$$

$$= \frac{\cos\theta - 1}{1 - \sec\theta} \times \frac{\cos\theta}{\cos\theta} \qquad = \frac{\cos\theta + 1}{1 + \sec\theta} \times \frac{\cos\theta}{\cos\theta}$$

$$= \frac{(\cos\theta - 1)\cos\theta}{\cos\theta - \sec\theta\cos\theta} \qquad = \frac{(\cos\theta + 1)\cos\theta}{\cos\theta + \sec\theta\cos\theta}$$

$$= \frac{(\cos\theta - 1)\cos\theta}{\cos\theta - 1} \qquad = \frac{(\cos\theta + 1)\cos\theta}{\cos\theta + 1}$$

$$= \cos\theta, \quad \cos\theta \neq 1 \qquad = \cos\theta, \quad \cos\theta \neq -1$$

$$\text{L.S.} = \text{R.S.} \quad \text{and} \quad \frac{\cos\theta - 1}{1 - \sec\theta} = \frac{\cos\theta + 1}{1 + \sec\theta}$$

EXAMPLE 3. *Express each of the trigonometric ratios in terms of* $\cos\theta$.

Solution
(i) $\sin\theta$:

$$\sin^2\theta + \cos^2\theta = 1$$

$$\sin^2\theta = 1 - \cos^2\theta$$

$$\sin\theta = \pm\sqrt{1 - \cos^2\theta}$$

(ii) $\tan\theta$:

$$\tan\theta = \frac{\sin\theta}{\cos\theta}$$

$$= \frac{\pm\sqrt{1 - \cos^2\theta}}{\cos\theta}$$

Determine the pattern.
Find the missing number.

56	47	20	29
33	61	46	18
45	55	31	21
80	56	▨	25

(iii) $\csc\theta$:

$$\csc\theta = \frac{1}{\sin\theta}$$

$$= \pm\frac{1}{\sqrt{1 - \cos^2\theta}}$$

(iv) $\sec\theta$:

$$\sec\theta = \frac{1}{\cos\theta}$$

(v) $\cot\theta$:

$$\cot\theta = \frac{\cos\theta}{\sin\theta}$$

$$= \pm\frac{\cos\theta}{\sqrt{1 - \cos^2\theta}}$$

EXERCISE 7-5

A **1.** State an equivalent expression for

(a) $\sin^2 \theta$ (b) $\cos^2 \theta$ (c) $\tan^2 \theta$

(d) $\csc^2 \theta$ (e) $\sec^2 \theta$ (f) $\cot^2 \theta$

(g) $1 - \sin^2 \theta$ (h) $\sec^2 \theta - 1$ (i) $1 - \csc^2 \theta$

(j) $\sec^2 \theta - \tan^2 \theta$ (k) $\cot^2 \theta - \csc^2 \theta$ (l) $\dfrac{1}{\sec^2 \theta}$

(m) $\dfrac{-1}{\csc^2 \theta}$ (n) $\dfrac{\cos^2 \theta}{\sin^2 \theta}$ (o) $\cos^2 \theta - 1$

B Prove the following identities by the method of Examples 1 and 2.

2. $\cos \theta \times \tan \theta = \sin \theta$

3. $\dfrac{\cot \theta}{\tan \theta} = \dfrac{1 - \sin^2 \theta}{1 - \cos^2 \theta}$

4. $\cot^2 \theta = \dfrac{\cos^2 \theta}{1 - \cos^2 \theta}$

5. $\dfrac{\csc t}{\sec t} = \cot t$

6. $(\sin \theta + \cos \theta)^2 = 1 + 2 \sin \theta \cos \theta$

7. $2 \sin^2 \theta - 1 = \sin^2 \theta - \cos^2 \theta$

8. $\dfrac{1}{\sin^2 \theta} + \dfrac{1}{\cos^2 \theta} = \dfrac{1}{\sin^2 \theta \cos^2 \theta}$

9. $\cos^2 t = \sin^2 t + 2 \cos^2 t - 1$

10. $\tan \theta = \tan^2 \theta \times \cot \theta$

11. $\sec^2 \theta + \csc^2 \theta = \sec^2 \theta \times \csc^2 \theta$

12. $\dfrac{1}{1 + \sin \theta} + \dfrac{1}{1 - \sin \theta} = 2 \sec^2 \theta$

13. $\tan^2 x - \sin^2 x = \sin^2 x \tan^2 x$

14. $\cot^2 \theta + \sec^2 \theta = \tan^2 \theta + \csc^2 \theta$

15. $\dfrac{1 + 2 \sin \theta \cos \theta}{\sin \theta + \cos \theta} = \sin \theta + \cos \theta$

16. $\dfrac{\sec \theta + 1}{\sec \theta - 1} + \dfrac{\cos \theta + 1}{\cos \theta - 1} = 0$

17. $\dfrac{\tan \theta \sin \theta}{\tan \theta + \sin \theta} = \dfrac{\tan \theta - \sin \theta}{\tan \theta \sin \theta}$

18. $\dfrac{\csc \theta + \cot \theta}{\csc \theta - \cot \theta} = \dfrac{1 + 2 \cos \theta + \cos^2 \theta}{\sin^2 \theta}$

19. $\sin \theta \times \cos \theta \times \tan \theta = 1 - \cos^2 \theta$

20. $\sin \theta + \tan \theta = \tan \theta (1 + \cos \theta)$

21. $\tan x + \text{Cot } x = \sec x \ \csc x$

22. $\dfrac{\csc \theta}{\csc \theta - 1} + \dfrac{\csc \theta}{\csc \theta + 1} = 2 \sec^2 \theta$

23. $(1 - \cos^2 t)(1 + \cot^2 t) = 1$

24. $\sec^4 \theta - \tan^4 \theta = 1 + 2 \tan^2 \theta$

WORD LADDER

Start with the word "river" and change one letter at a time to form a new word until you reach "lakes". The best solution has the fewest steps.

r i v e r

_ _ _ _ _

_ _ _ _ _

_ _ _ _ _

_ _ _ _ _

_ _ _ _ _

l a k e s

25. $\dfrac{\cos \theta}{\sec \theta} - \dfrac{\sin \theta}{\cot \theta} = \dfrac{\cos \theta \cot \theta - \tan \theta}{\csc \theta}$

26. $\sin^4 \theta - \cos^4 \theta = 1 - 2\cos^2 \theta$

27. $\sec^2 \theta - \sin^2 \theta = \cos^2 \theta + \tan^2 \theta$

C Determine which of the following are identities:

28. $\cot \theta + \cos \theta = \dfrac{\cos \theta (1 + \sin \theta)}{\sin \theta}$

29. $\cot \theta + \cos \theta = \dfrac{2\cos \theta}{\sin \theta}$

30. $\cot \theta + \cos \theta = \tan \theta + \sin \theta$

7.6 TRIGONOMETRIC EQUATIONS

Equations such as $\sin \theta = 0.5$, $-2\pi \leqslant \theta \leqslant 2\pi$, are called trigonometric equations. To solve these equations, we must find all values of θ within the stated domain for which $\sin \theta = 0.5$.

EXAMPLE 1. *Solve* $\sin \theta = 0.5$, $-2\pi \leqslant \theta \leqslant 2\pi$.

Solution
We take the graph of $y = \sin \theta$, $-2\pi \leqslant \theta \leqslant 2\pi$, and a draw a horizontal line at $y = 0.5$ as in the diagram.

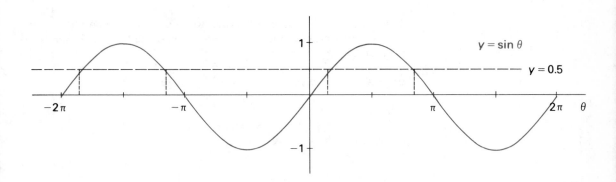

From the graph, we see that the horizontal line cuts the graph of
$y = \sin \theta$ at $\theta = -\dfrac{11\pi}{6}, -\dfrac{7\pi}{6}, \dfrac{\pi}{6}, \dfrac{5\pi}{6}$

$\therefore$ the solution set of $\sin \theta = 0.5$, $-2\pi \leqslant \theta \leqslant 2\pi$,

is $\left\{ \dfrac{-11\pi}{6}, \dfrac{-7\pi}{6}, \dfrac{\pi}{6}, \dfrac{5\pi}{6} \right\}$

$2n\pi \text{ rad} = (360n)^\circ$

If we remove the restriction $-2\pi \leqslant \theta \leqslant 2\pi$, the solution set is
$\left\{ \dfrac{\pi}{6} + 2n\pi, \dfrac{5\pi}{6} + 2n\pi \right\}$ where $n \in I$.

EXAMPLE 2. Solve $\cos^2 \theta - 1 = 0$, $\theta \in R$.

Solution
Since $\theta \in R$, we are looking for a general solution.

$$\cos^2 \theta - 1 = 0$$

$$(\cos \theta + 1)(\cos \theta - 1) = 0$$

$$\cos \theta + 1 = 0 \qquad \text{or} \quad \cos \theta - 1 = 0$$

$$\cos \theta = -1 \qquad\qquad \cos \theta = 1$$

$$\theta = \pi + 2n\pi \qquad\qquad \theta = 0 + 2n\pi$$

$$= (2n + 1)\pi$$

$$\text{where} \quad n \in I$$

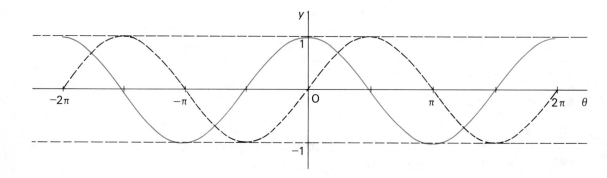

We add $2n\pi$, $n \in I$ to any solution to account for the periodic nature of the trigonometric functions, since it was given that $\theta \in R$. Hence the solution set is $\{k\pi \mid k \in I\}$.

EXAMPLE 3. Solve $\sqrt{2} \sin 2\theta = 1$, $0 \le \theta \le 3\pi$.

Solution
Since $0 \le \theta \le 3\pi$, then $0 \le 2\theta \le 6\pi$.
Considering the general solution:

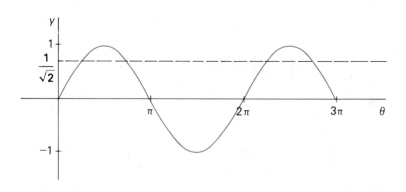

$$\sqrt{2} \sin 2\theta = 1$$

$$\sin 2\theta = \frac{1}{\sqrt{2}}$$

$$\therefore \quad 2\theta = \frac{\pi}{4} + 2n\pi \quad \text{or} \quad 2\theta = \frac{3\pi}{4} + 2n\pi$$

$$\theta = \frac{\pi}{8} + n\pi \qquad\qquad \theta = \frac{3\pi}{8} + n\pi$$

For $n = 0$, $\theta = \dfrac{\pi}{8}$ or $\dfrac{3\pi}{8}$

For $n = 1$, $\theta = \dfrac{9\pi}{8}$ or $\dfrac{11\pi}{8}$

For $n = 2$, $\theta = \dfrac{17\pi}{8}$ or $\dfrac{19\pi}{8}$

For $n > 2$, $\theta > 3\pi$, so that

the solution set is $\left\{\dfrac{\pi}{8}, \dfrac{3\pi}{8}, \dfrac{9\pi}{8}, \dfrac{11\pi}{8}, \dfrac{17\pi}{8}, \dfrac{19\pi}{8}\right\}$

As in Example 2, some trigonometric equations require an algebraic solution before the graphical method can be used. In some trigonometric equations it will be necessary to use the quadratic formula or tables.

EXERCISE 7-6

A 1. Solve for $0 \leqslant \theta \leqslant 2\pi$.

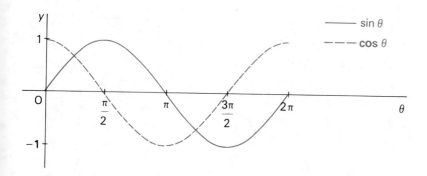

(a) $\sin \theta = 0$

(b) $\sin \theta = -1$

(c) $\cos \theta = 0.5$

(d) $\sin \theta = \dfrac{\sqrt{3}}{2}$

(e) $\cos \theta = -0.5$

(f) $\cos^2 \theta = 1$

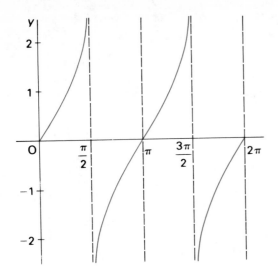

2. Solve for $\theta \in R$.
(a) $\tan \theta = 0$
(b) $\tan \theta = 1$
(c) $\tan 2\theta = 1$
(d) $\tan \theta = -1$
(e) $\tan \theta = -\sqrt{3}$

B Solve for $0 \leqslant \theta \leqslant 2\pi$ and then give the general solution.

3. $\cos \theta = 0.5$ **4.** $\sin \theta = -0.5$ **5.** $\tan \theta = 1$

6. $\cos 2\theta = 0$ **7.** $\sin 2\theta = 0.5$ **8.** $\tan 2\theta = -1$

9. $(\cos \theta + 0.5)(\cos \theta - 0.5) = 0$

10. $(\sin \theta - 0.5)(\sin \theta + 0.5) = 0$

11. $(\sin \theta - 1)(\tan \theta - 1) = 0$

12. $\sin \theta(\sin \theta + 1) = 0$

13. $\sin^2 \theta - 1 = 0$

14. $2 \cos^2 \theta + \cos \theta - 1 = 0$

15. $2 \sin^2 \theta + \sin \theta = 1$

16. $\sin 2\theta = -1$

17. $\cos 2\theta = 1$

18. $2 \sin 2\theta = 1$

19. $\cos^2 2\theta + \cos 2\theta = 0$

20. $\sin \frac{1}{2}\theta = 0.5$

C Solve the following.

21. $\sin 2\theta = 0.8910$

22. $4 \sin^2 \theta - 3 \sin \theta - 1 = 0$

23. $\sin^2 \theta - \cos^2 \theta = 0.25$

24. $\sin^2 \theta - 0.25 \sin \theta - 0.375 = 0$

25. $\sin 2\theta(\sin \theta - 1) = 0$

7.7 INVERSE TRIGONOMETRIC FUNCTIONS

The function $f(x) = \sin x$, $x \in R$ is not one-to-one and hence has no inverse, as shown using the horizontal line test. If we restrict the domain of f to $-\frac{\pi}{2} \leqslant x \leqslant \frac{\pi}{2}$, we define a new function $f(x) = \sin x$, $-\frac{\pi}{2} \leqslant x \leqslant \frac{\pi}{2}$. This new function is one-to-one and takes on all values that the function $f(x) = \sin x$ takes on. Because of the smaller domain, $f(x) = \sin x$, $-\frac{\pi}{2} \leqslant x \leqslant \frac{\pi}{2}$ takes on all values once and only once.

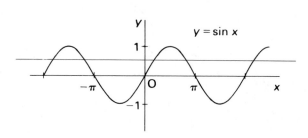

In Chapter 1, we denoted the inverse of $f(x)$ by the symbol $f^{-1}(x)$, and

$$y = f^{-1}(x) \quad \Leftrightarrow \quad f(y) = x$$

Here we shall write the inverse of $\sin x$, $-\frac{\pi}{2} \leqslant x \leqslant \frac{\pi}{2}$ as $\sin^{-1} x$ or $\arcsin x$

$$\left.\begin{array}{c} y = \sin^{-1} x \\ \text{or} \\ y = \arcsin x \end{array}\right\} \quad \Leftrightarrow \quad \sin y = x$$

In this text we use both $\sin^{-1} x$ and $\arcsin x$ and we read "the inverse sine of x" or "the number between $-\frac{\pi}{2}$ and $\frac{\pi}{2}$ whose sine is x."

EXAMPLE 1. *Evaluate* $y = \sin^{-1} 0.5$.

Solution
   We are looking for a number whose sine is 0.5. From previous work, we have

$$0.5 = \sin y$$
$$\sin y = 0.5 = \tfrac{1}{2}$$
$$\therefore \quad y = \frac{\pi}{6}$$

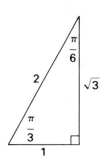

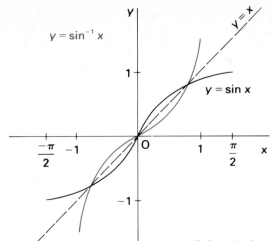

$y = \sin^{-1} x$

$y = \sin x$

The graph of $y = \sin^{-1} x$ is obtained by reflecting the graph of $y = \sin x$, $-\dfrac{\pi}{2} \leqslant x \leqslant \dfrac{\pi}{2}$ in the line $y = x$. The domain of $y = \sin x$ becomes the range of $y = \sin^{-1} x$, and likewise the range of $y = \sin x$ becomes the domain of $y = \sin^{-1} x$.

In defining the inverse functions for cosine and tangent we proceed as above, but restrict the functions to different intervals to obtain new one-to-one functions.

We restrict the cosine function to the interval

$$0 \leqslant x \leqslant \pi$$

to obtain the new function

$$y = \cos x, \qquad 0 \leqslant x \leqslant \pi$$

We reflect this graph in the line $y = x$ to obtain the graph of

$$y = \cos^{-1} x \quad \text{(also written } y = \arccos x)$$

We restrict the tangent function to the interval

$$-\dfrac{\pi}{2} < x < \dfrac{\pi}{2}$$

to obtain the new function

$$y = \tan x, \qquad -\dfrac{\pi}{2} < x < \dfrac{\pi}{2}$$

We reflect this graph in the line $y = x$ to obtain the graph of

$$y = \tan^{-1} x \quad \text{(also written } y = \arctan x)$$

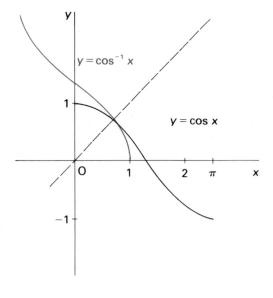

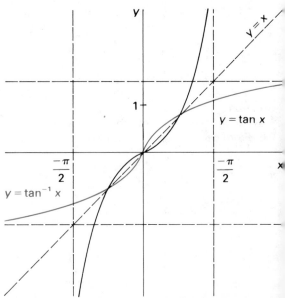

EXAMPLE 2. *Evaluate*

$$\text{(a)} \quad \sin^{-1}\frac{\sqrt{3}}{2} \qquad \text{(b)} \quad \sin{(\arccos 0.5)}$$

Solution

(a) $\sin^{-1}\dfrac{\sqrt{3}}{2} = \dfrac{\pi}{3}$ because $\sin\dfrac{\pi}{3} = \dfrac{\sqrt{3}}{2}$

(b) $\arccos 0.5 = \dfrac{\pi}{3}$ because $\cos\dfrac{\pi}{3} = 0.5$

$$\sin{(\arccos 0.5)} = \sin\frac{\pi}{3}$$

$$= \frac{\sqrt{3}}{2}$$

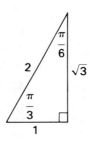

EXAMPLE 3. *Evaluate* $\cos{(\tan^{-1}5)}$

Solution

Let $\qquad\qquad \theta = \tan^{-1}5$

Then $\qquad\qquad \tan\theta = \frac{5}{1}$

If θ is the acute angle of a right triangle, then the side opposite is 5 units and the adjacent side is 1 unit so that the length of the hypotenuse is $\sqrt{26}$.

$$\therefore \quad \cos{(\tan^{-1}5)} = \cos\theta$$

$$= \frac{1}{\sqrt{26}}$$

EXERCISE 7-7

B 1. Evaluate.

(a) $\sin^{-1}\left(\dfrac{1}{\sqrt{2}}\right)$

(b) $\arccos\left(\frac{1}{2}\right)$

(c) $\arctan\dfrac{1}{\sqrt{3}}$

(d) $\cos^{-1}\left(\dfrac{\sqrt{3}}{2}\right)$

(e) $\arcsin\left(-\dfrac{1}{\sqrt{2}}\right)$

(f) $\arctan 1$

(g) $\arccos{(-0.5)}$

(h) $\tan^{-1}(-\sqrt{3})$

2. Evaluate:

(a) $\sin^{-1}0$

(b) $\cos^{-1}1$

(c) $\sin^{-1}\left(\dfrac{1}{\sqrt{2}}\right)$

(d) $\tan^{-1}1$

(e) $\tan^{-1}0$

(f) $\sin^{-1}\left(-\dfrac{1}{\sqrt{2}}\right)$

(g) $\tan^{-1} -1$ (h) $\cos^{-1} 0$

3. Evaluate the following.

(a) $\sin\left(\arccos\dfrac{1}{\sqrt{2}}\right)$ (b) $\tan(\cos^{-1} 0.5)$

(c) $\cos(\arctan 1)$ (d) $\sin(\cos^{-1} 0)$

(e) $\tan(\arcsin -\tfrac{1}{2})$ (f) $\cos(\tan^{-1} 2)$

(g) $\tan(\arctan 2)$ (h) $\cos\left(\sin^{-1}\left(\dfrac{\sqrt{3}}{2}\right)\right)$

(i) $\sin(\arctan \tfrac{4}{3})$ (j) $\cos(\sin^{-1} 0.6)$

4. State appropriate domains for x and sketch the graphs for

(a) $y = \csc^{-1} x$ (b) $y = \sec^{-1} x$ (c) $y = \cot^{-1} x$

5. Show the following.

(a) $\text{arccsc } u = \arcsin\dfrac{1}{u}$, where $u \geqslant 1$ or $u \leqslant -1$

(b) $\text{arcsec } u = \arccos\dfrac{1}{u}$, where $u \geqslant 1$ or $u \leqslant -1$

(c) $\cot^{-1} u = \tan^{-1}\dfrac{1}{u}$, where $u \in R$

7.8 ADDITION AND SUBTRACTION FORMULAS

We know

Find a four digit number in the form *xxyy* which is a perfect square.

$$\sin\frac{\pi}{6}=\frac{1}{2} \quad \text{and} \quad \sin\frac{\pi}{3}=\frac{\sqrt{3}}{2}$$

$$\therefore \sin\frac{\pi}{6}+\sin\frac{\pi}{3}=\frac{1}{2}+\frac{\sqrt{3}}{2}=\frac{1+\sqrt{3}}{2}$$

But

$$\sin\left(\frac{\pi}{6}+\frac{\pi}{3}\right)=\sin\frac{\pi}{2}=1$$

$$\therefore \sin\left(\frac{\pi}{6}+\frac{\pi}{3}\right)\neq \sin\frac{\pi}{6}+\sin\frac{\pi}{3}$$

In this section, we shall derive formulas for the sine and cosine of the sum and difference of two angles.

To derive formulas for functions of $\alpha + \beta$, we place the angles α and β with reference to coordinate axes as shown. Taking A on the terminal arm of $(\alpha + \beta)$ we draw the following perpendiculars—AD perpendicular to the terminal arm of α, $AB \perp OX$, $DC \perp OX$, $DE \perp AB$.

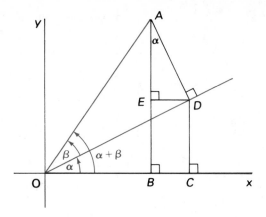

$$OB = OC - BC$$

But

$$\frac{OB}{OA} = \cos(\alpha + \beta) \Rightarrow OB = OA \cos(\alpha + \beta) \qquad ①$$

$$\frac{OC}{OD} = \cos\alpha \qquad \Rightarrow OC = OD \cos\alpha \qquad ②$$

In $\triangle AED$, $\angle EAD = \alpha$,

$$\therefore \quad \frac{ED}{AD} = \sin\alpha \Rightarrow ED = AD \sin\alpha$$

Since $\qquad BC = ED, \qquad BC = AD \sin\alpha \qquad ③$

Substituting ①, ② and ③ into $OB = OC - BC$,

$$OA \cos(\alpha + \beta) = OD \cos\alpha - AD \sin\alpha$$

Dividing by OA

$$\cos(\alpha + \beta) = \frac{OD}{OA} \cos\alpha - \frac{AD}{OA} \sin\alpha$$

But

$$\frac{OD}{OA} = \cos\beta \quad \text{and} \quad \frac{AD}{OA} = \sin\beta$$

Consequently

$$\boxed{\cos(\alpha + \beta) = \cos\alpha \cos\beta - \sin\alpha \sin\beta} \qquad \qquad \sin(-\theta) = -\sin\theta$$

Replacing β by $-\beta$, we have

$$\cos(\alpha + (-\beta)) = \cos\alpha \cos(-\beta) - \sin\alpha \sin(-\beta) \qquad \qquad \cos(-\theta) = \cos\theta$$

$$\boxed{\cos(\alpha - \beta) = \cos\alpha \cos\beta + \sin\alpha \sin\beta}$$

To develop formulas for $\sin(\alpha - \beta)$ and $\sin(\alpha + \beta)$ we replace α by $90° - \alpha$ and β by $-\beta$. Then

$$\cos((90° - \alpha) - \beta) = \cos(90° - \alpha)\cos\beta + \sin(90° - \alpha)\sin\beta$$

$$\cos(90° - (\alpha + \beta)) = \cos(90° - \alpha)\cos\beta + \sin(90° - \alpha)\sin\beta$$

Using $\cos(90° - \theta) = \sin\theta$ and $\sin(90° - \theta) = \cos\theta$ above, we get

$$\boxed{\sin(\alpha + \beta) = \sin\alpha\cos\beta + \cos\alpha\sin\beta}$$

Replacing β by $-\beta$, we get

$$\sin(\alpha - \beta) = \sin\alpha\cos(-\beta) + \cos\alpha\sin(-\beta)$$

or

$$\boxed{\sin(\alpha - \beta) = \sin\alpha\cos\beta - \cos\alpha\sin\beta}$$

These formulas are called the addition and subtraction formulas.

EXAMPLE 1. *Find $\sin 75°$ without using tables.*

Solution

Let $\alpha = 45°$ and $\beta = 30°$, and $\alpha + \beta = 75°$.

$$\sin(\alpha + \beta) = \sin\alpha\cos\beta + \cos\alpha\sin\beta$$

$$\sin 75° = \sin(45° + 30°)$$

$$= \sin 45°\cos 30° + \cos 45°\sin 30°$$

$$= \left(\frac{1}{\sqrt{2}}\right)\left(\frac{\sqrt{3}}{2}\right) + \left(\frac{1}{\sqrt{2}}\right)\left(\frac{1}{2}\right)$$

$$= \frac{1}{\sqrt{2}}\left(\frac{\sqrt{3} + 1}{2}\right)$$

$$= \tfrac{1}{4}(\sqrt{6} + \sqrt{2})$$

EXAMPLE 2. *Find a formula for $\tan(\alpha + \beta)$*

Solution

$$\tan(\alpha + \beta) = \frac{\sin(\alpha + \beta)}{\cos(\alpha + \beta)} = \frac{\sin\alpha\cos\beta + \cos\alpha\sin\beta}{\cos\alpha\cos\beta - \sin\alpha\sin\beta}$$

Dividing numerator and denominator by $\cos\alpha\cos\beta$

$$\tan(\alpha + \beta) = \frac{\dfrac{\sin\alpha\cos\beta}{\cos\alpha\cos\beta} + \dfrac{\cos\alpha\sin\beta}{\cos\alpha\cos\beta}}{\dfrac{\cos\alpha\cos\beta}{\cos\alpha\cos\beta} - \dfrac{\sin\alpha\sin\beta}{\cos\alpha\cos\beta}}$$

which reduces to

$$\tan (\alpha + \beta) = \frac{\tan \alpha + \tan \beta}{1 - \tan \alpha \tan \beta}$$

Replacing β by $(-\beta)$, we get

$$\tan (\alpha - \beta) = \frac{\tan \alpha - \tan \beta}{1 + \tan \alpha \tan \beta}$$

$\tan (-\theta) = -\tan \theta$

We can also use the addition formulas to find the functions of twice an angle as in the following example.

EXAMPLE 3. *Develop a formula for* $\cos 2\alpha$.

Solution

$$\cos (\alpha + \beta) = \cos \alpha \cos \beta - \sin \alpha \sin \beta$$

Replacing β by α, we have

$$\cos (\alpha + \alpha) = \cos \alpha \cos \alpha - \sin \alpha \sin \alpha$$

$$\cos 2\alpha = \cos^2 \alpha - \sin^2 \alpha$$

EXERCISE 7-8

B **1.** Find (a) $\cos 75°$ (b) $\tan 75°$ without using tables.

2. Find (a) $\sin 15°$ (b) $\cos 15°$ (c) $\tan 15°$ without using tables.

3. Prove the formulas for (a) $\sin (90° + \theta)$, (b) $\cos (90° + \theta)$ (c) $\tan (90° + \theta)$ by means of addition formulas.

4. Prove the formulas for (a) $\sin (180° - \theta)$ (b) $\cos (180° - \theta)$ (c) $\tan (180° - \theta)$ by means of subtraction formulas.

5. Simplify.
(a) $\sin (\theta + 30°) + \cos (\theta + 60°)$
(b) $\sin (\theta + 60°) - \cos (\theta + 30°)$
(c) $\cos (30° - \theta) - \cos (30° + \theta)$

6. Prove the identities:
(a) $\sin (\alpha + \beta) \times \sin (\alpha - \beta) = \sin^2 \alpha - \sin^2 \beta$
(b) $\cos (\alpha + \beta) \times \cos (\alpha - \beta) = \cos^2 \alpha - \sin^2 \beta$

7. Given $\sin \alpha = \frac{5}{13}$ and $\sin \beta = \frac{4}{5}$, and both α and β are acute, find
(a) $\sin (\alpha + \beta)$ (b) $\cos (\alpha + \beta)$ (c) $\tan (\alpha + \beta)$
(d) $\sin (\alpha - \beta)$ (e) $\cos (\alpha - \beta)$ (f) $\tan (\alpha - \beta)$
(g) $\sin (\beta - \alpha)$ (h) $\cos (90° - \alpha)$ (i) $\sin (90° - \alpha)$

C **8.** (a) Develop formulas for $\cot (\alpha + \beta)$ and $\cot (\alpha - \beta)$.
(b) Find $\cot 75° + \cot 15°$ without using tables.

9. (a) Develop a formula for $\sin 2\alpha$

(b) Without using tables, find $\sin 120° + \sin 45°$

(c) Find $\sin 2\alpha$ if $\sin \alpha = \frac{8}{17}$

10. (a) Develop formulas for (i) $\tan 2\alpha$ (ii) $\cot 2\alpha$

(b) Find $\tan 2\alpha$ if $\tan \alpha = \frac{3}{4}$

(c) Find $\cot 2\alpha$ if $\cot \alpha = \frac{12}{5}$

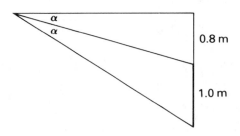

0.8 m

1.0 m

11. The top of a picture 1 m high is 0.8 m down from the ceiling. At a certain point on the ceiling directly in front of the picture, we wish to install a light so that the angle subtended by the picture equals the angle of depression of the top of the picture. How far out from the wall should the light be installed?

7.9 POLAR COORDINATES

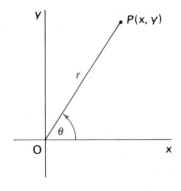

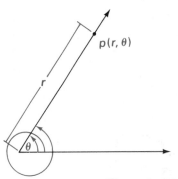

In a Cartesian coordinate system we identify each point in the plane according to a unique ordered pair of real numbers (x, y). We can also locate a point according to its distance from the origin and direction from the positive x-axis. If $P(x, y)$ is a point in the plane, r units from the origin, with $\angle POX = \theta$, then the ordered pair (r, θ) identifies the point in the plane. The components (r, θ) are called a pair of polar coordinates of P. The positive x-axis is the polar axis and the origin is called the pole.

In such a coordinate system, the angle θ is coterminal with infinitely many angles so that the location of P can be given by any of the ordered pairs

$$(r, \theta + 2\pi n) \quad \text{or} \quad (r, \theta + 360°n), \quad n \in I.$$

In polar coordinates the coordinates of the pole are $(0, \theta)$ for all values of θ.

The ordered pair (r, θ) is associated with one and only one point of the plane, but due to the cyclical nature of a polar coordinate system each point of the plane determines any number of ordered pairs (r, θ).

We can relate the polar coordinate system to the Cartesian system by letting the polar axis coincide with the positive *x*-axis so that the pole is at the origin. The polar and Cartesian coordinates of any point, *P*, are related by

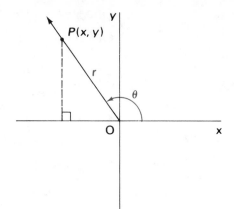

$$x = r \cos \theta$$
$$y = r \sin \theta$$

since $\cos \theta = \dfrac{x}{r}$ and $\sin \theta = \dfrac{y}{r}$

EXAMPLE 1. *Find the Cartesian coordinates of the point P with polar coordinates*

(a) (5, 120°)   (b) (7, −150°)

Solution
(a)

$x = r \cos \theta$	$y = r \sin \theta$
$= 5 \cos 120°$	$= 5 \sin 120°$
$= 5(-\tfrac{1}{2})$	$= 5\left(\dfrac{\sqrt{3}}{2}\right)$
$= -2.5$	$= \dfrac{5\sqrt{3}}{2}$
	$\doteq 4.33$

∴ the Cartesian coordinates are (−2.5, 4.33)

(b)

$x = r \cos \theta$	$y = r \sin \theta$
$= 7 \cos (-150°)$	$= 7 \sin (-150°)$
$= 7(-\cos 30°)$	$= 7(-\sin 30°)$
$\doteq -6.06$	$= -3.5$

∴ the Cartesian coordinates are (−6.06, −3.5)

We can find the polar coordinates of any point with Cartesian coordinates (*x, y*).

$$r^2 = x^2 + y^2$$

$$r = \pm\sqrt{x^2+y^2}, \quad \cos \theta = \frac{x}{\pm\sqrt{x^2+y^2}}, \quad \sin \theta = \frac{y}{\pm\sqrt{x^2+y^2}}$$

EXAMPLE 2. *Find a pair of polar coordinates of the point whose Cartesian coordinates are $\left(-\dfrac{1}{\sqrt{2}}, \dfrac{1}{\sqrt{2}}\right)$.*

Solution
(a) Using the above equations,

$$r = \pm\sqrt{\left(-\frac{1}{\sqrt{2}}\right)^2 + \left(\frac{1}{\sqrt{2}}\right)^2} = \pm\sqrt{\tfrac{1}{2}+\tfrac{1}{2}} = \pm 1$$

$$\cos\theta = \frac{x}{r} = \frac{-\dfrac{1}{\sqrt{2}}}{+1} = -\frac{1}{\sqrt{2}} \quad\text{OR}\quad \cos\theta = \frac{x}{r} = \frac{-\dfrac{1}{\sqrt{2}}}{-1} = \frac{1}{\sqrt{2}}$$

$$\therefore \quad \theta = 135° \qquad\qquad\qquad \therefore \quad \theta = 315°$$

One set of coordinates is   Another set of coordinates is

$$(1, 135°) \qquad\qquad\qquad\qquad (-1, 315°)$$

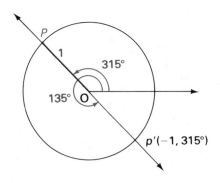

The polar coordinates $P(1, 135°)$ and $P(-1, 315°)$ are associated with the same point as shown in the accompanying diagram. Note that $P(-1, 315°)$ is the reflection of $P'(1, 315°)$ in the pole.

Equations such as $r = 2\sin\theta$, or $r = 5\cos\theta$ are called polar equations. These equations generate ordered pairs of the form (r, θ) and we can draw their graphs.

EXAMPLE 3. *Sketch the graph of $r = 2\sin\theta$*

Solution
We first plot a table of values:

θ	0°	30°	45°	60°	90°	120°	135°	150°	180°	210°
r	0	1	$\sqrt{2}$	$\sqrt{3}$	2	$\sqrt{3}$	$\sqrt{2}$	1	0	1
decimal approximation	0	1	1.4	1.7	2	1.7	1.4	1	0	1

Plotting these values in succession, produces the graph at right. The student should check that these values are repeated for $180° \leqslant \theta \leqslant 360°$. We join the points with a smooth curve to produce the required graph.

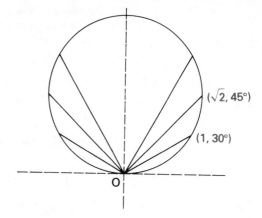

$(\sqrt{2}, 45°)$

$(1, 30°)$

In Example 4, we show how to transform equations from Cartesian form into polar form.

EXAMPLE 4. *Transform* $2x - 3y + 5 = 0$ *into an equation in polar form.*

Solution
We substitute $x = r \cos \theta$ and $y = r \sin \theta$ into the equation and solve for r.

$$2x - 3y + 5 = 0$$
$$2(r \cos \theta) - 3(r \sin \theta) + 5 = 0$$
$$r(2 \cos \theta - 3 \sin \theta) = -5$$
$$\therefore \ r = \frac{-5}{2 \cos \theta - 3 \sin \theta}$$

is the required equation.
To transform an equation in polar form into Cartesian form, we substitute

$$r = \pm\sqrt{x^2 + y^2}, \quad \sin \theta = \frac{y}{\pm\sqrt{x^2 + y^2}}, \quad \cos \theta = \frac{x}{\pm\sqrt{x^2 + y^2}}$$

EXERCISE 7-9

B 1. Find the Cartesian coordinates of the point with the given polar coordinates.

(a) $(3, 30°)$ (b) $(5, 45°)$ (c) $(4, 90°)$ (d) $(7, 150°)$
(e) $(4, -120°)$ (f) $(3, -180°)$ (g) $(2, 225°)$ (h) $(5, -330°)$

(i) $\left(5, \frac{\pi}{6}\right)$ (j) $(3, \pi)$ (k) $\left(3, \frac{3\pi}{2}\right)$ (l) $\left(5, -\frac{9\pi}{4}\right)$

(m) $(-3, 135°)$ (n) $(-5, -225°)$ (o) $\left(-2, \frac{3\pi}{4}\right)$ (p) $(-2, -\pi)$

2. Find two sets of polar coordinates for the point whose Cartesian coordinates are given, $-180° \le \theta \le 180°$.

(a) $(4, 4)$ (b) $(-3, 0)$ (c) $(0, 4)$ (d) $\left(\dfrac{\sqrt{3}}{2}, \dfrac{1}{2}\right)$

(e) $(3, 4)$ (f) $(5, 12)$ (g) $(-5, 12)$ (h) $(6, -8)$

(i) $\left(-\dfrac{\sqrt{3}}{2}, -\dfrac{1}{2}\right)$ (j) $\left(-\dfrac{5}{2}, -\dfrac{5\sqrt{3}}{2}\right)$ (k) $\left(\dfrac{3}{\sqrt{2}}, -\dfrac{3}{\sqrt{2}}\right)$ (l) $(8, -6)$

C 3. Graph the curves defined by

(a) $r = 4$ (b) $r = 2\cos\theta$ (c) $r = 1 - \sin\theta$
(d) $r = 1 + \sin\theta$ (e) $r = 2 - \cos\theta$ (f) $r = 1 - \cos\theta$

4. Graph the curves defined by

(a) $r = \sin 2\theta$ (b) $r = \sin 3\theta$ (c) $r = 2\cos 2\theta$
(d) $r = \tan\theta$ (e) $r = 3(1 - \sin\theta)$ (f) $r = 2(1 - \cos\theta)$

5. Graph the spiral of Archimedes defined by $r = \theta$.

6. Transform the following equations into polar form.
(a) $x - y - 1 = 0$ (b) $2x + 5y - 2 = 0$
(c) $x^2 + y^2 = 4$ (d) $y = 2x^2$

7. Transform the following equations into Cartesian form.
(a) $r = 2\sin\theta$ (b) $r = 3\cos\theta$

REVIEW EXERCISE

B 1. Convert the following degree measures to radian measure.
(a) $60°$ (b) $215°$ (c) $410°$ (d) $85°24'$ (e) $130°48'$

2. Convert the following radian measures to degree measure.
(a) $\dfrac{3\pi}{4}$ (b) $\dfrac{11\pi}{6}$ (c) $\dfrac{17\pi}{3}$ (d) $\dfrac{7\pi}{5}$ (e) $\dfrac{4\pi}{3}$

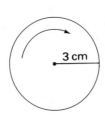
3 cm

3. A pulley makes 10 rotations in 1 s.
(a) Find the angular velocity in radians per second.
(b) How far does a point on the circumference travel in 1 s?

4. Sketch the following graphs on the same axes for $0 \le \theta \le 2\pi$.
(a) $y = \sin\theta$ and $y = |\sin\theta|$
(b) $y = \cos\theta$ and $y = -\cos\theta$
(c) $y = \tan\theta$ and $y = |\tan\theta|$

5. Sketch the graphs of the following functions.
(a) $y = 2\sin 3\theta$, $-\pi \le \theta \le 2\pi$.
(b) $y = \cos 2\left(\theta - \dfrac{\pi}{2}\right)$, $-2\pi \le \theta \le \pi$
(c) $y = 2\sin\frac{1}{2}(x + \pi)$, $-2\pi \le x \le 4\pi$
(d) $y = \sin(2\theta - \pi)$, $-\pi \le \theta \le 3\pi$

6. Write an equation and sketch the graph of the sine functions with the properties:

(a) amplitude 1, period π, phase shift $\dfrac{\pi}{2}$ left.

(b) amplitude 3, period π, phase shift $\dfrac{\pi}{3}$ right.

(c) amplitude 2, period 2π,

(d) amplitude $\frac{1}{2}$, period $\frac{1}{2}$, phase shift $\dfrac{\pi}{2}$ right.

7. A carnival ferris wheel with a radius of 9.5 m rotates once every 10 s. The bottom of the wheel is 1.2 m above the ground.
(a) Find the equations of the sine function that gives the rider's height above the ground with respect to time, starting at the bottom of the wheel.
(b) Sketch the graph showing three complete cycles.

8. In a colour television set, the alternating current is rated at 20 000 V (RMS) and 6000 Hz.
(a) Find the peak voltage.
(b) Write the equation of the sine function that describes this electrical power.

9. The electrical current (in amperes) in a circuit is given by the function

$$y = 5 \sin 120 \, \pi t$$

(a) State the values of t for which y is (i) a maximum (ii) a minimum.
(b) Find the effective current (RMS).
(c) Sketch the graph showing three complete cycles.

10. Prove the following identities:

(a) $2 \csc^2 \theta = \dfrac{1}{1 - \cos \theta} + \dfrac{1}{1 + \cos \theta}$

(b) $\tan \theta \cot \theta = \sec \theta \cos \theta$

(c) $\sin^4 \theta - \cos^4 \theta = 2 \sin^2 \theta - 1$

(d) $\dfrac{1}{1 + \cos \theta} = \csc^2 \theta - \csc \theta \cot \theta$

(e) $\dfrac{1 + \sin \theta + \cos \theta}{1 - \sin \theta + \cos \theta} = \dfrac{1 + \sin \theta}{\cos \theta}$

11. Solve for $0 \leqslant \theta \leqslant 2\pi$, then give the general solution.

(a) $\sin \theta = \dfrac{\sqrt{3}}{2}$ (b) $\cos \theta = -\sqrt{0.5}$ (c) $\tan \theta = -1$

(d) $\sin 2\theta = 1$ (e) $2 \sin \theta = 1$ (f) $\cos 2\theta = 0$

(g) $\sin \theta (2 \sin \theta - 1) = 0$

(h) $\sin^2 \theta - 1 = 0$

(i) $2 \sin^2 \theta - \sin \theta - 1 = 0$

12. Evaluate.

(a) $\arcsin \dfrac{\sqrt{3}}{2}$ (b) $\cos^{-1} \left(-\dfrac{1}{\sqrt{2}} \right)$ (c) $\arctan (-1)$

(d) $\sin^{-1} 1$ (e) $\arccos (-0.5)$ (f) $\operatorname{arcsec} \sqrt{2}$

13. (a) Express $(7, 210°)$ in Cartesian form.
(b) Express $(-5, 5)$ in polar form.

14. (a) Graph the curve defined by $r = 2(1 + \sin \theta)$.
(b) Transform $x^2 + y^2 = 25$ into an equation in polar form.

REVIEW AND PREVIEW TO CHAPTER 8

EXERCISE 1. EXPONENTS

$$a^m \times a^n = a^{m+n} \qquad\qquad a^m \div a^n = a^{m-n} \qquad\qquad (a^m)^n = a^{mn}$$

$$a^0 = 1 \qquad\qquad\qquad\quad a^{-n} = \frac{1}{a^n} \qquad\qquad\qquad a^{\frac{1}{n}} = \sqrt[n]{a}$$

$$(ab)^n = a^n b^n \qquad\qquad \left(\frac{a}{b}\right)^n = \frac{a^n}{b^n} \qquad\qquad a^{\frac{p}{q}} = \sqrt[q]{a^p} = (\sqrt[q]{a})^p$$

Simplify.

1. (a) $3a^5 \times 2a^3$ (b) $12x^7 \div 3x^4$ (c) $(2y^4)^3$ (d) $(3a^5b^2)^0$

2. (a) $3x^{-5} \times 5x^4$ (b) $\sqrt[4]{16x^4y^8}$ (c) $(a^4b^6)^{\frac{3}{2}}$ (d) $(3a^0b^3)^{\frac{1}{3}}$

3. (a) $\left(\dfrac{x^3}{y^0}\right)^2$ (b) $\dfrac{a^0}{b^0}$ (c) $(x^3)^{\frac{2}{3}}$ (d) $\sqrt{32a^5b^{10}}$

4. (a) $(a+b)^2$ (b) $(1+0.02)^2$ (c) $(1+0.03)^2$ (d) $(1.04)^2$

5. (a) $\dfrac{2^{-1}+3^{-1}}{2^{-1}-3^{-1}}$ (b) $\dfrac{3(5^2-1)}{5-1}$ (c) $\dfrac{2(1-3^3)}{1-3}$

   (d) $4^{\frac{3}{2}} - 2^0 + \left(\frac{1}{4}\right)^{-\frac{1}{2}}$ (e) $\left(\frac{3}{2}\right)^{-2} + \frac{4}{9}$ (f) $5^0 - 9^{\frac{1}{2}} - \left(\frac{1}{81}\right)^{-\frac{1}{4}}$

   (g) $\dfrac{3^{-1}}{3^{-2}+3^{-3}}$ (h) $\dfrac{2^{-1} \times 3^{-1}}{2^{-1}+3^{-1}}$ (i) $4^{\frac{1}{2}} \times \dfrac{2^{-1}}{2^{-2}}$

6. Solve the following equations:

   (a) $3^x = 9$ (b) $2^x = \frac{1}{4}$ (c) $3^{-x} = 27$

   (d) $8^x = 64$ (e) $4^x = 64$ (f) $2^x = 64$

   (g) $\left(\frac{3}{2}\right)^x = \frac{8}{27}$ (h) $2 \times 3^x = 162$ (i) $4^x = 8^5$

   (j) $3^{x+1} = 81$ (k) $5^x = 1$ (l) $0.5^x = 0.0625$

7. Express as the logarithm of a single number.

   (a) $\log a + \log b - \log c$

   (b) $\frac{1}{2}\log a - 2(\log a + \log b)$

   (c) $2\log a + 3\log b - 5\log c$

   (d) $3\log a - 2\log b + \log c$

   (e) $x\log a + y\log b - \log(a+b)$

   (f) $2\log(a+b) - 2(\log a - \log b)$

EXERCISE 2. SIMPLE INTEREST

Interest $I = Prt$ $\begin{cases} P = \text{principal} \\ r = \text{rate of interest} \\ t = \text{time} \end{cases}$

Amount $A = P + I$

1. Find the simple interest payable
(a) on $250 for 6 months at 8%/a
(b) on $3000 for 1.5a at 9%/a
(c) on $2200 for 3.5a at 11%/a

2. Find the amount due at simple interest
(a) on $500 for 3a at 9%/a
(b) on $750 for 2.5a at $8\frac{1}{2}$%/a
(c) on $2000 for 2a at 10%/a

3. Find the simple interest and amount payable
(a) on $890 for 90 days at 9%/a
(b) on $995 for 83 days at 11%/a
(c) on $1490 for 126 days at 12%/a

4. Find the rate of simple interest if
(a) the interest on $350 for 6 months is $14.00
(b) the interest on $2000 for 81 days is $39.95
(c) the interest on $2995 for 3a is $898.50

5. Find the time period if the interest
(a) on $250 at 8%/a is $40.00
(b) on $3500 at 11%/a is $1347.50
(c) on $1995 at 12%/a is $72.15

CHAPTER 8

Sequences and Series

Wherever there is number, there is beauty.

Proclus

When money is deposited on a regular basis, or a ball bounces, or a rocket is launched, or a body or plant grows, patterns occur. We can express these patterns mathematically, often using sequences and series. These same sequences and series are important later in our work with limits—the underlying idea of calculus.

8.1 SEQUENCES

Sandra buys a stereo paying $100 as a down payment, and then $10 every week until paid. We can express her payment plan as in the following table:

Week	1st	2nd	3rd	...	nth
Payment	$100	$10	$10	...	$10
Amount	$100	$110	$120	...	

$N = \{1, 2, 3, \ldots\}$

This table represents a function whose domain is a subset of the natural numbers.

> **Sequence**
> A sequence is a function whose domain is a subset of the natural numbers. The values in the range of the function are called the terms of the sequence.

The table can then be written:

n	1	2	3	...	n
$f(n)$	100	$100 + 10$	$100 + 20$	...	$100 + (n-1)10$

We use three dots to indicate that there are more terms than have been written. When we use the three dots we must be careful not to assume terms that are not there. For example, if we write

$$1, 2, 3, 4, \ldots$$

we cannot assume that the next term is 5 unless we know more about the sequence.

The sequence defined by

$$f(n) = n + (n-1)(n-2)(n-3)(n-4)(n^2+1)$$

has 1, 2, 3, 4 as its first four terms. However the fifth term is 629.

The terms of a sequence are often named using a single letter

$$t_1, t_2, t_3, t_4, \ldots, t_n$$

where t_n is the nth term or general term of the sequence. Relating this notation to our function notation

$$t_1 = f(1), t_2 = f(2), t_3 = f(3), \ldots, \text{and } t_n = f(n)$$

EXAMPLE 1. *Find the first 5 terms, given*

(a) $t_n = 2n + 1$ (b) $t_n = n^2 - 1$
(c) $f(n) = 3 - 2n$ (d) $f: x \rightarrow 2x$

Solution

(a) $t_n = 2n + 1$
$t_1 = 2(1) + 1 = 3$
$t_2 = 2(2) + 1 = 5$
$t_3 = 2(3) + 1 = 7$
$t_4 = 2(4) + 1 = 9$
$t_5 = 2(5) + 1 = 11$

(b) $t_n = n^2 - 1$
$t_1 = 1^2 - 1 = 0$
$t_2 = 2^2 - 1 = 3$
$t_3 = 3^2 - 1 = 8$
$t_4 = 4^2 - 1 = 15$
$t_5 = 5^2 - 1 = 24$

(c) $f(n) = 3 - 2n$
$f(1) = 3 - 2(1) = 1$
$f(2) = 3 - 2(2) = -1$
$f(3) = 3 - 2(3) = -3$
$f(4) = 3 - 2(4) = -5$
$f(5) = 3 - 2(5) = -7$

(d) $f: x \rightarrow 2x$
$f: 1 \rightarrow 2(1) = 2$
$f: 2 \rightarrow 2(2) = 4$
$f: 3 \rightarrow 2(3) = 6$
$f: 4 \rightarrow 2(4) = 8$
$f: 5 \rightarrow 2(5) = 10$

It is sometimes more convenient to describe the pattern of a sequence in terms of getting from one term to the next, rather than stating a general term. Given the terms of a sequence

$$1, 4, 7, 10, 13, \ldots$$

we can express the pattern using a recursion formula:

$$t_1 = 1$$

$$t_{n+1} = t_n + 3, \quad n \in N$$

This means that the first term, $t_1 = 1$, and that we add 3 to the nth term to get the $(n+1)$th term.

EXAMPLE 2. *Find the first five terms determined by the following recursion formulas:*

(a) $t_1 = 3$

$t_n = t_{n-1} - 2, n > 1$

(b) $t_1 = -2$

$t_{n+1} = t_n + (2n - 1)$

(c) $t_1 = 1$, $t_2 = 1$

$t_n = t_{n-1} + t_{n-2}$, $n > 2$

Solution

(a) $t_1 = 3$

$n = 2$, $t_2 = t_1 - 2 = 3 - 2 = 1$

$n = 3$, $t_3 = t_2 - 2 = 1 - 2 = -1$

$n = 4$, $t_4 = t_3 - 2 = -3 - 2 = -5$

$n = 5$, $t_5 = t_4 - 2 = -5 - 2 = -7$

∴ the first five terms are
3, 1, −1, −5, −7

(b) $t_1 = -2$

$n = 1$, $t_2 = t_1 + (2(1) - 1) = -2 + 1 = -1$

$n = 2$, $t_3 = t_2 + (2(2) - 1) = -1 + 3 = 2$

$n = 3$, $t_4 = t_3 + (2(3) - 1) = 2 + 5 = 7$

$n = 4$, $t_5 = t_4 + (2(4) - 1) = 7 + 7 = 14$

∴ the first five terms are
−2, −1, 2, 7, 14

(c) $t_1 = 1$, $t_2 = 1$

$t_n = t_{n-1} + t_{n-2}$, $n > 2$

$n = 3$, $t_3 = t_2 + t_1 = 1 + 1 = 2$

$n = 4$, $t_4 = t_3 + t_2 = 2 + 1 = 3$

$n = 5$, $t_5 = t_4 + t_3 = 3 + 2 = 5$

∴ the first five terms are
1, 1, 2, 3, 5

This is called the Fibonacci sequence, named after the Italian mathematician, Leonardo Fibonacci. The Fibonacci sequence is often seen in patterns involving growth of leaves on a stem, or the seed spirals in a sunflower.

EXERCISE 8-1

A 1. State the first five terms of the sequence whose *n*th term is given.

(a) $t_n = 2n$

(b) $t_n = 1 - 2n$

(c) $t_n = 2^n$

(d) $t_n = 2^{n-1}$

(e) $t_n = n^2$

(f) $t_n = 3(2^n)$

(g) $t_n = 1 + 2n$

(h) $t_n = 1 + 2(n - 1)$

(i) $t_n = \dfrac{1}{n}$

(j) $t_n = \dfrac{n+1}{n}$

(k) $t_n = 2^{-n}$

(l) $t_n = \dfrac{n-1}{2^n}$

2. State a possible rule that determines the following terms. Use your rule to find the next three terms.

(a) 5, 10, 15, 20, ...

(b) 5, 25, 125, ...

(c) 2, 4, 6, 8, ...

(d) 1, 3, 5, 7, ...

(e) 1, 4, 9, 16, ...

(f) 1, 3, 9, 27, ...

(g) $1, \frac{1}{2}, \frac{1}{3}, \frac{1}{4}, \dots$

(h) $1, \frac{1}{2}, \frac{2}{3}, \frac{3}{4}, \dots$

(i) $2, -1, \frac{1}{2}, -\frac{1}{4}, \dots$

(j) $a, 2a, 3a, 4a, \dots$

(k) $a, ar, ar^2, ar^3, \dots$

(l) $1, 1 + d, 1 + 2d, \dots$

B 3. List the first five terms of the sequences determined by each of the following.

(a) $t_n = 3n$

(b) $t_n = 2n - 5$

(c) $t_n = (n + 1)(n - 1)$

(d) $t_n = 3^n$

(e) $t_n = 3^{n-1}$

(f) $t_n = 3^n - 1$

(g) $t_n = (-1)^n$

(h) $t_n = (-1)^{n+1} 3n$

(i) $t_n = 2n - 3$

(j) $t_n = \dfrac{n-1}{n+1}$ (k) $t_n = \dfrac{n}{2}(n+1)$ (l) $t_n = \dfrac{n(n-1)}{2n+1}$

4. List the first five terms of the sequences determined by the following functions.

(a) $f(n) = 2n - 1$ (b) $f(n) = 2n$ (c) $f(k) = (-2)^k$

(d) $f(k) = \dfrac{2k}{2k-1}$ (e) $f(n) = \dfrac{1}{n}$ (f) $f(k) = 2^{-k}$

(g) $f : n \to 5n - 3$ (h) $f : k \to k^2$ (i) $f : k \to 2^k$

(j) $f : n \to \dfrac{n-1}{n+1}$ (k) $f : k \to \dfrac{k}{2}(k-1)$ (l) $f : n \to \dfrac{n^2-1}{n}$

5. Find a general term that determines the following sequences, then list the next three terms.

(a) $1, 2, 3, 4, \ldots$ (b) $4, 3, 2, 1, \ldots$

(c) $2, -1, \frac{1}{2}, -\frac{1}{4}, \ldots$ (d) $\frac{1}{8}, \frac{1}{4}, \frac{1}{2}, 1, \ldots$

(e) $4, 8, 16, 32, \ldots$ (f) $4, 1, -2, -5, \ldots$

(g) $1, -1, 1, -1, \ldots$ (h) $2, 6, 10, 14, \ldots$

(i) $2, 6, 18, 54, \ldots$ (j) $1, x, x^2, x^3, \ldots$

(k) $3a + b, 2a + 2b, a + 3b, \ldots$ (l) $a^3b, a^2b^2, ab^3, b^4, \ldots$

C 6. Write the first five terms of the sequence whose first term is 3 and every other term is 5 less than twice the preceding term.

7. Find an expression for the nth term of a sequence whose first term is 5 and every other term is 4 more than the preceding term.

8. A sequence has the first term 2 and every other term is 3 more than the preceding term.
(a) Find the first five terms.
(b) Find the nth term.
(c) Fing (i) t_{25} (ii) t_{1000}

9. A sequence has the first term 3 and every other term is 5 less than the preceding term.
(a) Find the first five terms.
(b) Find the nth term.
(c) Find (i) t_{50} (ii) t_{500}

10. Find the first five terms determined by the following recursion formulas.

(a) $t_1 = 3$ (b) $t_1 = 1$
      $t_{n+1} = t_n + 2$ $t_{n+1} = 2t_n + 4$

(c) $t_1 = 3$ (d) $t_1 = 0$
      $t_n = t_{n-1} - 2, \quad n > 1$ $t_n = t_{n-1} + 2, \quad n > 1$

(e) $t_1 = 2$ (f) $t_1 = 1, \quad t_2 = 1$
      $t_n = t_{n-1} + 2n, \quad n > 1$ $t_{n+2} = t_{n+1} + t_n$

8.2 ARITHMETIC SEQUENCES

Sequences such as $2, 5, 8, 11, \ldots$ where the difference between consecutive terms is constant are called arithmetic sequences. Each term of the sequence is formed by adding a fixed quantity to the preceding term. The arithmetic sequence is defined by a linear function. The above sequence is defined by the linear function

$$f(n) = 3n - 1$$

Computing the first four terms,

$$t_1 = 3(1) - 1 = 2$$
$$t_2 = 3(2) - 1 = 5$$
$$t_3 = 3(3) - 1 = 8$$
$$t_4 = 3(4) - 1 = 11$$

We can write the terms of the sequence as follows

$$
\begin{array}{cccc}
2 & 5 & 8 & 11 \quad \ldots \\
\updownarrow & \updownarrow & \updownarrow & \updownarrow
\end{array}
$$
$$2, 2 + 1(3), 2 + 2(3), 2 + 3(3), \ldots$$

The general arithmetic sequence is

$$a, a + d, a + 2d, a + 3d, \ldots$$

where a is the first term and d is the common difference.

$$t_1 = a$$
$$t_2 = a + d$$
$$t_3 = a + 2d$$
$$\vdots$$

$$\boxed{t_n = a + (n - 1)d}$$

EXAMPLE 1. *Find t_{10} and t_n for the arithmetic sequence*

$$2, 6, 10, 14, \ldots$$

Solution

$$a = 2 \quad \text{and} \quad d = 6 - 2 = 10 - 6 = 14 - 10 = 4$$
$$t_n = a + (n - 1)d$$
$$
\begin{array}{ll}
t_{10} = 2 + 9(4) & t_n = 2 + (n - 1)4 \\
\quad\;\; = 2 + 36 & \quad\;\; = 2 + 4n - 4 \\
\quad\;\; = 38 & \quad\;\; = 4n - 2
\end{array}
$$
$$\therefore \quad t_{10} = 38 \text{ and } t_n = 4n - 2$$

EXAMPLE 2. *How many terms are there in the arithmetic sequence*

$$-5, -2, 1, 4, \ldots, 103?$$

Solution

The sequence is arithmetic with

$$a = -5, \quad d = 3 \quad \text{and} \quad t_n = 103$$

$$t_n = a + (n-1)d$$
$$103 = -5 + (n-1)3$$
$$103 = -5 + 3n - 3$$
$$111 = 3n$$
$$37 = n$$

∴ the sequence has 37 terms.

EXAMPLE 3. *In an arithmetic sequence $t_8 = 130$ and $t_{12} = 166$. Find the first three terms and t_n.*

Solution

$$t_n = a + (n-1)d$$

$$t_{12} = 166 \qquad a + 11d = 166$$
$$t_8 = 130 \qquad \underline{a + 7d = 130}$$

By subtraction
$$4d = 36$$
$$d = 9$$

By substitution in t_8

$$a + 7(9) = 130$$
$$a + 63 = 130$$
$$a = 67$$

∴ the first three terms are 67, 76, and 85.

$$t_n = a + (n-1)d$$
$$t_n = 67 + (n-1)9$$
$$= 67 + 9n - 9$$
$$= 9n + 58$$
$$∴ \quad t_n = 9n + 58$$

The terms between any two given terms of an arithmetic sequence are called *arithmetic means* between the given terms.

EXAMPLE 4. Insert five arithmetic means between 5 and 29

Solution

The sequence will have seven terms:

$$5, t_2, t_3, t_4, t_5, t_6, 29$$

$$t_n = a + (n-1)d$$

where $a = 5$, $n = 7$, and $t_n = 29$

Substituting $\qquad\qquad 29 = 5 + (7-1)d$

$$24 = 6d$$

$$4 = d$$

$\therefore$ the terms of the sequence are

$$5, 9, 13, 17, 21, 25, 29$$

EXERCISE 8-2

A 1. Which of the following are successive terms of an arithmetic sequence? State the values of a and d for those that are arithmetic.

(a) $1, 5, 10, 15, \ldots$ (b) $1, 6, 11, 16, \ldots$ (c) $20, 16, 12, 8, \ldots$

(d) $2, 4, 8, 16, \ldots$ (e) $-2, -5, -8, -11, \ldots$ (f) $1, \frac{1}{2}, \frac{1}{4}, \frac{1}{8}, \ldots$

(g) $2, 2\frac{1}{2}, 2\frac{3}{4}, 3\frac{1}{4}, \ldots$ (h) $1, 1.6, 2.2, 2.8, \ldots$ (i) $5, 4.3, 3.7, 3.0, \ldots$

(j) $2x^2, 3x^2, 4x^2, \ldots$ (k) $x, x^2, x^3, x^4, \ldots$ (l) $a, a+b, a+2b, \ldots$

2. State the first five terms of the arithmetic sequence, given:

(a) $a = 1, d = 4$ (b) $a = 3, d = 5$ (c) $a = -8, d = -3$

(d) $a = x, d = y$ (e) $a = x+1, d = x+2$ (f) $a = 5, d = x$

(g) $t_1 = 5m, d = 3m$ (h) $t_1 = 3, d = x+1$ (i) $t_1 = 5+x, d = 3$

(j) $t_1 = 2a, d = -a$ (k) $t_1 = 0.5, d = 1.5$ (l) $t_1 = 3a, d = 2-a$

B 3. Find the indicated terms for each of the following arithmetic sequences.

(a) t_{10} and t_{44} for $8, 10, 12, \ldots$ (b) t_{16} and t_{51} for $10, 14, 18, \ldots$

(c) t_7 and t_{100} for $10, 17, 24, \ldots$ (d) t_{15} and t_{71} for $6, 0, -6, \ldots$

(e) t_5 and t_{62} for $-12, -8, -4, \ldots$ (f) t_7 and t_{93} for $a, a+2b, a+4b, \ldots$

(g) t_{11} and t_{101} for $x, 3x, 5x, \ldots$ (h) t_8 and t_{105} for $a+b, a, a-b, \ldots$

(i) t_{22} and t_n for $4, 7, 10, \ldots$ (j) t_{51} and t_n for $-11, -5, 1, \ldots$

(k) t_{30} and t_n for $2, 9, 16, \ldots$ (l) t_{24} and t_n for $a, a+6, a+12, \ldots$

4. Find a, d, and t_n for the following arithmetic sequences.

(a) $t_5 = 16, t_8 = 25$ (b) $t_{12} = 52, t_{22} = 102$

(c) $t_{50} = 140, t_{70} = 180$ (d) $t_2 = -12, t_5 = 9$

(e) $t_7 = 37, t_{10} = 22$ (f) $t_5 = -20, t_{18} = -53$

(g) $t_{13} = -177, t_{22} = -207$ (h) $t_7 = 3+5x, t_{11} = 3+23x$

5. Find the number of terms in each of the following arithmetic sequences.

(a) $3, 5, 7, \ldots, 129$ (b) $-1, 2, 5, \ldots, 164$

(c) $-29, -24, -19, \ldots, 126$ (d) $61, 55, 49, \ldots, -119$

(e) $5, 5.5, 6, \ldots, 87$ (f) $-53, -49, -45, \ldots, 51$

(g) $x, x+2, x+4, \ldots, x+256$ (h) $p+3q, p+7q, p+11q, \ldots, p+111q$

6. How many multiples of 5 are there from 25 to 750 inclusive?

7. How many multiples of 7 are there from -56 to 560 inclusive?

8. How many multiples of 6 are there between 65 and 391?

9. When money is lent at simple interest rates, the amounts required to pay off the loan at the end of each year are the terms of an arithmetic sequence.

Year	now	1	2	3	...	n
Amount	P	$P + Pi$	$P + 2Pi$	$P + 3Pi$	...	$P + nPi$

where P represents the principal, and i the interest rate.
(a) If $1000 is lent at 9%/a simple interest, find the amount at the end of 1, 2, 3, 4 and n years. Find a and d for the sequence.
(b) Find the amount required to repay a loan of $2500 at 7%/a simple interest after 12a.

10. Find t_{37} of an arithmetic sequence with $t_5 = 11$, $t_{18} = 65$

11. Find x so that x, $\frac{1}{2}x + 7$, $3x - 1$ are three terms of an arithmetic sequence.

12. Find x so that $2x$, $3x + 1$, $x^2 + 2$ are three terms of an arithmetic sequence.

13. Find the common difference of the sequence determined by $t_n = 5n + 4$

14. Given $t_n = 2n + 5$, find
(a) the first five terms   (b) t_k (c) t_{k-1} (d) $t_k - t_{k-1}$

15. (a) Insert one arithmetic mean between 11 and 17
(b) Insert two mathematical means between 5 and 23
(c) Insert seven arithmetic means between 15 and 39
(d) Insert six arithmetic means between 9 and -45
(e) Insert three arithmetic means between $x + 2y$ and $4x + 14y$.

Write 108 using five 3's.

16. The arithmetic mean of two numbers is 9 and the sum of their squares is 180. Find the numbers.

C **17.** Five fence posts are to be equally spaced between two corner posts that are 42 m apart. How far apart should the five line posts be installed?

18. A management trainee hires on at a salary of $15 000 with half-yearly raises of $375 until the maximum salary of $28 500 is reached. How long will it take to reach the maximum salary?

19. A small car depreciates $1500 the first year, and $600 each year thereafter. How long will it take a $5200 car to depreciate to $1300.?

20. The gas company charges a basic monthly rate plus a certain amount per unit of consumption. Consumption of 40 units gives a bill of $67.20, and 73 units gives a bill of $116.70. Find the basic monthly rate and the cost per unit.

8.3 GEOMETRIC SEQUENCES

Sequences such as

$$3, 6, 12, \ldots$$

$$\frac{6}{3} = \frac{12}{6} = \frac{24}{12} = \ldots = 2$$

where the ratio of consecutive terms is constant are called geometric sequences.

Each term of the sequence is found by multiplying the preceding term by a fixed quantity.

The geometric sequence is defined by an exponential function. The above sequence is defined by the exponential function

$$f(n) = 3 \times 2^{n-1}$$

Computing the first four terms

$$t_1 = 3 \times 2^{1-1} = 3$$
$$t_2 = 3 \times 2^{2-1} = 6$$
$$t_3 = 3 \times 2^{3-1} = 12$$
$$t_4 = 3 \times 2^{4-1} = 24$$

.
.
.

The general geometric sequence is $a, ar, ar^2, ar^3, \ldots$ where a is the first term and r is the common ratio.

$$t_1 = a$$
$$t_2 = ar$$
$$t_3 = ar^2$$

.
.
.

$$\boxed{t_n = ar^{n-1}}$$

EXAMPLE 1. *Find t_5 and t_n for the geometric sequence $2, 6, 18, \ldots$*

Solution

$$t_n = ar^{n-1}, \quad a = 2, \quad r = 3$$
$$t_5 = ar^4 \qquad t_n = ar^{n-1}$$
$$= 2 \cdot 3^4 \qquad = 3(2)^{n-1}$$
$$= 162$$

$$\therefore \quad t_5 = 162 \text{ and } t_n = 3(2)^{n-1}$$

EXAMPLE 2. *How many terms are there in the geometric sequence*

$$3, 6, 12, \ldots, 768?$$

Solution

The sequence is geometric: $a = 3$, $r = 2$, $t_n = 768$

$$t_n = ar^{n-1}$$
$$768 = 3(2^{n-1})$$
$$256 = 2^{n-1}$$
$$2^8 = 2^{n-1}$$
$$n - 1 = 8$$
$$n = 9$$

$\therefore$ the sequence has 9 terms.

EXAMPLE 3. In a geometric sequence of real numbers

$$t_5 = 1875, \quad \text{and} \quad t_7 = 46\,875.$$

Find t_1, t_2 and t_n.

Solution

$$t_7 = 46\,875 \quad \Rightarrow \quad ar^6 = 46\,875$$
$$t_5 = 1875 \quad \Rightarrow \quad ar^4 = 1875$$

By division,

$$\frac{ar^6}{ar^4} = \frac{46\,875}{1875}$$
$$r^2 = 25$$
$$r = \pm 5$$

This indicates that there are two possible solutions.

(i) $r = 5$	(ii) $r = -5$
Substituting in t_5	Substituting in t_5
$a(5)^4 = 1875$	$a(-5)^4 = 1875$
$625a = 1875$	$625a = 1875$
$a = 3$	$a = 3$
$\therefore \;\; t_1 = 3, \; t_2 = 15$	$\therefore \;\; t_1 = 3, \; t_2 = -15$
and $t_n = 3(5)^{n-1}$	and $t_n = 3(-5)^{n-1}$

The terms between any two given terms of a geometric progression are called *geometric means* between the two terms.

EXAMPLE 4. *Insert 3 geometric means between 5 and 80*

Solution

$$a = 5, \ t_5 = 80 \quad \text{and} \quad t_n = ar^{n-1}$$
$$80 = 5r^4$$
$$16 = r^4$$
$$r^2 = 4 \quad \text{or} \quad r^2 = -4$$
$$r = \pm 2 \qquad r = \pm 2i$$

We reject these roots since only real values are considered.

$$\therefore \quad r = \pm 2$$

Hence there are two sequences with terms:
$$\text{(i)} \ 5, 10, 20, 40, 80$$
$$\text{(ii)} \ 5, -10, 20, -40, 80$$

Unless otherwise stated, we shall assume that we are working with sequences of real numbers.

EXERCISE 8-3

A **1.** Which of the following are successive terms of a geometric sequence? State the values of a and r for those that are geometric.
(a) $1, 4, 9, 16, \ldots$ (b) $1, 2, 4, 8, \ldots$ (c) $5, 10, 15, 20, \ldots$
(d) $3, 12, 24, 72, \ldots$ (e) $32, 16, 8, 4, \ldots$ (f) $64, -16, 4, -1, \ldots$
(g) $x, x^3, x^5, x^7, \ldots$ (h) $x, x^3, x^6, x^9, \ldots$ (i) $x, -x^2, x^3, -x^4, \ldots$

(j) $2ax, 2x, 2\dfrac{x}{a}, \ldots$ (k) $3a^5b, a^4b^2, \tfrac{1}{3}a^3b^3, \ldots$ (l) $1, 2x, 3x^2, 4x^3, \ldots$

B **2.** Find the terms indicated for each of the following geometric sequences.
(a) t_5 and t_n for $2, 4, 8, \ldots$ (b) t_6 and t_n for $1, 5, 25, \ldots$
(c) t_6 and t_k for $3, 6, 12, \ldots$ (d) t_6 and t_k for $32, 16, 8, \ldots$
(e) t_5 and t_n for $2, -4, 8, \ldots$ (f) t_7 and t_n for $64, -32, 16, \ldots$
(g) t_8 and t_n for $81, -27, 9$ (h) t_6 and t_n for $\tfrac{1}{2}, \tfrac{1}{4}, \tfrac{1}{8}, \ldots$

(i) t_{10} and t_n for $2x, 4x^2, 8x^3, \ldots$ (j) t_8 and t_n for $1, \dfrac{x}{2}, \dfrac{x^2}{4}, \ldots$

(k) t_{25} and t_{50} for $\dfrac{1}{x^4}, \dfrac{1}{x^2}, 1, \ldots$ (l) t_{20} and t_{60} for $3x^{10}, -3x^9, 3x^8, \ldots$

3. How many terms are there in the following geometric sequences.
(a) $4, 12, 36, \ldots, 972$ (b) $3, 6, 12, \ldots, 768$
(c) $2, -4, 8, \ldots, 512$ (d) $\tfrac{1}{2}, \tfrac{1}{4}, \tfrac{1}{8}, \ldots, \tfrac{1}{1024}$
(e) $\tfrac{1}{25}, \tfrac{1}{5}, 1, \ldots, 625$ (f) $\tfrac{2}{81}, \tfrac{4}{27}, \tfrac{8}{9}, \ldots, 6912$
(g) $2x^2, 2x^3, 2x^4, \ldots, 2x^{16}$ (h) $3x^{13}, 3x^{12}, 3x^{11}, \ldots, 3$

(i) $1458, 486, 162, \ldots, 2$

(j) $\dfrac{1}{x}, \dfrac{1}{x^2}, \dfrac{1}{x^3}, \ldots, \dfrac{1}{x^{11}}$

(k) $\dfrac{5}{x}, \dfrac{1}{x^2}, \dfrac{1}{5x^3}, \ldots, \dfrac{1}{625x^6}$

(l) $2x, 2, \dfrac{2}{x}, \ldots, \dfrac{2}{x^{17}}$

4. Find a, r, and t_n for the following geometric sequences.

(a) $t_3 = 36, t_4 = 108$ (b) $t_5 = 48, t_8 = 384$ (c) $t_2 = 28, t_4 = 448$

(d) $t_3 = 64, t_8 = 2$ (e) $t_4 = -9, t_5 = -3$ (f) $t_2 = 12, t_4 = 192$

(g) $t_5 = 12, t_9 = 108$ (h) $t_5 = 3, t_{14} = 10$ (i) $t_6 = 486, t_9 = 2250$

(j) $t_3 = 5x^6, t_{10} = 5x^{20}$ (k) $t_4 = 8x^3, t_9 = 256x^8$ (l) $t_3 = 32k^8, t_7 = 2k^4$

5. Find the number of terms in the following geometric sequences.

(a) $t_1 = 8, r = 1.5, t_n = 40.5$ (b) $t_1 = 567, r = \frac{1}{3}, t_n = \frac{7}{9}$

(c) $t_1 = 6, r = 2, t_n = 1536$ (d) $5, 35, 245, \ldots, 588\,245$

(e) $3, 6, 12, \ldots, 96$ (f) $64, 32, 16, \ldots, 0.125$

(g) $\frac{1}{4}, \frac{1}{2}, 1, \ldots, 32$ (h) $b, ab, a^2b, \ldots, a^{12}b$

6. Find x so that $2x$, $x+5$, and $x-7$ are consecutive terms of a geometric sequence.

7. Find y so that $4y+1$, $y+4$, $10-y$ are consecutive terms of a geometric sequence.

8. A car depreciates 30% every year. Find the value of a car 5 years old if the original price was $9000.00

9. When money is lent and compound interest is charged, the amount required to repay the loan at the end of each year forms a geometric sequence.

Start with the word "beard" and change one letter at a time to form a new word until you reach "shave". The best solution has the fewest steps.

beard

− − − − −

− − − − −

− − − − −

− − − − −

− − − − −

shave

Year	Now	1	2	3	$\ldots$	n
Amount	P	$P(1+i)$	$P(1+i)^2$	$P(1+i)^3$	$\ldots$	$P(1+i)^n$

where P represents the principal and i the annual rate of interest.

If $300 is lent at 9%/a compounded annually, show the amount at the end of 1, 2, 3, and n years.

10. Find the amount of $500 invested for 4 years at 8% compounded annually.

11. A virus reproduces by dividing into two, and after a growth period by dividing again. How many virus will be in a system starting with a single virus and after ten divisions?

12. (a) Graph the sequence defined by $t_n = 3(2)^{n-1}$ for $1 \le n \le 5$
(b) What type of growth is illustrated here?

13. In a certain region, the number of highway accidents increased by 20%/a over a four year period. How many accidents were there in 1984 if there were 5120 in 1980?

14. The population of Satellite City increased from 12 000 to 91 125 over a 5 year period. Find the annual rate of increase assuming the increase was geometric.

15. A house worth $80 000 sold for $106 480 three years later. Find the annual rate of increase if the value of the house increased geometrically.

C **16.** (a) Insert 3 geometric means between 5 and 12 005
(b) Insert 3 geometric means between 27 and 2187
(c) Insert 4 geometric means between 48 and $1\frac{1}{2}$
(d) Insert 5 geometric means between 1458 and 2

17. If a, x, b are consecutive terms of a geometric sequence, then x is called the geometric mean of a and b.
(a) Find the geometric mean of 2 and 8
(b) Find the geometric mean of 5 and 180
(c) Find the geometric mean of m and n

18. Show that the sequence defined by $t_{n+1} = 2t_n$, $t_1 = x + y$ is a geometric sequence and state the values of a and r.

19. In case of disaster, St. Mary's General Hospital has a fan out system for calling in staff where each person makes two calls. How many people are called in the sixth level of calls if the person who initiates the first call is considered the first level?

20. The notes of the musical scale are based on frequency of vibration. A, above middle C, is 440 Hz, that is, 440 vibrations, or cycles, per second. The frequency of a note just above is given by

$$t_{n+1} = 2^{\frac{1}{12}} t_n$$

where t_n is the given note and t_{n+1} the note just above.
(a) Find the frequency of C, 3 notes above A.
(b) Find the frequency of F, 4 notes below A.
(c) Find the ratio of the frequencies $\dfrac{t_{13}}{t_1}$.

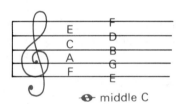
⦿ middle C

8.4 SERIES

We have studied sequences such as

$$1, 3, 9, 27, 81, 243$$

If we add the terms of a sequence, the resulting sum is called a series. The series that corresponds to this sequence is

$$1 + 3 + 9 + 27 + 81 + 243$$

A series is a sum of the terms of a sequence.
Given the sequence t_1, t_2, t_3, ..., t_n, the nth partial sum of the corresponding series is

$$S_n = t_1 + t_2 + t_3 + \cdots + t_n$$

If a series has a finite number of terms it has a sum which can be found. For example,

$$2 + 4 + 6 + 8 + 10 = 30$$

If there are infinitely many terms in a series, finding the sum when one exists is much more difficult. In this chapter, we shall restrict our discussions and work to finite series. Infinite series will be dealt with in Chapter 12.

Series can be described using the Greek letter Σ (sigma). For example the sum

$$2+4+6+8+10$$

can be written

$$\sum_{n=1}^{5} 2n$$

which is read

"the sum of $2n$ from $n=1$ to $n=5$"

EXAMPLE 1. *Find the sums of the following series.*

$$\text{(a)} \sum_{n=1}^{6} n \qquad \text{(b)} \sum_{n=1}^{5} (2n-1)$$

Solution

(a) $\displaystyle\sum_{n=1}^{6} n = 1+2+3+4+5+6$

$\qquad = 21$

(b) $\displaystyle\sum_{n=1}^{5} (2n-1) = [2(1)-1]+[2(2)-1]+[2(3)-1]+[2(4)-1]+[2(5)-1]$

$\qquad\qquad = 1+3+5+7+9$

$\qquad\qquad = 25$

Although we have used n as the index of *summation* other letters are also used.

EXAMPLE 2. *Write the following sums explicitly as series.*

$$\text{(a)} \sum_{i=1}^{5} ix \qquad \text{(b)} \sum_{j=1}^{6} x^i \qquad \text{(c)} \sum_{k=1}^{5} kx^k$$

Solution

(a) $\displaystyle\sum_{i=1}^{5} ix = 1x+2x+3x+4x+5x$

(b) $\displaystyle\sum_{j=1}^{6} x^i = x^1+x^2+x^3+x^4+x^5$

(c) $\displaystyle\sum_{k=1}^{5} kx^k = 1x^1+2x^2+3x^3+4x^4+5x^5$

EXERCISE 8-4

A **1.** State explicitly the series defined by each of the following.

(a) $\displaystyle\sum_{i=1}^{4}(2i+1)$ (b) $\displaystyle\sum_{j=1}^{6}2j$ (c) $\displaystyle\sum_{k=1}^{5}\frac{1}{k}$ (d) $\displaystyle\sum_{n=1}^{5}(-1)^n$

(e) $\displaystyle\sum_{i=1}^{4}2^i$ (f) $\displaystyle\sum_{i=1}^{5}\frac{1}{2i-1}$ (g) $\displaystyle\sum_{n=2}^{5}(2n-1)$ (h) $\displaystyle\sum_{k=1}^{6}k(k+1)$

B **2.** Write each series in expanded form and find the sum.

(a) $\displaystyle\sum_{n=1}^{5}(2-n)$ (b) $\displaystyle\sum_{n=1}^{4}(-1)^n n^2$ (c) $\displaystyle\sum_{k=1}^{5}(-1)^k(k^2-1)$

(d) $\displaystyle\sum_{i=1}^{5}(3i-1)$ (e) $\displaystyle\sum_{k=1}^{5}1-k$ (f) $\displaystyle\sum_{j=1}^{4}(1-j)^2$

(g) $\displaystyle\sum_{n=2}^{6}(2-n)$ (h) $\displaystyle\sum_{k=3}^{7}(-1)^k k^2$ (i) $\displaystyle\sum_{i=0}^{4}2^i$

(j) $\displaystyle\sum_{n=1}^{5}\frac{1}{n+1}$ (k) $\displaystyle\sum_{k=2}^{6}\frac{3}{k-1}$ (l) $\displaystyle\sum_{i=0}^{5}\frac{2i}{i+1}$

3. Use the summation sign to write each series.

(a) $2+4+6+8+10+12$ (b) $1+4+9+16+\cdots+n^2$

(c) $3+5+7+9+11$ (d) $1+2+4+8+\cdots+2^{n-1}$

(e) $1+4+7+10+\cdots+(3n-2)$ (f) $3+6+12+\cdots+3(2)^{n-1}$

(g) $5+5x+5x^2+5x^3$ (h) $3x+4x+5x+6x$

(i) $x-x^2+x^3-x^4+x^5$ (j) $a+2a^2+3a^3+4a^4$

(k) $\dfrac{1}{2}+\dfrac{1}{3}+\dfrac{1}{4}+\dfrac{1}{5}$ (l) $\dfrac{1}{x}+\dfrac{2}{x^2}+\dfrac{3}{x^3}+\dfrac{4}{x^4}$

8.5 ARITHMETIC SERIES

To the finite sequence 2, 4, 6, 8, 10 corresponds the finite series

$$2+4+6+8+10$$

In this series we write $S_5 = 30$ where the symbol S_5 denotes the *sum* of the first five terms of the series. In this section, we shall develop and use a formula to find the sum of a series.

Carl Friedrich Gauss, when only eight years old, used the following method to sum the natural numbers from 1 to 100. Letting S_{100} represent the sum of the first 100 natural numbers, we write out the series first explicitly and again in reverse:

$$S_{100} = \quad 1+ 2 + 3 +\cdots+99 +100$$

$$S_{100} = 100+99 +98 +\cdots+ 2 + 1$$

Adding $\qquad \overline{2S_{100} = 101+101+101+\cdots+101+101}$

$$= 100(101)$$

$$S_{100} = \tfrac{100}{2}(101) = 5050$$

This method of pairing terms can be used to find the sums of other series as in Example 1.

EXAMPLE 1. *Find the sum of 300 terms of the series* $1+5+9+13+\ldots$.

Solution

In order to use Gauss' method, we first find t_{300} from the corresponding sequence

$$t_n = a + (n-1)d$$

$$a = 1, \quad d = 4, \quad n = 300$$

$$t_{300} = 1 + (300-1)4$$

$$= 1197$$

$$S_{300} = \quad 1 + \quad 5 + \quad 9 + \cdots + 1193 + 1197$$

$$S_{300} = 1197 + 1193 + 1189 + \cdots + \quad 5 + \quad 1$$

$$\overline{2S_{300} = 1198 + 1198 + 1198 + \cdots + 1198 + 1198}$$

$$= 300(1198)$$

$$S_{300} = \tfrac{300}{2}(1198) = 179\,700$$

Arrange the digits 0, 1, 2, 3, 4, 5, 6, 7, 8, 9 in fractional form so that

We now use the method of Example 1 to derive a formula for the sum of the general arithmetic series.

The general arithmetic sequence

$$a, (a+d), (a+2d), \ldots, (t_n - d), t_n$$

has n terms with first term n and last term t_n. The corresponding arithmetic series is

$$S_n = a \quad + (a+d) + (a+2d) + \ldots + (t_n - d) + t_n$$

Reversing $\quad S_n = t_n \quad + (t_n - d) + (t_n - 2d) + \ldots + (a+d) + a$

Adding $\quad \overline{2S_n = (a + t_n) + (a + t_n) + (a + t_n) + \ldots + (a + t_n) + (a + t_n)}$

$$= n[a + t_n]$$

$$\boxed{S_n = \frac{n}{2}[a + t_n]} \quad (1)$$

Since $t_n = a + (n-1)d$, we can substitute for t_n in formula (1):

$$S_n = \frac{n}{2}[a + a + (n-1)d]$$

$$\boxed{S_n = \frac{n}{2}[2a + (n-1)d]} \quad (2)$$

EXAMPLE 2. *Find the sum of the first 50 terms of the arithmetic series*

(a) $5+8+11+14+\cdots$ (b) $-10-12-14-\cdots$

Solution

(a) $a = 5$, $d = 3$, $n = 50$

$$S_n = \frac{n}{2}[2a+(n-1)d]$$

$$S_{50} = \tfrac{50}{2}[2(5)+(50-1)3]$$

$$= 25[10+147]$$

$$= 25 \times 157$$

$$= 3925$$

(b) $a = -10$, $d = -2$, $n = 50$

$$S_n = \frac{n}{2}[2a+(n-1)d]$$

$$S_{50} = \tfrac{50}{2}[2(-10)+(50-1)(-2)]$$

$$= 25[-20-98]$$

$$= 25[-118]$$

$$= -2950$$

EXAMPLE 3. *Find the sum of the arithmetic series*
$3+7+11+\ldots+483$

Solution

Before we can use either formula (1) or formula (2) we must determine n, the number of terms.

$$t_n = a+(n-1)d$$

$$a = 3, \quad d = 4, \quad t_n = 483$$

$$483 = 3+(n-1)4$$

$$483 = 4n-1$$

$$484 = 4n$$

$$121 = n$$

Using formula (1)

$$S_n = \frac{n}{2}(t_1+t_n)$$

$$S_{121} = \tfrac{121}{2}(3+483)$$

$$= \frac{121 \times 486}{2}$$

$$= 29\,403$$

Using formula (2)

$$S_n = \frac{n}{2}[2a+(n-1)d]$$

$$S_{121} = \tfrac{121}{2}[2(3)+(121-1)4]$$

$$= \frac{121 \times 486}{2}$$

$$= 29\,403$$

Although both formulas gave the required answer in this example, the form that is used depends on the given data.

EXERCISE 8-5

A **1.** Find the sum of the arithmetic series given
(a) $a = 4$, $t_n = 9$, $n = 6$
(b) $a = 5$, $t_n = 29$, $n = 9$
(c) $a = 7$, $t_n = -22$, $n = 12$
(d) $a = -4$, $t_n = 17$, $n = 8$
(e) $a = 0$, $t_n = 64$, $n = 16$
(f) $a = 3x$, $t_n = 21x$, $n = 10$

2. Find the sum of the following series using Gauss' method as in example 1.

(a) $2+4+6+8+\ldots+2000$

(b) $1+3+5+7+\ldots+1999$

(c) $1+2+3+\ldots+1000$

(d) $1+2+3+\ldots+n$

(e) $3+6+9+\ldots$ to 150 terms

(f) $5+10+15+\ldots$ to 200 terms

3. Find the sum of the first 1000 terms of the following series.

(a) $1+4+7+\ldots$

(b) $10+8+6+\ldots$

(c) $5+8+11+\ldots$

(d) $0-2-4\ldots$

4. Find the indicated sums for the following.

(a) S_{15} of $5+9+13+\ldots$

(b) S_{20} of $20+25+30+\ldots$

(c) S_{14} of $-14-8-2+\ldots$

(d) S_{21} of $-2+6+14+\ldots$

(e) S_{50} of $50+48+46+\ldots$

(f) S_{15} of $20+15+10+\ldots$

(g) S_{50} of $\frac{1}{2}+\frac{3}{2}+\frac{5}{2}+\ldots$

(h) S_{61} of $\frac{1}{2}+\frac{3}{4}+1+\ldots$

5. Find the sums of the following series.

(a) $4+8+12+\ldots+400$

(b) $5+10+15+\ldots+265$

(c) $100+90+80+\ldots-100$

(d) $52+47+42+\ldots-48$

(e) $-17-10-3+\ldots+74$

(f) $2-5-12-\ldots-222$

(g) $\frac{5}{2}+\frac{11}{2}+\frac{17}{2}+\ldots+\frac{53}{2}$

(h) $\frac{1}{2}+\frac{1}{4}+0-\ldots-\frac{11}{2}$

6. Find the sums of the following series.

(a) $\sum\limits_{n=1}^{100}(2n-1)$

(b) $\sum\limits_{i=1}^{2000}2i$

(c) $\sum\limits_{n=1}^{80}(3n-2)$

7. Find the number of terms in the following arithmetic series.

(a) $78=1+2+3+\ldots$

(b) $1830=3+7+11+\ldots$

(c) $1250=15+20+25+\ldots$

(d) $-350=10+8+6+\ldots$

(e) $-120=-30-26-22-\ldots$

(f) $-345=5+1-3-\ldots$

8. A pile of logs is formed by first laying 12 logs side by side and piling others on top forming a prism tapering to one log at the top. How many logs are there in the pile?

9. A student is offered a job to last 20 h. The pay is $3.25 the first hour, $3.50 the second hour, $3.75 the third hour and so on, or a straight $6/h for the 20 h. Which system pays more?

10. An experimental theatre has 25 seats in the front row and one additional seat in each following row. How many seats are there if the theatre has 25 rows of seats?

11. An insurance broker earned $24 000/a and had increases of $800/a for the next 5 years. What was this person's total income over the 5 year period?

12. (a) Find a formula for $S_n=1+2+3+\ldots+n$
Find (b) S_{100} (c) S_{1000} (d) S_{2000} for this series.

13. Find a formula for the sum of
(a) the first n odd natural numbers.
(b) the first k even natural numbers.

14. A 12-h clock strikes the same number as the hour from 07:00 to 20:00 inclusive. How many times does the clock strike in one day?

15. In one type of billiards, number balls (1 to 15) are used and the player gets the number of points equal to the number on the ball he sinks.

(a) How many points are on the table at the start of the game?

(b) What is the least number of balls required to win if order is not important?

(c) How many balls must you sink to win if you must shoot the balls in order beginning with the 1?

C   **16**. Find an expression for the sum of n terms of a series with $t_n = 3n - 2$.

17. Find an expression for the sum of n terms of a series with $t_n = 1 - 4n$,

18. Find the first five terms of the arithmetic series with $t_{12} = 35$ and $S_{20} = 610$

19. A ball rolls down an inclined track and gains speed. If the distance the ball travels is 3 cm in the first second, 6 in the second, 9 in the third, and so on, find (a) the distance the ball travels in the 15 s, (b) the total distance travelled in 15 s.

20. Boxes are stored in a warehouse. The stack is 4 boxes wide, and 20 boxes long at the bottom. Each layer is one box shorter than the previous layer but the same width. How many boxes are there if the top layer is four boxes long?

8.6 GEOMETRIC SERIES

The sum of the terms of the finite geometric sequence 1, 3, 9, 27, 81, 243, 729 is the finite geometric series

$$1 + 3 + 9 + 27 + 81 + 243 + 729$$

We can find the sum of this series directly by addition, or by the following procedure.

$$S_7 = 1 + 3 + 9 + 27 + 81 + 243 + 729$$

$$3 \times S_7 = 3 + 9 + 27 + 81 + 243 + 729 + 2187$$

Subtracting top from bottom

$$2S_7 = -1 + 2187$$

$$2S_7 = 2186$$

$$S_7 = \frac{2186}{2} = 1093$$

This method is used to develop a formula for the sum of the general geometric series.

For the general geometric series,

$$S_n = a + ar + ar^2 + \ldots + ar^{n-1}$$

We now develop a formula for the sum of n terms of the geometric series:

$$S_n = a + ar + ar^2 + \ldots + ar^{n-1}$$
$$rS_n = \qquad ar + ar^2 + \ldots + ar^{n-1} + ar^n$$

Subtracting $S_n - rS_n = a \qquad\qquad\qquad - ar^n$

$$(1-r)S_n = a(1-r^n)$$

$$S_n = \frac{a(1-r^n)}{1-r}, \qquad r<1 \quad \text{or} \quad S_n = \frac{a(r^n-1)}{r-1}, \qquad r>1$$

We have stated two versions of the formula to avoid negative numbers.

EXAMPLE 1. *Find S_{10} for the series $1+2+4+\ldots$*

Solution

$$a=1, \quad r=2, \quad n=10$$

$$S_n = \frac{a(r^n-1)}{r-1}$$

$$S_{10} = \frac{1(2^{10}-1)}{2-1}$$

$$= \frac{1024-1}{1} = 1023$$

EXAMPLE 2. *Find the sum of the series*

$$5+15+45+\ldots+10\,935$$

Solution

$$S_n = \frac{a(r^n-1)}{r-1}$$

where $a=5$, $r=3$, and n is unknown.

$$t_n = ar^{n-1} \qquad\qquad S_8 = \frac{5(3^8-1)}{3-1}$$
$$10\,935 = 5(3)^{n-1} \qquad\qquad$$
$$3^{n-1} = 2187 \qquad\qquad = \frac{5(6561-1)}{2}$$
$$3^{n-1} = 3^7 \qquad\qquad$$
$$n-1 = 7 \qquad\qquad = \frac{5(6560)}{2} = 16\,400$$
$$n = 8$$

EXERCISE 8-6

1. Find the indicated sum for the following series.

(a) $S_8 = 10+20+40+\ldots$ (b) $S_5 = 2+6+18+\ldots$

(c) $S_6 = 3+15+75+\ldots$ (d) $S_8 = 2-6+18-\ldots$

(e) $S_6 = 256+128+64+\ldots$ (f) $S_6 = 972+324+108+\ldots$

2. Find the sum of the following series:

(a) $1+2+4+\ldots+256$

(b) $1+3+9+\ldots+2187$

(c) $2-4+8-\ldots+512$

(d) $5-15+45-\ldots+3645$

(e) $243+81+27+\ldots+\frac{1}{27}$

(f) $2700+270+27+\ldots+0.0027$

3. Every person has two natural parents, four grandparents and so on into the ancestral past. What is the total number of direct ancestors in six generations?

4. An emergency measures organization uses a fan-out system to alert staff. The executive officer who initiates the action makes four calls. Each of these in turn makes four calls, and so on. How many people have been alerted after the fifth level of calls if the executive officer is considered the first level?

5. A superball bounces to $\frac{3}{4}$ of its initial height when dropped on dry pavement. If the ball is dropped from a height of 16 m,

(a) how high does it bounce after the fifth bounce?

(b) how far does the ball travel by the time it hits the ground for the sixth time?

6. In a certain town the number of accident deaths decreased 20%/a over the last five years. How many people died accidentally during this period if there were 52 accidental deaths five years ago?

7. In a popular lottary, the first prize money was $10 000. Each succeeding ticket paid $\frac{1}{2}$ as much as the ticket before it. How much was paid out in prizes if six tickets were drawn?

C **8.** Evaluate the following expressions.

(a) $\sum_{n=1}^{4} (2^n + 3^n)$

(b) $\sum_{n=1}^{6} (2^n - 3^{n-1})$

(c) $\sum_{n=1}^{5} (3^n + 2^{-n})$

(d) $\sum_{n=1}^{1000} 5^n$

(e) $\sum_{n=1}^{96} \frac{1}{2^n}$

8.7 APPLICATION: AMOUNT OF A LUMP SUM

When money is borrowed from a bank, or other lending institution, interest is charged for the use of the money. If the interest is payable at regular intervals during the duration of the loan, and it is not actually paid but added on to the principal for the next interest period, it is called compound interest.

EXAMPLE 1. *If $100 is invested at 8%/a compounded annually, show how the amount grows over a term of* (b) *20 years* (b) *n years.*

Solution

After 1 year, $100 accumulates to

$$100 + 100(0.08)$$

principal   interest

$$= 100(1 + 0.08)$$
$$+ 100(1.08)$$

This amount, $100(1.08) now becomes the principal for the following year's investment. After 2 years, we have

$$100(1.08) + 100(1.08)(0.08)$$

$\uparrow$ principal $\uparrow$ interest

$$= 100(1.08)(1 + 0.08)$$
$$= 100(1.08)(1.08)$$
$$= 100(1.08)^2$$

We continue this process until we have $100(1.08)^n$ for n years.

It is convenient to present the data on a time line.

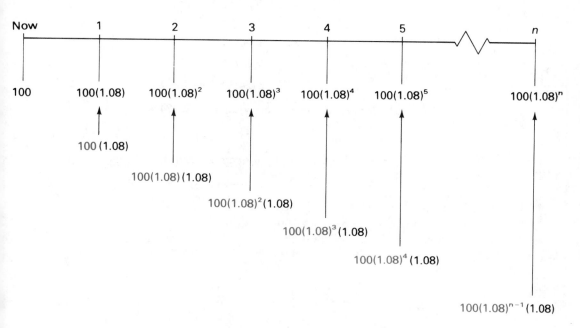

The amount at the end of each year forms the terms of a geometric sequence where $a = 100(1.08)$, $r = 1.08$, and n is the number of years.

$$t_n = ar^{n-1}$$
$$t_n = 100(1.08)(1.08)^{n-1}$$
$$= 100(1.08)^n$$

For $n = 20$, $t_{20} = 100(1.08)^{20}$
$$= 100(4.660\ 957\ 1)$$
$$\doteq 466.10$$

$\therefore$ the money accumulates to $466.10.

In these sections, a calculator was used to 8 figure accuracy. For added convenience, five place tables are provided in the appendix. However, calculations using the five place tables are generally accurate only to four figures.

EXAMPLE 2. *Find the amount of $3000 invested for 5 years at 11%/a compounded semi-annually.*

Solution

The 11%/a compounded semi-annually for 5 years is equivalent to 5.5% per conversion period (in this case 6 months) for 10 conversion periods (twice a year for 5 years). For this geometric sequence,

$$a = 3000(1.055) \qquad r = 1.055 \qquad n = 10$$

$$t_n = ar^{n-1}$$

$$t_{10} = 3000(1.055)(1.055)^{10-1}$$

$$t_{10} = 3000(1.055)^{10}$$

$$= 3000(1.708\ 145)$$

$$\doteq 5124.43$$

∴ the amount after 5 years would be $5124.43.

We generalize the results of example 2 in the following formula:

$$A = P(1+i)^n \text{ where}$$

A is the amount
P is the principal,
i is the rate of interest per conversion period,
n is the total number of conversion periods.

EXAMPLE 3. *Find the amount of $5000 invested for 10 years at 9% compounded semiannually.*

Solution

At 9% compounded semiannually, $i = 0.045$
For 10 years compounded semiannually, $n = 20$

$$A = P(1+i)^n$$

$$A = 5000(1+0.045)^{20}$$

$$= 5000(2.411\ 711\ 4)$$

$$= 12\ 058.57$$

∴ the amount would be $12 058.57.

EXERCISE 8-7

1. (a) Find n and i for a 10%/a semi-annual rate for 7 years.
(b) Find n and i for an 8%/a quarterly rate for 10 years.
(c) Find the per annum rate and conversion period if there are 10 conversion periods in 5 years and $i = 4.5\%$.
(d) Find the per annum rate if the rate per conversion period is 2% compounded quarterly.

2. Find the amount of each of the following investments.
(a) $5000 at 10%/a compounded semi-annually for 5 years.
(b) $7500 at 9%/a compounded semi-annually for 3 years.
(c) $2000 at 8%/a compounded quarterly for 4 years.
(d) $20 000 at 10%/a compounded semi-annually for 10 years.
(e) $250 at 12%/a compounded monthly for 3 years.

3. Albert Catello invests $5000 for 5 years at 9%/a compounded semi-annually.
(a) What is his investment worth after 5 years?
(b) How much interest has been earned?

4. Find the amounts that $1000 invested at 12%/a for 3 years will grow to if the interest is compounded
(a) monthly   (b) quarterly   (c) semi-annually.

5. Find the length of time to the nearest half year that it would take a sum of money to double if it is invested at
(a) 8% semi-annually.
(b) 9% semi-annually.
(c) 10% semi-annually.

6. Bob Brown invests $5000 in an account that pays 9%/a compounded semi-annually. How long must he wait (to the nearest half year) in order to have $8400 for the purchase of a new car?

7. Marie Dubois is saving money for a vacation. On June 1, she invests $800 at 10% compounded semi-annually, and on Dec. 1, she invests an additional $700 at the same rate. How much does she have the following Dec. 1?

8. Sam Jones borrowed $10 000 at 9%/a semi-annually using his insurance policy for collateral. He then reinvested the $10 000 in second mortgages at 16%/a compounded quarterly.
(a) What profit did he make over 5 years?
(b) What did Mr. Jones do to "earn" this profit?

9. Debbie Lubinski borrows money at 8%/a compounded quarterly and reinvests it at 12%/a compounded monthly. Find the annual rate of return by considering an investment of $1 for 1 year.

10. The sum of $20 000 was invested 5 years ago at 11% compounded semiannually. Since then, interest rates have dropped and today the principal and interest were reinvested at 9%/a compounded semiannually for an additional 5 years. What will the investment be worth in 5 years?

8.8 APPLICATION: PRESENT VALUE OF A LUMP SUM

The *Present Value* of an amount is the sum of money that must be invested today to produce a desired amount at a later date.

EXAMPLE 1. *What principal invested now at 10%/a compounded semiannually will produce an amount of $7000 for the purchase of a new car in 3 years?*

Solution
The principal to be invested is called the present value *PV*. Using the formula $A = P(1+i)^n$,

$$A = 7000 \qquad i = 0.05 \qquad P = PV \qquad n = 6$$

$$A = P(1+i)^n$$

$$7000 = PV(1+0.05)^6$$

$$\frac{7000}{(1.05)^6} = PV$$

$$\frac{7000}{1.340\,095\,6} = PV$$

$$5223.51 \doteq PV$$

∴ $5223.51 should be invested today to give $7000 in 3 years.
The results of example 1 can be generalized to the formula

$$PV = \frac{A}{(1+i)^n} \quad \text{where}$$

PV is the present value
A is the amount to be achieved
i is the interest rate per conversion period
n is the number of conversion periods

A table of values for $\dfrac{1}{(1+i)^n}$ is provided in the appendix.

EXAMPLE 2. *Mr. and Mrs. John Conrad have sold their present home for $70 000 and moved into an apartment nearer their jobs. When they retire in 12 years they would like to have $100 000 for the purchase of a retirement home. How much of the $70 000 should they invest in bonds that pay 9% semiannually in order to have $100 000 in 12 years?*

Solution
Mr. and Mrs. Conrad should invest the present value of $100 000 at 9%/a for 12 years. In this case,

$$A = 100\,000 \qquad i = 0.045 \qquad n = 24$$

$$PV = \frac{A}{(1+i)^n}$$

$$PV = \frac{100\,000}{(1.045)^{24}}$$

$$= \frac{100\,000}{2.876\,013\,8}$$

$$= 34\,770.35$$

∴ they should invest $34 770.35 to produce the desired $100 000 in 12 years.

EXERCISE 8-8

Find three integers in arithmetic progression whose product is prime.

1. Find the present value of each of the following amounts.
(a) $15 000 in 10 years at 9% compounded semiannually.
(b) $2500 in 5 years at 8% compounded quarterly.
(c) $500 in 2 years at 12% compounded monthly.
(d) $1575 in 3 years at 12% compounded quarterly.
(e) $25 000 in 5.75 years at 10% compounded quarterly.

2. How much money should be invested today at 10% compounded semi-annually in order to have $8750 in 7 years for the purchase of a new automobile?

3. Mary Boucher has a paid-up policy that will pay her $20 000 at age 65. What is the value of the policy at age 58? Money is worth 5%/a.

4. Find the present values of $1000 due in 3 years at 12%/a if the interest is compounded (a) monthly (b) quarterly (c) semi-annually.

5. George Fontaine has signed a promissory note to pay $1500 on Dec. 1. What is the value of the note on April 1 if money is worth 1%/month on the unpaid balance?

6. John and Vera wish to provide for their new baby's education. How much should they invest on the day the child is born in order to have $16 000 on the child's 18th birthday, if money is worth 9%/a compounded semi-annually?

7. Louis Vanderman owes $1000 in 1 year and $3000 in 2.5 years. How much money is required to retire both debts if money is worth 11%/a compounded semi-annually?

8. Anne White has won a lottery and wishes to set up educational funds for her two children. How much must she invest today at 10% compounded semi-annually in order to have $10 000 each for George in 7 years and Dorothy in 12 years if money is worth 9%/a compounded semi-annually?

9. What principal invested for the next 5 years at 10% semi-annually and for the following 4 years at 12%/a compounded quarterly will amount to $20 000 in 9 years?

10. A standard sized station wagon sells today for $9400. In 3 years, the cost of a new model will increase by 16%. How much should you invest today at 9% compounded semi-annually in order to buy the new model in 3 years with a $2500 trade-in allowance?

8.9 APPLICATION: AMOUNT OF AN ANNUITY

An annuity is a sum of money paid as a series of regular equal payments. Although the word annuity suggests annual or yearly, payments can be made semiannually, quarterly, or monthly. Payments are usually made at the end of the payment interval unless otherwise stated. The amount of an annuity is the sum of the amounts of the individual payments invested from the time of payment until the last payment is made, including all the interest.

EXAMPLE 1. *Joanne Tate deposits $500 into a high interest bearing savings account every Dec. 15 and June 15 for 8 years. How much will she have in the account at the time of the last payment if interest is earned at 8%/a compounded semiannually?*

Solution
We are asked to find the amount of an annuity of 16 semiannual payments of $500 each at 8%/a compounded semiannually, so that $i = 0.04$
The last payment receives no interest.
The second last payment is in for one conversion period.
The first payment is in for 15 conversion periods.

The problem can be illustrated on a time line.

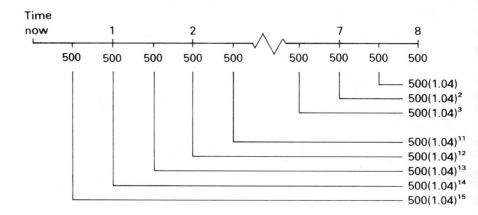

The amount of the annuity is the sum of the amount of the 16 lump sums.

$$A = 500 + 500(1.04) + 500(1.04)^2 + \ldots + 500(1.04)^{15}$$

which is a geometric series with

$$a = 500 \qquad r = 1.04 \qquad n = 16$$

$$S_n = \frac{a(r^n - 1)}{r - 1}$$

$$S_{16} = \frac{500(1.04^{16} - 1)}{1.04 - 1}$$

$$= \frac{500(1.872\,981\,2 - 1)}{0.04}$$

$$= \frac{500(0.872\,981\,2)}{0.04}$$

$$= 10\,912.27$$

∴ the amount of the annuity after 8 years is \$10 912.27

The regular annuity payment is called the periodic rent, R. As in the study of lump sums, i is the interest rate per conversion period and n is the number of payments. We shall assume that the conversion period is equal to the time between payments.

The general annuity is

$$R + R(1 + i) + R(1 + i)^2 + \ldots + R(1 + i)^{n-1}$$

a geometric series with

$a = R, r = (1 + i)$, and there are n terms

$$S_n = \frac{a(r^n - 1)}{r - 1}$$

$$A = \frac{R((1 + i)^n - 1)}{(1 + i) - 1}$$

$$= \frac{R((1 + i)^n - 1)}{i}$$

Solving this formula for R,

$$Ai = R((1 + i)^n - 1)$$

so that

$$R = \frac{Ai}{(1 + i)^n - 1}$$

EXAMPLE 2. *How much money should be invested every month at 12%/a compounded monthly in order to have \$5000 in 18 months?*

Solution

12%/a compounded monthly gives $i = 0.01$

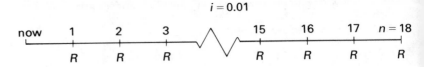

$$i = 0.01$$

The annuity is

$$R + R(1.01) + R(1.01)^2 + \ldots + R(1.01)^{17} = 5000$$

where $a = R$, $r = 1.01$, $n = 18$ and $A = 5000$

$$S_n = \frac{a(r^n - 1)}{r - 1}$$

$$5000 = \frac{R(1.01^{18} - 1)}{1.01 - 1}$$

$$5000 = \frac{R(1.196\ 147\ 5 - 1)}{0.01}$$

$$\frac{5000 \times 0.01}{0.196\ 147\ 5} = R$$

$$R = 254.91$$

∴ the monthly investment should be $254.91

EXERCISE 8-9

B **1.** Find the amount of each of the following annuities.

(a) 20 semi-annual payments of $500 each into an account that pays 8%/a compounded semiannually.

(b) 16 quarterly payments of $300 each into an account that pays 10%/a compounded quarterly.

(c) 36 monthly payments of $50 each into an account that pays 12%/a compounded monthly.

(d) 10 semi-annual payments of $1000 into an account that pays 10% compounded semiannually.

2. Find the periodic rent in each of the following annuities.

(a) 40 semi-annual payments amounting to $20 000 at 10% compounded semiannually.

(b) an amount of $8000 in 6 years if money is worth 12%/a compounded quarterly.

(c) 24 monthly payments amounting to $3200 at 12%/a compounded monthly.

(d) an amount of $12 000 in 4 years if money is worth 12%/a compounded every two months.

3. John Vogel bought a small tractor for his lawn care business. He expects this machine to last for 3 years, and then he will buy a new one for about $11 000. How much must he invest at 1%/month, each month in order to meet this expense in 3 years?

This type of investment plan to meet a future expense is called a sinking fund.

4. The ABC Arena Company wishes to establish a sinking fund to replace the ice making equipment in 12 years. How much should be deposited every 6 months into an account that pays 9%/a compounded semiannually in order to have $42 000 for the replacement in 12 years?

5. Mrs. Benton makes provision for her own pension. She invests $1000 every 6 months starting 6 months before her 35th birthday, into an account that pays 9%/a compounded semiannually. How much will she have on her 50th birthday?

6. Jones Printing has a small press worth $230 000 with a useful life expectancy of 20 years. How much should the company invest semiannually in a sinking fund that pays 9%/a compounded semiannually to meet this expense in 20 years?

7. The Direct Route Courier Service purchased a new van for $9700. In 3 years the van will have a trade-in value of $2000 and will be traded in on a similar vehicle expected to cost $11 200. How much should the company invest semiannually in a sinking fund that pays 10%/a compounded semiannually to meet this expense in 3 years?

8. Find the amounts of the following annuities after the last payment has been made.
a) 12 semiannual payments of $500 at 8%/a compounded semiannually.
b) 36 quarterly payments of $200 at 12%/a compounded quarterly.
c) 24 semiannual payments of $1000 at 9%/a compounded semiannually.
d) 36 monthly payments of $100 at 18%/a compounded monthly.

9. Mrs. Shuster has purchased a small new car for $6200. She realizes that due to driving conditions, she will have to replace the car in 4 years. In that time, new car prices will increase by 40%, and her present car will depreciate 70%. There will be a 7% retail sales tax on the difference between the trade-in value and the new car price. How much should she invest every 3 months in a sinking fund in order to purchase a new car with cash in 4 years if money is worth 12%/a compounded quarterly?

10. Anne and Todd add to the family allowances received for their son Jason so that they save $50/month for his education. Every 6 months the funds are deposited into an account that pays 10%/a compounded semiannually. How much will be in the account when Jason is 18 if his parents started saving on the day he was born?

Determine the pattern.
Find the missing number.

36	15	40	19
29	27	19	17
42	33	/////	22

8.10 APPLICATION: PRESENT VALUE OF AN ANNUITY

The present value of an annuity is the principal which must be invested now at a given rate of interest in order to provide a given periodic rent. We find the present value of the annuity by finding the present values of all of the lump sums.

EXAMPLE 1. *How much money must be invested now at 9%/a compounded semiannually to provide an annuity of 10 payments of $200 every 6 months, the first payment being in 6 months.*

Solution
We can illustrate the problem on a time line.

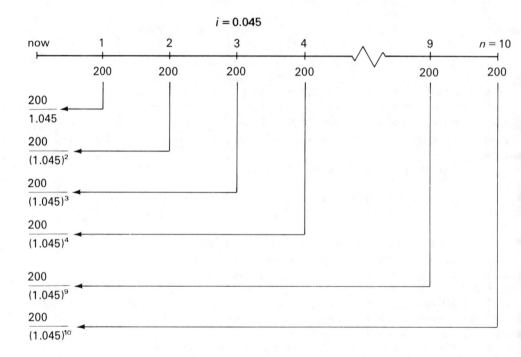

The present value of the annuity is

$$PV = \frac{200}{1.045} + \frac{200}{(1.045)^2} + \frac{200}{(1.045)^3} + \ldots + \frac{200}{(1.045)^{10}}$$

which is a geometric series with

$$a = \frac{200}{1.045}, \quad r = \frac{1}{1.045}, \quad \text{and} \quad n = 10$$

$$S_n = \frac{a(1 - r^n)}{1 - r}$$

$$PV = \frac{200}{1.045}\left(\frac{1 - \dfrac{1}{1.045^{10}}}{1 - \dfrac{1}{1.045}}\right)$$

$$= \frac{200(1 - 0.643\,927\,7)}{1.045(1 - 0.956\,94)}$$

$$= \frac{200(0.356\,072\,3)}{1.045(0.043\,062\,201)}$$

$$\doteq 1582.54$$

∴ investing $1582.54 now at 9%/a compounded semiannually will provide an annuity of $200 every 6 months for 5 years.

EXAMPLE 2. *Rod Carter plans to retire at age 57, and to receive a cash payment of $50 000 from a profit sharing plan. The total sum received will be used to set up an annuity with an insurance company at 8%/a compounded semiannually until age 65. How large is each payment if Rod is to receive two equal payments per year?*

Solution
Let each payment in dollars be R.

$$\text{Time (a)} \quad i = 0.04 \quad n = 16$$

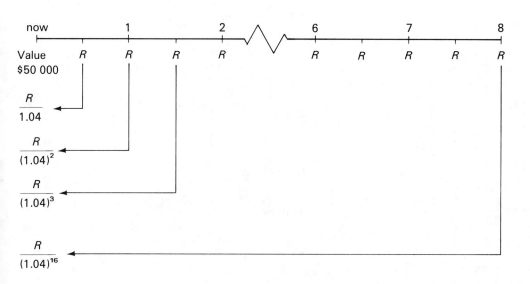

The present value, $50 000, is the sum of the present values:

$$50\,000 = \frac{R}{1.04} + \frac{R}{(1.04)^2} + \frac{R}{(1.04)^3} + \ldots + \frac{R}{(1.04)^{16}}$$

which is a geometric series with

$$S_{16} = 50\,000, \quad a = \frac{R}{1.04}, \quad r = \frac{1}{1.04}, \quad n = 16$$

$$S_n = \frac{a(1 - r^n)}{1 - r}$$

$$50\,000 = \frac{\dfrac{R}{1.04}\left(1 - \dfrac{1}{1.04^{16}}\right)}{1 - \dfrac{1}{1.04}}$$

$$50\,000 = \frac{\dfrac{R}{1.04}(1 - 0.533\,908\,2)}{1 - 0.961\,538\,5}$$

$$= \frac{\dfrac{R}{1.04}(0.466\,091\,8)}{0.038\,461\,539}$$

$$\frac{50\,000 \times 1.04 \times 0.038\,461\,539}{0.466\,091\,8} = R$$

$$R \doteq 4291.00$$

Calculations are simplified if we reverse the series.

$$50\,000 = \frac{R}{1.04^{16}} + \frac{R}{1.04^{15}} + \frac{R}{1.04^{14}} + \ldots + \frac{R}{1.04}$$

where $r = 1.04$

$$S_n = \frac{a(r^n - 1)}{r - 1}$$

$$50\,000 = \frac{R}{1.04^{16}}\left(\frac{1.04^{16} - 1}{1.04 - 1}\right)$$

$$50\,000 = R\left(\frac{1 - \dfrac{1}{1.04^{16}}}{0.04}\right)$$

$$50\,000 = R\left(\frac{1 - 0.533\,908\,2}{0.04}\right)$$

$$50\,000 = R\left(\frac{0.466\,091\,8}{0.04}\right)$$

$$\frac{50\,000 \times 0.04}{0.466\,091\,8} = R$$

$$4291.00 = R$$

$\therefore$ each semiannual payment is \$4291.00

EXERCISE 8-10

1. Find the present value of each of the following.
(a) 20 payments of $300 each at 8%/a compounded semiannually.
(b) 24 payments of $1000 each at 12%/a compounded quarterly.
(c) 36 payments of $75 each at 12%/a compounded monthly.
(d) 10 payments of $5000 each at 10%/a compounded semiannually.

2. Find the periodic rent of each of the following.
(a) 40 semiannual payments of 8%/a with a present value of $10 000.
(b) 12 quarterly payments at 12%/a with a present value of $8000.
(c) 24 monthly payments at 12%/a with a present value of $5600.
(d) 15 semiannual payments at 10%/a with a present value of $9000.

3. Find the present value of $200/month for 2 years beginning in 1 month if interest is earned at 2%/month.

4. John Banks has won $5000 to attend university. If he invests the money in a small second mortgage at 12%/a compounded monthly, how much can he draw monthly for the next 3 years starting 1 month later?

5. Tom Sullivan retires from the Acme Steel Company with his choice of $50 000 cash or 30 equal half-yearly payments earning interest at 9%/a compounded semiannually. If the first payment is made 6 months after he retires, how large is each payment?

6. W. "Bill" Harvey pays into an annuity with interest at 9% semiannually that will pay him $5000 every 6 months for 10a starting at age 65. Find the present value of the annuity on his 65th birthday.

7. An annuity pays $3000 every 6 months for 10 years from an account that pays 9%/a compounded semiannually. Find the present value of the annuity if the first payment is due
(a) now   (b) in 6 months.

8. Find the monthly payment required to pay off an automobile worth $10 125 including taxes, if the down payment was $2500 and the balance was financed over 2 years at 12%/a compounded monthly.

9. Mr. and Mrs. Ed Yates win $250 000 in a lottery on Mr. Yates' 45th birthday. How much should they invest as a lump sum today in order to have 10 payments of $10 000 each every 6 months starting 6 months after Mr. Yates' 60th birthday? The money is invested at 10% compounded semiannually.

10. Tom Stevens signs a professional baseball contract that will pay him $25 000/a for 5 years plus a bonus for signing in the form of an annuity of $5000/a for 20 years to follow. Money is worth 6%/a, compounded annually. Find
(a) the present value of the annuity at the time of signing.
(b) the total cost of the contract to the club.
(c) Compare the total cost of the contract to the club with the total amount of money Tom Stevens will receive.

REVIEW EXERCISE

B **1.** Identify each of the following sequences as arithmetic or geometric, and find t_n.

(a) $2, 7, 12, \ldots$ (b) $2, 4, 8, \ldots$

(c) $x, x^3, x^5, \ldots$ (d) $x, x+a, x+2a, \ldots$

(e) $5, 1, -3, \ldots$ (f) $3, -6, 12, \ldots$

2. Write the first three terms and identify each of the following as arithmetic or geometric. Find the sum of the first 8 terms.

(a) $t_n = 2 + 3n$ (b) $t_n = 2(3^{n-2})$

(c) $t_n = 3n + 1$ (d) $t_n = 21 - 3n$

(e) $t_n = 5(2^n)$ (f) $t_n = 3(2^{-n})$

3. Find the number of terms if the sequences are either arithmetic or geometric.

(a) $8, 12, 16, \ldots, 100$ (b) $5, 10, 20, \ldots, 1280$

4. If $t_4 = 24$ and $t_7 = 192$, find the first four terms if the sequence is

(a) arithmetic   (b) geometric

5. Find t_{20} and S_{50} for the following arithmetic series.

(a) $t_{10} = 16$, $t_{18} = 40$ (b) $t_5 = 15$, $t_9 = 31$

6. Find t_5 and S_6 for the following geometric series.

(a) $t_3 = 6$, $t_6 = 48$ (b) $t_2 = 10$, $t_5 = 1250$

7. If a town has an 8% population growth each year and its present population is 7000, what will the population be in 4 years?

8. The present population of a town is 13 000. What was the population 5 years ago if the growth rate was 6% each year?

9. There is a legend that the inventor of chess chose the following as his reward.

One grain of wheat on the first square, two grains on the second square, four on the third and so on for all 64 squares on the chessboard. Find an expression for the amount of wheat required to fulfill his request.

10. Write explicitly and find the sum.

(a) $\sum_{n=1}^{6} \dfrac{n+1}{n}$ (b) $\sum_{k=2}^{6} \dfrac{k-2}{k}$ (c) $\sum_{i=1}^{5} 2^{i-1}$

11. Find the amount of

(a) $5000 invested for 6 years at 9%/a compounded semiannually.

(b) $360 invested for 1 year at 12%/a compounded monthly.

12. Find the present value of

(a) $12 000 in 5 years at 10%/a compounded semiannually.

(b) $8500 in 4 years at 8%/a compounded quarterly.

13. Find the amount of an annuity of

(a) 30 payments of $500 every 6 months if money is worth 9%/a compounded semiannually.

(b) 24 payments of $100/month if money is worth 24%/a compounded monthly.

14. Find the periodic rent for
(a) an amount of \$10 000 in 10 years if money is worth 9%/a compounded semiannually and payments are made every 6 months.
(b) 16 payments amounting to \$6000 in 4 years if money is worth 8% compounded quarterly.

15. Find the present value of an annuity of
(a) 24 payments of \$100 each if money is worth 10%/a compounded quarterly.
(b) 10 semiannual payments of \$1000 each at 10%/a compounded semiannually.

16. Find the periodic rent if
(a) the present value is \$10 500 and there are 30 semiannual payments with interest at 10%/a compounded semiannually.
(b) the present value is \$695 and there are 24 monthly payments at 1%/month.

17. If $t_1, t_2, t_3, \ldots$ is a geometric sequence with $t_n = xy^{n-1}$, prove $\log t_1$, $\log t_2$, $\log t_3, \ldots$ is an arithmetic sequence.

18. Prove $\sqrt{xy} \leqslant \frac{1}{2}(x+y)$.
The geometric mean of two positive real numbers is less than or equal to the arithmetic mean of the numbers.

19. (a) If $t_1, t_2, t_3, \ldots$ is a geometric sequence with $t_n = ab^{n-1}$, determine whether $t_1^2, t_2^2, t_3^2, \ldots$ is a geometric sequence.
(b) State the common ratio of the second sequence.

20. If $t_1, t_2, t_3, \ldots$ is an arithmetic sequence with $t_n = 2n-1$, find a corresponding geometric sequence with $a = t_1$ and $r = t_2$.

REVIEW AND PREVIEW TO CHAPTER 9

EXERCISE 1   LINEAR SYSTEMS

1. Solve the following systems of equations.

(a) $y = 2x - 1$
$y = 3x - 4$

(b) $y = -x + 6$
$y = x + 8$

(c) $y = 3x - 1$
$y = x + 5$

(d) $x + y = 7$
$x - y = 13$

(e) $2x + y = 7$
$3x - 2y = 7$

(f) $3x + 2y = -8$
$5x + 3y = -14$

(g) $5x - 6y = -1$
$7x + 4y = 11$

(h) $3x - 5y = 9$
$4x - 7y = 13$

(i) $6x - 7y = -72$
$4x - 5y = -50$

(j) $3x - 8y + 7 = 0$
$2x + 9y = -19$

(k) $y = 8x - 9$
$10x + 3y = -10$

(l) $9x - 8y + 7 = 0$
$3x + 10y - 4 = 0$

(m) $8x = 7y + 4$
$5y = 3x - 11$

(n) $5x + 6y = 3.8$
$4x - 7y = -0.5$

(o) $6x + y = 0.9$
$2x - 3y = 1.3$

(p) $\dfrac{x + y}{2} = 4$

$\dfrac{2x - 3y}{3} = -3$

(q) $\dfrac{x}{2} - \dfrac{y}{6} = 9$

$\dfrac{x}{4} + \dfrac{y}{3} = -3$

(r) $\dfrac{4x + 2}{5} = -\dfrac{y}{2}$

$\dfrac{3y + 4}{4} = -\dfrac{4x}{3}$

2. Solve the following systems of equations.

(a) $4x + 3y + 2z = 8$
$5x + 3y - z = 1$
$2x + 5y - 3z = -15$

(b) $3x + y - 2z = 16$
$2x + 3y - z = 3$
$4x - 2y - 3z = 32$

(c) $4x + 2y + 3z = -5$
$5x - 5y + 4z = 25$
$6x + y + 3z = -7$

(d) $2x + y - z = 3$
$4x - 2y + 3z = -5$
$6x - 3y - 4z = 18$

(e) $4x - 2y - 5z = -27$
$3x + y = 2z - 19$
$x - 3z = -3y - 18$

(f) $x + y = 8$
$z - y = 1$
$x - z = 1$

(g) $2x - 3y + 4z = -1.2$
$5x - 2y - 3z = 2.4$
$3x - 4y - 5z = 3.6$

(h) $x + 2y = 3z + 1$
$3x + 6z = 4y + 3$
$3z + 5x = 5 + 2y$

(i) $4w + 3x + 2y - z = -5$
$3w + x - y + z = 4$
$2w + 2x + y - 2z = -6$
$w + 4x - 2y + 2z = 17$

(j) $3w + 2x + y = 6 + z$
$2w + 2y - z = 9 + 3x$
$w - 2x + z = 2 + 3y$
$3x - y - z = 3 - 2w$

Matrices and Vectors

Algebra is the intellectual instrument for rendering clear the quantitative aspects of the world.

Alfred North Whitehead

9.1 BASIC MATRIX OPERATIONS

A matrix is a rectangular array of numbers enclosed by parentheses or brackets. The following are examples of matrices

$$\begin{pmatrix} 3 & 4 \\ -1 & 2 \end{pmatrix}, \quad \begin{bmatrix} 5 & 1 & 7 \\ -2 & -5 & 6 \end{bmatrix}, \quad (4 \quad 0 \quad 5 \quad -2), \quad \begin{bmatrix} 1 \\ 3 \\ 5 \\ 2 \end{bmatrix}$$

The numbers in the matrix are called the *entries, elements* or *components* of the matrix. The number of rows (horizontal) and columns (vertical) determine the *dimension* or *order* of the matrix. The matrices given above have dimensions 2×2 (two by two), 2×3, 1×4 and 4×1. The number of rows is always given first.

A matrix that has the same number of rows as columns is called a *square matrix*. A matrix whose entries are all zero is called a *zero matrix*. A matrix containing only one row, such as (3   5   6) is called a *row matrix*, while a matrix containing only one column is called a *column matrix*.

Two matrices are *equal* when they have the same order and have equal elements in corresponding positions.

In general we represent a matrix as follows

$$A = \begin{pmatrix} a_{11} & a_{12} & a_{13} \ldots a_{1n} \\ a_{21} & a_{22} & a_{23} \ldots a_{2n} \\ a_{31} & a_{32} & a_{33} \ldots a_{3n} \\ \cdot & \cdot & \cdot \quad \cdot \\ \cdot & \cdot & \cdot \quad \cdot \\ \cdot & \cdot & \cdot \quad \cdot \\ a_{m1} & a_{m2} & a_{m3} \ldots a_{mn} \end{pmatrix}$$

or in shorter notation

$$A = (a_{ij})$$

This matrix has m rows and n columns. It is an $m \times n$ matrix. The numbers $a_{ij} (i = 1, \ldots, m; j = 1, \ldots, n)$ are the entries of the matrix. The entry a_{ij} is in the ith row and jth column of the matrix.

The *sum* of two matrices is found by adding the corresponding components of the two matrices.

For example, if

$$A = \begin{pmatrix} 3 & -1 & -5 \\ 5 & -3 & 6 \end{pmatrix} \quad \text{and} \quad B = \begin{pmatrix} 0 & 5 & -2 \\ 7 & 8 & 3 \end{pmatrix}$$

then

$$A + B = \begin{pmatrix} 3 & -1 & -5 \\ 5 & -3 & 6 \end{pmatrix} + \begin{pmatrix} 0 & 5 & -2 \\ 7 & 8 & 3 \end{pmatrix}$$

$$= \begin{pmatrix} 3+0 & -1+5 & -5+(-2) \\ 5+7 & -3+8 & 6+3 \end{pmatrix}$$

$$= \begin{pmatrix} 3 & 4 & -7 \\ 12 & 5 & 9 \end{pmatrix}$$

$$\boxed{A + B = (a_{ij}) + (b_{ij}) = (a_{ij} + b_{ij})}$$

By this definition of sum, two matrices may be added only if they contain the same number of rows and the same number of columns.

The *negative* of matrix A is the matrix $-A$, each of whose entries is the negative of the corresponding entry in A.

If $\qquad A = \begin{pmatrix} 2 & -4 \\ -3 & 5 \end{pmatrix} \quad \text{then} \quad -A = \begin{pmatrix} -2 & 4 \\ 3 & -5 \end{pmatrix}$

We now define subtraction of matrices in terms of addition.

If $\qquad A = \begin{pmatrix} 5 & -8 \\ -4 & -6 \end{pmatrix} \quad \text{and} \quad B = \begin{pmatrix} -1 & 3 \\ -2 & 4 \end{pmatrix}$

then $\qquad A - B = A + (-B)$

$$= \begin{pmatrix} 5 & -8 \\ -4 & -6 \end{pmatrix} + \begin{pmatrix} 1 & -3 \\ 2 & -4 \end{pmatrix}$$

$$= \begin{pmatrix} 6 & -11 \\ -2 & -10 \end{pmatrix}$$

or $\qquad A - B = \begin{pmatrix} 5 & -8 \\ -4 & -6 \end{pmatrix} - \begin{pmatrix} -1 & 3 \\ -2 & 4 \end{pmatrix}$

$$= \begin{pmatrix} 5-(-1) & -8-3 \\ -4-(-2) & -6-4 \end{pmatrix}$$

$$= \begin{pmatrix} 6 & -11 \\ -2 & -10 \end{pmatrix}$$

$$\boxed{A - B = (a_{ij}) - (b_{ij}) = (a_{ij} - b_{ij})}$$

When working with matrices we call any real number a *scalar*.

The *scalar product* of a number k and a matrix A is a matrix kA where each element of A is multiplied by k. For example, if $\qquad A = \begin{pmatrix} 2 & 3 & -1 \\ 4 & 0 & -3 \end{pmatrix}$ and $k = 3$

then $\qquad kA = 3\begin{pmatrix} 2 & 3 & -1 \\ 4 & 0 & -3 \end{pmatrix}$

$$= \begin{pmatrix} 6 & 9 & -3 \\ 12 & 0 & -9 \end{pmatrix}$$

$$\boxed{kA = k(a_{ij}) = (ka_{ij})}$$

EXAMPLE 1. *Express as a single matrix*

$$4\begin{pmatrix} 3 & -2 \\ -1 & -5 \end{pmatrix} - 2\begin{pmatrix} -1 & 5 \\ 2 & 3 \end{pmatrix}$$

Solution

$$4\begin{pmatrix} 3 & -2 \\ -1 & -5 \end{pmatrix} - 2\begin{pmatrix} -1 & 5 \\ 2 & 3 \end{pmatrix} = \begin{pmatrix} 12 & -8 \\ -4 & -20 \end{pmatrix} + \begin{pmatrix} 2 & -10 \\ -4 & -6 \end{pmatrix}$$

$$= \begin{pmatrix} 14 & -18 \\ -8 & -26 \end{pmatrix}$$

EXERCISE 9-1

1. Given the matrices

$$A = \begin{pmatrix} 3 & -2 & -3 \\ -1 & 4 & 5 \\ 7 & -6 & 8 \end{pmatrix}, \qquad B = \begin{pmatrix} 2 & 1 \\ -3 & 4 \\ 5 & 8 \end{pmatrix}, \qquad C = \begin{pmatrix} 0 \\ 3 \\ -5 \\ -6 \end{pmatrix}$$

and $\qquad D = (0 \quad 4 \quad 3 \quad -8 \quad -1),$

(a) state the dimension of each matrix
(b) state the matrix $-B$
(c) identify the entries a_{22}, a_{13}, a_{31}
(d) identify the entries b_{21}, b_{12}, b_{32}
(e) identify the entries c_{31}, d_{14}, d_{15}

2. State the indicated sum, difference or product.

(a) $\begin{pmatrix} 5 & -6 \\ 3 & -4 \end{pmatrix} + \begin{pmatrix} -4 & 7 \\ -5 & 8 \end{pmatrix}$

(b) $\begin{pmatrix} 6 & -7 \\ -9 & 3 \end{pmatrix} - \begin{pmatrix} 8 & 6 \\ -2 & -1 \end{pmatrix}$

(c) $3\begin{pmatrix} 5 & -7 \\ -4 & 0 \end{pmatrix}$

(d) $\begin{pmatrix} 5 \\ 4 \\ -2 \end{pmatrix} - \begin{pmatrix} -3 \\ 7 \\ -1 \end{pmatrix}$

(e) $\begin{pmatrix} 6 & 0 & -1 \\ -3 & -4 & 5 \\ 2 & 1 & -2 \end{pmatrix} + \begin{pmatrix} -6 & 8 & 2 \\ 4 & -1 & 0 \\ -3 & -2 & 5 \end{pmatrix}$

(f) $-4\begin{pmatrix} 6 & -3 \\ -2 & 1 \end{pmatrix}$

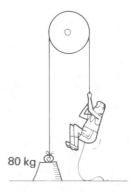

80 kg

A rope passes over a pulley. A block of iron with a mass of 80 kg is attached to one end. A man with a mass of 80 kg starts to climb steadily up the rope. Will the block of iron rise or fall?

B 3. If $A = \begin{pmatrix} 3 & -1 & -2 \\ 2 & 4 & 0 \end{pmatrix}$, $B = \begin{pmatrix} -5 & 4 & -3 \\ -3 & -1 & 6 \end{pmatrix}$ and $C = \begin{pmatrix} 6 & -2 & 4 \\ -1 & -3 & 2 \end{pmatrix}$, find

(a) $A + B$ (b) $A + C$ (c) $A + B + C$
(d) $-2A$ (e) $B - C$ (f) $C - B$
(g) $2B + 3C$ (h) $3A - B$ (i) $2C - 3B$
(j) $2A - \frac{1}{2}C$ (k) $2(3B - 2C)$ (l) $3C - (2A + B)$

4. Express as a single matrix.

(a) $5\begin{pmatrix} -3 & 4 \\ 0 & 1 \end{pmatrix} - 2\begin{pmatrix} 0 & -5 \\ -6 & 1 \end{pmatrix} - 4\begin{pmatrix} 1 & 5 \\ -1 & -2 \end{pmatrix}$

(b) $3(4 \quad 1 \quad 3 \quad 0) - (-2 \quad 4 \quad -1 \quad -3) - 5(0 \quad 3 \quad -1 \quad -2)$

(c) $4\begin{pmatrix} 3 \\ 1 \\ 5 \end{pmatrix} + 2\begin{pmatrix} -4 \\ -3 \\ -1 \end{pmatrix} - 5\begin{pmatrix} 6 \\ -4 \\ -7 \end{pmatrix}$

(d) $2\begin{pmatrix} 1 & 5 & 6 \\ -4 & -3 & 2 \\ 2 & 0 & -1 \end{pmatrix} - \begin{pmatrix} -3 & -5 & 6 \\ 4 & -2 & 3 \\ 3 & 1 & -4 \end{pmatrix} - 3\begin{pmatrix} 2 & 1 & 5 \\ -3 & -1 & 4 \\ 1 & -3 & 4 \end{pmatrix}$

5. Find the 2×2 matrix X in each of the following.

(a) $X + \begin{pmatrix} 3 & -4 \\ -1 & 2 \end{pmatrix} = \begin{pmatrix} -1 & 5 \\ -4 & -6 \end{pmatrix}$ (b) $X - \begin{pmatrix} 3 & -4 \\ 1 & 2 \end{pmatrix} = \begin{pmatrix} -1 & -4 \\ 6 & 3 \end{pmatrix}$

(c) $X - \begin{pmatrix} 5 & 3 \\ -1 & -2 \end{pmatrix} = 2\begin{pmatrix} 3 & -1 \\ 5 & -2 \end{pmatrix}$ (d) $X + \begin{pmatrix} 5 & 6 \\ -1 & -4 \end{pmatrix} = -3\begin{pmatrix} 1 & -4 \\ 3 & -2 \end{pmatrix}$

(e) $2X - \begin{pmatrix} 6 & -4 \\ 8 & -7 \end{pmatrix} = \begin{pmatrix} 8 & 6 \\ -4 & 3 \end{pmatrix}$ (f) $2X + 3\begin{pmatrix} 1 & 4 \\ -2 & -1 \end{pmatrix} = -2\begin{pmatrix} -1 & -3 \\ 5 & 6 \end{pmatrix}$

9.2 MULTIPLICATION OF MATRICES

It would seem that we should multiply matrices in a manner similar to the way we add them. However, experience has shown that the method which is most useful is what is often called row-by-column multiplication.

Consider the following example.

The Besco Motor Company makes limited edition models of cars by taking standard new cars and replacing the body. The company produces three models—the Manta, the Python and the Lynx. The following table gives the units of material and units of labour required for the production of each model.

	Manta	Python	Lynx
Units of Material	9	7	6
Units of Labour	38	42	33

This information can be represented by the matrix A

$$A = \begin{pmatrix} 9 & 7 & 6 \\ 38 & 42 & 33 \end{pmatrix}$$

Suppose that the cost of each unit of material is $50 and the cost of each unit of labour is $80. We can represent these costs by the row matrix C.

$$C = (50 \quad 80)$$

The total cost of production will be $C \times A$.
The total cost for a Manta is $50 \times 9 + 80 \times 38 = 3490$
The total cost for a Python is $50 \times 7 + 80 \times 42 = 3710$
The total cost for a Lynx is $50 \times 6 + 80 \times 33 = 2940$
We can represent the total cost for each by the matrix

$$(3490 \quad 3710 \quad 2940)$$

We arrive at this matrix by

$$CA = (50 \quad 80)\begin{pmatrix} 9 & 7 & 6 \\ 38 & 42 & 33 \end{pmatrix}$$

$$= (50 \times 9 + 80 \times 38 \quad 50 \times 7 + 80 \times 42 \quad 50 \times 6 + 80 \times 33)$$

$$= (3490 \quad 3710 \quad 2940)$$

Notice that the number of columns in C is the same as the number of rows in A.

To multiply matrices it is not necessary that they have the same dimensions. What is necessary is that the number of columns of the first matrix be the same as the number of rows of the second matrix. With this in mind we shall define the product of two matrices.

> The product of an $m \times n$ matrix A and an $n \times p$ matrix B is the $m \times p$ matrix whose entry in row i and column j is the sum of the products of corresponding elements of row i in A and column j in B.

If
$$A = \begin{pmatrix} a_{11} & a_{12} \\ a_{21} & a_{22} \end{pmatrix} \quad \text{and} \quad B = \begin{pmatrix} b_{11} & b_{12} \\ b_{21} & b_{22} \end{pmatrix}$$

then
$$AB = \begin{pmatrix} a_{11} & a_{12} \\ a_{21} & a_{22} \end{pmatrix}\begin{pmatrix} b_{11} & b_{12} \\ b_{21} & b_{22} \end{pmatrix} = \begin{pmatrix} (a_{11}b_{11} + a_{12}b_{21}) & (a_{11}b_{12} + a_{12}b_{22}) \\ (a_{21}b_{11} + a_{22}b_{21}) & (a_{21}b_{12} + a_{22}b_{22}) \end{pmatrix}$$

The rule for multiplication is illustrated by the following example.

EXAMPLE 1. *Find the product*

$$\begin{pmatrix} 4 & -1 \\ 2 & -3 \end{pmatrix}\begin{pmatrix} 2 & -1 & -3 \\ 4 & -2 & 0 \end{pmatrix}$$

Solution

$$\begin{pmatrix} 4 & -1 \\ 2 & -3 \end{pmatrix}\begin{pmatrix} 2 & -1 & -3 \\ 4 & -2 & 0 \end{pmatrix} = \begin{pmatrix} 4 & & \end{pmatrix} \qquad (4)(2) + (-1)(4)$$

$$\begin{pmatrix} 4 & -1 \\ 2 & -3 \end{pmatrix}\begin{pmatrix} 2 & -1 & -3 \\ 4 & -2 & 0 \end{pmatrix} = \begin{pmatrix} 4 & -2 & \end{pmatrix} \qquad (4)(-1) + (-1)(-2)$$

$$\begin{pmatrix} 4 & -1 \\ 2 & -3 \end{pmatrix}\begin{pmatrix} 2 & -1 & -3 \\ 4 & -2 & 0 \end{pmatrix} = \begin{pmatrix} 4 & -2 & -12 \\ & & \end{pmatrix} \qquad (4)(-3)+(-1)(0)$$

$$\begin{pmatrix} 4 & -1 \\ 2 & -3 \end{pmatrix}\begin{pmatrix} 2 & -1 & -3 \\ 4 & -2 & 0 \end{pmatrix} = \begin{pmatrix} 4 & -2 & -12 \\ -8 & & \end{pmatrix} \qquad (2)(2)+(-3)(4)$$

$$\begin{pmatrix} 4 & -1 \\ 2 & -3 \end{pmatrix}\begin{pmatrix} 2 & -1 & -3 \\ 4 & -2 & 0 \end{pmatrix} = \begin{pmatrix} 4 & -2 & -12 \\ -8 & 4 & \end{pmatrix} \qquad (2)(-1)+(-3)(-2)$$

$$\begin{pmatrix} 4 & -1 \\ 2 & -3 \end{pmatrix}\begin{pmatrix} 2 & -1 & -3 \\ 4 & -2 & 0 \end{pmatrix} = \begin{pmatrix} 4 & -2 & -12 \\ -8 & 4 & -6 \end{pmatrix} \qquad (2)(-3)+(-3)(0)$$

$$\therefore \ \begin{pmatrix} 4 & -1 \\ 2 & -3 \end{pmatrix}\begin{pmatrix} 2 & -1 & -3 \\ 4 & -2 & 0 \end{pmatrix} = \begin{pmatrix} 4 & -2 & -12 \\ -8 & 4 & -6 \end{pmatrix}$$

Matrix multiplication is not always possible.
If

$$A = \begin{pmatrix} 2 & -3 \\ 1 & 4 \end{pmatrix} \quad \text{and} \quad B = \begin{pmatrix} 2 \\ 5 \end{pmatrix}$$

then it is possible to find the product AB.

$$AB = \begin{pmatrix} 2 & -3 \\ 1 & 4 \end{pmatrix}\begin{pmatrix} 2 \\ 5 \end{pmatrix}$$
$$= \begin{pmatrix} -11 \\ 22 \end{pmatrix},$$

but not possible to find the product BA since the number of columns of the first matrix must equal the number of rows of the second matrix.

EXAMPLE 2. *The General Computer Company distributes 3 types of home computers—HCA, HCB, and HCC. The following table gives the number of each type ordered by 4 stores.*

	HCA	HCB	HCC
Store 1	10	8	6
Store 2	7	9	5
Store 3	8	4	3
Store 4	6	7	3

If each HCA, HCB and HCC cost $800, $900 and $1000 respectively, use matrix multiplication to determine the income from each store.

Solution

We first write the order as a matrix

$$\begin{pmatrix} 10 & 8 & 6 \\ 7 & 9 & 5 \\ 8 & 4 & 3 \\ 6 & 7 & 3 \end{pmatrix}$$

Now we write the costs as a column matrix

$$\begin{pmatrix} 800 \\ 900 \\ 1000 \end{pmatrix}$$

Then

$$\begin{pmatrix} 10 & 8 & 6 \\ 7 & 9 & 5 \\ 8 & 4 & 3 \\ 6 & 7 & 3 \end{pmatrix} \begin{pmatrix} 800 \\ 900 \\ 1000 \end{pmatrix} = \begin{pmatrix} 21\,200 \\ 18\,700 \\ 13\,000 \\ 14\,100 \end{pmatrix}$$

The product matrix represents the income from each store, \$21 200 from Store 1, \$18 700 from Store 2, \$13 000 from Store 3 and \$14 100 from Store 4.

Recall that the number 1 is the identity element over multiplication for all real numbers x because $1 \times x = x \times 1 = x$.
Similarly the 2×2 matrix

$$I = \begin{pmatrix} 1 & 0 \\ 0 & 1 \end{pmatrix}$$

is the multiplicative identity matrix for all 2×2 matrices because

$$\begin{pmatrix} 1 & 0 \\ 0 & 1 \end{pmatrix}\begin{pmatrix} a & b \\ c & d \end{pmatrix} = \begin{pmatrix} a & b \\ c & d \end{pmatrix}\begin{pmatrix} 1 & 0 \\ 0 & 1 \end{pmatrix} = \begin{pmatrix} a & b \\ c & d \end{pmatrix}$$

Similarly the identity matrix for 3×3 matrices is

$$\begin{pmatrix} 1 & 0 & 0 \\ 0 & 1 & 0 \\ 0 & 0 & 1 \end{pmatrix}$$

In general a square matrix whose main diagonal from upper left to lower right has entries 1 while all other entries are 0 is an identity matrix.

MULTIPLICATION

$$\frac{\begin{array}{r} EAU \\ EAU \end{array}}{OCEAN}$$

EXERCISE 9-2

A **1.** The table indicates the number of rows and columns in Matrices A, B, C, D and E.

Matrix	Number of Rows	Number of Columns
A	2	3
B	2	2
C	3	2
D	3	3
E	1	2

Which of the following multiplications are possible?
(a) AB　　(b) BA　　(c) EC　　(d) CE　　(e) AD
(f) DE　　(g) CE　　(h) BD　　(i) DB

B **2.** Write each product as a single matrix, where possible.

(a) $\begin{pmatrix} 3 & 1 \\ 2 & 4 \end{pmatrix}\begin{pmatrix} 1 & 3 \\ 5 & 6 \end{pmatrix}$　　(b) $\begin{pmatrix} -3 & 2 \\ -4 & 0 \end{pmatrix}\begin{pmatrix} 5 & -1 \\ -3 & 2 \end{pmatrix}$

(c) $\begin{pmatrix} 2 & 5 \\ -1 & 7 \end{pmatrix}\begin{pmatrix} -4 & -3 \\ 6 & -2 \end{pmatrix}$　　(d) $\begin{pmatrix} 7 & 11 \\ -2 & -3 \end{pmatrix}\begin{pmatrix} -6 & 5 \\ 0 & 8 \end{pmatrix}$

(e) $\begin{pmatrix} 1 & 0 \\ 0 & 1 \end{pmatrix}\begin{pmatrix} 5 & -3 \\ 2 & 9 \end{pmatrix}$　　(f) $\begin{pmatrix} 6 & 2 & 1 \\ 3 & 4 & -2 \\ 5 & -1 & 3 \end{pmatrix}\begin{pmatrix} 7 & -3 & 4 \\ 6 & 5 & -2 \\ -1 & -4 & 8 \end{pmatrix}$

(g) $\begin{pmatrix} -1 & 2 & 1 \\ -2 & 3 & 6 \\ 0 & 5 & -2 \end{pmatrix}\begin{pmatrix} 7 & 2 & -4 \\ 1 & 9 & -6 \\ 8 & -3 & -5 \end{pmatrix}$　　(h) $(7 \quad 3 \quad 1 \quad -2)\begin{pmatrix} 7 \\ -1 \\ 3 \end{pmatrix}$

(i) $\begin{pmatrix} 6 \\ -2 \end{pmatrix}(-4 \quad -2 \quad -3)$　　(j) $\begin{pmatrix} 3 & 5 & 0 \\ 6 & -1 & 2 \\ -4 & 3 & 0 \end{pmatrix}\begin{pmatrix} 1 & 0 & 0 \\ 0 & 1 & 0 \\ 0 & 0 & 1 \end{pmatrix}$

(k) $\begin{pmatrix} 1 & 0 & 0 \\ 0 & 1 & 0 \\ 0 & 0 & 1 \end{pmatrix}\begin{pmatrix} 3 \\ -5 \\ 2 \end{pmatrix}$　　(l) $\begin{pmatrix} 5 \\ 1 \\ 3 \end{pmatrix}\begin{pmatrix} 2 & 2 \\ -3 & 6 \\ -5 & -3 \end{pmatrix}$

(m) $\begin{pmatrix} 5 & 1 & 7 & 6 \\ 4 & -2 & -3 & 0 \\ 6 & -1 & 3 & 4 \end{pmatrix}\begin{pmatrix} 4 & 9 \\ 3 & -2 \\ -1 & -1 \\ 7 & 0 \end{pmatrix}$　　(n) $\begin{pmatrix} 2 & 3 \\ 4 & -1 \\ -5 & -2 \end{pmatrix}\begin{pmatrix} 5 & -3 & -2 & 1 \\ 4 & -1 & 6 & 2 \end{pmatrix}$

(o) $\begin{pmatrix} 3 & 1 & -2 \\ 1 & -4 & 1 \\ 0 & 3 & -1 \end{pmatrix}\begin{pmatrix} 5 & 0 \\ 1 & 2 \\ 0 & 4 \end{pmatrix}$　　(p) $\begin{pmatrix} 2 & -1 \\ 3 & 4 \\ -1 & 2 \end{pmatrix}\begin{pmatrix} 1 & 0 & 0 \\ 0 & 1 & 0 \\ 0 & 0 & 1 \end{pmatrix}$

3. The Best Book Company bought the publishing rights to an exciting novel, "Diary of a Mad Mathematician". The book was published in hard cover and paperback. The following table gives the number of each type ordered by 4 stores.

	HC	PB
Store A	100	300
Store B	150	300
Store C	200	400
Store D	75	500

(a) If each hardcover edition costs $8 and each paperback $1.50, use matrix multiplication to determine the amount owing to the company by each store.

(b) The stores sell each hardcover book for $10 and each paperback for $2. The book is an instant best seller, naturally, and each store sells all its copies. Use matrix multiplication to determine the gross profit for each store.

4. The Deuce Racquet Company makes and distributes 3 models of tennis racquets—ACE, STAR and PRO. The following table indicates the number of each type ordered by 5 stores.

	ACE	STAR	PRO
Store 1	15	6	9
Store 2	13	9	10
Store 3	20	5	3
Store 4	25	8	8
Store 5	17	4	12

If the ACE, STAR and PRO models cost $15, $30 and $60 respectively, use matrix multiplication to find the amount owing to the company by each store.

5. If $A = \begin{pmatrix} 2 & 3 \\ 1 & -1 \end{pmatrix}$, $B = \begin{pmatrix} 3 & -2 \\ -1 & 0 \end{pmatrix}$ and $C = \begin{pmatrix} 0 & -1 \\ -2 & 3 \end{pmatrix}$ show that

(a) $AC \neq CA$
(b) $A(BC) = (AB)C$
(c) $A(B+C) = AB + AC$
(d) $(A+C)B = AB + CB$
(e) $(A+B)^2 = A^2 + 2AB + B^2$
(f) $(B+C)(B-C) = B^2 - C^2$
(g) $(B-C)^2 = B^2 - 2BC + C^2$
(h) $A^2 \neq A^3$

C **6.** Solve the following matrix equations.

(a) $\begin{pmatrix} 2 & 3 \\ 3 & -1 \end{pmatrix}\begin{pmatrix} x \\ y \end{pmatrix} = \begin{pmatrix} 7 \\ 5 \end{pmatrix}$

(b) $\begin{pmatrix} 4 & 1 \\ 1 & 3 \end{pmatrix}\begin{pmatrix} x \\ y \end{pmatrix} = \begin{pmatrix} 5 \\ -7 \end{pmatrix}$

(c) $\begin{pmatrix} 5 & -2 \\ 7 & -3 \end{pmatrix}\begin{pmatrix} x \\ y \end{pmatrix} = \begin{pmatrix} 4 \\ 5 \end{pmatrix}$

(d) $\begin{pmatrix} 2 & 1 & 3 \\ 3 & -2 & -1 \\ 3 & 3 & -2 \end{pmatrix}\begin{pmatrix} x \\ y \\ z \end{pmatrix} = \begin{pmatrix} 14 \\ 1 \\ 3 \end{pmatrix}$

9.3 DETERMINANTS

Associated with each square matrix M is a real number called the determinant of the matrix. Determinants will be used later to solve systems of equations.

For a 2×2 matrix, if

$$A = \begin{pmatrix} a & b \\ c & d \end{pmatrix}$$

then

$$\boxed{\det A = ad - bc}$$

For example, if

$$X = \begin{pmatrix} 3 & -1 \\ 2 & 4 \end{pmatrix}$$

then

$$\det X = (3)(4) - (-1)(2)$$
$$= 12 + 2$$
$$= 14$$

To denote the determinant of a matrix we place vertical lines left and right of the entries. Therefore if $A = \begin{pmatrix} a & b \\ c & d \end{pmatrix}$ we write the determinant of A as $\det A$ or $\begin{vmatrix} a & b \\ c & d \end{vmatrix}$.

Rewriting the result of the example above we have

$$\begin{vmatrix} 3 & -1 \\ 2 & 4 \end{vmatrix} = 14$$

To find the determinant of a 3×3 matrix we use the idea of a minor.

The minor of the entry 3 in the matrix $\begin{pmatrix} 3 & 1 & 4 \\ -2 & 5 & -3 \\ -4 & -1 & 2 \end{pmatrix}$ is the determinant of the 2×2 matrix remaining when the row and column containing 3 are removed

The minor of 3 is $\begin{vmatrix} 5 & -3 \\ -1 & 2 \end{vmatrix} = 10-(3)=7$

The minor of 5 is $\begin{vmatrix} 3 & 4 \\ -4 & 2 \end{vmatrix} = 6-(-16)=22$

The minor of -3 is $\begin{vmatrix} 3 & 1 \\ -4 & -1 \end{vmatrix} = -3-(-4)=1$

To find the determinant of a square matrix of order higher than 2 we expand the determinant by minors about any row or column.

To do this we

1. choose any row of column
2. find the minor of each element in that row or column
3. multiply each element by its minor and by $(-1)^{i+j}$ where i and j are the row and column numbers of the given element
4. add the values found in step 3

It turns out that we always get the same result no matter which row or column we choose in step one.

EXAMPLE 1. *Find the determinant of*

$$\begin{pmatrix} 3 & -2 & -3 \\ 1 & -1 & 6 \\ 2 & 4 & -4 \end{pmatrix}$$

Solution 1

Expand by minors of the first column

$$\begin{vmatrix} 3 & -2 & -3 \\ 1 & -1 & 6 \\ 2 & 4 & -4 \end{vmatrix} = (-1)^{1+1} \times 3 \times \begin{vmatrix} -1 & 6 \\ 4 & -4 \end{vmatrix} + (-1)^{2+1} \times 1 \times \begin{vmatrix} -2 & -3 \\ 4 & -4 \end{vmatrix} + (-1)^{3+1} \times 2 \times \begin{vmatrix} -2 & -3 \\ -1 & 6 \end{vmatrix}$$

$$= 1 \times 3 \times (-20) + (-1) \times 1 \times 20 + 1 \times 2 \times (-15)$$

$$= -60 - 20 - 30$$

$$= -110$$

Solution 2

Expand by minors of the second row

$$\begin{vmatrix} 3 & -2 & -3 \\ 1 & -1 & 6 \\ 2 & 4 & -4 \end{vmatrix} = (-1)^{2+1} \times 1 \times \begin{vmatrix} -2 & -3 \\ 4 & -4 \end{vmatrix} + (-1)^{2+2} \times (-1) \times \begin{vmatrix} 3 & -3 \\ 2 & -4 \end{vmatrix} + (-1)^{2+3} \times 6 \times \begin{vmatrix} 3 & -2 \\ 2 & 4 \end{vmatrix}$$

$$= (-1) \times 1 \times 20 + 1 \times (-1) \times (-6) + (-1) \times 6 \times 16$$

$$= -20 + 6 - 96$$

$$= -110$$

Expansion by minors can be used to evaluate determinants of fourth and higher order.

EXAMPLE 2. *Evaluate*

$$\begin{vmatrix} 3 & 2 & 0 & 1 \\ 1 & -1 & 3 & 0 \\ 0 & 0 & 2 & 1 \\ 2 & 0 & -2 & 0 \end{vmatrix}$$

Solution

Expanding by elements of a row or column that contain zeros simplifies calculations.

$$\begin{vmatrix} 3 & 2 & 0 & 1 \\ 1 & -1 & 3 & 0 \\ 0 & 0 & 2 & 1 \\ 2 & 0 & -2 & 0 \end{vmatrix} = (-1) \times 1 \times \begin{vmatrix} 1 & -1 & 3 \\ 0 & 0 & 2 \\ 2 & 0 & -2 \end{vmatrix} + 0 \times \begin{vmatrix} 3 & 2 & 0 \\ 0 & 0 & 2 \\ 2 & 0 & -2 \end{vmatrix} + (-1) \times 1 \times \begin{vmatrix} 3 & 2 & 0 \\ 1 & -1 & 3 \\ 2 & 0 & -2 \end{vmatrix} + 0 \times \begin{vmatrix} 3 & 2 & 0 \\ 1 & -1 & 3 \\ 0 & 0 & 2 \end{vmatrix}$$

$$= (-1) \times \begin{vmatrix} 1 & -1 & 3 \\ 0 & 0 & 2 \\ 2 & 0 & -2 \end{vmatrix} + (-1) \times \begin{vmatrix} 3 & 2 & 0 \\ 1 & -1 & 3 \\ 2 & 0 & -2 \end{vmatrix}$$

$$= -\left((-1) \times (-1) \times \begin{vmatrix} 0 & 2 \\ 2 & -2 \end{vmatrix} + 0 \times \begin{vmatrix} 1 & 3 \\ 2 & -2 \end{vmatrix} + 0 \times \begin{vmatrix} 1 & 3 \\ 0 & 2 \end{vmatrix} \right)$$

$$-\left(2 \times \begin{vmatrix} 2 & 0 \\ -1 & 3 \end{vmatrix} + 0 \times \begin{vmatrix} 3 & 0 \\ 1 & 3 \end{vmatrix} + (-2) \times \begin{vmatrix} 3 & 2 \\ 1 & -1 \end{vmatrix} \right)$$

$$= -\left(\begin{vmatrix} 0 & 2 \\ 2 & -2 \end{vmatrix} \right) - \left(2 \begin{vmatrix} 2 & 0 \\ -1 & 3 \end{vmatrix} - 2 \begin{vmatrix} 3 & 2 \\ 1 & -1 \end{vmatrix} \right)$$

$$= -(-4) - (12 + 10)$$

$$= -18$$

The following is an important property that can be used to simplify the computation of determinants.

> An equal determinant results if each element of one *row* is multiplied by *k* and each resulting product is added to the corresponding elements of a different *row*. (*Row* can be replaced by *column*)

We use this property to obtain a determinant having at most one non-zero element in a selected row or column.

EXAMPLE 3. *Evaluate*

$$\begin{vmatrix} 3 & 1 & -3 \\ -1 & 2 & -2 \\ 2 & 4 & 1 \end{vmatrix}$$

Solution

Multiply row 3 by 2 and add to row 2

$$\begin{vmatrix} 3 & 1 & -3 \\ -1 & 2 & -2 \\ 2 & 4 & 1 \end{vmatrix} = \begin{vmatrix} 3 & 1 & -3 \\ 2\times(2)+(-1) & 2\times(4)+2 & 2\times(1)+(-2) \\ 2 & 4 & 1 \end{vmatrix} = \begin{vmatrix} 3 & 1 & -3 \\ 3 & 10 & 0 \\ 2 & 4 & 1 \end{vmatrix}$$

Multiply row 3 by 3 and add to row 1

$$\begin{vmatrix} 3 & 1 & -3 \\ 3 & 10 & 0 \\ 2 & 4 & 1 \end{vmatrix} = \begin{vmatrix} 3\times(2)+3 & 3\times(4)+1 & 3\times(1)+(-3) \\ 3 & 10 & 0 \\ 2 & 4 & 1 \end{vmatrix} = \begin{vmatrix} 9 & 13 & 0 \\ 3 & 10 & 0 \\ 2 & 4 & 1 \end{vmatrix}$$

Expand by minors of the third column

$$\begin{vmatrix} 9 & 13 & 0 \\ 3 & 10 & 0 \\ 2 & 4 & 1 \end{vmatrix} = (-1)^{1+3}\times0\times\begin{vmatrix} 3 & 10 \\ 2 & 4 \end{vmatrix} + (-1)^{2+3}\times0\times\begin{vmatrix} 9 & 13 \\ 2 & 4 \end{vmatrix} + (-1)^{3+3}\times1\times\begin{vmatrix} 9 & 13 \\ 3 & 10 \end{vmatrix}$$

$$= \begin{vmatrix} 9 & 13 \\ 3 & 10 \end{vmatrix}$$

$$= 51$$

EXERCISE 9-3

1. Evaluate the determinant of each matrix.

(a) $\begin{pmatrix} 5 & 4 \\ 1 & 2 \end{pmatrix}$ (b) $\begin{pmatrix} 6 & 4 \\ 3 & 1 \end{pmatrix}$ (c) $\begin{pmatrix} 7 & 3 \\ -2 & -4 \end{pmatrix}$ (d) $\begin{pmatrix} -2 & 0 \\ -1 & -3 \end{pmatrix}$

(e) $\begin{pmatrix} 2 & 4 \\ 6 & 5 \end{pmatrix}$ (f) $\begin{pmatrix} -3 & -1 \\ 3 & 1 \end{pmatrix}$ (g) $\begin{pmatrix} 1 & 0 \\ 0 & 1 \end{pmatrix}$ (h) $\begin{pmatrix} 0 & 1 \\ 1 & 0 \end{pmatrix}$

2. Evaluate the following.

(a) $\begin{vmatrix} 3 & 1 & -2 \\ -3 & 0 & 1 \\ -1 & 0 & 2 \end{vmatrix}$ (b) $\begin{vmatrix} -1 & -2 & 5 \\ 2 & 3 & 4 \\ 0 & 0 & 1 \end{vmatrix}$ (c) $\begin{vmatrix} -1 & 2 & 3 \\ 1 & 0 & -2 \\ 3 & -2 & 4 \end{vmatrix}$ (d) $\begin{vmatrix} 2 & 1 & -4 \\ 4 & -2 & 2 \\ -1 & 3 & 0 \end{vmatrix}$

(e) $\begin{vmatrix} 2 & -1 & 1 \\ 3 & -2 & -3 \\ 4 & -4 & 5 \end{vmatrix}$ (f) $\begin{vmatrix} 0 & 3 & -2 \\ -2 & 1 & 4 \\ 5 & -1 & 3 \end{vmatrix}$ (g) $\begin{vmatrix} 2 & 5 & -3 \\ 4 & -1 & 3 \\ -2 & -5 & 2 \end{vmatrix}$ (h) $\begin{vmatrix} 3 & 2 & -1 \\ -1 & 4 & 2 \\ -2 & -3 & 1 \end{vmatrix}$

3. Evaluate the following.

(a) $\begin{vmatrix} 2 & -1 & 3 & 1 \\ 0 & -2 & 0 & 0 \\ -3 & 1 & 2 & 0 \\ 0 & 3 & -3 & 0 \end{vmatrix}$ (b) $\begin{vmatrix} 5 & 1 & -1 & -2 \\ 0 & 2 & 0 & 0 \\ 4 & 0 & -1 & 1 \\ -2 & 0 & -3 & 3 \end{vmatrix}$ (c) $\begin{vmatrix} 1 & -1 & 1 & 0 \\ -1 & 1 & 2 & -1 \\ 1 & -2 & 2 & 1 \\ 1 & 1 & -2 & 1 \end{vmatrix}$

C **4.** Evaluate the following.

(a) $\begin{vmatrix} 0 & 0 & 0 & 1 & 0 \\ -1 & 0 & 1 & 0 & 2 \\ 1 & -1 & 2 & 0 & 1 \\ 2 & 0 & -1 & 1 & 2 \\ 1 & 1 & 1 & 0 & -1 \end{vmatrix}$ (b) $\begin{vmatrix} 1 & -1 & 0 & 0 & 1 \\ 0 & 0 & 2 & 1 & 0 \\ 0 & 1 & -1 & 0 & 2 \\ 0 & 0 & 0 & 0 & -1 \\ 1 & 1 & -1 & 1 & 2 \end{vmatrix}$

5. Solve the following equations for x.

(a) $\begin{vmatrix} x & 0 & -2 \\ -1 & x & -1 \\ 1 & 0 & 1 \end{vmatrix} = 8$ (b) $\begin{vmatrix} x & 3 & 2 \\ 1 & 1 & 1 \\ 0 & 0 & x \end{vmatrix} = 10$

6. Prove that $\begin{vmatrix} a & b \\ c+ka & d+kb \end{vmatrix} = \begin{vmatrix} a & b \\ c & d \end{vmatrix}$

7. Prove that (a) $\begin{vmatrix} a & b & c \\ b & c & a \\ c & a & b \end{vmatrix} = a^3 + b^3 + c^3 - 3abc$

(b) $\begin{vmatrix} a^2 & a & 1 \\ b^2 & b & 1 \\ c^2 & c & 1 \end{vmatrix} = (a-b)(a-c)(b-c)$

9.4 INVERSES OF 2×2 MATRICES

If x is any non-zero real number, then its inverse for multiplication is

$$\frac{1}{x} \quad \text{or} \quad x^{-1}$$

That is

$$x \times x^{-1} = x^{-1} \times x = 1$$

Similarly matrices A and A^{-1} are inverses with respect to matrix multiplication if

$$A \times A^{-1} = A^{-1} \times A = I$$

where I is the identity matrix and A and A^{-1} are square matrices of the same order. I must be of the same order as A and A^{-1}.
For example, if

$$A = \begin{pmatrix} 2 & 2 \\ 3 & 4 \end{pmatrix} \quad \text{and} \quad A^{-1} = \begin{pmatrix} 2 & -1 \\ -\frac{3}{2} & 1 \end{pmatrix}$$

then

$$AA^{-1} = \begin{pmatrix} 2 & 2 \\ 3 & 4 \end{pmatrix}\begin{pmatrix} 2 & -1 \\ -\frac{3}{2} & 1 \end{pmatrix} = \begin{pmatrix} 1 & 0 \\ 0 & 1 \end{pmatrix}$$

and

$$A^{-1}A = \begin{pmatrix} 2 & -1 \\ -\frac{3}{2} & 1 \end{pmatrix}\begin{pmatrix} 2 & 2 \\ 3 & 4 \end{pmatrix} = \begin{pmatrix} 1 & 0 \\ 0 & 1 \end{pmatrix}$$

EXAMPLE 1. *Find the inverse of*

$$M = \begin{pmatrix} 1 & -2 \\ 3 & -4 \end{pmatrix}$$

Solution

Let

$$M^{-1} = \begin{pmatrix} a & b \\ c & d \end{pmatrix}$$

Then

$$M \times M^{-1} = I$$

$$\begin{pmatrix} 1 & -2 \\ 3 & -4 \end{pmatrix}\begin{pmatrix} a & b \\ c & d \end{pmatrix} = \begin{pmatrix} 1 & 0 \\ 0 & 1 \end{pmatrix}$$

$$\begin{pmatrix} a-2c & b-2d \\ 3a-4c & 3b-4d \end{pmatrix} = \begin{pmatrix} 1 & 0 \\ 0 & 1 \end{pmatrix}$$

Placing corresponding entries equal we have

				and		
	$a-2c=1$	①			$b-2d=0$	③
	$3a-4c=0$	②			$3b-4d=1$	④
①×2	$2a-4c=2$	①		③×2	$2b-4d=0$	③
	$3a-4c=0$	②			$3b-4d=1$	④
subtract	$-a=2$			subtract	$-b=-1$	
	$a=-2$				$b=1$	

substitute $a=-2$ in ②   substitute $b=1$ in ④

$$3(-2)-4c=0 \qquad\qquad 3(1)-4d=1$$
$$-6-4c=0 \qquad\qquad\quad 3-4d=1$$
$$-4c=6 \qquad\qquad\quad -4d=-2$$
$$c=-\tfrac{3}{2} \qquad\qquad\qquad d=\tfrac{1}{2}$$

$$\therefore \quad M^{-1} = \begin{pmatrix} -2 & 1 \\ -\dfrac{3}{2} & \dfrac{1}{2} \end{pmatrix}$$

Check:

$$\begin{pmatrix} 1 & -2 \\ 3 & -4 \end{pmatrix}\begin{pmatrix} -2 & 1 \\ -\tfrac{3}{2} & \tfrac{1}{2} \end{pmatrix} = \begin{pmatrix} 1 & 0 \\ 0 & 1 \end{pmatrix}$$

$$\begin{pmatrix} -2 & 1 \\ -\tfrac{3}{2} & \tfrac{1}{2} \end{pmatrix}\begin{pmatrix} 1 & -2 \\ 3 & -4 \end{pmatrix} = \begin{pmatrix} 1 & 0 \\ 0 & 1 \end{pmatrix}$$

EXAMPLE 2. *Find the inverse of*

$$M = \begin{pmatrix} a & b \\ c & d \end{pmatrix}$$

Solution

Let

$$M^{-1} = \begin{pmatrix} v & w \\ x & y \end{pmatrix}$$

Then

$$M \times M^{-1} = I$$

Write 100 using five 7's.

$$\begin{pmatrix} a & b \\ c & d \end{pmatrix}\begin{pmatrix} v & w \\ x & y \end{pmatrix} = \begin{pmatrix} 1 & 0 \\ 0 & 1 \end{pmatrix}$$

$$\begin{pmatrix} av + bx & aw + by \\ cv + dx & cw + dy \end{pmatrix} = \begin{pmatrix} 1 & 0 \\ 0 & 1 \end{pmatrix}$$

Placing corresponding entries equal we have

$$av + bx = 1 \quad ① \qquad aw + by = 0 \quad ③$$
$$cv + dx = 0 \quad ② \qquad cw + dy = 1 \quad ④$$

By solving each system we find that

$$v = \frac{d}{ad - bc} \qquad w = \frac{-b}{ad - bc}$$

$$x = \frac{-c}{ad - bc} \qquad y = \frac{a}{ad - bc}$$

providing that $ad - bc \neq 0$. Notice that $ad - bc = \det M$
Substituting the results for v, w, x and y in M^{-1}, we have

$$M^{-1} = \begin{pmatrix} \dfrac{d}{ad - bc} & \dfrac{-b}{ad - bc} \\ \dfrac{-c}{ad - bc} & \dfrac{a}{ad - bc} \end{pmatrix}$$

$$= \frac{1}{ad - bc} \times \begin{pmatrix} d & -b \\ -c & a \end{pmatrix}$$

$$\boxed{M^{-1} = \frac{1}{\det M} \times \begin{pmatrix} d & -b \\ -c & a \end{pmatrix}}$$

We can start with $A^{-1} \times A = I$ instead of $A \times A^{-1} = I$ and get the same result. You can find the inverse of a 2×2 matrix provided that its determinant is not 0. If $\det M = 0$, M has no inverse.

Given $M = \begin{pmatrix} a & b \\ c & d \end{pmatrix}$, to find M^{-1} we

(i) interchange a and d
(ii) replace b and c by their negatives
(iii) multiply the resulting matrix by $\dfrac{1}{\det M}$.

A matrix which has an inverse is said to be *invertible*.

EXAMPLE 3. *If*

$$A = \begin{pmatrix} 3 & -1 \\ 4 & -2 \end{pmatrix}$$

find A^{-1}

Solution

Since $\det A = -6 - (-4) = -2$, A^{-1} exists.

$$A = \begin{pmatrix} 3 & -1 \\ 4 & -2 \end{pmatrix}$$

$$A^{-1} = \frac{1}{-2} \begin{pmatrix} -2 & 1 \\ -4 & 3 \end{pmatrix}$$

$$= \begin{pmatrix} 1 & -\frac{1}{2} \\ 2 & -\frac{3}{2} \end{pmatrix}$$

EXERCISE 9-4

1. Find the inverse of each of the following, if one exists.

(a) $\begin{pmatrix} 3 & 1 \\ 5 & 2 \end{pmatrix}$ (b) $\begin{pmatrix} 4 & 3 \\ 3 & 2 \end{pmatrix}$ (c) $\begin{pmatrix} 4 & 6 \\ 2 & 3 \end{pmatrix}$ (d) $\begin{pmatrix} -2 & -3 \\ -3 & 5 \end{pmatrix}$

(e) $\begin{pmatrix} 1 & 0 \\ 0 & 1 \end{pmatrix}$ (f) $\begin{pmatrix} 0 & 1 \\ 1 & -3 \end{pmatrix}$ (g) $\begin{pmatrix} 6 & 11 \\ 2 & 4 \end{pmatrix}$ (h) $\begin{pmatrix} -1 & 2 \\ 2 & -4 \end{pmatrix}$

(i) $\begin{pmatrix} 2 & 2 \\ 1 & \frac{1}{2} \end{pmatrix}$ (j) $\begin{pmatrix} 3 & -3 \\ -1 & 2 \end{pmatrix}$ (k) $\begin{pmatrix} \frac{1}{2} & -12 \\ \frac{1}{3} & 6 \end{pmatrix}$ (l) $\begin{pmatrix} 0.5 & 3 \\ -1 & 4 \end{pmatrix}$

9.5   2×2 MATRIX EQUATIONS

The linear system

$$2x + y = 5$$
$$x - 2y = -5$$

can be expressed as a matrix equation

$$\begin{pmatrix} 2 & 1 \\ 1 & -2 \end{pmatrix} \begin{pmatrix} x \\ y \end{pmatrix} = \begin{pmatrix} 5 \\ -5 \end{pmatrix}$$

Since

$$\begin{pmatrix} 2 & 1 \\ 1 & -2 \end{pmatrix} \begin{pmatrix} x \\ y \end{pmatrix} = \begin{pmatrix} 2x + y \\ x - 2y \end{pmatrix}$$

The matrix

$$\begin{pmatrix} 2 & 1 \\ 1 & -2 \end{pmatrix}$$

is called the *coefficient matrix*. The determinant of this matrix is -5 and its inverse is

$$-\frac{1}{5}\begin{pmatrix} -2 & -1 \\ -1 & 2 \end{pmatrix} \quad \text{or} \quad \begin{pmatrix} \frac{2}{5} & \frac{1}{5} \\ \frac{1}{5} & -\frac{2}{5} \end{pmatrix}$$

Multiplying both sides of the matrix equation by this inverse we have

$$\begin{pmatrix} \frac{2}{5} & \frac{1}{5} \\ \frac{1}{5} & -\frac{2}{5} \end{pmatrix}\begin{pmatrix} 2 & 1 \\ 1 & -2 \end{pmatrix}\begin{pmatrix} x \\ y \end{pmatrix} = \begin{pmatrix} \frac{2}{5} & \frac{1}{5} \\ \frac{1}{5} & -\frac{2}{5} \end{pmatrix}\begin{pmatrix} 5 \\ -5 \end{pmatrix}$$

$$\begin{pmatrix} 1 & 0 \\ 0 & 1 \end{pmatrix}\begin{pmatrix} x \\ y \end{pmatrix} = \begin{pmatrix} 2-1 \\ 1+2 \end{pmatrix}$$

$$\begin{pmatrix} x \\ y \end{pmatrix} = \begin{pmatrix} 1 \\ 3 \end{pmatrix}$$

$\therefore \quad x = 1$ and $y = 3$.

If the coefficient matrix is not invertible the equations are either inconsistent or dependent.

EXERCISE   9-5

A **1.** State the matrix equation for each system.

(a) $2x + 3y = 5$
$3x - y = 2$

(b) $4x - y = -7$
$3x + y = 0$

(c) $x + 3y = -4$
$3x - y = 8$

(d) $3x + 4y = -15$
$5x - 2y = 1$

(e) $2x + 7y = -6$
$3x - y = 14$

(f) $5x + y - 7 = 0$
$2y - x = 3$

2. Determine the determinant of the coefficient matrix of each of the following systems.

(a) $2x + y = 7$
$3x + 5y = 4$

(b) $-3x + y = 8$
$4x - y = 7$

(c) $3x + 2y = 5$
$6x + 4y = 1$

(d) $5x - y = 6$
$4x + 2y = 9$

(e) $-3x + 2y = -1$
$4x - 3y = 3$

(f) $2x - 3y = 8$
$-6x + 9y = -2$

B **3.** Solve each system by the method of this section.

(a) $2x - y = 4$
$x + 2y = 7$

(b) $3x - y = 5$
$2x + 3y = 7$

(c) $2x + y = 1$
$5x - y = -8$

(d) $3x + 5y = -27$
$5x - 4y = -8$

(e) $8x + y = -1$
$4x + 3y = 7$

(f) $-2x - 3y = 5$
$7x - 12y = -10$

(g) $4x = 3 - 3y$
$1 = 3x + 2y$

(h) $2y = -8x - 5$
$12x + 11 = 4y$

(i) $5x - 4y = 1$
$-7x + 3y = 9$

4. Solve by the method of this section.

(a) $\frac{3}{2}x + y = 7$

$x - \frac{y}{4} = 1$

(b) $\frac{5}{2}x + y = -5\frac{1}{2}$

$x - \frac{3}{2}y = -6$

(c) $\frac{x}{3} + y = -\frac{2}{3}$

$\frac{3}{4}x + y = 1$

(d) $x + y = -\frac{1}{4}$

$3x - 4y = -\frac{5}{2}$

(e) $\dfrac{x+1}{3} - \dfrac{y-2}{4} = -1$

$\dfrac{5x-1}{3} - \dfrac{6+y}{4} = -1$

5. Flying with the wind a plane travels 3000 km in 5 h. The return trip against the same wind takes one hour longer. Find the wind speed.

9.6 CRAMER'S RULE

We shall now develop another method for solving systems of linear equations.

We first solve the following system using the elimination method.

$$ax + by = e \quad \text{①}$$
$$cx + dy = f \quad \text{②}$$

Solving for x

① $\times d$	$adx + bdy = de$
② $\times b$	$cbx + bdy = bf$
subtract	$adx - bcx = de - bf$

$$x(ad - bc) = de - bf$$
$$x = \frac{de - bf}{ad - bc}$$

Solving for y

① $\times c$	$acx + bcy = ce$
② $\times a$	$acx + ady = af$
subtract	$bcy - ady = ce - af$

$$y(bc - ad) = ce - af$$
$$y = \frac{ce - af}{bc - ad}$$
$$\text{or} \quad y = \frac{af - ce}{ad - bc}$$

$$\therefore \quad x = \frac{\begin{vmatrix} e & b \\ f & d \end{vmatrix}}{\begin{vmatrix} a & b \\ c & d \end{vmatrix}} \quad \text{and} \quad y = \frac{\begin{vmatrix} a & e \\ c & f \end{vmatrix}}{\begin{vmatrix} a & b \\ c & d \end{vmatrix}}$$

These two equations are called Cramer's Rule for 2×2 systems.

Cramer's Rule is often written as

$$x = \frac{D_x}{D}, \quad y = \frac{D_y}{D}, \quad D \neq 0$$

where D is the determinant of the coefficient matrix, D_x is the determinant formed by replacing the coefficients of x in D by the constant terms and D_y is the determinant formed by replacing the coefficients of y in D by the constant terms.

For

$$ax + by = e$$
$$cx + dy = f$$

$$D = \begin{vmatrix} a & b \\ c & d \end{vmatrix}$$

$$D_x = \begin{vmatrix} e & b \\ f & d \end{vmatrix}$$

$$D_y = \begin{vmatrix} a & e \\ c & f \end{vmatrix}$$

EXAMPLE 1. *Use Cramer's Rule to solve*

$$3x + 2y = -9$$
$$4x - 3y = 5$$

Solution

$$x = \frac{D_x}{D} \qquad\qquad y = \frac{D_y}{D}$$

$$= \frac{\begin{vmatrix} -9 & 2 \\ 5 & -3 \end{vmatrix}}{\begin{vmatrix} 3 & 2 \\ 4 & -3 \end{vmatrix}} \qquad\qquad = \frac{\begin{vmatrix} 3 & -9 \\ 4 & 5 \end{vmatrix}}{\begin{vmatrix} 3 & 2 \\ 4 & -3 \end{vmatrix}}$$

$$= \frac{27 - 10}{-9 - 8} \qquad\qquad = \frac{15 - (-36)}{-9 - 8}$$

$$= \frac{17}{-17} \qquad\qquad = \frac{51}{-17}$$

$$= -1 \qquad\qquad = -3$$

Determine the pattern.
Find the missing number.

91	8	7	35
82	4	4	66
53	3	9	26
	5	7	12

Cramer's Rule can be extended to solve a system of n equations in n variables, provided the determinant of the coefficient matrix is not 0. For a system of 3 equations in 3 variables

$$a_1 x + b_1 y + c_1 z = d_1$$
$$a_2 x + b_2 y + c_2 z = d_2$$
$$a_3 x + b_3 y + c_3 z = d_3$$

$$D = \begin{vmatrix} a_1 & b_1 & c_1 \\ a_2 & b_2 & c_2 \\ a_3 & b_3 & c_3 \end{vmatrix} \qquad D_x = \begin{vmatrix} d_1 & b_1 & c_1 \\ d_2 & b_2 & c_2 \\ d_3 & b_3 & c_3 \end{vmatrix}$$

$$D_y = \begin{vmatrix} a_1 & d_1 & c_1 \\ a_2 & d_2 & c_2 \\ a_3 & d_3 & c_3 \end{vmatrix} \qquad D_z = \begin{vmatrix} a_1 & b_1 & d_1 \\ a_2 & b_2 & d_2 \\ a_3 & b_3 & d_3 \end{vmatrix}$$

If $D \neq 0$ then $x = \dfrac{D_x}{D}$, $y = \dfrac{D_y}{D}$ and $z = \dfrac{D_z}{D}$

EXAMPLE 2. *Solve by Cramer's Rule*

$$2x + y + 3z = -2$$
$$x - 2y + 2z = -7$$
$$3x - y - z = 3$$

Solution

$$D = \begin{vmatrix} 2 & 1 & 3 \\ 1 & -2 & 2 \\ 3 & -1 & -1 \end{vmatrix}$$

add row 3
to row 1

$$= \begin{vmatrix} 5 & 0 & 2 \\ 1 & -2 & 2 \\ 3 & -1 & -1 \end{vmatrix}$$

add $(-2) \times$ row
3 to row 2

$$= \begin{vmatrix} 5 & 0 & 2 \\ -5 & 0 & 4 \\ 3 & -1 & -1 \end{vmatrix}$$

$$= (-1)^{2+3} \times (-1) \times \begin{vmatrix} 5 & 2 \\ -5 & 4 \end{vmatrix}$$

$$= 30$$

$$D_x = \begin{vmatrix} -2 & 1 & 3 \\ -7 & -2 & 2 \\ 3 & -1 & -1 \end{vmatrix}$$

add row 3
to row 1

$$= \begin{vmatrix} 1 & 0 & 2 \\ -7 & -2 & 2 \\ 3 & -1 & -1 \end{vmatrix}$$

add $(-2) \times$ column
1 to column 3

$$= \begin{vmatrix} 1 & 0 & 0 \\ -7 & -2 & 16 \\ 3 & -1 & -7 \end{vmatrix}$$

$$= (-1)^{1+1} \times (1) \times \begin{vmatrix} -2 & 16 \\ -1 & -7 \end{vmatrix}$$

$$= 30$$

$$D_y = \begin{vmatrix} 2 & -2 & 3 \\ 1 & -7 & 2 \\ 3 & 3 & -1 \end{vmatrix}$$

add $2 \times$ row 3
to row 2

$$= \begin{vmatrix} 2 & -2 & 3 \\ 7 & -1 & 0 \\ 3 & 3 & -1 \end{vmatrix}$$

add $3 \times$ row 3
to row 1

$$= \begin{vmatrix} 11 & 7 & 0 \\ 7 & -1 & 0 \\ 3 & 3 & -1 \end{vmatrix}$$

$$= (-1)^{3+3} \times (-1) \times \begin{vmatrix} 11 & 7 \\ 7 & -1 \end{vmatrix}$$

$$= 60$$

$$D_z = \begin{vmatrix} 2 & 1 & -2 \\ 1 & -2 & -7 \\ 3 & -1 & 3 \end{vmatrix}$$

add row 1
to row 3

$$= \begin{vmatrix} 2 & 1 & -2 \\ 1 & -2 & -7 \\ 5 & 0 & 1 \end{vmatrix}$$

add $2 \times$ row 1
to row 2

$$= \begin{vmatrix} 2 & 1 & -2 \\ 5 & 0 & -11 \\ 5 & 0 & 1 \end{vmatrix}$$

$$= (-1)^{1+2} \times (1) \times \begin{vmatrix} 5 & -11 \\ 5 & 1 \end{vmatrix}$$

$$= -60$$

$$\therefore \quad x = \frac{D_x}{D} = \frac{30}{30} = 1, \qquad y = \frac{D_y}{D} = \frac{60}{30} = 2, \qquad z = \frac{D_z}{D} = \frac{-60}{30} = -2$$

EXERCISE 9-6

A **1.** Evaluate the following determinants.

(a) $\begin{vmatrix} 5 & 3 \\ 2 & 4 \end{vmatrix}$
(b) $\begin{vmatrix} 3 & 2 \\ 7 & 4 \end{vmatrix}$
(c) $\begin{vmatrix} 6 & 3 \\ -1 & 4 \end{vmatrix}$
(d) $\begin{vmatrix} -3 & 4 \\ 1 & -2 \end{vmatrix}$

(e) $\begin{vmatrix} -1 & -3 \\ 2 & 4 \end{vmatrix}$
(f) $\begin{vmatrix} \frac{1}{2} & -1 \\ 3 & 8 \end{vmatrix}$
(g) $\begin{vmatrix} -2 & 6 \\ -4 & 3 \end{vmatrix}$
(h) $\begin{vmatrix} -8 & 3 \\ 5 & 0 \end{vmatrix}$

2. If Cramer's Rule is used to solve $2x + 3y = 7$
$$4x + 5y = 8$$

then $x = \dfrac{\begin{vmatrix} ? \end{vmatrix}}{\begin{vmatrix} ? \end{vmatrix}}$ and $y = \dfrac{\begin{vmatrix} ? \end{vmatrix}}{\begin{vmatrix} ? \end{vmatrix}}$.

3. If Cramer's Rule is used to solve $3x - y = -4$
$$2x - 5y = 7$$

then $x = \dfrac{\begin{vmatrix} ? \end{vmatrix}}{\begin{vmatrix} ? \end{vmatrix}}$ and $y = \dfrac{\begin{vmatrix} ? \end{vmatrix}}{\begin{vmatrix} ? \end{vmatrix}}$.

B **4.** Solve the following systems of equations using Cramer's Rule.

(a) $2x + 3y = 4$
$3x + y = 7$

(b) $x - 3y = 5$
$4x + 5y = 9$

(c) $3x - 4y = 6$
$2x - 5y = 8$

(d) $7x + 2y = -2$
$4x - y = -4$

(e) $5x - 3y + 4 = 0$
$6x + 5y = 4$

(f) $2x + 3y = 5$
$4x - y = 7$

(g) $3y - 2x = 5$
$4x + 5y = 1$

(h) $3x = 2y - 4$
$4x - y + 6 = 0$

5. Solve the following systems of equations using Cramer's Rule.

(a) $\frac{1}{2}x - 4y = 6$
$2x - 5y - 2 = 0$

(b) $2x + 9y = -1$
$4x + y = 15$

(c) $2x - 3y = 0$
$4x + y = -14$

(d) $0.5x + y = 4$
$0.2x + 0.3y = 1.3$

6. Solve using Cramer's Rule.

(a) $2x + y + z = 3$
$x + 2y - z = -3$
$3x - y + 2z = 8$

(b) $x + 2y + 3z = 14$
$2x + 3y - 2z = 2$
$3x - 2y + 4z = 11$

(c) $3x + y + z = 4$
$2x + 2y + z = 1$
$x - 2y - 3z = 7$

(d) $2x + y - z = -3$
$x + 3y + z = 0$
$3x - 2y + 2z = -1$

(e) $3x - 2y + z = 1$
$x + 2y - 3z = 9$
$4x + y - 2z = 12$

(f) $x + 2y + 3z = -13$
$2x - y + 2z = -4$
$3x + 2y - z = -1$

C **7.** Solve the following systems using Cramer's Rule.

(a) $w - x - y + z = -2$
$2w - x - y + z = -1$
$w + x + y - 2z = 6$
$w - x + 2y - z = 8$

(b) $2w + x + y - z = -2$
$w - x - y + z = 2$
$w + 2x + y - 2z = -3$
$2w - x + y - z = -4$

8. Show that $k \begin{vmatrix} a & c \\ b & d \end{vmatrix} = \begin{vmatrix} ka & kc \\ b & d \end{vmatrix} = \begin{vmatrix} a & c \\ kb & kd \end{vmatrix}$

9. Find the value of $\begin{vmatrix} a & c \\ b & d \end{vmatrix} - \begin{vmatrix} b & d \\ a & c \end{vmatrix}$

10. Verify that Cramer's Rule is correct for 3×3 systems.

9.7 SOLVING SYSTEMS USING THE AUGMENTED MATRIX

For the system of equations

$$2x + 3y - z = -2$$
$$3x + 4y + 2z = 5$$
$$2x - 2y + z = 12$$

the matrix

$$\begin{pmatrix} 2 & 3 & -1 \\ 3 & 4 & 2 \\ 2 & -2 & 1 \end{pmatrix}$$

is called the coefficient matrix.

The augmented matrix for this system is

$$\begin{pmatrix} 2 & 3 & -1 & | & -2 \\ 3 & 4 & 2 & | & 5 \\ 2 & -2 & 1 & | & 12 \end{pmatrix}$$

The vertical line segment in the matrix is just a reminder that the first three columns come from the left side of the equations and the last column from the right side. The augmented matrix is a notation that avoids repeatedly writing variables and equal signs when solving linear systems.

Three row operations are permitted. They produce equivalent matrices because the related linear systems are equivalent.
The operations are
1. the interchange of any two rows
2. the multiplication of all elements of a row by the same non-zero number
3. the addition of the same multiple of the elements of one row to the corresponding elements of another row.

The goal is to get an equivalent matrix in the trianglar form

$$\begin{pmatrix} a_1 & 0 & 0 & | & d_1 \\ b_1 & b_2 & 0 & | & d_2 \\ c_1 & c_2 & c_3 & | & d_3 \end{pmatrix} \quad \text{or} \quad \begin{pmatrix} a_1 & a_2 & a_3 & | & d_1 \\ b_1 & b_2 & 0 & | & d_2 \\ c_1 & 0 & 0 & | & d_3 \end{pmatrix}$$

EXAMPLE 1. *Solve*

$$2x + 3y - z = -2$$
$$3x + 4y + 2z = 5$$
$$2x - 2y + z = 12$$

Solution

The corresponding augmented matrix is
$$\begin{pmatrix} 2 & 3 & -1 & -2 \\ 3 & 4 & 2 & 5 \\ 2 & -2 & 1 & 12 \end{pmatrix}$$

Add row 3 to row 1 and replace row 1 with the result.
$$\begin{pmatrix} 4 & 1 & 0 & 10 \\ 3 & 4 & 2 & 5 \\ 2 & -2 & 1 & 12 \end{pmatrix}$$

Multiply row 3 by -2 and add to row 2 and replace row 2 with the result.
$$\begin{pmatrix} 4 & 1 & 0 & 10 \\ -1 & 8 & 0 & -19 \\ 2 & -2 & 1 & 12 \end{pmatrix}$$

Multiply row 1 by -8 and add to row 2 and replace row 1 with the result.
$$\begin{pmatrix} -33 & 0 & 0 & -99 \\ -1 & 8 & 0 & -19 \\ 2 & -2 & 1 & 12 \end{pmatrix}$$

The matrix is now in triangular form which represents the following system, which can be solved readily.

$$-33x = -99 \quad \text{①}$$
$$-x + 8y = -19 \quad \text{②}$$
$$2x - 2y + z = 12 \quad \text{③}$$

Since $-33x = -99$, $x = 3$.
Replace x by 3 in equation 2 to give $y = -2$.
Now replace x by 3 and y by -2 in equation 3 to give $z = 2$.

$\therefore$ $x = 3$, $y = -2$ and $z = 2$

EXERCISE   9-7

Solve the following systems by the method of this section.

B   **1.** $x + y + z = 2$
$\quad$ $2x - y + z = 2$
$\quad$ $x + 2y - z = 5$

2. $2x + y + z = 6$
$\quad$ $-x + y - z = -5$
$\quad$ $3x + 3y - 2z = -5$

3. $x + y + z = 6$
$\quad$ $3x - 2y + 2z = 10$
$\quad$ $2x + y - z = 2$

4. $3x - 2y + 3z = 21$
$\quad$ $2x + y - 2z = -7$
$\quad$ $3x + 2y - z = 5$

5. $2x + y + z = 3$
$\quad$ $3x - y + z = 9$
$\quad$ $x + 2y - 2z = -4$

6. $x + 2y - z = -3$
$\quad$ $2x - 2y - z = 8$
$\quad$ $3x + 3y + 2z = 7$

7. $3x + y + z = -10$
$2x + 3y - 2z = -1$
$4x - 2y + 3z = -15$

8. $2x + y - 2z = 16$
$3x - 2y + 3z = -1$
$4x - 3y + z = 7$

9. $w + x - y + z = 2$
$w - x + 2y - z = 6$
$2w - x + y - 2z = 5$
$3w + 2x - y + 2z = -1$

10. $2w + x - 2y - 2z = 5$
$w + 2x + y + 3z = 6$
$3w - x + y - 2z = 2$
$2w - 3x + 2y - z = -2$

11. $2x + 3y = 8$
$2z - y = 4$
$3x + 2z = 9$

12. $4y - 3z = -10$
$3x - 2y = -4$
$2z + 5x = -6$

9.8 VECTORS

A vector is a mathematical object which has both magnitude and direction. For example, a force is a vector because to describe it you must state in which direction it is acting and with what strength. Velocity is another example of a vector. To describe the velocity of a jet you give the direction and speed of the jet.

We denote a vector by an arrow on a letter, such as $\vec{v}$, or by an arrow on a line segment such as $\overrightarrow{AB}$. Figure 9-1 shows three parallel line segments which represent three equal vectors $\overrightarrow{AB}$, $\overrightarrow{CD}$ and $\overrightarrow{EF}$, since they have *the same length and direction*. In Figure 9–1, each terminal point of the vector is reached from its initial point by a displacement of 2 units to the right and 3 units upward. We indicate this by writing $\overrightarrow{AB} = [2, 3]$, $\overrightarrow{CD} = [2, 3]$ and $\overrightarrow{EF} = [2, 3]$.

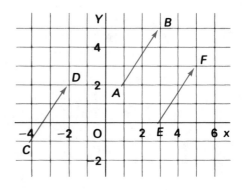

Figure 9-1

In general, if a and b are real numbers then $\vec{v} = [a, b]$ defines a vector which is represented geometrically by a displacement of a horizontal units and b vertical units.

The magnitude of a vector $\vec{v}$ is the length of the line segment which represents it.

If $\overrightarrow{AB} = [2, 3]$, then $|\overrightarrow{AB}|$ is the length of AB which can be found using the Pythagorean Theorem

$$|\overrightarrow{AB}| = \sqrt{(2)^2 + (3)^2}$$
$$= \sqrt{13}$$

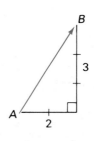

> The magnitude of the vector $\vec{v} = [a, b]$ is
> $$|\vec{v}| = \sqrt{a^2 + b^2}$$

There are two ways of determining whether vectors are equal.

Algebraically	Geometrically

If

$$\vec{u} = [a, b]$$

and

$$\vec{v} = [c, d]$$

then

$$\vec{u} = \vec{v}$$

if and only if
 (i) $a = c$
(ii) $b = d$

Geometrically

$$\overrightarrow{AB} = \overrightarrow{CD}$$

if and only if
 (i) $|\overrightarrow{AB}| = |\overrightarrow{CD}|$
(ii) $AB \parallel CD$ and have the same direction

When working with vectors we call real numbers scalars. The operation of multiplying a vector $\vec{v}$ by a scalar k is called scalar multiplication and the result of this multiplication is another vector. The following diagram illustrates scalar multiplication

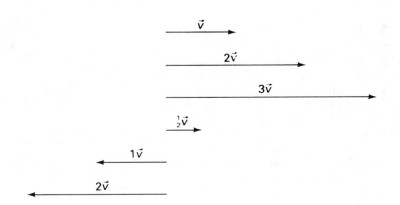

In general for any real number k we define $k\vec{v}$ as follows.

> If $\vec{v} = [a, b]$, then $k\vec{v} = [ka, kb]$
> or $k[a, b] = [ka, kb]$

We compare $k\vec{v}$ with $\vec{v}$:
 (i) The magnitude of $k\vec{v}$ is

$$|k\vec{v}| = \sqrt{(ka)^2 + (kb)^2}$$
$$= \sqrt{k^2 a^2 + k^2 b^2}$$
$$= \sqrt{k^2(a^2 + b^2)}$$
$$= \sqrt{k^2}\sqrt{a^2 + b^2}$$
$$= k|\vec{v}|$$

The magnitude of kv is $|k|$ times the magnitude of $\vec{v}$.

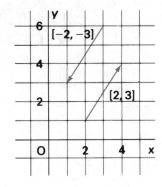

(ii) The slope of $k\vec{v}$ is $\dfrac{kb}{ka} = \dfrac{b}{a} = $ slope of $\vec{v}$ $(a \neq 0)$

Thus $k\vec{v}$ is parallel to $\vec{v}$.
If $k > 0$, $k\vec{v}$ and $\vec{v}$ are in the same direction. If $k < 0$, $k\vec{v}$ has the opposite direction to $\vec{v}$.

EXERCISE 9-8

1. Determine the following vectors.
(a) $A(3, 2)$ to $B(5, 6)$ (b) $M(1, 0)$ to $N(7, 9)$
(c) $C(-2, 3)$ to $D(-4, 7)$ (d) $E(-3, -1)$ to $F(5, -4)$
(e) $R(3, -7)$ to $S(-2, -3)$ (f) $G(-2, -9)$ to $H(-7, 5)$
(g) $K(2, 0)$ to $L(-5, -3)$ (h) $S(4, -5)$ to $T(-11, -9)$
(i) $P(-1, 7)$ to $Q(4, -11)$ (j) $A(-5, -3)$ to $B(2, 3)$

2. Find the terminal points of the directed line segments which represent the vector $[4, -3]$ if the initial points are as follows.
(a) $(3, 2)$ (b) $(-1, -3)$ (c) $(-7, 7)$ (d) $(6, -9)$
(e) $(-4, 3)$

3. Find the initial points of the directed line segments which represent the vector $[-2, 5]$ if the terminal points are as follows.
(a) $(6, 2)$ (b) $(-7, -3)$ (c) $(-6, 7)$ (d) $(8, -9)$
(e) $(2, 5)$

4. Express each of the following vectors in the form $[a, b]$.
(a) $2[3, -4]$ (b) $-3[2, 5]$ (c) $-2[-4, -1]$
(d) $\frac{1}{2}[8, -14]$ (e) $-\frac{1}{3}[-15, 9]$ (f) $4[-3, 0]$

5. (a) Plot the points $A(3, 2)$, $B(-2, 5)$, $C(-4, -6)$ and $D(1, -7)$.
(b) Draw the following vectors and express each of them in algebraic form.
(i) $\overrightarrow{AB}$ (ii) $\overrightarrow{CD}$ (iii) $\overrightarrow{DA}$ (iv) $\overrightarrow{CA}$
(v) $\overrightarrow{CB}$ (vi) $\overrightarrow{BA}$ (vii) $\overrightarrow{BC}$ (viii) $\overrightarrow{DB}$

6. Determine the magnitude of each of the following vectors.
(a) $A(3, 1)$ to $B(-4, 6)$ (b) $C(-3, -5)$ to $D(5, -2)$
(c) $E(0, -5)$ to $F(-3, 7)$ (d) $G(2, -9)$ to $H(-5, -6)$
(e) $M(-1, 6)$ to $N(6, 4)$ (f) $P(-7, 0)$ to $Q(-3, 6)$
(g) $R(7, 7)$ to $S(-5, 4)$ (h) $A(-11, -2)$ to $B(-5, -8)$

7. Determine the magnitude of the following vectors
(a) $2[-3, 4]$ (b) $-3[1, -2]$ (c) $\frac{1}{2}[-4, -8]$ (d) $-\frac{1}{3}[-12, 15]$

9.9 ADDITION AND SUBTRACTION OF VECTORS

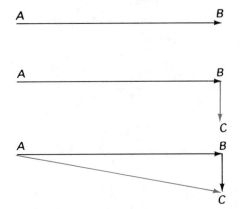

Consider a plane flying due east at 300 km/h. We represent this velocity by the vector $\vec{AB}$. A south wind of 50 km/h is encountered. We represent this velocity by the vector $\vec{BC}$. The resulting velocity of the plane is represented by the vector $\vec{AC}$.

This method of adding vectors uses the Triangle Law. The initial point of the second vector coincides with the terminal point of the first vector.

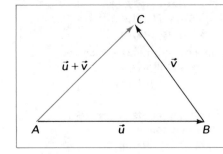

The Triangle Law
If $\vec{u} = \vec{AB}$ and $\vec{v} = \vec{BC}$ then $\vec{u} + \vec{v}$ is represented by the third side of $\triangle ABC$: $\vec{u} + \vec{v} = \vec{AC}$. In short

$$\vec{AB} + \vec{BC} = \vec{AC}$$

The Triangle Law illustrates how vectors can be added geometrically. This method is especially useful when adding three or more vectors.

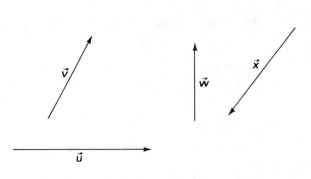
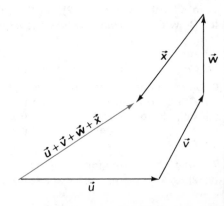

The Triangle Law leads to the algebraic addition of vectors. In Figure 9-2 $\vec{u} = [4, 2]$ and $\vec{v}$ [1, 5]. We can see from the figure that $\vec{u} + \vec{v} = [5, 7]$. Therefore

$$[4, 2] + [1, 5] = [5, 7]$$

Algebraic vectors can be added simply by adding the corresponding components.

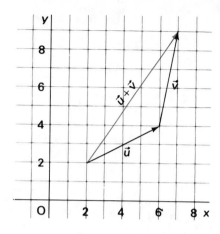

Figure 9-2

Algebraic Vector Addition
If $\vec{u} = [a, b]$ and $\vec{v} = [c, d]$ then
$\vec{u} + \vec{v} = [a + c, b + d]$. In short

$$[a, b] + [c, d] = [a + c, b + d].$$

A second geometric method for adding vectors is called the Parallelogram Law.

In Figure 9-3, $ABCD$ is a parallelogram.

$$BA = CD$$

$$BA \parallel CD$$

and BA and CD have the same direction.

$$\therefore \quad \vec{BA} = \vec{CD}$$

By the Triangle Law

$$\vec{BC} + \vec{CD} = \vec{BD}$$
$$\therefore \quad \vec{BC} + \vec{BA} = \vec{BD}$$

This proves the Parallelogram Law.

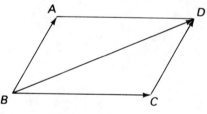

Figure 9-3

The Parallelogram Law
If $\vec{u} = \vec{BA}$ and $\vec{v} = \vec{BC}$ then $\vec{u} + \vec{v}$
is represented by the diagonal
of the parallelogram deter-
mined by $\vec{BC}$ and $\vec{BA}$. In short

$$\vec{BC} + \vec{BA} = \vec{BD}$$

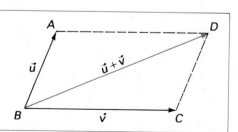

In summary

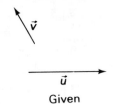

Given

Triangle Law

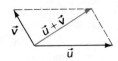

Parallelogram Law

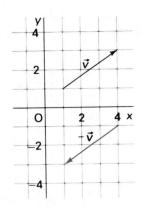

The opposite (or negative) of a vector $\vec{v}$ (written $-\vec{v}$) is the vector having the same slope and length as $\vec{v}$ but with the opposite direction.

> The opposite (or negative) of the vector $\vec{v} = [a, b]$ is the vector $-\vec{v} = [-a, -b]$

Also

$$\vec{v} + (-\vec{v}) = [a, b] + [-a, -b]$$
$$= [a - a, b - b]$$
$$= [0, 0]$$

The vector $[0, 0]$ is a special vector which we call the *zero vector* and denote by $\vec{0}$. It has a magnitude of 0 but is not considered to have a direction.

The difference of two vectors $\vec{u}$ and $\vec{v}$, $\vec{u} - \vec{v}$, is $\vec{u} + (-\vec{v})$

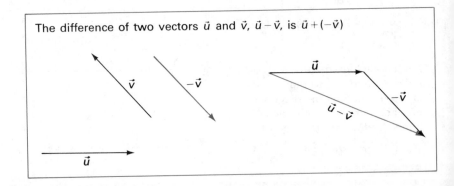

If $\vec{u} = [a, b]$ and $\vec{v} = [c, d]$ then

$$\vec{u} - \vec{v} = \vec{u} + (-\vec{v})$$
$$= [a, b] + [-c, -d]$$
$$= [a - c, b - d]$$

Thus

$$\boxed{[a, b] - [c, d] = [a - c, b - d]}$$

EXAMPLE 1. *Express the following in the form* $[a, b]$.

$$3[2, -4] - 2[-2, 1] - [-3, -1]$$

Solution

$$3[2, -4] - 2[-2, 1] - [-3, -1]$$
$$= [6, -12] + [4, -2] + [3, 1]$$
$$= [13, -13]$$

EXERCISE 9-9

A **1.** Find the following sums of vectors.
(a) $[3, 2] + [-4, -1]$ (b) $[-3, -4] + [2, 1]$
(c) $[-5, 1] + [6, -3]$ (d) $[2, -3] + [1, 4] + [0, 5]$
(e) $[0, 2] + [-3, -5] + [1, -1]$ (f) $[3, -5] + [-4, -1] + [-3, -7]$

2. Find the following differences of vectors.
(a) $[5, 3] - [2, 2]$ (b) $[6, -3] - [-4, -2]$
(c) $[-1, -3] - [-2, 5]$ (d) $[6, 0] - [2, -7]$
(e) $[8.5, -1.3] - [7.1, -2.1]$ (f) $[p, q] - [m, n]$

3. Express each vector as the sum of two other vectors.

(a)

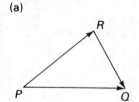

(b)

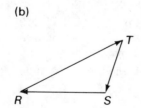

(c)

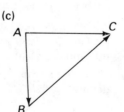

4. Given that *ABCD* is a parallelogram, name a single vector equal to
(a) $\overrightarrow{AD}$ (b) $\overrightarrow{ED}$
(c) $\overrightarrow{AE}$ (d) $\overrightarrow{CD}$
(e) $\overrightarrow{AE} + \overrightarrow{EB}$ (f) $\overrightarrow{BC} + \overrightarrow{CD}$
(g) $\overrightarrow{AE} + \overrightarrow{EC}$ (h) $\overrightarrow{AB} + \overrightarrow{BC}$
(i) $\overrightarrow{BC} + \overrightarrow{CD} + \overrightarrow{DE}$
(j) $\overrightarrow{BA} + \overrightarrow{AE} + \overrightarrow{ED} + \overrightarrow{DC}$

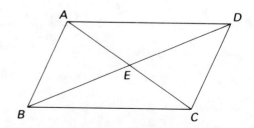

B **5.** Redraw the following pairs of vectors and find their sum using
   (i) the triangle law
   (ii) the parallelogram law

(a)

(b)

6. Redraw the following pairs of vectors and find their difference $\vec{u} - \vec{v}$ geometrically.

(a)

(b)

7. Find the following sums and differences of vectors
(i) algebraically, and (ii) geometrically
(a) $[3, 2] + [4, -2]$ (b) $[-2, 5] + [-3, -1]$
(c) $[4, 2] - [3, 5]$ (d) $[-3, -2] - [4, -5]$
(e) $[2, 1] + [-4, 4] + [-2, -5]$ (f) $[6, -5] + [2, -5] - [-3, -7]$

8. Express each of the following vectors in the form $[a, b]$.
(a) $2[3, -5] + 3[-4, -2]$ (b) $6[-2, -1] - 3[-2, 5]$
(c) $4[-1, -2] - 2[3, -2] - [-1, 0]$ (d) $-[-2, -3] + 5[-4, -2] - 3[-1, 3]$
(e) $2[1, -5] - 3[4, -2] - [3, -7]$ (f) $\frac{1}{2}[4, -8] - \frac{1}{3}[9, 12] - \frac{1}{5}[-10, -20]$

9. Given the vectors $\vec{u} = [3, -1]$, $\vec{v} = [-2, 5]$ and $\vec{w} = [-1, -4]$.
(a) Find $\vec{u} + \vec{w}$, $\vec{w} - \vec{v}$ and $\vec{v} - \vec{u}$ algebraically and geometrically.
(b) Find $|\vec{u}|, |\vec{v}|, |\vec{w}|, |\vec{u} + \vec{w}|, |\vec{w} - \vec{v}|, |\vec{v} - \vec{u}|$

10. Redraw the following vectors and find the sum $\vec{u} + \vec{v} + \vec{w} + \vec{x}$ geometrically.

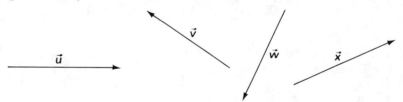

C **11.** Prove algebraically and geometrically that for any two vectors $\vec{u}$ and $\vec{v}$,

$$\vec{u} + \vec{v} = \vec{v} + \vec{u}$$

12. Prove algebraically that for any two non-zero vectors $\vec{u}$ and $\vec{v}$

$$|\vec{u}| + |\vec{v}| \geq |\vec{u} + \vec{v}|$$

9.10 APPLICATIONS OF VECTORS

Problems involving forces are simplified using some of the vector techniques we have just studied.

To describe a force it is necessary to state
(i) the direction
(ii) the point of application
(iii) the magnitude.

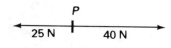

Figure 9-4

Figure 9-4 shows forces of 40 N and 25 N acting, in opposite directions, at point P. The combined effect of these two forces is a 15 N force acting to the right. This single force that has the same effect as the other forces is called the *resultant*. The resultant is the sum of the vectors representing the two forces.

EXAMPLE 1. *Two forces of 30 N and 40 N act at a point at an angle of 60° to each other. Find the magnitude and direction (to the nearest degree) of the resultant.*

One Newton is roughly the force exerted by your hand when supporting two golf balls.

$$1\,N = 1\,kg \cdot m/s^2$$

Solution

We find the resultant of the two forces by adding the two forces using the parallelogram law.

In $\triangle BDC$, since $AB \parallel DC$,

$$\angle C = 180° - \angle B = 120°\,(TPT)$$

also

$$BA = CD = 40$$

Using the Law of Cosines in $\triangle BDC$

$$(BD)^2 = (BC)^2 + (CD)^2 - 2(BC)(CD)(\cos C)$$

$$R^2 = 30^2 + 40^2 - 2(30)(40)(\cos 120°)$$

$$= 900 + 1600 + 1200$$

$$= 3700$$

$$\therefore \quad R \doteq 61\,N$$

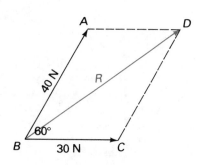

By the Law of Sines

$$\frac{\sin \angle DBC}{CD} = \frac{\sin C}{BD}$$

$$\frac{\sin \angle DBC}{40} = \frac{\sin 120°}{61}$$

$$\sin \angle DBC = \frac{40(0.866)}{61}$$

$$\doteq 0.5679$$

$$\angle DBC \doteq 35°$$

∴ the resultant force has a magnitude of 61 N and acts at an angle of 35° to the 30 N force.

Since velocity is speed in a direction, velocity can be represented by a vector.

When a plane flies its velocity relative to the earth is the resultant of
(i) the plane's velocity through still air, and
(ii) the velocity of the wind

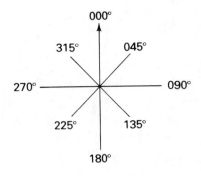

EXAMPLE 2. *A plane is steering a heading of 045° at an air speed (speed in still air) of 500 km/h. The wind is from 300° at 100 km/h (the direction from which the wind blows is always given). Find the ground speed and track (or course) of the plane.*

Solution

Adding the vectors using the triangle law gives a true picture of what is happening.

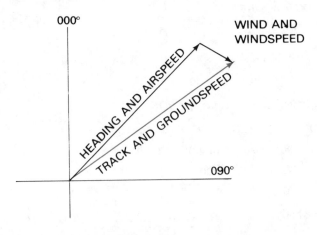

The parallelogram law gives a simpler solution.

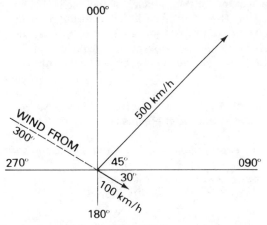

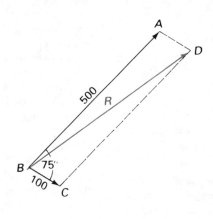

By the Law of Cosines in $\triangle BDC$

$$(BD)^2 = (BC)^2 + (CD)^2 - 2(BC)(CD)(\cos C)$$

$$= 100^2 + 500^2 - 2(100)(500)(\cos 105°)$$

$$\doteq 234\,000$$

$$\therefore \quad BD \doteq 484$$

By the Law of Sines in $\triangle ABD$

$$\frac{\sin \angle ABD}{AD} = \frac{\sin A}{BD}$$

$$\frac{\sin \angle ABD}{100} = \frac{\sin 105°}{484}$$

$$\sin \angle ABD \doteq \frac{100(0.9659)}{484}$$

$$\doteq 0.1996$$

$$\therefore \quad \angle ABD \doteq 12°$$

$\therefore$ the plane's ground speed is 484 km/h and it is making a track of 057° (45° + 12°).

The topic of *relative velocity* is another important application of vectors.

Consider the following highway situation (Figure 9-5) involving a car (C) travelling at 100 km/h, a bus (B) travelling at 80 km/h and a truck (T) travelling at 90 km/h.

To an observer in a helicopter hovering over the vehicles their actual velocities are 100 km/h west, 80 km/h west and 90 km/h east. To someone sitting in the bus the car is passing at 20 km/h. We say that the velocity of the car *relative* to the bus is 20 km/h west. The velocity of the truck relative to the car is 190 km/h east.

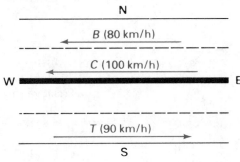

Figure 9-5

This phenomenon occurs because all velocities are relative to something else. In the strictest sense the velocity of the car is 100 km/h west *relative to the earth*. The earth itself is flying through space at approximately 100 000 km/h and spinning as it goes yet we don't notice it. In other words, when we look at a moving object, even though we are moving ourselves, we see the object as though we are stationary. The following, then, is the important principle for relative velocity problems.

The velocity of an object A relative to an object B is $v_A - v_B$ where v_A is the actual velocity of A and v_B the actual velocity of B.

EXAMPLE 3. *A ship is steering 090° at 15 kn. A tug 2 M to the south is steering 045° at 20 kn.*
(a) *Find the velocity of the ship relative to the tug.*
(b) *Will the ship pass in front of or behind the tug?*

1 M = 1 nautical mile
   = 1.852 km

1 kn = 1 M/h

Note: The nautical mile and the nautical mile per hour, or knot, are not SI units. And M and kn are not SI symbols (though M, k, and n are SI prefixes, meaning 10^6, 10^3, and 10^{-9} respectively). The nautical mile and knot are permitted for use in SI for the time being because of their wide use in navigation. The nautical mile is based on the geometry of the earth. It is the mean length of an arc of 1' along a great circle route of the earth.

Solution
To an observer above the two vessels the vector diagrams would appear as in Figure 9-6
(a) To an observer on the tug the velocity of the ship is $v_s - v_t$ or $v_s + (-v_t)$. By the Law of Cosines

$$R^2 = 15^2 + 20^2 - 2(15)(20) \cos 45°$$
$$R \doteq 14.2 \text{ kn}$$

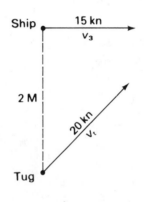

By the Law of Sines,

$$\frac{\sin \theta}{20} = \frac{\sin 45°}{14.2}$$
$$\sin \theta \doteq 0.996$$
$$\theta \doteq 85°$$

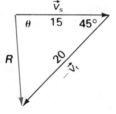

To an observer on the tug the ship is steering 175° at 14.2 kn.

Figure 9-6

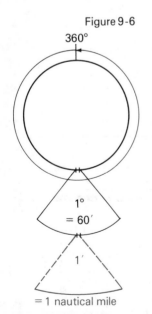

360°

1°
= 60'

1'

= 1 nautical mile

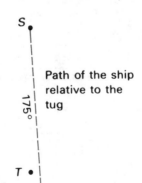

S

Path of the ship relative to the tug

175°

T

(b) A scale diagram best illustrates the path of the ship relative to the tug.
The ship passes in front of the tug. The point of closest approach is calculated by finding the perpendicular distance from T to the path of the ship.

EXERCISE 9-10

1. The diagram shows a highway situation involving a bus (*B*), car (*C*), truck (*T*) and van (*V*).
Determine
(a) the velocity of the car relative to the truck.
(b) the velocity of the bus relative to the car.
(c) the velocity of the bus relative to the van.
(d) the velocity of the van relative to the bus.
(e) the velocity of the truck relative to the van.
(f) the velocity of the car relative to the van.
(g) the velocity of the truck relative to the car.

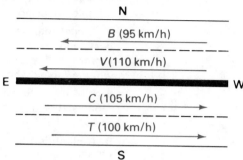

2. State the resultant of the following systems of forces acting at a point *P*.

(a)
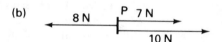

(b)

(c)
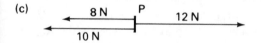

(d)
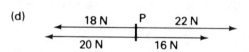

(e)
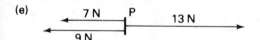

(f)
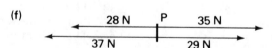

3. Determine the magnitude and direction (to the nearest degree) of the resultant of the following systems of forces.
(a) Forces of 60 N and 50 N acting at a point at an angle of 60° to each other.
(b) Forces of 50 N and 40 N acting at a point at an angle of 30° to each other.
(c) Forces of 7 N and 8 N acting at a point at an angle of 90° to each other.
(d) Forces of 10 N and 9 N acting at a point at an angle of 120° to each other.
(e) Forces of 20 N and 30 N acting at a point at an angle of 153° to each other.
(f) Forces of 11 N and 15 N acting at a point at an angle of 34° to each other.

4. A plane is steering a heading of 060° at an airspeed of 500 km/h. The wind is from 000° at 100 km/h. Find the ground speed and track of the plane.

5. If the wind is from 090° at 90 km/h and a plane is steering 225° at an air speed of 350 km/h, find the ground speed and track of the plane.

6. A pilot wants his plane to track 300° with a ground speed of 400 km/h. If the wind is from 100° at 80 km/h, what heading should the pilot steer and at what airspeed should he fly?

7. A pilot maps out his flight plan and determines that to reach his destination on time his plane must track 170° at 500 km/h. If the wind is from 220° at 50 km/h, what heading should the pilot steer and at what air speed should he fly?

8. A plane is steering a heading of 070° at an air speed of 300 km/h. A radar station reports that the plane is tracking 050° with a ground speed of 550 km/h. Find the wind speed and wind direction.

9. A plane is tracking 250° with a ground speed of 400 km/h. If the pilot is steering a heading of 270° at an air speed of 750 km/h, find the windspeed and wind direction.

10. A ship is steering 270° at 12 kn. A submarine 3 M to the north is steering 225° at 16 kn.
(a) Find the velocity of the submarine relative to the ship.
(b) Will the submarine pass in front of or behind the ship?

11. An aircraft carrier is steering 135° at 20 kn. A submarine 5 M to the east is steering 180° at 15 kn.
(a) Find the velocity of the submarine relative to the aircraft carrier.
(b) Find the velocity of the aircraft carrier relative to the submarine.
(c) Will the aircraft carrier pass in front of or behind the submarine?

12. A ship is steering 000° at 16 kn. Radar detects a submarine 2 M to the east with a relative velocity of 13 kn at 105°. What is the actual velocity of the submarine?

13. The radar, on a ship steering 135° at 18 kn, detects a submarine 3 M to the south with relative velocity of 010° at 16 kn. What is the actual velocity of the submarine?

C **14.** A submarine detects a ship 5 M to the north. The ship is steering 090° at 20 kn. The submarine's attack speed is 30 kn. What course should the submarine steer to intercept the ship?

15. A destroyer detects a submarine 4 M to the south steering 225° at 20 kn. If the destroyer's attack speed is 30 kn what course should the destroyer steer to intercept the sub?

9.11 TRAJECTORIES

In this section we shall consider the motions of objects whose trajectories lead to quadratic equations. To simplify calculations we shall neglect air resistance.

For a bomber flying at 200 m/s its horizontal movement can be expressed as $x = 200t$, where x is in metres and t in seconds. If there were no gravitational force and a bomb were released it would continue to move horizontally according to the equation $x = 200t$.

However, an object falls according to $d = \frac{1}{2}gt^2$ where d is distance, t is time and $g = 9.8 \, \text{m/s}^2$ (acceleration due to gravity).

If an object is dropped from a height of 4500 m its distance above ground after t seconds can be expressed as

$$y = 4500 - 4.9t^2$$

or simply $y = 4500 - 5t^2$

Suppose a bomb is dropped from an aircraft flying at 200 m/s from an altitude of 4500 m. The path of the bomb can be described by two equations.

Horizontal movement $x = 200t$ ①

Vertical movement $y = 4500 - 5t^2$ ②, $t \geqslant 0$

Equations such as $x = 200t$ and $y = 4500 - 5t^2$ are called parametric equations and t is called a parameter. If the parameter can be eliminated then y can be expressed in terms of x.

Solving for t in ① we have $t = \dfrac{x}{200}$

Substituting in ② $y = 4500 - 5\left(\dfrac{x}{200}\right)^2$

$$= 4500 - \dfrac{x^2}{8000}$$

or $y = -\dfrac{x^2}{8000} + 4500$

The graph of this function is a parabola with vertex $(0, 4500)$. The bomb strikes the ground when $y = 0$.

$$0 = -\dfrac{x^2}{8000} + 4500$$

$$x^2 - 36\,000\,000 = 0$$

$$(x - 6000)(x + 6000) = 0$$

$$x = 6000 \text{ or } -6000$$

$\therefore$ the bomb strikes the ground 6000 m from the point where it was released.

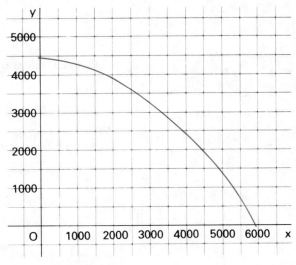

To find the time of flight for the bomb we substitute $x = 6000$ in equation ①.

$$x = 200t$$

$$6000 = 200t$$

$$t = 30$$

Therefore to hit a designated target the bomb must be released 6000 m before the target. The bomb will strike the target 30 s after release.

It is sometimes convenient to resolve a vector into its components. The components of a vector are found by projecting the vector onto the x-axis and y-axis.

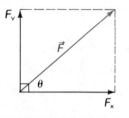

For $\vec{F} = [F_x, F_y]$,
F_x is the horizontal component of $\vec{F}$ and $F_x = |\vec{F}| \cos \theta$
F_y is the vertical component of $\vec{F}$ and $F_y = |\vec{F}| \sin \theta$

EXAMPLE 3. *A sled is pulled along the ground with a force of 60 N applied to the handle at an angle of 30° to the horizontal. Find the force that moves the sled forward and the force that lifts the sled.*

Solution

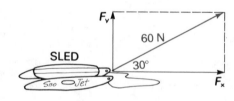

$$\frac{F_x}{60} = \cos 30° \qquad \frac{F_y}{60} = \sin 30°$$

$$F_x = 60(\cos 30°) \qquad F_y = 60(\sin 30°)$$

$$\doteq 60(0.866) \qquad = 60(0.5)$$

$$\doteq 52 \qquad = 30$$

A 52 N force moves the sled forward and a 30 N force tends to lift the sled.

Cannon Ball Trajectories

We shall now use our knowledge of vectors to determine the equation of the path of a cannon ball.

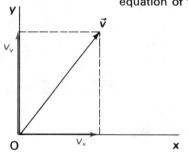

The initial velocity of the cannon ball is represented by the vector $\vec{v}$. This vector is resolved into the components v_x and v_y which are the horizontal and vertical components of $\vec{v}$ as the ball leaves the cannon's mouth.

The horizontal displacement along the x-axis is given by

$$x = v_x t \qquad \text{①}$$

If there were no gravitational pull vertically downward the displacement along the y-axis would be

$$y = v_y t$$

However, bodies fall according to the formula $y = \frac{1}{2}gt^2$. Since the gravitational force is having a negative effect on the vertical displacement we write

$$y = v_y t - \frac{1}{2}gt^2 \quad ②$$

Solving for t in ① we have

$$t = \frac{x}{v_x}$$

Substituting in ②

$$y = v_y t - \frac{1}{2}gt^2$$

$$= v_y \left(\frac{x}{v_x}\right) - \frac{1}{2}g\left(\frac{x}{v_x}\right)^2$$

$$= \frac{v_y x}{v_x} - \frac{gx^2}{2v_x^2}$$

Completing the square.

$$y = \frac{-gx^2}{2v_x^2} + \frac{v_y x}{v_x}$$

$$= -\frac{g}{2v_x^2}\left[x^2 - \frac{2v_x v_y x}{g} + \frac{v_x^2 v_y^2}{g^2} - \frac{v_x^2 v_y^2}{g^2}\right]$$

$$= -\frac{g}{2v_x^2}\left[\left(x - \frac{v_x v_y}{g}\right)^2 - \frac{v_x^2 v_y^2}{g^2}\right]$$

$$= -\frac{g}{2v_x^2}\left(x - \frac{v_x v_y}{g}\right)^2 + \frac{v_y^2}{2g}$$

From this we see that the cannon ball reaches a maximum height of $\frac{v_y^2}{2g}$ when $x = \frac{v_x v_y}{g}$

Graphically we display the path of a cannon ball as follows.

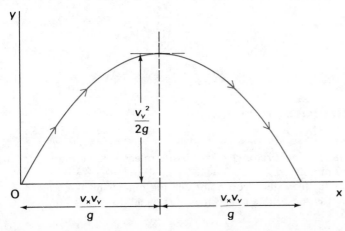

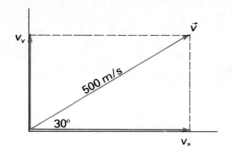

EXAMPLE 4. *A cannon is fired at an angle of elevation of 30°. The cannon ball leaves the barrel at 500 m/s. Determine*
(a) *the maximum height reached by the ball*
(b) *the horizontal distance travelled*
(c) *the time of flight.*

Solution

We first determine v_x and v_y.

$$v_x = |\vec{v}| \cos \theta$$

$$= 500(\cos 30°)$$

$$\doteq 433 \text{ m/s}$$

$$v_y = |\vec{v}| \sin \theta$$

$$= 500(\sin 30°)$$

$$= 250 \text{ m/s}$$

(a) The maximum height is given by $\dfrac{v_y^2}{2g}$

$$\frac{v_y^2}{2g} = \frac{(250)^2}{2(9.81)}$$

$$\doteq 3200 \text{ m}$$

(b) The horizontal distance travelled is given by $\dfrac{2v_x v_y}{g}$

$$\frac{2v_x v_y}{g} = \frac{2(433)(250)}{9.81}$$

$$\doteq 22\,000 \text{ m}$$

(c) The time of flight is given by $t = \dfrac{x}{v_x}$

$$t = \frac{22\,000}{433}$$

$$\doteq 51 \text{ s}$$

EXERCISE 9-11

B   **1.** A plane flying over a lake at 100 m/s releases a die marker from an altitude of 4500 m.
(a) How far from the drop point will the marker hit the water?
(b) What is the time elapsed from "release" to "splash"?

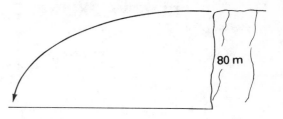

2. A rifle is fired horizontally from a cliff 80 m high with a muzzle velocity of 800 m/s.
(a) What is the horizontal distance travelled by the bullet?
(b) What is the time elapsed before the bullet hits the ground?

3. A baseball is thrown horizontally with a velocity of 40 m/s at a height of 2 m. How far will the ball travel before it hits the ground?

4. Resolve the following into their horizontal and vertical components.

(a)   (b)   (c)

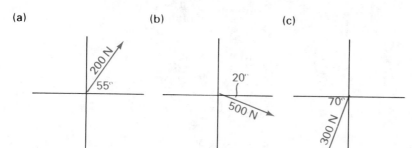

5. A ball is thrown with a force of 80 N at an angle of 25° with the horizontal. Determine the magnitude of the force that

(a) propels the ball forward
(b) propels the ball upward

6. A football is punted with a force of 100 N at an angle of 50° to the horizontal. What is the magnitude of the force that
(a) propels the ball forward?
(b) propels the ball upward?

7. A rifle is fired at an angle of elevation of 10°. The bullet leaves the barrel at 400 m/s. Determine
(a) the maximum height reached by the bullet.
(b) the horizontal distance travelled.
(c) the time of flight.

8. In 1918 the Germans built a huge gun so they could shell Paris from great distances. It was nicknamed Big Bertha in honour of Bertha Krupp who owned the Krupp works where the gun was built. The gun was fired at an angle of elevation of 55°. The shell left the gun at 2000 m/s. Determine
(a) the horizontal distance travelled by the shell.
(b) the time of flight of the shell.
(c) the maximum height reached by the shell.

REVIEW EXERCISE

B **1.** If $A = \begin{pmatrix} 2 & -1 & 2 \\ 1 & 0 & 3 \end{pmatrix}$, $B = \begin{pmatrix} -1 & -3 & 0 \\ 2 & 1 & -2 \end{pmatrix}$ and $C = \begin{pmatrix} -3 & 1 & -2 \\ -2 & -1 & 4 \end{pmatrix}$, find

(a) $A + C$ (b) $B + C + A$ (c) $B - C$

(d) $C - B$ (e) $2A + 3B$ (f) $2C - 3A$

(g) $2B - (A - 2C)$ (h) $-3(B - 3A)$ (i) $-(3C + B) - 2A$

2. Write each product as a single matrix, where possible.

(a) $\begin{pmatrix} 2 & 1 \\ 3 & -1 \end{pmatrix} \begin{pmatrix} 1 & -2 \\ -3 & 0 \end{pmatrix}$ (b) $\begin{pmatrix} -3 & 4 \\ 1 & -2 \end{pmatrix} \begin{pmatrix} 0 & -1 \\ 3 & 2 \end{pmatrix}$

(c) $\begin{pmatrix} 3 & 5 \\ -2 & 1 \end{pmatrix} \begin{pmatrix} 2 & 0 \\ 1 & 2 \\ -2 & 3 \end{pmatrix}$ (d) $\begin{pmatrix} 3 & -2 \\ 0 & -1 \\ 2 & 4 \end{pmatrix} \begin{pmatrix} 2 & -1 \\ 1 & -3 \end{pmatrix}$

(e) $\begin{pmatrix} -1 & 2 & 3 \\ 0 & -2 & 1 \\ 1 & -4 & 2 \end{pmatrix} \begin{pmatrix} 3 & 1 & -2 \\ -2 & 0 & 0 \\ 1 & 3 & -5 \end{pmatrix}$ (f) $\begin{pmatrix} 1 & 0 & 0 \\ 0 & 1 & 0 \\ 0 & 0 & 1 \end{pmatrix} \begin{pmatrix} 2 & 1 \\ -1 & -2 \\ 3 & 0 \end{pmatrix}$

(g) $\begin{pmatrix} 1 & 3 & -2 \\ 2 & -1 & 4 \\ -2 & 0 & -1 \end{pmatrix} \begin{pmatrix} 2 \\ 0 \\ -2 \end{pmatrix}$ (h) $\begin{pmatrix} 3 & -1 & 2 & 1 \\ 0 & 1 & -1 & -2 \\ 1 & 2 & 0 & 3 \end{pmatrix} \begin{pmatrix} 3 & 4 \\ 1 & -2 \\ 2 & 0 \end{pmatrix}$

3. Evaluate the following.

(a) $\begin{vmatrix} 2 & -3 \\ 4 & 5 \end{vmatrix}$ (b) $\begin{vmatrix} 3 & 1 & 2 \\ 4 & -3 & 0 \\ 1 & -2 & 0 \end{vmatrix}$ (c) $\begin{vmatrix} 3 & 2 & -1 \\ 1 & 0 & 2 \\ -2 & 5 & 1 \end{vmatrix}$ (d) $\begin{vmatrix} 1 & 4 & -2 \\ -2 & -3 & 3 \\ -1 & 4 & 2 \end{vmatrix}$

4. Find the inverse of each of the following.

(a) $\begin{pmatrix} 3 & 3 \\ 1 & 2 \end{pmatrix}$ (b) $\begin{pmatrix} -2 & -3 \\ -1 & 4 \end{pmatrix}$ (c) $\begin{pmatrix} -1 & 2 \\ 0 & 1 \end{pmatrix}$ (d) $\begin{pmatrix} 2 & -4 \\ -3 & -2 \end{pmatrix}$

5. Solve the system by the method of section 9.5.

(a) $2x + y = 7$ (b) $2x - 3y = -14$ (c) $4x + 7y = -5$

     $3x - 2y = 0$ $3x + 2y = -8$ $6x - 5y = 8$

6. Solve the following using Cramer's Rule.

(a) $5x + 3y = -4$ (b) $4x + 5y = -17$ (c) $2x + y + 1 = 0$

     $3x - 2y = -10$ $3x - 7y = -2$ $4x - 3y = -17$

(d) $3x - 2y = -12$ (e) $2x + 3y - z = 7$ (f) $3x + y - z = -7$

     $4x + 5y = 7$ $x + 2y + 3z = -3$ $2x - y + z = 2$

                        $3x - y + z = 0$ $x + 2y - z = -7$

7. Solve the following using the augmented matrix.

(a) $2x + 3y - z = -1$ (b) $2x + 3y + 2z = -2$ (c) $2w + x - y + 2z = -2$

     $3x - 2y + 2z = -4$ $3x - y + 4z = -15$ $3w - 2x + y - 2z = -9$

     $x + 2y - 3z = -7$ $x + y - 2z = -1$ $w + 2x - 2y + 3z = 0$

                                                   $2w - 3x + 2y - z = -3$

(d) $3x + y - 2z = 3$ (e) $4y + 3x + 2z = -18$ (f) $2x + 3y = 6$

     $x + 2y + 4z = 0$ $z - 2y + 5x = -4$ $2y - 3z = 14$

     $2x + 3y - 6z = -5$ $3y - 3z + 2x = -13$ $3x - z = -7$

8. Determine the vector and its magnitude.

(a) $A\,(2, 4)$ to $B\,(3, 7)$ (b) $C\,(-1, 2)$ to $D\,(3, 5)$

(c) $E\,(-3, -1)$ to $F\,(4, -2)$ (d) $G\,(-4, 2)$ to $H\,(0, -5)$

(e) $K\,(6, -2)$ to $L\,(4, -5)$ (f) $M\,(-7, 6)$ to $N\,(-3, -1)$

9. Find the following sums and differences of vectors
(i) algebraically and (ii) geometrically
(a) $[2, 1] + [3, -2]$ (b) $[-1, 0] - [-3, -2]$
(c) $[3, 4] - [-2, 5]$ (d) $[4, -3] + [-2, -3]$

10. Express each of the following in the form $[a, b]$.
(a) $2[3, 2] + 4[-1, 5]$ (b) $6[-2, -1] - 3[1, -4]$
(c) $5[1, -1] - [-3, 1] + 2[6, 0]$ (d) $\frac{1}{2}[4, -6] - 2[-1, -3] - 3[-2, 5]$

11. Determine the magnitude and direction of the resultant of the following systems of forces.
(a) Forces of 30 N and 50 N acting at a point at an angle of 40° to each other.
(b) Forces of 9 N and 12 N acting at a point at an angle of 100° to each other.

12. A plane is steering a heading of 050° at an airspeed of 300 km/h. The wind is from 000° at 50 km/h. Find the ground speed and track of the plane.

13. A plane is tracking 270° with a ground speed of 400 km/h. If the pilot is steering a heading of 300° at an airspeed of 350 km/h, find the wind speed and wind direction.

14. A ship is steering 090° at 15 kn. A submarine 5 M to the north is steering 120° at 20 kn.
(a) Find the velocity of the submarine relative to the ship.
(b) Will the submarine pass in front of or behind the ship?

15. A gun is fired at an angle of elevation of 40°. The shell leaves the barrel at 1000 m/s. Determine
(a) the horizontal distance travelled by the shell
(b) the maximum height reached by the shell
(c) the time of flight.

16. A rifle is fired horizontally from a cliff 50 m high with a muzzle velocity of 700 m/s.
(a) What is the horizontal distance travelled by the bullet?
(b) What is the time elapsed before the bullet hits the ground?

17. A ball is batted with a force of 100 N at an angle of 40° to the horizontal. What is the magnitude of the force that
(a) propels the ball upward?
(b) propels the ball forward?

REVIEW AND PREVIEW TO CHAPTER 10

EXERCISE 1   MEAN, MEDIAN AND MODE

The MEAN: the average
   The mean or average of a set of numbers is found by adding them together and dividing the total by the number of numbers added.
   For a set of values $x_1, x_2, x_3, \ldots, x_n$ the mean is

$$\bar{x} = \frac{x_1 + x_2 + x_3 + \ldots + x_n}{n}$$

The MEDIAN: the halfway
   When a set of numbers is arranged in order (smallest to largest), then the middle number is the median. If there is an even number of numbers, then the median is the average of the middle two numbers. Knowing the median enables one to tell whether any number is in the top half or bottom half of the group.

The MODE: the most common
   The mode of a set of numbers is the number that occurs most often. If every number occurs only once, then we say there is no mode. It is also possible, however, for a set of numbers to have several modes.

1. Calculate the mean, median and mode for the following data.
(a) 5, 7, 9, 7, 8, 6, 4, 3, 14
(b) 12, 13, 16, 20, 11, 14, 22, 18, 16, 12
(c) 27, 21, 19, 23, 22, 21, 24
(d) 47, 58, 63, 55, 52, 50, 46, 69
(e) 107, 134, 102, 101, 105, 111, 121, 107, 97, 102

2. Calculate the mean, median and mode for the following data.

(a)

Value	Frequency
1	5
3	7
4	6
5	8
6	4

(b)

Value	Frequency
7	2
10	3
12	6
13	4
15	2
18	5

(c)

Value	Frequency
10	9
13	6
15	1
18	7
25	6

3. The following are the results of a grade 12 math test.

$$73, \quad 56, \quad 40, \quad 64, \quad 63,$$
$$66, \quad 10, \quad 59, \quad 57, \quad 20,$$
$$67, \quad 70, \quad 71, \quad 61, \quad 40$$

Calculate the mean, median and mode. Which is more useful?

4. The following are the weekly earnings (in dollars) of 20 students who work part time.

$$32, \quad 34, \quad 38, \quad 36, \quad 30,$$
$$26, \quad 28, \quad 32, \quad 40, \quad 32,$$
$$34, \quad 36, \quad 40, \quad 42, \quad 38,$$
$$32, \quad 28, \quad 30, \quad 32, \quad 34$$

Calculate the mean, median and mode.

5. The following are the annual salaries of people employed by a company.

Title	Number	Annual Salary
President	1	$100 000
Vice President	2	$ 50 000
Treasurer	1	$ 40 000
Accountant	3	$ 35 000
Salesman	5	$ 30 000
Secretary	8	$ 20 000

(a) Determine the mean, median and mode.
(b) Which measure best represents the salary paid by the company?

6. A shoe store manager records the sizes of shoes sold in order to determine what shoe sizes to order. What measure of central tendency is most meaningful to him—the mean, median or mode?

7. The mean mass of the students at Northern High School is 54 kg. The mean mass at Southern High School is 52 kg. Can we conclude that the mean mass of both groups together is 53 kg? Explain.

CHAPTER 10

Probability and Statistics

We see ... that the theory of probabilities is at bottom only common sense reduced to calculations; it makes us appreciate with exactitude what reasonable minds feel by a sort of instinct, often without being able to account for it. It is remarkable that this science, which originated in the consideration of games of chance, should have become the most important object of human knowledge.

Pierre Laplace

Blaise Pascal (1623–1666)

Pascal's father was a mathematician who at first kept mathematics books away from Blaise so that he would develop other interests. But by the time he was 12 Blaise had discovered so many geometrical facts on his own that his father finally encouraged him. Pascal was so much a child prodigy that by the time he was 14 he was meeting regularly with the leading French mathematicians of the day. When he was 16 he discovered what we call Pascal's Theorem: If a hexagon is inscribed in a conic, then the opposite sides intersect in 3 collinear points.

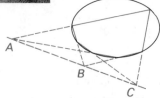

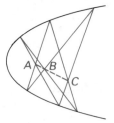

Pascal's Theorem: *A*, *B*, *C* lie in a straight line

In 1642, when he was only 19, Pascal invented the first calculating machine and eventually built and sold about 50 such machines.

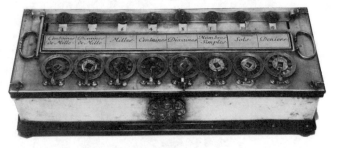

Pascal's calculating machine (from an original model in the collection of Arts and Sciences Department of IBM).

In 1654 his friend, the Chevalier de Méré, who was an able and experienced gambler, wrote to Pascal about a gambling problem. The Chevalier had made a lot of money betting that he could get at least one 6 out of 4 rolls of a die. But eventually nobody would bet against him, and so he bet he would roll at least one double 6 out of 24 rolls of two dice. When he lost much of his fortune on this bet he wrote to Pascal asking what had gone wrong. Pascal corresponded with Pierre Fermat about this problem and they both solved it by finding the appropriate probabilities. In the previous century Girolamo Cardano had founded the theory of probability, but Cardano's work had been forgotten. The modern theory of probability has its origins in the correspondence between Pascal and Fermat.

Pascal is also famous for Pascal's Triangle. (See Section 10-4.) This arithmetic triangle originated in China about 1100 A.D. but it is called Pascal's Triangle because Pascal rediscovered it and developed and applied many of its properties.

This chapter is mainly concerned with the principles of probability and statistics. However before starting our study of probability theory we shall first look at some techniques for counting collections and outcomes which will be useful when we come to compute probabilities.

10.1 COUNTING PRINCIPLES

Suppose that A, B and C are three towns and there are 3 roads from A to B and 2 roads from B to C. How many routes are there from A to C via B?

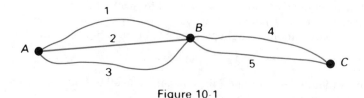

Figure 10-1

If the roads are numbered as in Figure 10-1, then we can list all of the possible routes as

14   15   24   25   34   35

and so there are 6 routes. We could also use a tree diagram:

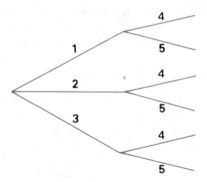

and again count 6 routes.

For each of the 3 choices of road from A to B, there are 2 choices of road from B to C. So the number of routes from A to C is $3 \times 2 = 6$.

Similarly if there were m roads from A to B and n roads from B to C, then by visualizing a road or tree diagram you can see that the number of possible routes from A to C via B is mn.

The kind of reasoning used in this example is called the Fundamental Counting Principle.

> ### The Fundamental Counting Principle
>
> If the first choice can be made in m ways and the second choice can be made in n ways, then the number of ways of making the two choices is mn.

EXAMPLE 1. *John Dapper owns twelve shirts and seven pairs of pants. How many different outfits can he wear?*

Solution

John can choose a shirt in 12 ways, and for each of these choices he can choose a pair of pants in 7 ways.

∴ by the Fundamental Counting Principle he can choose an outfit in

$$12 \times 7 = 84 \text{ ways.}$$

The Fundamental Counting Principle can be used to find the number of elements in the Cartesian product of two sets.

If A is a finite set, the number of elements in A is called the cardinality (or cardinal number) of A and is denoted by $n(A)$. Recall that the Cartesian product of two sets A and B is $A \times B = \{(x, y) \mid x \in A, y \in B\}$. If $n(A) = r$ and $n(B) = s$, then in forming an ordered pair (x, y) with $x \in A$ and $y \in B$ there are r choices for the first component and s choices for the second component. Thus by the Fundamental Counting Principle the total number of ordered pairs is $n(A \times B) = rs$.

$$\boxed{n(A \times B) = n(A)n(B)}$$

For example if $A = \{1, 3, 5, 7, 9\}$ and $B = \{2, 4, 6, 8\}$, then

$$n(A \times B) = n(A)n(B)$$
$$= 5 \times 4$$
$$= 20$$

When there are several choices to be made, the Fundamental counting Principle can be extended as follows.

If the first choice can be made in n_1 ways, the second choice in n_2 ways, ..., and the rth choice in n_r ways, then the total number of ways of making all the choices is the product $n_1 n_2 \ldots n_r$.

EXAMPLE 2. *Jane wants to choose an outfit from a selection of 2 skirts (green, brown), 3 blouses (white, green, brown) and 2 pairs of shoes (white, brown). In how many ways can she do this?*

Solution

Jane can choose a skirt in 2 ways, a blouse in 3 ways and a pair of shoes in 2 ways.

∴ by the Fundamental Counting Principle she can choose an outfit in

$$2 \times 3 \times 2 = 12 \text{ ways.}$$

The tree diagram illustrates the process:

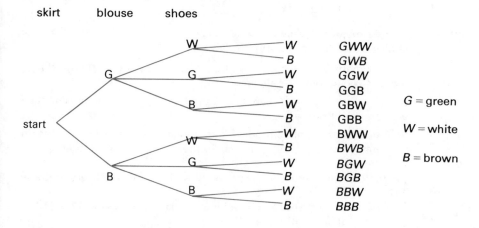

EXAMPLE 3. *A test consists of ten true-false questions. How many different sets of answers can be given?*

Solution

There are 2 choices (true or false) for each of the ten questions.

∴ by the Fundamental Counting Principle, the total number of choices is

$$2 \times 2 \times 2 \times 2 \times 2 \times 2 \times 2 \times 2 \times 2 \times 2 = 2^{10} = 1024$$

EXERCISE 10-1

B **1.** A car purchaser has a choice of two upholstery materials (leather, nylon) and four colours (blue, white, black, red). How many different choices are there? Draw a tree diagram.

2. Show by a tree diagram the number of methods of travelling from Toronto to Vancouver via Calgary, if you can go from Toronto to Calgary by plane or train and from Calgary to Vancouver by bus, plane, or train.

3. An all-star baseball team has 7 pitchers and 3 catchers. How many different batteries consisting of a pitcher and a catcher can the manager select?

4. (a) If repetitions are allowed, how many two-digit numbers can be formed from the set of digits $D = \{1, 2, 3, 4, 5\}$?
(b) How many numbers consisting of two different digits can be formed from D?

5. If repetitions are allowed, how many two-digit even numbers can be formed from the set $\{1, 2, 3, 4, 5, 6, 7, 8, 9\}$?

6. The Tiffany Restaurant offers the following menu:

Main Course	Dessert	Beverage
Chicken	Cheesecake	Coffee
Ham	Ice cream	Tea
Steak	Apple pie	Milk
Prime Rib		Lemonade
Roast Pork		

In how many ways can a customer order a meal consisting of one choice from each category?

7. How many license plates can be made using 3 letters followed by 3 digits if repetitions are allowed?

What is the next year that you will be able to use this year's calendar?

8. In how many ways can a 15-member club elect a president, a vice-president and a secretary?

9. A club consists of 10 grade 12 students and 8 grade 11 students. In how many ways can this club elect a president, a vice-president and a secretary if
(a) the president must be in grade 12 and the other officers in grade 11?
(b) the president and vice-president must be in grade 12 and the secretary must be in grade 11?

10. In a combination lock there are 60 different positions. To open the lock you move to a certain number in the clockwise direction, then to a number in the counterclockwise direction and finally to a third number in the clockwise direction. How many different combinations are there?

11. If 4 coins are tossed in succession, in how many ways can they come up? Illustrate with a tree diagram. What if there are r coins?

12. If 3 dice are rolled in succession, in how many ways can they come up?

13. In how many ways can 6 books be arranged on a shelf?

14. There are 5 people in the Johnson family. If you go to visit them, how many different combinations of them might you find at home?

10.2 PERMUTATIONS

An investment club has five members and wants to choose a president and a vice-president. In how many ways can this be done?

The president can be chosen in 5 ways and after one is chosen the vice-president can be chosen in 4 ways. Thus, by the Fundamental Counting Principle, both can be chosen in

$$5 \times 4 = 20 \text{ ways.}$$

To illustrate this, let us call the five members of the club A, B, C, D and E. Then the 20 choices can be written as

$$\begin{array}{ccccccccc}
AB & AC & AD & AE & BA & BC & BD & BE & CA & CB \\
CD & CE & DA & DB & DC & DE & EA & EB & EC & ED
\end{array}$$

Notice that the order of the members is important here: AB means that A is president and B is vice-president, while BA means that B is president and A is vice-president.

An *arrangement* of things in a *definite order* is called a permutation.

> A permutation of n objects taken r at a time is an arrangement of r of the n objects in a definite order. The total number of permutations of n objects taken r at a time is denoted by $_nP_r$.

In the preceding example the objects are club members and $n = 5$, $r = 2$. We saw that the number of ways of choosing a president and a vice-president from a 5-member club is

$$_5P_2 = 5 \times 4 = 20$$

Similarly the Fundamental Counting Principle shows that the number of ways of choosing a president, vice-president, and secretary is

$$_5P_3 = 5 \times 4 \times 3 = 60$$

In general suppose that we want to form an arrangement of r objects chosen from a set of n objects. The first object can be chosen in n ways. After it is chosen, there are only $n - 1$ choices for the second object. There are $n - 2$ choices for the third object, and so on.

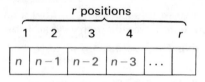

r positions

1	2	3	4	r

| n | $n-1$ | $n-2$ | $n-3$ | $\ldots$ | |

number of choices

Finally the number of choices for the rth object is $n-(r-1)=n-r+1$. By the Fundamental Counting Principle the total number of choices in forming an arrangement of r objects is

$$n\times(n-1)\times(n-2)\times\ldots\times(n-r+1)$$

$$\boxed{_nP_r=n(n-1)(n-2)\ldots(n-r+1)}$$

EXAMPLE 1. *Margaret has 12 books, but she has space for only 8 of them on the shelf of her locker. In how many ways can she arrange her books on the shelf?*

Solution

In this example we want to know the number of permutations of 12 objects (books) taken 8 at a time.
Here

$$n=12 \quad \text{and} \quad r=8$$

$$_{12}P_8=12\times11\times10\times9\times8\times7\times6\times5$$

$$=19\,958\,400$$

∴ Margaret can arrange her books on the shelf in 19 958 400 ways.

EXAMPLE 2. *Find the number of different orders in which a disc jockey can play 6 records.*

Solution

This is the number of permutations of 6 objects taken 6 at a time.

$$\therefore \quad n=6 \quad \text{and} \quad r=6$$

$$_6P_6=6\times5\times4\times3\times2\times1=720$$

∴ a disc jockey can play 6 records in 720 different orders.

In Example 2 we found the number of permutations of *all* of the objects. In general

$$_nP_n=n(n-1)(n-2)\ldots3\times2\times1$$

This expression, the product of the first n natural numbers, occurs so frequently in mathematics that we give it a special symbol $n!$ and a special name, n factorial.

$$\boxed{n!=n(n-1)(n-2)\ldots2\times1}$$

For example
$$1! = 1$$
$$2! = 2 \times 1 = 2$$
$$3! = 3 \times 2 \times 1 = 6$$
$$4! = 4 \times 3 \times 2 \times 1 = 24$$
$$5! = 5 \times 4 \times 3 \times 2 \times 1 = 120$$

By convention

$$0! = 1$$

We can write $_nP_r$ in terms of factorials as follows.

$$_nP_r = n(n-1)(n-2) \ldots (n-r+1)$$

$$= n(n-1)(n-2) \ldots (n-r+1) \times \frac{(n-r)(n-r-1) \ldots 3 \times 2 \times 1}{(n-r)(n-r-1) \ldots 3 \times 2 \times 1}$$

$$= \frac{n(n-1)(n-2) \ldots (n-r+1)(n-r)(n-r-1) \ldots 3 \times 2 \times 1}{(n-r)(n-r-1) \ldots 3 \times 2 \times 1}$$

$$= \frac{n!}{(n-r)!}$$

$$_nP_r = \frac{n!}{(n-r)!}$$

EXAMPLE 3. *How many permutations are there of the letters in the words* (a) ROAM (b) ROOM?

Solution

(a) Since the letters in the word ROAM are all different, the number of permutations of them is

$$_4P_4 = 4! = 4 \times 3 \times 2 \times 1 = 24$$

(b) If we attempt to solve this problem as in part (a) we would get 4! = 24 as the answer. But if we list the possibilities we only get 12 permutations. The difficulty here is that 2 of the letters in the word ROOM (the two O's) are *indistinguishable*. If we write the two O's in different colors we find additional possibilities:

ROOM   ROOM
ROMO   ROMO
.   .
.   .
.   .

ROOM
ROMO
RMOO
OROM
ORMO
OORM
OOMR
OMRO
OMOR
MOOR
MORO
MROO

If we completed this list we would get 4! = 24 possibilities. Since the 2 different permutations ROOM, ROOM would be the same without the colours, we counted twice as many arrangements as there really are. So we must divide by 2 to take care of this.

∴ the number of permutations of the letters in the word ROOM is

$$\frac{4!}{2} = 12$$

EXAMPLE 4. *In how many ways can the letters of the word MINIMUM be arranged?*

Solution

If the 7 letters of the word MINIMUM were all different, then there would be 7! permutations. Let us label the 3 M's with numbers. The 6 different arrangements

$M_1INIM_2UM_3$ $M_1INIM_3UM_2$ $M_2INIM_1UM_3$
$M_2INIM_3UM_1$ $M_3INIM_1UM_2$ $M_3INIM_2UM_1$

would be the same without the numbers. Thus in counting the 7! permutations we counted 6 times as many permutations as there really are. So we must divide 7! by 6 = 3! (the number of ways of arranging the M's).

Similarly the two different arrangements

MI_1NI_2MUM and MI_2NI_1MUM

would be the same without the numbers. So we must also divide by 2 = 2! to make up for this.

∴ the number of arrangements of the letters of the word MINIMUM is

$$\frac{7!}{3!\,2!} = \frac{7 \times 6 \times 5 \times 4 \times 3 \times 2 \times 1}{3 \times 2 \times 1 \times 2 \times 1}$$

$$= 420$$

The same reasoning used in Example 4 demonstrates the following general principle.

> The number of permutations of n objects, of which a objects are alike, another b objects are alike, another c objects are alike, and so on is
>
> $$\frac{n!}{a!\,b!\,c!\ldots}$$

EXERCISE 10-2

B   **1.** Evaluate the following.

(a) $_6P_3$ (b) $_{10}P_4$ (c) 7!

(d) 10!   (e) $\dfrac{12!}{8!}$ (f) $\dfrac{20!}{18!}$

2. (a) How many permutations are there of the letters a, b, c, d taken 2 at a time? Write out all these permutations.

(b) Do the same if the letters are taken 3 at a time.

3. The manager of a baseball team has chosen the 9 players for his starting lineup. In how many ways can he arrange the batting order?

4. A club has 28 members. In how many ways can the president, vice-president, secretary, and treasurer be chosen?

5. If 1000 people enter a contest in which there is a first prize, a second prize, and a third prize, in how many ways can the prizes be given?

6. In how many ways can 4 cards be dealt in succession from a deck of 52 cards?

7. A mathematics text, a history text, a biology text, a French text, and a chemistry text are to be placed on a shelf. In how many ways can they be arranged?

8. Four people get onto a bus in which there are six empty seats. In how many different ways can they seat themselves?

9. Three people arrive in a town which has four hotels. They have become angry at each other on the trip and so they all want to stay in different hotels. In how many ways can this be done?

10. (a) How many permutations are there of the letters of the word *sandwich*?

(b) How many of these begin with a *w*?
(c) How many end with an *h*?
(d) How many have *s* first and *a* second?

11. In how many ways can the letters of the following words be arranged?

(a) feast
(b) famine
(c) idiot
(d) assist
(e) Manitoba
(f) maximum
(g) Canada
(h) Saskatchewan
(i) interesting
(j) uninteresting
(k) ukulele
(l) Mississippi

12. How many 7 digit integers are there which contain
(a) two 3's, three 2's, and two 8's?
(b) four 3's and three 4's?

13. A man bought 2 vanilla ice cream cones, 3 chocolate cones, 4 strawberry cones and 1 maple walnut cone for his 10 children. In how many different ways can he distribute the flavours among his children?

14. A soap company will give away a million dollars to anyone who guesses the one way in which they have arranged the letters of the word SUPERCLEANER. Each entry must be in a separate envelope. How much would it cost you in postage to submit all possible entries?

15. Simplify the following.

(a) $\dfrac{96!}{95!}$

(b) $\dfrac{n!}{(n-1)!}$

(c) $37 \times 36!$

(d) $n \times (n-1)!$

(e) $(n+1) \times n!$

(f) $\dfrac{(n+1)!}{(n-1)!}$

16. In how many ways can 12 basketball players be assigned to
(a) 6 double rooms?   (b) 4 triple rooms?

10.3 COMBINATIONS

An investment club has five members and wants to choose a committee of two members. In how many ways can this be done?

In the preceding section we made a list of the 20 possibilities in choosing a president and vice-president. Notice that *AB* and *BA* represent the same committee. Order is not important in choosing a committee. Since each committee has been counted twice we must divide by 2. The number of ways of selecting a committee of 2 from a 5-member club is

$$\frac{5 \times 4}{2} = 10$$

A *selection* of things in which the *order does not matter* is called a combination.

> A combination of *n* objects taken *r* at a time is a selection of *r* of the *n* objects without regard to order. The total number of combinations of *n* objects taken *r* at a time is denoted by
> $$_nC_r \text{ or } \binom{n}{r}.$$

In the preceding example the objects are club members and $n = 5$, $r = 2$. We say that the number of ways of choosing a 2-person committee from a 5-member club is

$$_5C_2 = \frac{5 \times 4}{2} = 10$$

Similarly if we want to choose a committee of 3, notice that any such committee (for instance *ABC*) can be arranged in 3! ways (*ABC, ACB, BAC, BCA, CAB, CBA*). Therefore we must divide the total number of permutations of the 5 members taken 3 at a time by 3! to get the number of combinations. The number of ways that a committee of 3 can be chosen from 5 club members is

$$_5C_3 = \frac{_5P_3}{3!} = \frac{5 \times 4 \times 3}{3 \times 2 \times 1} = 10$$

In general to find the number of combinations of *n* objects taken *r* at a time we first use the Fundamental Counting Principle to find the total number of permutations $_nP_r$, then we divide by the number of ways of arranging the *r* objects, namely *r*!

$$_nC_r = \frac{_nP_r}{r!} = \frac{n(n-1)(n-2)\dots(n-r+1)}{r!}$$

Recalling that $_nP_r = \frac{n!}{(n-r)!}$ we have

$$\binom{n}{r} = {_nC_r} = \frac{n!}{(n-r)!\, r!}$$

EXAMPLE 1. (a) *In how many ways can 3 men be chosen out of a group of 8 men?*
(b) *In how many ways can 8 men finish 1st, 2nd, and 3rd in a race?*

Solution
(a) Here the order of the 3 men is *not* important.
∴ the number of ways of choosing 3 men from 8 is

$$_8C_3 = \frac{_8P_3}{3!} = \frac{8 \times 7 \times 6}{3 \times 2 \times 1} = 56$$

or equivalently

$$_8C_3 = \frac{8!}{(8-3)!\, 3!}$$

$$= \frac{8 \times 7 \times 6}{3 \times 2 \times 1} = 56$$

(b) In a race the order of the 3 men is important.
∴ the number of ways they can finish 1st, 2nd, and 3rd is

$$_8P_3 = 8 \times 7 \times 6 = 336$$

The physique of a human being is determined by 20 distinct characteristics and each characteristic has about 10 variations. How many different individuals can there be?

EXAMPLE 2. *A gardener bought 5 geraniums and 3 rose bushes from a nursery that had 14 geraniums and 12 rose bushes. How many choices did the gardener have?*

Solution
Order is not important in this example. The number of ways of choosing 5 geraniums from 14 is $_{14}C_5$.
The number of ways of choosing 3 rose bushes from 12 is $_{12}C_3$.
By the Fundamental Counting Principle the total number of choices is

$$_{14}C_5 \times {_{12}C_3} = \frac{14!}{9!\, 5!} \times \frac{12!}{9!\, 3!}$$

$$= \frac{14 \times 13 \times 12 \times 11 \times 10}{5 \times 4 \times 3 \times 2 \times 1} \times \frac{12 \times 11 \times 10}{3 \times 2 \times 1}$$

$$= 440\,440$$

EXERCISE 10-3

1. Evaluate the following.

(a) $_6C_2$

(b) $_{12}C_4$

(c) $_9C_9$

(d) $_8C_5$

(e) $_{10}C_3$

(f) $_{10}C_7$

(g) $\binom{16}{2}$

(h) $\binom{7}{0}$

(i) $_5C_2 \times {_4C_2}$

(j) $_7C_5 \times {_6C_4}$

(k) $\binom{12}{4} \times \binom{5}{3}$

(l) $\binom{8}{4} \times \binom{5}{2}$

2. A club has 25 members.

(a) In how many ways can a committee of 3 members be chosen?

(b) In how many ways can the offices of president, secretary, and treasurer be filled?

3. There are 12 books on a shelf. In how many ways can you choose 5 books from the shelf?

4. If you are going on a trip, in how many ways can you pick 5 pairs of socks from a drawer with 8 pairs?

5. There are 13 players on a basketball team.

(a) In how many ways can the coach select a 5-man team for the starting lineup?

(b) In how many ways can he do this if one particular player must be on the starting lineup?

6. Find the number of ways that a 5-card hand can be dealt from a deck of 52 cards.

7. In how many ways can a hand of 5 diamonds (a diamond flush) be dealt in poker?

8. Given 8 points in a plane, no 3 of which are collinear, how many lines can be drawn passing through 2 of the points?

9. A club consists of 5 boys and 5 girls. How many committees of 4 members can be formed with

(a) no restrictions?   (b) 4 boys?

(c) 3 boys and a girl?   (d) 2 boys and 2 girls?

(e) a boy and 3 girls?   (f) 4 girls?

10. Five people go to dinner at a Chinese restaurant. The menu contains 14 dishes in column A and 10 dishes in Column B. The "dinner for 5" consists of 3 dishes from Column A and 2 dishes from Column B. How many different dinners for 5 could they choose?

11. In how many ways can the 5 starting positions on a basketball team be filled

(a) from 10 men who can play any position?

(b) from 2 men who play centre and 8 other men who can play any of the other positions?

(c) from 2 men who play centre, 4 other men who play either of the forward positions and 4 other men who can play either of the two guard positions?

12. From a group of 14 Liberals, 12 Conservatives, 6 N.D.P. and 2 Social Credit Members of Parliament, how many different committees can be formed consisting of 3 Liberals, 3 Conservatives, 2 N.D.P. and 1 Social Credit member?

13. How many poker hands (5 cards) are there with 3 aces and 2 kings?

14. How many bridge hands (13 cards) contain 5 spades, 2 hearts, 3 diamonds, and 3 clubs?

15. (a) Compute

$$_0C_0$$
$$_1C_0 \qquad _1C_1$$
$$_2C_0 \qquad _2C_1 \qquad _2C_2$$
$$_3C_0 \qquad _3C_1 \qquad _3C_2 \qquad _3C_3$$
$$_4C_0 \qquad _4C_1 \qquad _4C_2 \qquad _4C_3 \qquad _4C_4$$
$$_5C_0 \qquad _5C_1 \qquad _5C_2 \qquad _5C_3 \qquad _5C_4 \qquad _5C_5$$

(b) Do you see a pattern occurring in this triangle of numbers? For example how is $_4C_2$ related to $_3C_1$ and $_3C_2$? How is $_5C_2$ related to $_4C_1$ and $_4C_2$?

(c) Use this pattern to extend the triangle for four more rows.

(d) Read the numbers $_8C_3$, $_8C_5$, $_9C_6$ from the triangular array of numbers.

C   **16.** How many bridge hands contain exactly 5 spades?

17. In how many ways can 12 things be divided equally

(a) between 2 people?

(b) among 3 people?

(c) among 4 people?

10.4 PASCAL'S TRIANGLE AND THE BINOMIAL THEOREM

You are familiar with such binomial expansions as

$$(a+b)^2 = a^2 + 2ab + b^2$$

and

$$(a+b)^3 = a^3 + 3a^2b + 3ab^2 + b^3$$

Binomial expansions for $(a+b)^n$, where n is any positive integer, can also be found. For instance

$$(a+b)^4 = (a+b)^3(a+b)$$
$$= (a^3 + 3a^2b + 3ab^2 + b^3)(a+b)$$
$$= a^4 + 4a^3b + 6a^2b^2 + 4ab^3 + b^4$$

It would be very laborious to use this method to find the binomial expansion of $(a+b)^n$ for large values of n. Instead we shall look for a pattern.

Examine the following binomial expansions.

$$(a+b)^0 = 1$$
$$(a+b)^1 = a+b$$
$$(a+b)^2 = a^2+2ab+b^2$$
$$(a+b)^3 = a^3+3a^2b+3ab^2+b^3$$
$$(a+b)^4 = a^4+4a^3b+6a^2b^2+4ab^3+b^4$$
$$(a+b)^5 = a^5+5a^4b+10a^3b^2+10a^2b^3+5ab^4+b^5$$
$$(a+b)^6 = a^6+6a^5b+15a^4b^2+20a^3b^3+15a^2b^4+6ab^5+b^6$$

.

.

.

If we write down just the numerical coefficients in these expansions we get the following triangular array.

```
            1
          1   1
        1   2   1
      1   3   3   1
    1   4   6   4   1
  1   5  10  10   5   1
1   6  15  20  15   6   1
```

This triangular array of numbers is called Pascal's Triangle. Notice that it is the same as the triangle of the combinations $_nC_r$ that you computed in question 17 of Exercise 10-3. For example the coefficients of the binomial expansion of $(a+b)^6$ are

$$_6C_0 \quad _6C_1 \quad _6C_2 \quad _6C_3 \quad _6C_4 \quad _6C_5 \quad _6C_6$$

or, in the alternate notation,

$$\binom{6}{0} \quad \binom{6}{1} \quad \binom{6}{2} \quad \binom{6}{3} \quad \binom{6}{4} \quad \binom{6}{5} \quad \binom{6}{6}$$

This suggests that the coefficients in the binomial expansion of $(a+b)^n$, n a positive integer, are

$$\binom{n}{0} \quad \binom{n}{1} \quad \binom{n}{2} \quad \binom{n}{3} \quad \binom{n}{4} \cdots \binom{n}{n}$$

This is in fact correct and is called the Binomial Theorem.

> **The Binomial Theorem**
>
> If $n \in N$, then
>
> $$(a+b)^n = \binom{n}{0}a^n + \binom{n}{1}a^{n-1}b + \binom{n}{2}a^{n-2}b^2 + \binom{n}{3}a^{n-3}b^3$$
>
> $$+ \ldots + \binom{n}{k}a^{n-k}b^k + \ldots + \binom{n}{n}b^n$$

Using the formula

$$\binom{n}{k} = {}_nC_k = \frac{n!}{(n-k)!\,k!}$$

$$= \frac{n(n-1)(n-2)\ldots(n-k+1)}{k!}$$

we have the following form of the Binomial Theorem.

If $n \in N$, then

$$(a+b)^n = a^n + na^{n-1}b + \frac{n(n-1)}{2!}a^{n-2}b^2 + \frac{n(n-1)(n-2)}{3!}a^{n-3}b^3$$

$$+ \ldots + \frac{n(n-1)\ldots(n-k+1)}{k!}a^{n-k}b^k + \ldots + nab^{n-1} + b^n$$

To see why this is true look at the expansion

$$(a+b)^n = (a+b)(a+b)\ldots(a+b)$$

$$= aa\ldots a \qquad\qquad\qquad\qquad\qquad\qquad\qquad \text{no } b\text{'s}$$

$$+ aa\ldots ab + aa\ldots aba + \ldots + ba\ldots a \qquad\qquad 1\ b$$

$$+ aa\ldots abb + aa\ldots bab + \ldots + bbaa\ldots a \qquad 2\ b\text{'s}$$

$$+\ldots \qquad\qquad\qquad\qquad\qquad\qquad\qquad\qquad \cdot$$

$$+ bb\ldots b \qquad\qquad\qquad\qquad\qquad\qquad\qquad n\ b\text{'s}$$

Each term is obtained by choosing a term (either a or b) from each of the n factors $(a+b)$ and then multiplying the n chosen factors. The coefficient of $a^{n-1}b$ is the number of ways of choosing one b from the n factors. We know that this is ${}_nC_1 = \binom{n}{1} = n$. The coefficient of $a^{n-2}b^2$ is the number of ways of choosing 2 b's from the n factors, namely ${}_nC_2$. In general, the coefficient of $a^{n-k}b^k$ is the number of ways of choosing k b's from the n factors. We know that this number is ${}_nC_k = \binom{n}{k}$. This concludes the proof of the Binomial Theorem.

EXAMPLE 1. *Expand* $(a+b)^7$.

Solution 1

$$(a+b)^7 = a^7 + \binom{7}{1}a^6b + \binom{7}{2}a^5b^2 + \binom{7}{3}a^4b^3 + \binom{7}{4}a^3b^4 + \binom{7}{5}a^2b^5 + \binom{7}{6}ab^6 + b^7$$

$$= a^7 + 7a^6b + \frac{7 \times 6}{2 \times 1}a^5b^2 + \frac{7 \times 6 \times 5}{3 \times 2 \times 1}a^4b^3 + \frac{7 \times 6 \times 5 \times 4}{4 \times 3 \times 2 \times 1}a^3b^4 + \frac{7 \times 6 \times 5 \times 4 \times 3}{5 \times 4 \times 3 \times 2 \times 1}a^2b^5 + 7ab^6 + b^7$$

$$= a^7 + 7a^6b + 21a^5b^2 + 35a^4b^3 + 35a^3b^4 + 21a^2b^5 + 7ab^6 + b^7$$

Solution 2

Use the fact that the binomial coefficients in $(a + b)^7$ are just the numbers in the 7th row of Pascal's Triangle (not counting the 0th row) and the pattern that each number in Pascal's Triangle is the sum of the two numbers immediately above it.

```
                    1       1
                1       2       1
            1       3       3       1
        1       4       6       4       1
     1      5      10      10       5      1
  1      6      15      20      15      6      1
1     7      21      35      35      21      7      1
```

Thus

$$(a + b)^7 = a^7 + 7a^6b + 21a^5b^2 + 35a^4b^3 + 35a^3b^4 + 21a^2b^5 + 7ab^6 + b^7$$

EXAMPLE 2. *Expand* $(x - 2)^6$

Solution

Use the binomial expansion for $(a + b)^n$ where $a = x$, $b = -2$ and $n = 6$.

$$(x - 2)^6 = x^6 + \binom{6}{1}x^5(-2) + \binom{6}{2}x^4(-2)^2 + \binom{6}{3}x^3(-2)^3 + \binom{6}{4}x^2(-2)^4 + \binom{6}{5}x(-2)^5 + (-2)^6$$

$$= x^6 + 6x^5(-2) + \frac{6 \times 5}{2 \times 1}x^4 \times 4 + \frac{6 \times 5 \times 4}{3 \times 2 \times 1}x^3(-8) + \frac{6 \times 5 \times 4 \times 3}{4 \times 3 \times 2 \times 1}x^2 \times 16 + 6x(-32) + 64$$

$$= x^6 - 12x^5 + 60x^4 - 160x^3 + 240x^2 - 192x + 64$$

EXAMPLE 3. *Expand* $(3x + y^2)^4$

Solution

Use the binomial expansion for $(a + b)^n$ where $a = 3x$, $b = y^2$ and $n = 4$

$$(3x+y^2)^4 = (3x)^4 + \binom{4}{1}(3x)^3 y^2 + \binom{4}{2}(3x)^2(y^2)^2 + \binom{4}{3}(3x)(y^2)^3 + (y^2)^4$$

$$= 3^4 x^4 + 4 \times 3^3 x^3 y^2 + 6 \times 3^2 x^2 y^4 + 4 \times 3xy^6 + y^8$$

$$= 81x^4 + 108x^3 y^2 + 54x^2 y^4 + 12xy^6 + y^8$$

EXAMPLE 4. *Find the term containing x^4 in the expansion of* $(1-x)^{100}$

Solution
In the expansion of $(a+b)^n$ the term containing b^k is

$$\binom{n}{k} a^{n-k} b^k$$

Here $a = 1$, $b = -x$, $n = 100$ and $k = 4$
$\therefore$ the term containing x^4 in the expansion of $(1-x)^{100}$ is

$$\binom{100}{4} 1^{96}(-x)^4 = \frac{100 \times 99 \times 98 \times 97}{4 \times 3 \times 2 \times 1} x^4$$

$$= 3\,921\,225 x^4$$

EXAMPLE 5. *Compute* $(1.02)^{10}$ *correct to 3 decimal places.*

Solution

$$(1.02)^{10} = (1+0.02)^{10}$$

So we take $a = 1$, $b = 0.02$, $n = 10$ in the Binomial Theorem.

$$(1.02)^{10} = 1^{10} + \binom{10}{1} 1^9(0.02) + \binom{10}{2} 1^8(0.02)^2 + \binom{10}{3} 1^7(0.02)^3$$

$$+ \binom{10}{4} 1^6(0.02)^4 + \ldots$$

$$= 1 + 10(0.02) + \frac{10 \times 9}{2}(0.0004) + \frac{10 \times 9 \times 8}{3 \times 2 \times 1}(0.000\,008)$$

$$+ \frac{10 \times 9 \times 8 \times 7}{4 \times 3 \times 2 \times 1}(0.000\,000\,16) + \ldots$$

$$= 1 + 0.2 + 0.018 + 0.000\,96 + 0.000\,033\,6 + \ldots$$

$$\doteq 1.219 \quad \text{(correct to 3 decimal places)}$$

Note that the neglected terms will not affect the fourth decimal place.

The "Pascal" Triangle as depicted in a Chinese manuscript of 1303

EXERCISE 10-4

B
1. Expand the following.
(a) $(a+b)^6$ (b) $(a+b)^8$ (c) $(x+y)^5$

(d) $(2+x)^7$	(e) $(a-3)^4$	(f) $(x-y)^{10}$
(g) $(1+a)^9$	(h) $(x+2y)^6$	(i) $(2x+3)^4$
(j) $(3a-2b)^5$	(k) $(a^2+b^3)^5$	(l) $\left(x+\dfrac{1}{x}\right)^6$
(m) $(x^2-2y)^8$	(n) $(r+\frac{1}{2})^4$	(o) $(c^2-\sqrt{d})^5$

2. Write out the first four terms in the binomial expansions of the following.

(a) $(a+b)^{12}$	(b) $(x-y)^{12}$	(c) $(x+2)^{14}$
(d) $(c-5d)^{10}$	(e) $(x^2-3y)^9$	(f) $\left(a+\dfrac{4}{b}\right)^{20}$

3. Find the term containing
(a) a^4b^5 in the expansion of $(a+b)^9$
(b) x^6 in the expansion of $(4-x)^8$
(c) $x^{15}y^5$ in the expansion of $(x+y)^{20}$
(d) $x^{12}y^4$ in the expansion of $(x^3+y)^8$
(e) a^{26} in the expansion of $\left(2+\dfrac{a^2}{2}\right)^{16}$

4. Find the term which does not contain x in the expansion of $\left(x^3+\dfrac{3}{x^2}\right)^{15}$.

5. Use the Binomial Theorem to compute the following correct to 3 decimal places.
(a) $(1.03)^9$ (b) $(1.008)^6$
(c) $(0.98)^{10}$ (d) $(2.004)^8$

6. Use the Binomial Theorem to compute 101^{10} to 3 significant figures.

7. (a) Expand $(1+1)^7$ using the Binomial Theorem.
(b) Prove that

$$\binom{n}{0}+\binom{n}{1}+\binom{n}{2}+\binom{n}{3}+\ldots+\binom{n}{n}=2^n$$

10.5 PROBABILITY

Suppose that a card is drawn from a standard deck of 52 playing cards. If the cards have been well shuffled, then there are 52 equally likely outcomes of which 13 are hearts. We say that the probability of drawing a heart is

$$P(\text{heart})=\tfrac{13}{52}=\tfrac{1}{4}$$

Drawing a card from a deck is an example of an experiment. Other examples of experiments are "tossing a coin", "rolling a pair of dice" and "drawing 2 cards and rolling 3 dice". The set of all possible outcomes of an experiment is called the sample space of the experiment. An event is a set of possible outcomes (a subset of the sample space). If the sample space of an experiment consists of N equally likely outcomes and if S of those outcomes are considered successful (or favourable) for an event E, we define the probability of E as follows.

$$\text{probability of an event } E = \frac{\text{number of successful outcomes}}{\text{total number of possible outcomes}}$$

$$P(E) = \frac{S}{N}$$

We can also write the definition of probability as

$$P(E) = \frac{n(E)}{N}$$

where $n(E) = S$ is the number of outcomes favourable to E, i.e., the cardinality of the set E.

In computing probabilities we must first find the numbers S and N. To calculate S and N we often use the counting principles developed in the first three sections of this chapter.

EXAMPLE 1. *Four coins are tossed. What is the probability of obtaining 2 heads and 2 tails?*

Solution

Each coin can fall in 2 ways. By the Fundamental Counting Principle the number of ways that the 4 coins can fall is

$$2 \times 2 \times 2 \times 2 = 16$$

$$\therefore \quad N = 16$$

We could list the sample space as

$$\{HHHH, HHHT, HHTH, HTHH, THHH, HHTT, HTHT, HTTH,$$

$$THHT, THTH, TTHH, HTTT, THTT, TTHT, TTTH, TTTT\}$$

The event of obtaining 2 heads and 2 tails is

$$E = \{HHTT, HTHT, HTTH, THHT, THTH, TTHH\}$$

$$\therefore \quad S = 6$$

$$P(E) = \frac{S}{N} = \frac{6}{16} = \frac{3}{8}$$

$\therefore$ the probability of obtaining 2 heads and 2 tails is $\frac{3}{8}$

However we can avoid listing the event by using permutations or combinations.

The number of ways of obtaining 2 heads and 2 tails is the number of permutations of 4 objects of which 2 are alike (the H's) and another 2 are alike (the T's), and so it is

$$\frac{4!}{2! \, 2!} = \frac{4 \times 3 \times 2 \times 1}{2 \times 1 \times 2 \times 1} = 6$$

$$\therefore \quad S = 6 \text{ as before.}$$

Alternatively, observe that S is the number of ways of choosing 2 objects (the H's) from 4 objects.

$$\therefore \quad S = {}_4C_2 = 6$$

Sometimes it is easier to find the probability of an event by first finding the probability that the event does not occur.
Let

$p = p(E) = $ probability that E occurs
$q = $ probability that E does not occur
$S = $ number of successful outcomes
$N = $ total number of outcomes

$\therefore$ the number of unsuccessful outcomes is $N - S$.

$$\therefore \quad q = \frac{N - S}{N}$$

$$\therefore \quad p + q = \frac{S}{N} + \frac{N - S}{N} = \frac{S + N - S}{N} = \frac{N}{N} = 1$$

$$p + q = 1$$

> If the probability that an event will occur is p, then the probability that it will not occur is
>
> $$q = 1 - p$$

The next example illustrates why this equation is useful.

EXAMPLE 2. *Once a year the New York Millionaires Club has a draw. The 3 prizes in the draw are 3 compact cars. Mrs. Pearson bought 5 of the 50 tickets that were sold at $1000 a ticket.*
(a) *What is the probability that she will win at least one car?*
(b) *What is the probability that she will win all 3 cars?*

Solution
(a) The number of ways that 3 tickets can be drawn from 50 is

$$_{50}C_3 = \frac{50 \times 49 \times 48}{3 \times 2 \times 1} = 19\,600$$

The number of ways that 3 tickets can be drawn from the 45 that Mrs. Pearson did not buy is

$$_{45}C_3 = \frac{45 \times 44 \times 43}{3 \times 2 \times 1} = 14\,190$$

$\therefore$ the probability that she will not win anything is

$$q = \frac{14\,190}{19\,600}$$

$\therefore$ the probability that she will win at least one car is

$$p = 1 - q$$

$$= 1 - \frac{14\,190}{19\,600} = \frac{5\,410}{19\,600} = \frac{541}{1960} \quad (\doteq 0.276)$$

(b) The number of ways that all 3 tickets can be drawn from the 5 bought by Mrs. Pearson is

$$_5C_3 = \frac{5 \times 4 \times 3}{3 \times 2 \times 1} = 10$$

∴ the probability that she will win all 3 cars is

$$\frac{10}{19\,600} = \frac{1}{1960}$$

EXAMPLE 3. *Five cards are dealt from a deck of 52 cards. Find the probability that 3 are queens and two are jacks.*

SUBTRACTION

NEVER
DRIVE
___
RIDE

Solution

The number of ways of dealing 3 of the 4 queens is

$$_4C_3 = 4$$

The number of ways of dealing 2 of the 4 jacks is

$$_4C_2 = 6$$

∴ by the Fundamental Counting Principle the number of ways of dealing 3 queens and 2 jacks is

$$S = 4 \times 6 = 24$$

The total number of ways of dealing 5 cards from a deck of 52 cards is

$$N = {}_{52}C_5 = \frac{52 \times 51 \times 50 \times 49 \times 48}{5 \times 4 \times 3 \times 2 \times 1}$$

$$= 2\,598\,960$$

∴ the probability of dealing 3 queens and 2 jacks is

$$P = \frac{S}{N} = \frac{24}{2\,598\,960} = \frac{1}{108\,290}$$

EXERCISE 10-5

1. A single card is selected from a deck of 52 playing cards. Find the probability that the card is

(a) an ace   (b) not an ace
(c) a diamond   (d) not a diamond
(e) a red card   (f) the 4 of spades
(g) a face card   (h) a black queen

2. The integers from 1 to 15 inclusive are painted on 15 balls. One of these balls is drawn at random. Find the probability that the number on the ball is

(a) odd   (b) even
(c) 13   (d) a multiple of 5

(e) a multiple of 3   (f) less than 5
(g) a 2-digit number   (h) a prime number

3. Two dice are rolled. Find the probability of getting

(a) 1   (b) 3   (c) 6
(d) 3 or less   (e) 10 or less   (f) an even number

4. Three coins are tossed. Find the probability of getting

(a) 3 heads   (b) no heads
(c) 2 heads and a tail   (d) at least one tail

5. Seven coins are tossed. Find the probability of getting

(a) 7 heads   (b) at least one head
(c) 6 heads and a tail   (d) 3 heads and 4 tails
(e) 2 heads and 5 tails   (f) 5 heads and 2 tails

6. Five dice are rolled. Find the probability of getting

(a) two 3's and three 4's   (b) five 6's
(c) four 3's and one 4   (d) three 1's, one 4 and one 5
(e) exactly three 1's   (f) at least three 1's
(g) two 1's, two 2's and a 3   (h) five different numbers

7. A bag contains 4 green balls and 5 yellow balls.

(a) If 5 balls are chosen at random, what is the probability that they are all yellow?

(b) If only 3 balls are chosen at random, what is the probability that they are all yellow?

8. In the game of bridge, 13 cards are dealt to each of 4 people. [Leave your answer in terms of the symbol $_nC_r$.]

(a) What is the total possible number of bridge hands?

(b) What is the probability that a bridge hand will consist of 13 hearts?

(c) What is the probability that a bridge hand will consist of 13 cards in the same suit?

(d) What is the probability of one person getting all 4 aces?

(e) What is the probability of one person getting all 4 aces, all 4 kings and all 4 queens?

(f) What is the probability that every card in a bridge hand is 9 or lower? (Ace is high in bridge.)

9. If a committee of 3 members is chosen at random from a club consisting of 6 girls and 10 boys, find the probability that the committee will contain

(a) 3 boys   (b) 3 girls
(c) 2 boys and a girl   (d) 2 girls and a boy
(e) at least one boy   (f) at least one girl

10. In the game of poker a 5-card hand is dealt from a deck of 52 cards. Find the probability of getting the following poker hands.

(a) royal flush: ace, king, queen, jack, 10 in the same suit
(b) five diamonds
(c) five cards in the same suit
(d) four of a kind (for example, four jacks or four 7's)
(e) three 5's and two 7's
(f) full house: three of a kind and two of another kind

11. There are 15 prizes in a lottery and 1000 tickets are sold. If you buy 10 tickets what is the probability that you will win at least one prize? (Leave your answer in terms of factorials.)

10.6 MUTUALLY EXCLUSIVE EVENTS

Consider the experiment of drawing a single card from a well-shuffled deck of 52 cards. What is the probability of the event E that the card drawn is a diamond or an ace?

Let E_1 be the event that a diamond is drawn and E_2 the event that an ace is drawn. E, E_1 and E_2 are all subsets of the sample space. Notice that $E = E_1 \cup E_2$. Therefore we need a rule for finding $P(E_1 \cup E_2)$ in terms of $P(E_1)$ and $P(E_2)$.

In general let E_1 and E_2 be any two events in a sample space. If the number of points in E_1 is $S_1 = n(E_1)$ and the number of points in E_2 is $S_2 = n(E_2)$, then

$$P(E_1) = \frac{S_1}{N} = \frac{n(E_1)}{N} \quad \text{and} \quad P(E_2) = \frac{S_2}{N} = \frac{n(E_2)}{N}$$

where N is the total number of possible outcomes of the experiment.

$$\therefore P(E_1 \cup E_2) = \frac{n(E_1 \cup E_2)}{N}$$

$$= \frac{n(E_1) + n(E_2) - n(E_1 \cap E_2)}{N}$$

$$= \frac{n(E_1)}{N} + \frac{n(E_2)}{N} - \frac{n(E_1 \cap E_2)}{N}$$

$$= P(E_1) + P(E_2) - P(E_1 \cap E_2)$$

$$\boxed{P(E_1 \cup E_2) = P(E_1) + P(E_2) - P(E_1 \cap E_2)}$$

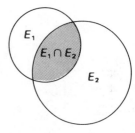

We subtract $n(E_1 \cap E_2)$ because $n(E_1) + n(E_2)$ counts the elements in $E_1 \cap E_2$ twice.

Let us now use this to solve the example given at the beginning of this section.

EXAMPLE 1. *What is the probability of drawing a diamond or an ace from a deck of 52 playing cards?*

Solution
Let E_1 be the event that a diamond is drawn.

$$P(E_1) = \tfrac{13}{52} = \tfrac{1}{4}$$

Let E_2 be the event that an ace is drawn.

$$P(E_2) = \tfrac{4}{52} = \tfrac{1}{13}$$

Then $E_1 \cap E_2$ is the event that an ace and a diamond is drawn, i.e., that the ace of diamonds is drawn.

$$\therefore \quad P(E_1 \cap E_2) = \tfrac{1}{52}$$

$E = E_1 \cup E_2$ is the event that an ace or a diamond is drawn.

$$P(E) = P(E_1 \cup E_2) = P(E_1) + P(E_2) - P(E_1 \cap E_2)$$
$$= \tfrac{1}{4} + \tfrac{1}{13} - \tfrac{1}{52}$$
$$= \tfrac{4}{13}$$

This solution can be abbreviated as follows:

$$P(\text{diamond or ace}) = P(\text{diamond}) + P(\text{ace}) - P(\text{ace and diamond})$$
$$= \tfrac{1}{4} + \tfrac{1}{13} - \tfrac{1}{52}$$
$$= \tfrac{4}{13}$$

Two events are called mutually exclusive if they cannot both occur simultaneously. For instance the events of drawing a diamond and drawing a club are mutually exclusive because they cannot both occur at once. But the two events in Example 1 are *not* mutually exclusive because they can occur simultaneously when the ace of diamonds is drawn.

If two events E_1 and E_2 are mutually exclusive, then $E_1 \cap E_2 = \emptyset$ and so

$$P(E_1 \cap E_2) = P(\emptyset) = 0$$
$$\therefore \quad P(E_1 \cup E_2) = P(E_1) + P(E_2) - P(E_1 \cap E_2)$$
$$= P(E_1) + P(E_2)$$

If E_1 and E_2 are mutually exclusive events, then to find the probability of the occurrence of E_1 or E_2 we add their probabilities.

$$P(E_1 \cup E_2) = P(E_1) + P(E_2)$$

EXAMPLE 2. *What is the probability of drawing a 5 or a face card from a deck of cards.*

Solution

Let E_1 be the event of drawing a 5

$$P(E_1) = \tfrac{4}{52} = \tfrac{1}{13}$$

Let E_2 be the event of drawing a face card. There are 12 face cards (4 kings, 4 queens, 4 jacks).

$$P(E_2) = \tfrac{12}{52} = \tfrac{3}{13}$$

Since E_1 and E_2 are mutually exclusive, we have

$$P(5 \text{ or face card}) = P(E_1 \cup E_2)$$

$$= P(E_1) + P(E_2)$$

$$= \tfrac{1}{13} + \tfrac{3}{13}$$

$$= \tfrac{4}{13}$$

EXERCISE 10-6

B **1.** A box contains 3 blue balls, 6 green balls, 4 red balls and 5 black balls. One ball is drawn at random. Find the probability of choosing
(a) a blue ball   (b) a green ball
(c) a blue or a green ball   (d) a green or a red ball
(e) a blue or a black ball   (f) a blue or a green or a black ball

2. A single card is drawn from a deck of playing cards. What is the probability that the card is
(a) a spade or a heart?   (b) a spade or a red jack?
(c) a black ace or a red face card?
(d) a club or a 4?   (e) a heart or a face card?
(f) neither a king nor a heart?

3. The integers from 1 to 24 inclusive are written on 24 slips of paper and placed in a hat. One slip is picked at random. Find the probability that the number drawn is
(a) odd   (b) divisible by 4
(c) odd or divisible by 4   (d) divisible by 5
(e) odd or divisible by 5   (f) even or a perfect square

4. In a class of 35 students, 25 are taking mathematics, 8 are taking history and 5 are taking both mathematics and history. If a student is chosen at random from this class, what is the probability that he or she is taking mathematics or history?

5. A coin is tossed 3 times. Find the probability of obtaining
(a) 3 heads or 3 tails   (b) 2 or 3 heads
(c) 2 or 3 heads or all tosses the same

10.7 INDEPENDENT EVENTS

Suppose that a deck of playing cards is shuffled and a card is drawn from it. Let E_1 be the event of drawing a diamond. Now suppose that the card is replaced in the deck, the deck is again shuffled, and another card is drawn. Let E_2 be the event of drawing a king on this second draw. What is the probability that both E_1 and E_2 occur?

Notice that what happens in the first draw does not affect what happens in the second draw because the first card is replaced in the deck before the second is drawn.

E_1 and E_2 are called independent events because neither has an influence on the other.

The number of ways of drawing a card on the first draw is 52. The number of ways of drawing a card on the second draw is also 52. So by the Fundamental Counting Principle the number of ways of drawing 2 cards is

$$N = 52 \times 52$$

The number of ways of drawing a diamond is 13. Since the first card is replaced, the number of ways of drawing a king is 4. By the Fundamental Counting Principle the number of ways of drawing a diamond and a king is

$$S = 13 \times 4$$

∴ the probability of drawing a diamond and a king (i.e. both E_1 and E_2 occur) is

$$p = \frac{13 \times 4}{52 \times 52} = \frac{1}{52}$$

Note that we could have calculated the required probability by multiplying the probabilities of the events E_1 and E_2.

$$P(E_1)P(E_2) = \tfrac{13}{52} \times \tfrac{4}{52}$$

$$= \tfrac{1}{52}$$

$$= P(E_1 \text{ and } E_2)$$

> If the events E_1 and E_2 are independent, then the probability that both events occur is the product of the probabilities of E_1 and E_2.
>
> $$P(E_1 \cap E_2) = P(E_1)P(E_2)$$

This can be proved by using the Fundamental Counting Principle as in the preceding example. The Fundamental Counting Principle tells us to multiply the number of successes of the two events (in the numerator) and to multiply the number of outcomes (in the denominator).

EXAMPLE 1.   *What is the probability of rolling two 4's in a row with a single die?*

Solution
   The probability of rolling the first 4 is

$$P(4) = \tfrac{1}{6}$$

the probability of rolling another 4 is still $\tfrac{1}{6}$. These two events are independent.

$$\therefore \quad P(4 \text{ and } 4) = P(4) \times P(4)$$

$$= \tfrac{1}{6} \times \tfrac{1}{6}$$

$$= \tfrac{1}{36}$$

What is the probability of rolling two 4's with a single roll of a pair of dice? The probability is again $\tfrac{1}{36}$ because neither die affects the other.

EXERCISE 10-7

1. A coin is tossed twice. Find the probability that
(a) the coin comes up heads twice in a row
(b) the coin comes up heads first, then tails.

2. What is the probability of tossing 8 heads in a row with a coin?

3. If a coin comes up heads 8 times in a row, what is the probability of a head on the 9th toss?

4. A player rolls a pair of dice, one blue and one white. Find the probability of rolling
(a) 6 with the blue die and 4 with the white die
(b) 6 with one die and 4 with the other die

5. A pair of dice is rolled twice. Find the probability of rolling 7 the first time and 8 the second time.

6. A box contains 3 black balls, 4 blue balls and 5 green balls. A ball is selected at random from the box, it is replaced and another ball is selected. Find the probability that
(a) the first ball is green and the second is blue
(b) both balls are black
(c) both balls are blue
(d) the first ball is black and the second is green
(e) the first ball is green and the second is black
(f) one ball is black and the other is green
(g) the first ball is green and the second is green or blue

7. A card is drawn from a deck of 52 playing cards. It is replaced, the deck reshuffled and a second card is drawn. Find the probabilities of the following events.
(a) the first card is a spade and the second is a diamond
(b) both cards are hearts
(c) the first card is an ace and the second is a spade
(d) one card is an ace and the other is a spade
(e) one card is a 5 and the other is a face card
(f) the jack of hearts is drawn twice
(g) the same card is drawn twice

8. Three cards are drawn in succession from a deck and each is replaced after each drawing. Find the probabilities of the following events.
(a) all 3 cards are aces
(b) all 3 cards are diamonds
(c) all 3 cards are of the same suit
(d) a diamond, a club, and a heart are drawn in that order
(e) a 5, a diamond, and a red card are drawn in that order
(f) a 5, a diamond, and a red card are drawn in any order

Determine the pattern.
Find the missing number.

25	52	31	26
9	4	7	5
38	28	18	19
7	20	7	

10.8 CONDITIONAL PROBABILITY

Sometimes we want to find the probability of an event E but we are given additional information that changes the sample space and therefore changes the probabilities.

The conditional probability of an event E, given A, is the probability that the event E occurs, given that another event A has occurred. It is denoted by $P(E \mid A)$.

For instance if 2 coins are tossed and E is the event that 2 heads are obtained, then the sample space is

$$HH$$
$$HT$$
$$TH$$
$$TT$$

and $$P(E) = \tfrac{1}{4}$$

However if it is known that the first coin is a head, then we have an altered sample space:

$$\left.\begin{array}{c} HH \\ HT \end{array}\right\} \text{ new sample space}$$
$$\cancel{TH}$$
$$\cancel{TT}$$

If A is the event that the first coin comes up heads, then

$$P(E \mid A) = \tfrac{1}{2}$$

Now suppose it is known that at least one coin has turned up heads. Again the sample space is altered.

$$\left.\begin{array}{c} HH \\ HT \\ TH \end{array}\right\} \text{ new sample space}$$
$$\cancel{TT}$$

If B is the event that at least one coin is heads, then

$$P(E \mid B) = \tfrac{1}{3}$$

EXAMPLE 1. *Suppose that 2 cards are drawn in succession from a deck of playing cards without replacing the first card.*
(a) *Find the probability that the second card is a king, given that the first card is a queen.*
(b) *Find the probability that the first card is a queen and the second card is a king.*

Solution
(a) Let E_1 be the event of drawing a queen on the first draw and E_2 the event of drawing a king on the second draw.

If E_1 has occurred, then there are 51 cards remaining of which 4 are kings.

$$\therefore \quad P(E_2 \mid E_1) = \tfrac{4}{51}$$

(b) By the Fundamental Counting Principle the number of ways of drawing 2 cards without replacement is

$$52 \times 51.$$

Again by the Fundamental Counting Principle, the number of ways of drawing a queen, then a king, is

$$4 \times 4$$

$\therefore$ the probability of drawing a queen, then a king, is

$$P(E_1 \text{ and } E_2) = \frac{4 \times 4}{52 \times 51} = \frac{4}{663}$$

Notice that we could have calculated the required probability by multiplying the probability of E_1 by the conditional probability of E_2, given E_1.

$$P(E_1)P(E_2 \mid E_1) = \tfrac{4}{52} \times \tfrac{4}{51}$$

$$= \tfrac{4}{663}$$

$$= P(E_1 \text{ and } E_2)$$

By using the Fundamental Counting Principle as in Example 1 we could prove this equation for any pair of events E_1 and E_2.

The probability that both E_1 and E_2 occur is the product of the probability of E_1 and the conditional probability of E_2, given E_1.

$$P(E_1 \cap E_2) = P(E_1)P(E_2 \mid E_1)$$

or

$$P(E_1 \cap E_2) = P(E_2)P(E_1 \mid E_2)$$

In Example 1, E_1 and E_2 are not independent; clearly E_2 depends on E_1.

If E_1 and E_2 *are* independent events (as in the preceding section) then E_1 cannot influence E_2 and so $P(E_2 \mid E_1) = P(E_2)$. Therefore for the case of independent events the above equations reduce to the equation $P(E_1 \cap E_2) = P(E_1)P(E_2)$ given in the last section.

EXAMPLE 2. *A box contains 5 red balls and 3 green balls. Two balls are drawn in succession without replacement. Find the probability of drawing first a red, then a green ball.*

Solution

Let E_1 be the event of drawing a red ball on the first draw and E_2 the event of drawing a green ball on the second draw.

Then

$$P(E_1) = \tfrac{5}{8}$$

After the red ball has been drawn there are 7 balls remaining, of which 3 are green.

$$\therefore \quad P(E_2 \,|\, E_1) = \tfrac{3}{7}$$

$\therefore$ the probability of drawing a red and then a green ball is

$$P(E_1 \cap E_2) = P(E_1)P(E_2 \,|\, E_1)$$

$$= \tfrac{5}{8} \times \tfrac{3}{7}$$

$$= \tfrac{15}{56}$$

EXERCISE 10-8

B **1.** A box contains 6 white balls and 9 black balls. Two balls are drawn in succession without replacement. Let W_1 be the event of getting a white ball on the first draw, W_2 be the event of getting a white ball on the second draw, B_1 be the event of getting a black ball on the first draw, B_2 be the event of getting a black ball on the second draw. Find the following conditional probabilities.

(a) $P(W_2 \,|\, W_1)$ (b) $P(W_2 \,|\, B_1)$
(c) $P(B_2 \,|\, W_1)$ (d) $P(B_2 \,|\, B_1)$

2. On a single roll of a pair of dice what is the probability
(a) of obtaining 7?
(b) of obtaining 7, given that at least one die is a 2?

3. Three coins are tossed. Find the probability of obtaining
(a) two heads and a tail
(b) two heads and a tail, given that at least one head appears
(c) two heads and a tail, given that at least two heads appear
(d) at least two heads
(e) at least two heads, given that at least one head appears

4. It is known that among the families in Utopia, 25% have no children, 30% have one child, 26% have two children, 12% have 3 children and 7% have 4 children or more. If a Utopian family is selected at random, what is the probability that they have
(a) 2 or more children?
(b) 2 or more children, given that they have at least one child?

5. Two cards are drawn in succession from a deck without replacement. Find the probability that
(a) the second card is a diamond, given that the first is a club
(b) the first card is a club and the second is a diamond
(c) the second card is red, given that the first is a heart
(d) the first card is a heart and the second is red
(e) both cards are aces
(f) the first card is an ace and the second is a face card
(g) both cards are diamonds
(h) both cards are of the same suit

6. A box contains 5 red, 6 white, and 9 blue balls. Two balls are selected at random in succession without replacement. Find the probabilities of the following events.
(a) the first is red and the second is white

(b) the first is white and the second is red

(c) one ball is red and the other is white

(d) both balls are blue

(e) neither ball is white

7. Three cards are identical except for colour. One is black on both sides, one is red on both sides, and one is red on one side and black on the other side. One of the cards is chosen at random from a hat and is placed on a table. The side that is up is red. What is the probability that the side that is down is black?

8. Three cards are drawn in succession from a deck without replacement. Find the probabilities of the following events.

(a) all 3 cards are aces

(b) all 3 cards are diamonds

(c) all 3 cards are of the same suit

(d) a diamond, a club, and a heart are drawn in that order

(e) a diamond, a club, and a heart are drawn in any order

(f) a 5, a 6, and a 7 are drawn in that order

(g) a 5, a 6, and a 7 are drawn in any order

9. A box contains 15 coloured balls which are drawn without replacement. 7 of the balls are green, 5 are blue, and 3 are red. Find the probabilities of the following events.

(a) the first ball is red and the second is green

(b) at least one of the first two balls is blue

(c) exactly one of the first two balls is green

(d) the first ball is green, the second is blue, the third is red

(e) the first five balls drawn are all blue

(f) at least one of the first five balls is blue

10. Box A contains 3 red and 4 black balls. Box B contains 6 red and 5 black balls. Box C contains 5 red and 8 black balls. A box is selected at random and a ball is chosen from that box. Find the probability of drawing a red ball.

10.9 DISTRIBUTIONS

Probability uses assumed knowledge of a situation to determine the likelihoods of certain outcomes for an experiment. We shall now take a brief look at the topic of statistics as it relates to probability.

In order to determine whether or not a die is "loaded" you could roll the die a large number of times, say 1000. If the die is a fair one the proportion of times that each number occurs should approach $\frac{1}{6}$.

Outcome	Proportion
1	$\frac{1}{12}$
2	$\frac{1}{3}$
3	$\frac{1}{12}$
4	$\frac{1}{12}$
5	$\frac{1}{3}$
6	$\frac{1}{12}$

Table 10-1

However, suppose the resulting proportions are as shown in Table 10-1. Clearly 2 and 5 occur more often than expected and it appears that the die is "loaded" in favour of 2 and 5. Since our results were determined by a series of experiments, rather than by assuming equal likelihood, they are called statistical probabilities.

With probability theory we assume knowledge of the population and then make predictions about specific portions of the population. With statistics we make measurements on a sample of the population and then generalize about the nature of the population as a whole. In our "loaded" die problem we used a sample of 1000 rolls to predict the probabilities of rolling each number.

A random variable is a number determined by the outcome of an experiment. Thus we cannot predict which value a random variable will have from one time to the next. The set of possible values is the sample space of the variable. For example, the number showing on a rolled die is a random variable with sample space 1, 2, 3, 4, 5, 6.

Suppose we roll a die 60 times with the following results

OUTCOME	FREQUENCY
1	9
2	12
3	10
4	8
5	11
6	10

To make the results more apparent we can present them in the form of a bar graph or histogram. Sometimes a frequency polygon is constructed by joining the midpoints of the tops of the bars. (Figure 10-2)

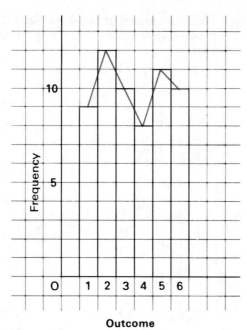

Outcome

Figure 10-2

If the die that is being rolled is fair, in the long run each number should come up as frequently as the others. In such cases we say that the random variable obeys a constant frequency distribution.

In Section 10.5, Example 1, we determined the probability of obtaining 2 heads and 2 tails when four coins are tossed. Suppose we toss 4 coins 16 times and record the number of tails showing each time. By using the method of Example 1 in Section 10.5 we can make a prediction as to the number of times each possible value of the random variable will occur.

Number of Tails	Frequency
4	1
3	4
2	6
1	4
0	1

Table 10-2

Sample Space

HHHH, HHHT, HHTH, HTHH
THHH, HHTT, HTHT, HTTH
THHT, THTH, TTHH, HTTT
THTT, TTHT, TTTH, TTTT

Row 4 of Pascal's Triangle gives the frequencies entered in Table 10-2.

If 5 coins are tossed 32 times the theoretical frequencies for the number of tails showing each time is given by row 5 of Pascal's

Triangle. When 4 coins are tossed 32 times the theoretical frequencies for the number of tails showing each time are found by doubling row 4 of Pascal's Triangle.

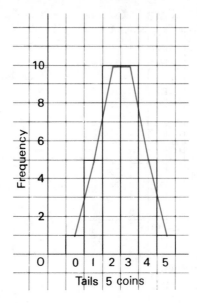 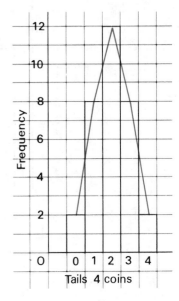

These are examples of what are called binomial frequency distributions. As with the constant frequency distribution they are likely to be approximated by the collection of an actual data sample. The binomial distribution occurs when each trial can result in either success or failure and when the random variable is the number of successes for a given number of trials. (In the preceding examples with coins, a success was tossing a tail.) When the probabilities of success and failure are equal, (both $\frac{1}{2}$), the binomial graph is symmetric.

So far we have been dealing with random variables that are discrete-valued, that is they could only take on certain isolated values. For example a rolled die could show either 1, 2, 3, 4, 5 or 6 but never $5\frac{1}{2}$. Many random variables are not restricted to discrete values. Examples of these are

(i) the speed of the wind
(ii) the atmospheric pressure
(iii) the height of a tree

We classify these variables as continuous-valued. The quantities are not limited to whole number values.

Suppose that there is a weather station on the top of a lighthouse with an instrument capable of measuring the speed of the wind very accurately. Let us assume that the average speed of the wind is 50 km/h. If the wind speed is recorded each minute, a few minutes will be enough to show that the wind does not blow at a constant speed:

its speed changes from minute to minute. After taking measurements for a whole day a graph of the results is drawn.

Write 5 using four 6's.

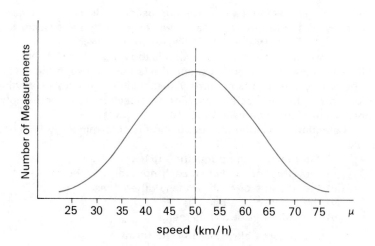

speed (km/h)

The curve representing the frequency distribution has the shape of a bell. Such a bell-shaped curve is known as the normal or Gaussian curve after the mathematician, Karl Gauss, who explained its special shape.

Any set of data which produces such a curve is said to obey a normal frequency distribution.

If the number of coins and the number of tosses is increased without bound in our coin tossing experiments, the resulting binomial polygons would approach the shape of a perfect normal curve.

EXERCISE 10-9

1. An experiment of tossing 6 fair coins is to be repeated 64 times.
(a) Construct a frequency table for the expected number of times we would obtain 0, 1, 2, 3, 4, 5, and 6 tails.
(b) Construct a histogram and a frequency polygon.

2. An experiment of tossing 7 fair coins is to be repeated 384 times.
(a) Construct a frequency table for the expected number of times we would obtain 0, 1, 2, 3, 4, 5, 6 and 7 heads.
(b) Construct a histogram and a frequency polygon.

3. 160 families, each with five children, were surveyed to determine how many of the children were girls. Assume that the probability of a newborn baby being a girl is $\frac{1}{2}$
(a) Construct a frequency table for the expected number of times there would be 0, 1, 2, 3, 4 and 5 girls.
(b) Construct a histogram and a frequency polygon.

10.10   STANDARD DEVIATION

The mean, median and mode are used to describe the central tendency of a collection of data. However it is often necessary to be able to describe how the data is dispersed or spread out.

The simplest measure of dispersion is the range. It is defined as the difference between the smallest and the largest values in the set. The range is very sensitive to extreme values and does not tell us anything about how the numbers vary. For this reason we need another measure of dispersion called the standard deviation (σ).

The standard deviation of a population is determined by finding (in order)

(i) the mean of the population (μ)
(ii) the difference between each number and the mean
(iii) the squares of each of these differences
(iv) the mean of the squares
(v) the square root of this mean.

The five steps are abbreviated in the formula

$$\sigma = \sqrt{\frac{(x_1 - \mu)^2 + (x_2 - \mu)^2 + \ldots + (x_n - \mu)^2}{n}}$$

In most statistical problems we do not have all the data for the population, but usually we have only a sample or small part of the population. The mean of the sample is denoted by $\bar{x}$. This is an estimate of the true mean of the population μ. To calculate the sample standard deviation (s) we use the formula

$$s = \sqrt{\frac{(x_1 - \bar{x})^2 \times (x_2 - \bar{x})^2 + \ldots + (x_n - \bar{x})^2}{n - 1}}$$

s is an estimate of σ.

For a population standard deviation we divide by n whereas for a sample standard deviation we divide by $n - 1$. Statisticians have found that dividing by $n - 1$ instead of n makes s a better estimate of σ. (It is conventional in statistics to reserve μ and σ for the mean and standard deviation of the underlying probability distribution.)

Normal curves can take on various sizes and shapes. Each is characterized by two numbers—the mean and standard deviation. The

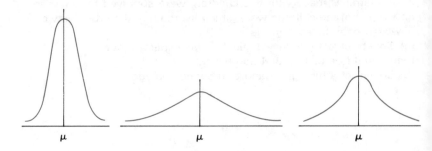

mean gives the central value or point of symmetry. The standard deviation tells us the amount of spread. The larger the standard deviation, the greater the spread. Very few values are more than three standard deviations away from the mean on either side.

Most data do not produce a perfect normal curve but the discrepancy is only slight for a large number of natural phenomena.

EXAMPLE 1. *Determine the sample standard deviation s for the following set of data.*

Value	Frequency
1	3
2	4
3	9
4	6
5	2

Solution

To determine the mean we divide the sum of the values by the number of values.

$$\bar{x} = \frac{1 \times 3 + 2 \times 4 + 3 \times 9 + 4 \times 6 + 5 \times 2}{3 + 4 + 9 + 6 + 2}$$

$$= \frac{3 + 8 + 27 + 24 + 10}{24}$$

$$= 3$$

Value	Frequency	$x_n - \bar{x}$	$(x_n - \bar{x})^2$	$(x_n - \bar{x})^2 \times f$
1	3	−2	4	12
2	4	−1	1	4
3	9	0	0	0
4	6	1	1	6
5	2	2	4	8

$$s = \sqrt{\frac{12 + 4 + 0 + 6 + 8}{24 - 1}}$$

$$= \sqrt{\frac{30}{23}}$$

$$\doteq 1.1$$

When treating a sample of values for a continuously distributed variable we commonly group the data into classes and record frequencies for each class interval. The width and number of intervals depends on the number of values and the purpose of the analysis. To calculate the mean of grouped data we use the midpoint of the value's class interval as an approximation of each value in the interval. If there are k intervals and m_i is the midpoint of an interval and f_i is the frequency then the mean for the sample is approximated by

$$\bar{x} = \frac{(m_1 \times f_1) + (m_2 \times f_2) + \ldots + (m_k \times f_k)}{f_1 + f_2 + \ldots + f_k}$$

EXAMPLE 2. *Determine the sample standard deviation for the following set of data.*

Interval Boundaries	Frequency
0–10	2
10–20	4
20–30	9
30–40	7
40–50	3

Solution

Interval Boundaries	Frequency f	Interval Midpoint (m)	$m \times f$	$(m - \bar{x})^2$	$(m - \bar{x})^2 \times f$
0–10	2	5	10	484	968
10–20	4	15	60	144	576
20–30	9	25	225	4	36
30–40	7	35	245	64	448
40–50	3	45	135	324	972
sums	25		675		3000

$$\bar{x} = \tfrac{675}{25} = 27$$

$$s = \sqrt{\frac{3000}{24}} \doteq 11.2$$

When the mean and standard deviation are calculated for a normal population distribution, it turns out that approximately 68% of the data values are within 1 standard deviation of the mean, approximately 95% within 2 standard deviations and approximately 99% within three standard deviations.

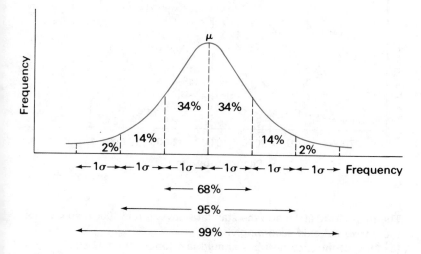

In order to facilitate calculations the distribution is simplified as follows.

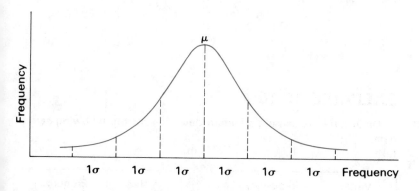

EXAMPLE 3. *A TV manufacturer advertises that the mean life of picture tubes in new TV sets is* 10 000 h *with a standard deviation of* 1000 h. *A local hotel buys 200 TV sets. Assuming a normal distribution,*

(a) *what percent of the picture tubes should last longer than* 11 000 h?
(b) *what percent of the picture tubes should last less than* 8000 h?
(c) *how many picture tubes should last longer than* 9000 h?

Solution

Draw a normal curve.

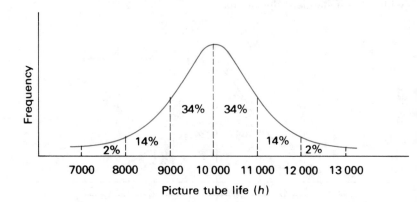

Picture tube life (*h*)

The mean is 10 000 h and the standard deviation is 1000 h so we mark the horizontal axis accordingly.

(a) 16% of the picture tubes should last longer than 11 000 h
(b) 2% of the picture tubes should last less than 8000 h
(c) 84% of the picture tubes should last longer than 9000 h

$$0.84 \times 200 = 168$$

168 tubes should last longer than 9000 h

EXERCISE 10-10

B **1.** Determine the sample standard deviation for the following sets of data.

(a)

Value	Frequency
3	2
4	8
5	9
6	6
7	3

(b)

Value	Frequency
8	2
10	3
12	5
16	4
25	1

2. Determine the sample standard deviation for the following set of data.

Interval Boundaries	Frequency
0–20	3
20–40	6
40–60	11
60–80	8
80–100	2

3. An IQ test was given to all members of the armed forces. The results were normally distributed with a mean of 110 and a standard deviation of 15.
(a) What percent of the scores were greater than 125?
(b) What percent of the scores were less than 80?
(c) If 75 000 personnel took the test, how many scored higher than 140?
(d) How many scored between 110 and 125?

4. A turkey farm manager has determined the masses of his turkeys are normally distributed with a mean of 5 kg and a standard deviation of 0.2 kg. A supermarket chain purchased 10 000 turkeys.
(a) How many will have masses greater than 4.8 kg?
(b) How many will have masses between 4.6 and 5.2 kg?

5. In order to decide whether or not to install a traffic light at an intersection the speeds of the vehicles using the intersection were recorded for a one month period. The results were normally distributed with a mean of 47 km/h and a standard deviation of 3 km/h.
(a) What percent of the vehicles had speeds less than 44 km/h?
(b) If the speed limit is 50 km/h, what percent of the vehicles were speeding?
(c) If 12 000 vehicles use the intersection each day, how many are speeding?

6. The life of a toaster is normally distributed with a mean of 7 a and a standard deviation of 1 a. During one year a company sold 3000 toasters.
(a) How many toasters should last longer than 8 a?
(b) If the manufacturer will replace a toaster that lasts less than 5 a, how many will be replaced?

7. The time required for a student to register at a university is normally distributed with a mean of 33 min and a standard deviation of 6 min. What percent of the registrations will last
(a) more than 45 min?
(b) less than 27 min?
(c) between 21 min and 39 min?

10.11 PERCENTILES AND z-SCORES

We have seen how mean, median, mode, range and standard deviation are used to analyze the central tendency and dispersion of data. However quite often one is also interested in knowing the position of a term in a distribution.

Suppose that Marie got 72 on her final mathematics exam. There were 120 students, including Marie, who wrote the exam. She knows that 20% of the students scored higher than 72, 6% scored 72 and 74% scored lower than 72.

Lower than 72	72	Higher than 72
74%	6%	20%

Since

$$74 + \tfrac{1}{2}(6) = 77$$

we say that Marie's percentile rank is 77.

What this means is that she did better than approximately 77% of the students and approximately 23% of the students did better than she did.

The percentile rank of a term in a distribution is found by adding the percentage of terms below it to $\tfrac{1}{2}$ of the percentage of terms equal to it.

If X represents a given term, B the number of terms below X, E the number of terms equal to X and n the total number of terms then the percentile rank of X is $\dfrac{B + \tfrac{1}{2}E}{n} \times 100$

EXAMPLE 1. *Pete got 64 on a history test. The grades of the other students in his class were 59, 64, 48, 53, 78, 81, 60, 53, 62, 71, 40, 58, 53, 59, 90, 30, 51, 65, 59, 70, 50, 45, 58, 62. Find Pete's percentile rank.*

Solution

There are 25 students, including Pete.

There are 17 scores below 64.

There are 2 scores (including Pete's) equal to 64

∴ Pete's percentile rank

$$= \frac{B + \tfrac{1}{2}E}{n} \times 100$$

$$= \frac{17 + \tfrac{1}{2}(2)}{25} \times 100$$

$$= 72$$

We say that Pete's grade is in the 72nd percentile. Approximately 72% of the class scored lower than Pete.

EXAMPLE 2. *On a grade 12 English test Sam got 72. The marks for the other students in his class were*

$$60, 50, 42, 81, 85, 88, 90, 94, 96, 75$$
$$80, 43, 72, 70, 75, 76, 72, 84, 60, 91$$
$$90, 50, 88, 80, 60, 57, 91, 73, 77, 80$$

Susan also got 72 on her grade 12 English test and the marks for the other students in her class were

$$60, 66, 68, 80, 50, 48, 37, 50,$$
$$72, 51, 54, 62, 66, 67, 90, 60,$$
$$55, 70, 71, 88, 40, 42, 70, 63$$

Find the percentile rank of Sam and Susan.

Solution
  There are 31 students in Sam's class
  9 scored below 72
  3 scored 72
∴ Sam's percentile rank

$$= \frac{9 + \frac{1}{2}(3)}{31} \times 100$$

$$\doteq 34$$

There are 25 students in Susan's class.
20 scored below 72
2 scored 72
∴ Susan's percentile rank

$$= \frac{20 + \frac{1}{2}(2)}{25} \times 100$$

$$= 84$$

Although Susan and Sam both had marks of 72, Susan's percentile rank is considerably higher. If we assume that the levels of competition are equivalent in both classes, this may indicate something about their level of performance or the difficulty of the respective tests.

However using a percentile rank alone can sometimes be misleading. Another measure of the performance of an individual score in a population is called the z-score. The z-score measures how many standard deviations a score is away from the mean.

The z-score of a term X in a population distribution whose mean is μ and whose standard deviation is σ is given by

$$z = \frac{X - \mu}{\sigma}$$

Since σ is always positive, z will be positive when X is greater than μ and negative when X is less than μ. A z-score of 0 means that the term has the same value as the mean.

WORD LADDER

Start with the word "tooth" and change one letter at a time to form a new word until you reach "brush". The best solution has the fewest steps.

t o o t h
– – – – –
– – – – –
– – – – –
– – – – –
– – – – –
b r u s h

EXAMPLE 3. *On a nationwide math test the mean was 70 and the standard deviation 10. Robert scored 86, Sharon 62 and Anne 70. Find their z-scores.*

Solution

$$z = \frac{X - \mu}{\sigma}$$

$$\text{For Robert} \quad z = \frac{86 - 70}{10} = 1.6$$

$$\text{For Sharon} \quad z = \frac{62 - 70}{10} = -0.8$$

$$\text{For Anne} \quad z = \frac{70 - 70}{10} = 0$$

EXAMPLE 4. *On a college entrance exam the mean was 70 and the standard deviation 8. If Mary's z-score was −1.5, what was her exam mark?*

Solution

$$z = \frac{X - \mu}{\sigma}$$

$$\therefore \quad z \times \sigma = X - \mu$$

$$\text{and} \quad X = \mu + z \times \sigma$$

$$= 70 + (-1.5) \times (8)$$

$$= 58$$

∴ Mary's mark was 58.

In the following section we shall see how z-scores are used to determine the probability of an event.

EXERCISE 10-11

A **1.** Mary has a high school average of 86. The college that she wants to attend will not accept a student if the percentile rank is lower than 90. Is it possible that Mary will be accepted by the college? Explain.

2. The mean on a physics contest was 71 with a standard deviation of 6.
(a) If Sarah's z-score was 1, what was her mark?
(b) If Ed's z-score was −2, what was his mark?

3. Can a percentile rank of 60 have a negative z-score? Explain.

B **4.** Mark got 70 on an English exam. The grades of the other students in his class were

60, 59, 82, 47, 75, 72
70, 66, 66, 50, 30, 91
55, 80, 69, 62, 60, 73

Find Mark's percentile rank.

5. On a college entrance exam, the mean was 60 and the standard deviation 6. Sue scored 70, Bill 58 and Tom 61. Find their z-scores.

6. For a national physical fitness test conducted on 18 year olds the mean was 72 with a standard deviation of 5. Jim had a z-score of -1.2 and Shelly a z-score of 1.8. Determine their actual test marks.

7. A brand of transistor radio battery has a mean life of 50 h with a standard deviation of 5 h. Find the z-score of a battery which lasts
(a) 58 h
(b) 48 h
(c) 53 h.

8. In order to help him decide what his major should be in college, Ralph took an aptitude test. The results of the test are as follows

Subject	National Mean	Standard Deviation	Ralph's Score
Pure Science	75	5	83
Languages	70	7	78
Business	56	6	61
Social Science	68	4	77

(a) Change Ralph's scores to z-scores.
(b) What should he major in?
(c) In what subject is he least talented?

10.12 THE STANDARD NORMAL CURVE

A normal distribution is completely specified by its mean and standard deviation. Different means and different standard deviations will describe different bell shaped curves. However it is possible to convert each of these different normal distributions into one standardized form. The following example illustrates the reason for doing this.

It was stated in Section 10.9 that frequency polygons associated with binomial coin tossing distributions approach a normal curve as the number of coins and tosses increases to very large values.

The following figure shows the bar graph and the approximating normal curve for the experiment of tossing 8 coins 2560 times. The random variable represents the number of tails obtained.

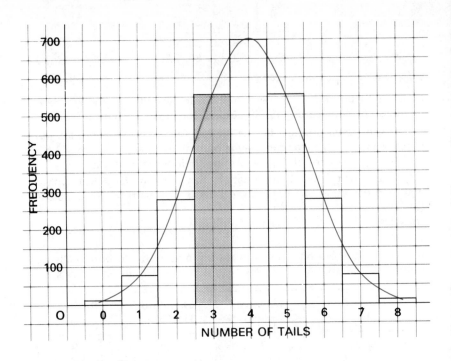

Suppose we wanted to know the probability that exactly 3 of the coins turned up tails. We could use the method of Section 10.5.

$$P(3 \text{ tails}) = \frac{{}_8C_3}{2^8}$$

$$= \frac{56}{256}$$

$$\doteq 0.2186$$

Geometrically this probability represents the area of the shaded bar divided by the total area of the 9 bars. The area of the shaded bar is approximately equal to the area under the normal curve from 2.5 to 3.5.

Since areas under normal curves are related to probabilities, we use a special normal distribution table to calculate probabilities. Such a table is given in the Appendix at the end of the book. However, since the mean and standard deviation can take on many values, it would appear that we would need many tables.

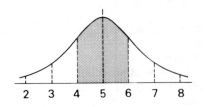

This is not the case. We need only one standardized table. To determine probabilities using areas under a normal curve we are interested in the ratios of areas and not the specific areas themselves. If approximately 68% of the total area under a normal curve lies within 1 standard deviation of the mean for a distribution with a mean of 5 and a standard deviation of 1, then approximately 68% of the total area lies within 1 standard deviation of the mean for a distribution with a mean of 50 and a standard deviation of 15. For this reason statisticians use a standard distribution.

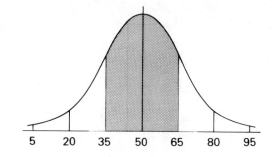

The standardized normal distribution is a normal distribution with a mean of 0 and a standard deviation of 1.

If X is a random variable with mean μ and standard deviation σ, then $z = \dfrac{X - \mu}{\sigma}$ has a mean of 0 and a standard deviation of 1.

The Table in the Appendix gives the areas under the Standard Normal Curve between $z = 0$ and $z = 0.00, 0.01, 0.02, \ldots, 3.99$.

EXAMPLE 1. *For a standard normal distribution, find the area between $z = 0$ and $z = 1.14$.*

Solution

We first draw a sketch. From the Table we see that the area between $z = 0$ and $z = 1.14$ is 0.3729. This means that the probability of a z-score falling between $z = 0$ and $z = 1.14$ is 0.3729.

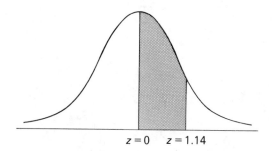

$z = 0$ $z = 1.14$

EXAMPLE 2. *For a standard normal distribution find the area between $z = 0$ and $z = -2.13$.*

Solution

We first draw a sketch. From the table we see that the area between $z = 0$ and $z = 2.13$ is 0.4834. Due to the symmetry of the curve, the area between $z = 0$ and $z = -2.13$ is also 0.4834. A negative value of z just tells us that z is to the left of the mean. The probability of getting a z-score between 0 and -2.13 is 0.4834.

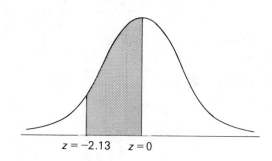

$z = -2.13$ $z = 0$

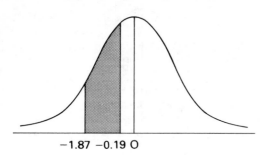

EXAMPLE 3. *For a standard normal distribution, find the area between* $z = -0.19$ *and* $z = -1.87$.

Solution
From the table the area between $z = 0$ and $z = 0.19$ is 0.0754. The area between $z = 0$ and $z = 1.87$ is 0.4693. Subtraction gives the area between $z = -0.19$ and $z = -1.87$ as 0.3939. The probability of getting a z-score between -0.19 and -1.87 is 0.3939

EXAMPLE 4. *For a standard normal distribution, find the probability of getting a z-value less than 1.2.*

Solution
The probability of getting a z value less than 1.2 means the area under the curve to the left of $z = 1.2$. The area from $z = 0$ to $z = 1.2$ is 0.3849. The area to the left of $z = 0$ is 0.5000. Therefore the probability of getting a z-value less than 1.2 is $0.3849 + 0.5000$ or 0.8849.

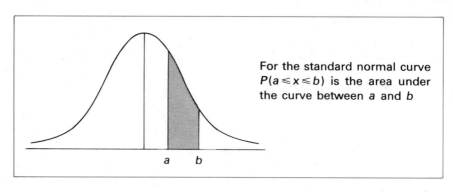

For the standard normal curve $P(a \leqslant x \leqslant b)$ is the area under the curve between a and b

EXAMPLE 5. *In a normal distribution, $\mu = 20$ and $\sigma = 5$. What is the probability of obtaining a value*
(a) *greater than 24?*
(b) *less than 21?*

Solution

(a) For $X = 24$

$$z = \frac{X - \mu}{\sigma}$$

$$= \frac{24 - 20}{5}$$

$$= 0.8$$

(b) For $X = 21$

$$z = \frac{X - \mu}{\sigma}$$

$$= \frac{21 - 20}{5}$$

$$= 0.2$$

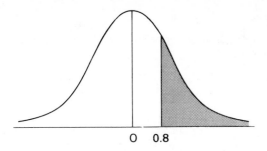

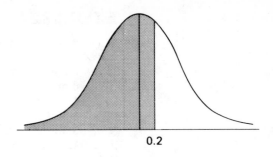

We are interested in the area of the curve to the right of 0.8. From the table, the area from $z = 0$ to $z = 0.8$ is 0.2881.
∴ the area to the right of 0.8 is

$$0.5000 - 0.2881 = 0.2119$$

∴ the probability of obtaining a value greater than 24 is 0.2119.

We are interested in the area to the left of 0.2. The area from $z = 0$ to $z = 0.2$ is 0.0793.
∴ the area to the left of 0.2 is

$$0.5000 + 0.0793 = 0.5793$$

∴ the probability of obtaining a value less than 21 is 0.5793

EXAMPLE 6. *A manufacturer advertizes that his movie projector bulbs have a mean life of 25 h with a standard deviation of 2 h. Assuming a normal distribution, what is the probability that a bulb will*
(a) *last longer than 28 h?*
(b) *last between 21 h and 30 h?*

Solution
(a) For $X = 28$

$$z = \frac{28 - 25}{2}$$

$$= 1.5$$

(b) For $X = 21$

$$z = \frac{21 - 25}{2}$$

$$= -2$$

For $X = 30$

$$z = \frac{30 - 25}{2}$$

$$= 2.5$$

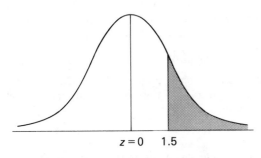

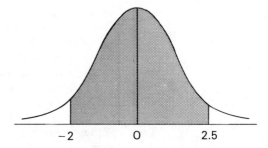

The area from $z = 0$ to $z = 1.5$ is 0.4332. The area to the right of $z = 1.5$ is

$$0.5000 - 0.4332 = 0.0668$$

The probability of a bulb lasting longer than 28 h is 0.0668 or approximately 7% of the bulbs last longer than 28 h.

The area between $z = 0$ and $z = -2$ is 0.4772.
The area between $z = 0$ and $z = 2.5$ is 0.4938.
The area between $z = -2$ and $z = 2.5$ is 0.9710.
∴ the probability of a bulb lasting between 21 and 30 h is 0.9710.

B   **1.** For a standard normal distribution, approximately what percent of the population lies between
(a) $z = 0$ and $z = 1.83$?
(b) $z = 0$ and $z = -0.56$?
(c) $z = 1$ and $z = -1$?
(d) $z = 2$ and $z = -2$?
(e) $z = 3$ and $z = -3$?
(f) $z = 1.12$ and $z = 2.44$?
(g) $z = -0.82$ and $z = -2.41$?
(h) $z = -0.73$ and $z = 1.98$?

2. For a standard normal distribution find the probability of getting a z value
(a) less than 1.9
(b) greater than -1.57
(c) less than 2.41
(d) less than 0.33
(e) between 1.29 and 2.56
(f) between -2.03 and -1.06
(g) between 1.75 and -0.08
(h) less than -1.66 or greater than 0.81

3. For a normal distribution, $\mu = 30$ and $\sigma = 5$. What is the probability of obtaining a value
(a) greater than 35?
(b) less than 28?
(c) between 31 and 37?
(d) between 19 and 29?
(e) between 26 and 41?

4. A supermarket has determined that the average waiting time at an express counter is 200 s with a standard deviation of 40 s. Assuming a normal distribution, what is the probability that you will wait longer than 3 min?

5. The average "life" of a certain car engine is 110 000 km with a standard deviation of 12 000 km. Assuming a normal distribution, what is the probability that the engine will last
(a) longer than 120 000 km?
(b) between 95 000 km and 115 000 km?

6. The mean life of a certain brand of TV picture tube is 9000 h with a standard deviation of 600 h. Assuming a normal distribution, what is the probability that a tube will
(a) last less than 8000 h?
(b) last more than 9500 h?

7. The label on a box of paper clips states that the box contains 100 clips. The manufacturer has determined that the mean number is 102 with a standard deviation of 3. Assuming a normal distribution, what is the probability that a box will contain
(a) more than 100 clips?
(b) less than 100 clips?

8. The life of a blender is normally distributed with a mean of 7 a and a standard deviation of 1.5 a. What is the probability that a blender will
(a) last longer than 8 a?
(b) last less than 5 a?

9. The neck size of men is normally distributed with a mean of 40 and a standard deviation of 1. A manufacturer is going to produce 10 000 shirts with the following sizes: 37, 38, 39, 40, 41, 42, 43 and 44. Assuming a normal distribution, how many of each size should he produce?

10. A manufacturer has determined that the life of his mixers is normally distributed with a mean of 10 a and a standard deviation of 3 a. If he guarantees his mixers for 7 a, what percent can he expect to replace?

C **11.** A car manufacturer has determined that the engines in the Python car have a mean life of 80 000 km with a standard deviation of 10 000 km. For how many kilometres should he guarantee the engine if he does not want to replace more than 2% of them?

39   40

REVIEW EXERCISE

B **1.** Evaluate.
(a) $_9P_4$
(b) $_9C_4$
(c) $12!$
(d) $_7P_2$
(e) $\binom{10}{5}$
(f) $\dfrac{20!}{18!}$
(g) $\binom{100}{98}$
(h) $\binom{100}{2}$

2. A store sells 25 flavours of ice cream. In how many ways can you choose
(a) a double scoop cone?
(b) a triple scoop cone?
(c) a triple scoop cone if you decide to have 3 different flavours?

3. The Cupid Computer Dating Service has cards for 194 boys and 110 girls. How many different dates can it arrange?

4. In going through a maze there are 9 places where you can go to the left or to the right. How many different paths are there through the maze, if all paths lead to the exit?

5. A club has 26 members. In how many ways can it choose
(a) a president, a secretary, and a treasurer?
(b) a committee of 3 members?

6. There are 7 candidates for the office of mayor. In how many ways can their names be listed on the ballot?

7. There are 48 people at a party. If everybody shakes hands once with everybody else, how many handshakes will there be?

8. There are 12 players on a basketball team and all of them can play each of the 5 positions.
(a) In how many ways can the coach select 5 players to start the game?
(b) Once he has selected these 5 players, in how many ways can the coach assign them to the 5 positions?

9. A new musical group called "The Birds" is being formed. It will consist of 3 guitarists, 1 drummer, and 2 vocalists. Auditions are held and 12 guitarists, 5 drummers and 7 vocalists try out. How many different sets of musicians could be chosen for the group?

10. How many poker hands are there which consist of 2 jacks, 2 queens, and a king?

11. In how many ways can the letters of the following words be arranged?
(a) mustard (b) unusual (c) Toronto

12. Expand the following.
(a) $(a+b)^9$ (b) $(1-x)^7$ (c) $(x^2+2y)^6$

13. Write out the first 4 terms in the binomial expansion of the following.
(a) $(a+b)^{16}$ (b) $(x-2)^{13}$

14. Find $(1.015)^7$ correct to 3 decimal places by using the Binomial Theorem.

15. A single card is dealt from a deck of 52 playing cards. Find the probability that the card is
(a) a jack (b) not a jack
(c) a heart (d) a jack or a king
(e) a jack or a heart (f) neither a jack nor a heart

16. Six coins are tossed. Find the probability of getting
(a) 6 tails (b) at least one tail
(c) 2 heads and 4 tails (d) 3 heads and 3 tails

17. A box contains 8 red balls and 6 blue balls. Four balls are drawn at random from the box. Find the probabilities of the following events.
(a) All 4 balls are red.
(b) 3 balls are red and 1 is blue.
(c) 2 balls are red and 2 are blue.
(d) At least one ball is blue.

18. A box contains 2 white balls, 3 red balls, 4 brown balls, and 1 yellow ball. A ball is chosen at random from the box, it is replaced, and another ball is chosen. Find the probabilities of the following events.
(a) The first ball is brown and the second is white.
(b) The first ball is red and the second is yellow.
(c) One ball is red and the other is white.
(d) Both balls are brown.
(e) Both balls are yellow.

19. Do question 18 assuming that the ball is not replaced.

20. At a charity bazaar 40 lottery tickets were sold. Dale bought 10 tickets and Bruce bought 5 tickets. There are 5 prizes. Find the probabilities of the following events.
(a) Dale wins all 5 prizes.
(b) Bruce wins all 5 prizes.
(c) Dale wins at least one prize.
(d) Bruce wins at least one prize.
(e) Dale or Bruce wins at least one prize.

21. Determine the sample standard deviation for the following set of data.

Value	Frequency
2	4
4	6
6	10
8	9
10	8
12	3

22. Sandra got 73 on a geography exam. Frank got 68. The marks of the other students in their class were

$$50, 78, 82, 67, 73$$
$$68, 40, 52, 66, 81$$
$$53, 56, 90, 71, 75$$
$$30, 52, 66, 70, 84$$

Find the percentile rank of Sandra and Frank.

23. On a national mathematics contest the mean was 80 and the standard deviation 20. Al scored 66, Terry 82, and Sue 70. Find their z-scores.

24. For a standard normal distribution, approximately what percent of the population lies between
(a) $z = 1.03$ and $z = 2.56$
(b) $z = -2.13$ and $z = -0.49$
(c) $z = -1.72$ and $z = 1.14$

25. For a normal distribution, $\mu = 24$ and $\sigma = 4$. What is the probability of obtaining a value
(a) greater than 26?
(b) greater than 17?
(c) less than 30?
(d) between 25 and 31?

26. A soda cracker manufacturer has determined that the masses of boxes of crackers are normally distributed with a mean of 250 g and a standard deviation of 4 g. What is the probability that a box of crackers will have a mass
(a) greater than 252 g?
(b) less than 247 g?
(c) between 245 g and 255 g?

REVIEW AND PREVIEW TO CHAPTER 11.

EXERCISE 1 THE DISTANCE FORMULA AND MIDPOINT

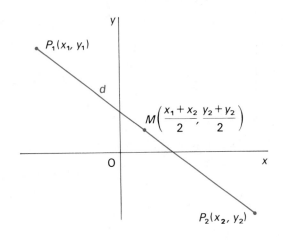

$$d = \sqrt{(x_2 - x_1)^2 + (y_2 - y_1)^2}$$

$$M\left(\frac{x_1 + x_2}{2}, \frac{y_1 + y_2}{2}\right)$$

Find the distance between the following pairs of points.

1. $A(2, 5)$, $B(4, 8)$ **2.** $C(-2, -1)$, $D(5, 4)$ **3.** $E(-3, 5)$, $F(5, 7)$

4. $G(-2, -6)$, $H(-7, -6)$ **5.** $I(-3, -4)$, $J(-8, -6)$ **6.** $K(0, 7)$, $L(-5, 2)$

7. Find the radius of a circle with centre $(2, 9)$ if $(8, 12)$ is a point on the circumference.

Find the midpoint of the line segment having the endpoints

8. $A(3, 4)$, $B(9, 12)$ **9.** $C(-3, 5)$, $D(5, -5)$ **10.** $E(4, -11)$, $F(8, -5)$

11. $G(5, -3)$, $H(-5, 3)$ **12.** $L(-2, 6)$, $J(-5, 3)$ **13.** $K(0, -7)$, $L(5, 3)$

14. Find the centre of the circle having $A(2, 5)$ and $B(-3, 7)$ as endpoints of a diameter.

15. Use the distance formula to show that $\left(\dfrac{a+b}{2}, \dfrac{c+d}{2}\right)$ is the midpoint of the line segment having endpoints (a, c) and (b, d).

EXERCISE 2 CIRCUMFERENCE AND AREA

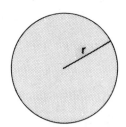

Circumference: $C = 2\pi r = \pi d$

Area: $A = \pi r^2$

Find the perimeter and area of the shaded region.

1.

2.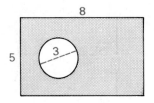

3.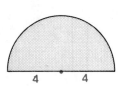

4

5.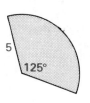

6.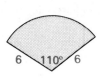

7.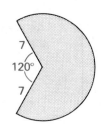

8.

EXERCISE 3   CHORDS

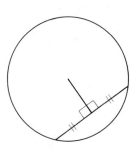

The right bisector of the chord passes
through the centre of the circle.

Find the value of the variables:

1.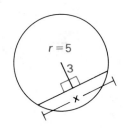

2.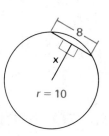

3.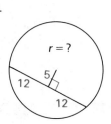

4.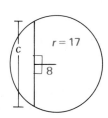

5.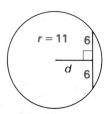

6.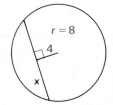

7.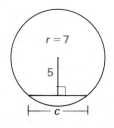

8.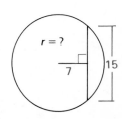

EXERCISE 4   ANGLES IN A CIRCLE

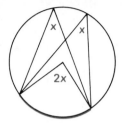

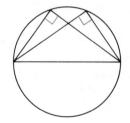

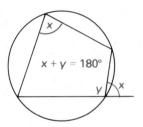

Angles subtended by the same arc are equal

An angle in a semicircle is 90°.

In a Cyclic Quadrilateral opposite angles are supplementary.

Find the value of the variables.

1.

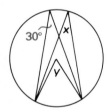

2.

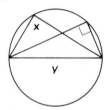

3.

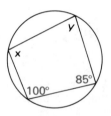

4.

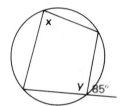

5.

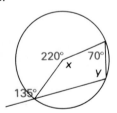

6.

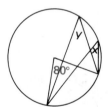

7.

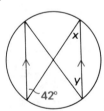

8.

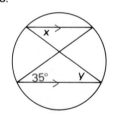

EXERCISE 5   TANGENTS TO A CIRCLE

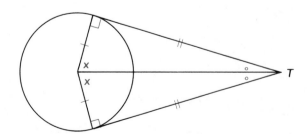

Tangents drawn to a circle from an external point are equal.

Find the value of the variables.

1.

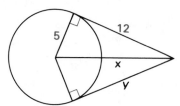

2.

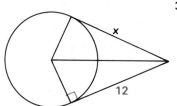

3.

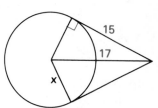

4.

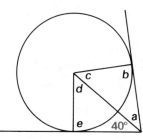

5.

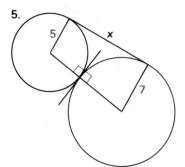

6.

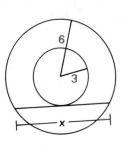

EXERCISE 6   TANGENTS, CHORDS AND SECANTS

Tangent Chord Theorem:
The angle between the tangent and the chord is equal to the angle inscribed in the circle on the opposite side of the chord.

Tangent Secant Theorem:
If a secant and a tangent are drawn from the same external point, then

$$PT^2 = PA \times PB$$

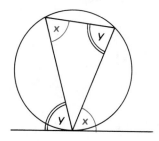

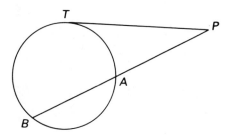

Find the values of the variables.

1.

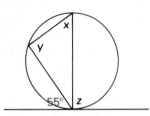

2.

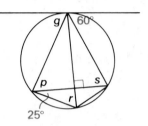

3.

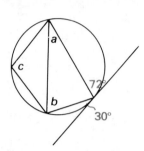

4.

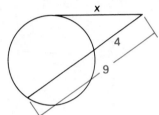

5.

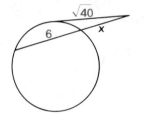

6.

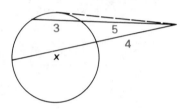

7.

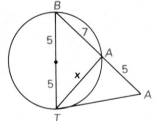

8.

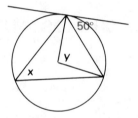

9.

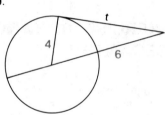

Analytic Geometry

CHAPTER 11

Geometry will draw the soul toward truth and create the spirit of philosophy.

Plato

JOHANN KEPLER (1571—1630)

Kepler, an astronomer and mathematician, was born near Stuttgart in Germany. He had a readiness to look for new relations between familiar things. At the age of twenty-two he went to Gratz in Austria, where he was appointed professor, then on to join another astronomer, Tycho Brahe, at a new observatory near Prague. It was here that he also came under the influence of Galileo. He eventually published his great laws of planetary motion:

1. (1609) The orbit of each planet is an ellipse, with the sun at a focus.
2. (1609) The line joining the planet to the sun sweeps out equal areas in equal times.
3. (1619) The square of the period of the planet is proportional to the cube of its mean distance from the sun.

Kepler pointed out many details in abstract theory that his predecessors had missed—such as the importance of the focus of a conic. He was the first to use the word "focus" (meaning "hearth" in Latin). As well as working in algebra and logarithms, Kepler was also a geometer, finding the area of the ellipse to be πab.

11.1 THE EQUATION OF A CIRCLE

A locus is a set of points that obey a rule or satisfy a given condition. The locus of points in the plane that are a fixed distance from a fixed point is called a circle—the fixed distance is the radius and the fixed point is called the centre.

In order to find the equation of a locus, we go through the following three steps:

1. Name a point such as $P(x, y)$ to represent a typical point in the locus.
2. State the locus in geometric form.
3. Express the law of the locus in algebraic form.

These three steps are illustrated in the following example.

EXAMPLE 1. *Find an equation of the locus of a point equidistant from*
$A(2, 5)$ and $B(6, 9)$

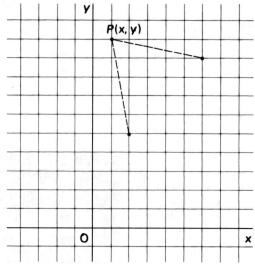

1. Let $P(x, y)$ be any point equidistant from $A(2, 5)$ and $B(6, 9)$
2. P is equidistant from A and B if, and only if, $AP = BP$
3. Using the distance formula

$$d = \sqrt{(x_2 - x_1)^2 + (y_2 - y_1)^2}$$

$$AP = \sqrt{(x - 2)^2 + (y - 5)^2}$$

$$BP = \sqrt{(x - 6)^2 + (y - 9)^2}$$

$$\because \quad AP = BP$$

$$\sqrt{(x - 2)^2 + (y - 5)^2} = \sqrt{(x - 6)^2 + (y - 9)^2}$$

$$(x - 2)^2 + (y - 5)^2 = (x - 6)^2 + (y - 9)^2$$

$$x^2 - 4x + 4 + y^2 - 10y + 25 = x^2 - 12x + 36 + y^2 - 18y + 81$$

$$8x + 8y - 88 = 0$$

$$x + y - 11 = 0$$

$\therefore$ an equation of the locus is $x + y - 11 = 0$
It turns out that the locus is the right bisector of AB.

EXAMPLE 2. *Find an equation of the circle having centre $C(2, 5)$ and radius 4*

Solution

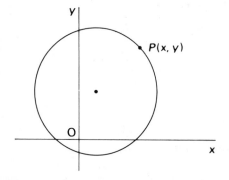

Let $P(x, y)$ be any point on the circle. P is on the circle if, and only if, $CP = 4$

$$\sqrt{(x - 2)^2 + (y - 5)^2} = 4$$

$$(x - 2)^2 + (y - 5)^2 = 16$$

Since these steps can be reversed, a point belongs to the circle if and only if its coordinates satisfy $(x - 2)^2 + (y - 5)^2 = 16$
$\therefore$ an equation of the circle is
$(x - 2)^2 + (y - 5)^2 = 16$

We can use the method of Example 2 to find the general form of the equation of the circle having

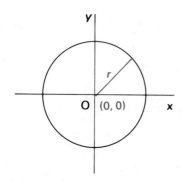

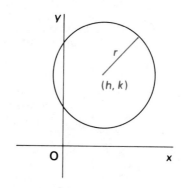

Centre 0(0, 0), radius r

Let $P(x, y)$ be any point on the circle.
P is on the circle if and only if $OP = r$

$$\sqrt{(x-0)^2 + (y-0)^2} = r$$
$$(x-0)^2 + (y-0)^2 = r^2$$
$$x^2 + y^2 = r^2$$

Centre C(h, k), radius r

Let $P(x, y)$ be any point on the circle.
P is on the circle if and only if $CP = r$

$$\sqrt{(x-h)^2 + (y-k)^2} = r$$
$$(x-h)^2 + (y-k)^2 = r^2$$

An equation of the circle with radius r, and centre

$0(0, 0)$ is $x^2 + y^2 = r^2$

$C(h, k)$ is $(x-h)^2 + (y-k)^2 = r^2$

EXAMPLE 3. *Find the equations of the following circles*
(a) *centre 0(0, 0) and radius 5*
(b) *centre C(-3, 5) and radius 6*

Solution
(a) Using the formula $x^2 + y^2 = r^2$

$$x^2 + y^2 = 5^2$$

∴   an equation of the circle is

$$x^2 + y^2 = 25$$

(b) Using the formula $(x - h)^2 + (y - k)^2 = r^2$,

$$(x - (-3))^2 + (y - 5)^2 = 6^2$$

∴ $(x + 3)^2 + (y - 5)^2 = 36$ is an equation of the circle.

EXAMPLE 4. *Find the centre and radius of the circles defined by*
(a) $x^2+y^2=49$
(b) $x^2+y^2-6x=7$
(c) $x^2+y^2+4x-10y-7=0$

Solution

(a) $x^2+y^2=49$ can be written

$$x^2+y^2=7^2$$

∴ the centre is $(0,0)$ and the radius is 7

(b) We wish to express the equation in the form $(x-h)^2+(y-k)^2=r^2$.

$$x^2+y^2-6x=7$$
$$x^2-6x+y^2=7$$

Completing the square

$$x^2-6x+9+y^2=7+9$$

Factoring

$$(x-3)^2+(y-0)^2=16$$

∴ the centre is $(3,0)$ and the radius is 4

(c) $x^2+y^2+4x-10y-7=0$

$$x^2+4x+y^2-10y=7$$

Completing the square,

$$x^2+4x+4+y^2-10y+25=7+4+25$$

Factoring

$$(x+2)^2+(y-5)^2=36$$

∴ the centre is $(-2,5)$ and the radius is 6

EXAMPLE 5. *Sketch the graph of the region defined by*
(a) $x^2+y^2<25$
(b) $x^2+y^2-6x-8y-11\geqslant0$

Solution

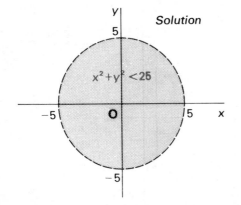

(a) We sketch the graph of the boundary first.

$$x^2+y^2=25$$

and

$$\sqrt{x^2+y^2}<5$$

∴ we shade the interior of the circle.

(b) We sketch the graph of the boundary first.

$$x^2 + y^2 - 6x - 8y - 11 = 0$$
$$x^2 - 6x + y^2 - 8y = 11$$
$$x^2 - 6x + 9 + y^2 - 8y + 16 = 11 + 9 + 16$$
$$(x-3)^2 + (y-4)^2 = 36$$
$$\sqrt{(x-3)^2 + (y-4)^2} \geqslant 6$$

$\therefore$ we shade the exterior of the circle.

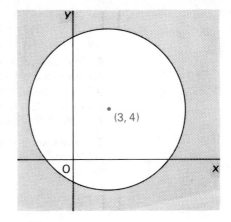

EXERCISE 11-1

1. State the location of the centre and the radius of the following circles.
(a) $x^2 + y^2 = 1$ (b) $x^2 + y^2 = 49$ (c) $x^2 + y^2 = 81$
(d) $x^2 + (y-2)^2 = 25$ (e) $(x+3)^2 + y^2 = 36$ (f) $(x-5)^2 + (y+4)^2 = 100$
(g) $x^2 + y^2 = 20$ (h) $x^2 + y^2 = 17$ (i) $x^2 + y^2 = 50$
(j) $2x^2 + 2y^2 = 50$ (k) $3(x-2)^2 + 3(y+1)^2 = 10$
(l) $(x-a)^2 + (y-b)^2 = c^2$

2. State the equation of each of the following circles, given
(a) centre $(0, 0)$, radius 3   (b) centre $(0, 0)$, radius 7
(c) centre $(0, 0)$, radius $\sqrt{5}$ (d) centre $(2, 5)$, radius $\sqrt{7}$
(e) centre $(-2, 3)$, radius 5   (f) centre $(-3, -4)$, radius 5
(g) centre $(5, -2)$, radius 3   (h) centre $(0, 3)$, radius 6
(i) centre $(-4, 0)$, radius $4\sqrt{2}$ (j) centre $(-3, -8)$, radius 10
(k) centre (a, b), radius c (l) centre $(a, -b)$, radius c

3. Find an equation of the locus of each of the following.
(a) points 5 units above the x-axis.
(b) points 2 units to the left of the y-axis.
(c) points 5 units from the origin.
(d) points 7 units from $A(2, 5)$.
(e) points equidistant from $B(0, 5)$ and $C(0, -1)$.
(f) points equidistant from $D(-3, 2)$ and $E(5, -6)$.
(g) points on the right bisector of the line segment joining $A(5, 2)$ to $B(3, 8)$.

4. Find the equation of each of the following circles.
(a) centre $(0, 0)$, passing through $(-3, 4)$.
(b) centre $(2, 5)$, passing through $(2, 8)$.
(c) centre $(-3, -2)$, passing through $(-3, 8)$.
(d) centre $(0, 5)$, passing through $(3, -4)$.
(e) centre $(-3, 0)$, passing through $(0, 4)$.

5. Find the location of the centre and length of the radius of each of the following circles.
(a) $x^2 + y^2 + 6x - 27 = 0$
(b) $x^2 + y^2 - 4y - 5 = 0$
(c) $x^2 + y^2 + 10x - 8y + 16 = 0$
(d) $x^2 + y^2 - 2x - 2y - 3 = 0$

(e) $x^2 + y^2 - 4x + 2y - 4 = 0$
(f) $x^2 + y^2 - 10x + 12y - 3 = 0$
(g) $x^2 + y^2 + 5x - 3y + \frac{1}{2} = 0$

6. Find the equation of each of the following circles.
(a) having a diameter with endpoints $A(2, -5)$ and $B(2, 5)$.
(b) having a diameter with endpoints $A(2, -5)$ and $B(8, 3)$.
(c) centre $(0,0)$ and x-intercept 7
(d) centre $(0, 0)$ and y-intercept -3

7. Sketch graphs of the following relations, $x, y \in R$.
(a) $x^2 + y^2 \leqslant 16$ (b) $x^2 + y^2 < 9$ (c) $x^2 + y^2 - 25 > 0$
(d) $(x - 2)^2 + (y - 3)^2 \leqslant 25$ (e) $(x + 3)^2 + (y - 5)^2 \geqslant 16$
(f) $x^2 + y^2 + 6y < 16$ (g) $x^2 + y^2 + 6x - 8y > 0$
(h) $x^2 + y^2 - 12x + 6y - 4 \leqslant 0$

11.2 CHORDS AND TANGENTS

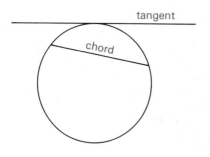

A chord is a line segment having its endpoints on the circle. A tangent is a line that intersects the circle in only one point.

In this section you will require the following formulas from your previous work:

Equations of Lines	Midpoint
$y - y_1 = m(x - x_1)$ $y = mx + b$ $y = m(x - a)$ $\dfrac{x}{a} + \dfrac{y}{b} = 1$	$\left(\dfrac{x_1 + x_2}{2}, \dfrac{y_1 + y_2}{2}\right)$
	Distance between two points $d = \sqrt{(x_2 - x_1)^2 + (y_2 - y_1)^2}$
	Slope $m = \dfrac{y_2 - y_1}{x_2 - x_1}$

EXERCISE 11-2

1. Given the circle defined by $x^2 + y^2 = 25$ and endpoints $A(3, 4)$ and $B(-4, 3)$
(a) show that AB is a chord of the circle.
(b) find the equation of the right bisector of AB.
(c) show that the centre of the circle lies on the right bisector of AB.

2. Given the circle defined by $x^2 + y^2 = 40$ and the points $C(2, 6)$, and $D(-6, 2)$
(a) show that CD is a chord of the circle.
(b) find the midpoint, M, of CD.
(c) find the slope of OM.
(d) find the slope of CD.
(e) show that $CD \perp OM$.

3. Given the circle $x^2 + y^2 = 16$ and the point $P(5, 9)$ and T, the point of contact of a tangent from P,
(a) show that P lies in the exterior of the given circle.
(b) find the lengths of OT and OP.
(c) find the length of the tangent PT.

4. Find the length of the tangent to the given circle from the given point.
(a) $x^2 + y^2 = 25$, $P(6, 8)$ (b) $x^2 + y^2 = 9$, $P(7, -6)$
(c) $x^2 + y^2 = 16$, $P(0, 10)$ (d) $x^2 + y^2 = 40$, $P(5, -5)$
(e) $x^2 + y^2 = 50$, $P(-8, 10)$ (f) $x^2 + y^2 = 1$, $P(8, 1)$
(g) $(x - 5)^2 + y^2 = 36$, $P(8, -8)$ (h) $(x + 3)^2 + (y - 2)^2 = 25$, $P(8, 8)$

5. Given the circle defined by $x^2 + y^2 = 25$ and the point $T(-3, 4)$,
(a) show that T is a point of the circle.
(b) find the slope of OT.
(c) find the slope of the tangent at T, perpendicular to OT.
(d) find an equation of the tangent to the circle at T.

6. Find an equation of the tangent to the given circle at the given point of contact.
(a) $x^2 + y^2 = 13$, $T(2, 3)$ (b) $x^2 + y^2 = 34$, $T(3, 5)$
(c) $x^2 + y^2 = 74$, $T(-5, -7)$ (d) $x^2 + y^2 = 20$, $T(2, -4)$
(e) $x^2 + y^2 = 36$, $T(0, 6)$ (f) $x^2 + y^2 = 34$, $T(-5, 3)$
(g) $(x - 2)^2 + (y - 3)^2 = 20$, $T(4, 7)$ (h) $(x + 3)^2 + (y - 4)^2 = 25$, $T(0, 0)$

7. Given the circle defined by $x^2 + y^2 = r^2$ and the points $A(a, b)$ and $B(-b, a)$ on the circle,
(a) find the equation of the right bisector of the chord.
(b) show that the right bisector of the chord AB passes through the centre of the circle.

8. Given the circle defined by $x^2 + y^2 = r^2$ and the points $P(p, q)$ and $Q(q, -p)$ on the circle,
(a) find the midpoint, M, of PQ.
(b) find the slope of OM.
(c) find the slope of PQ.
(d) show that $OM \perp PQ$.

9. Given the circle defined by $x^2 + y^2 = r^2$ and the point $P(a, b)$ in the exterior of the circle, T is the point of contact on the circle of a tangent from P.
(a) Find the lengths OT and OP.
(b) Find the length of the tangent PT and write a formula for length of tangent from a point.

10. Given the circle defined by $x^2 + y^2 = r^2$ and the point $T(a, b)$ on the circle,
(a) find the slope of OT.
(b) find the slope of the tangent at T, perpendicular to OT.
(c) find an equation of the tangent to the circle at T.

11.3 THE PARABOLA: FOCUS-DIRECTRIX DEFINITION

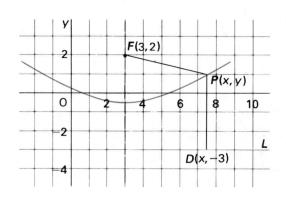

Suppose that a point $P(x, y)$ moves so that its perpendicular distance from line L ($y = -3$) is always equal to its distance from point $F(3, 2)$. We can find an equation of the path of P since

$$PF = PD$$

$$\sqrt{(x-3)^2 + (y-2)^2} = y + 3$$

Squaring both sides of the equation we have

$$(x-3)^2 + (y-2)^2 = (y+3)^2$$

$$(x-3)^2 + y^2 - 4y + 4 = y^2 + 6y + 9$$

$$(x-3)^2 - 5 = 10y$$

$$y = \tfrac{1}{10}(x-3)^2 - \tfrac{1}{2}$$

Since the equation of the path of P is in the form $y = a(x - h)^2 + k$, the path of P is a parabola. This leads to a geometric definition of a parabola.

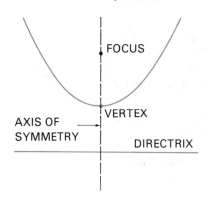

A parabola is the set of all points which are equidistant from a fixed line (called the *directrix*) and a fixed point not on the line (called the *focus*).

Notice that the vertex of the parabola is midway between the focus and the directrix.

EXAMPLE 1. *Find an equation of the parabola whose focus is (2, 1) and whose directrix is the line x = 4.*

Solution

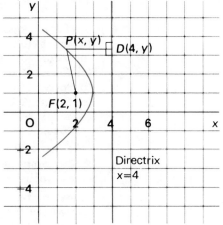

Let $P(x, y)$ be any point on the parabola.

$$PF = PD$$

$$\sqrt{(x-2)^2 + (y-1)^2} = \sqrt{(x-4)^2 + (y-y)^2}$$

$$(x-2)^2 + (y-1)^2 = (x-4)^2$$

$$x^2 - 4x + 4 + (y-1)^2 = x^2 - 8x + 16$$

$$(y-1)^2 - 12 = -4x$$

$$\therefore \quad x = -\tfrac{1}{4}(y-1)^2 + 3$$

is an equation of the parabola

The method of Example 1 suggests the following method to derive a general equation of a parabola with focus on the x-axis.

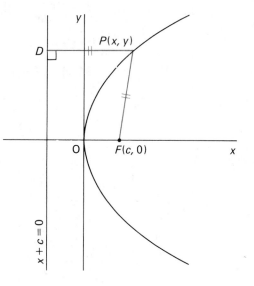

Let the focus be $F(c, 0)$ and the equation of the directrix be $x + c = 0$. If $P(x, y)$ is any point on the parabola, then

$$FP = PD$$

$$\sqrt{(x-c)^2 + y^2} = x + c$$

Squaring both sides,

$$x^2 - 2cx + c^2 + y^2 = x^2 + 2cx + c^2$$

$$y^2 = 4cx$$

> The general equation of a parabola
> with horizontal axis of symmetry is
>
> $$y^2 = 4cx$$
>
> where the focus is $(c, 0)$ and the equa-
> tion of the directrix is $x + c = 0$.

Examination of the equation shows that the parabola opens to the right for $c > 0$ and to the left for $c < 0$. For a parabola with a vertical axis of symmetry, the equation is of the form $x^2 = 4cy$, where the focus is $(0, c)$.

EXERCISE 11-3

B **1.** Find an equation of the parabola with the given focus and directrix.
(a) focus: $(0, 2)$; directrix: $y = -4$
(b) focus: $(0, -3)$; directrix: $y = 2$
(c) focus: $(4, 0)$; directrix: $x = 1$
(d) focus: $(-3, 0)$; directrix: $x = 2$
(e) focus: $(2, 2)$; directrix: $y = -1$
(f) focus: $(-3, -2)$; directrix: $x = -1$
(g) focus: $(-5, -1)$; directrix: $x = 5$
(h) focus $(-4, 3)$; directrix: $y = 5$

2. Determine an equation of the parabola whose vertex is at $(4, 2)$ and whose focus is 3 units to the left of the vertex.

3. Determine an equation of the parabola whose vertex is at $(-3, -1)$ and whose directrix is 2 units above the vertex.

C **4.** Determine an equation of the parabola whose vertex is $(a, 0)$ and whose directrix is the line $x = -a$.

5. Determine an equation of the parabola whose vertex is $(1, 3)$ and whose directrix is the line $y = x$.

11.4 THE EQUATION OF AN ELLIPSE

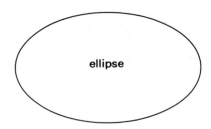

ellipse

When the earth revolves about the sun it does so in an orbit which we call an ellipse. Also, when most satellites revolve about the earth they do so in elliptical orbits.

If we take two points F_1 and F_2, and a piece of string longer than F_1F_2 fastened at F_1 and F_2, then we can draw an ellipse as shown below.

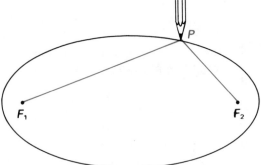

From the diagram above we see that the sum of the distances $F_1P + PF_2$, namely the length of the string, is a constant for all positions that P takes. This leads us to make the following definition.

> Ellipse
> An ellipse is a locus such that the sum
> of the distances from any point on the
> locus to two fixed points is a constant.
>
> $$F_1P + PF_2 = k$$

Each of the fixed points is called a focus (the plural is foci) and the lengths F_1P and PF_2 are called focal radii. The constant value must be greater than the distance between the foci.

EXAMPLE 1. *Find an equation of an ellipse with foci at $(-4, 0)$ and $(4, 0)$ and constant sum of the focal radii 10.*

Solution

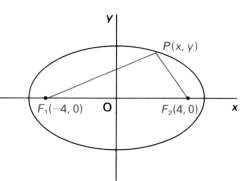

Let $P(x, y)$ be any point on the ellipse.

$$F_1P + PF_2 = 10$$

Using the distance formula

$$d = \sqrt{(x_2 - x_1)^2 + (y_2 - y_1)^2}$$
$$F_1P = \sqrt{(x+4)^2 + (y-0)^2}$$
$$F_2P = \sqrt{(x-4)^2 + (y-0)^2}$$

The required equation for the set of points is

$$\sqrt{(x+4)^2 + y^2} + \sqrt{(x-4)^2 + y^2} = 10$$
$$\sqrt{(x-4)^2 + y^2} = 10 - \sqrt{(x+4)^2 + y^2}$$

Squaring both sides

$$(x^2 - 8x + 16) + y^2 = 100 - 20\sqrt{(x+4)^2 + y^2} + (x^2 + 8x + 16) + y^2$$
$$5\sqrt{(x+4)^2 + y^2} = 4x + 25$$

Squaring both sides again

$$25x^2 + 200x + 400 + 25y^2 = 16x^2 + 200x + 625$$
$$9x^2 + 25y^2 = 225$$

Dividing both sides by 225 we get the equation in a convenient form.

$$\frac{x^2}{25} + \frac{y^2}{9} = 1$$

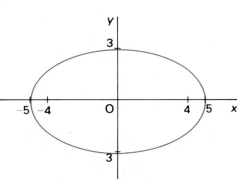

Rewriting the equation

$$\frac{x^2}{5^2} + \frac{y^2}{3^2} = 1$$

we immediately see other important features of the graph—the x-intercepts are ± 5, and the y-intercepts are ± 3.

We use the method of Example 1 to derive the general equation of an ellipse.

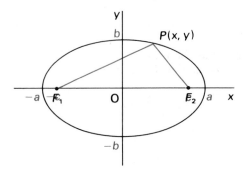

If $P(x, y)$ is any point on the ellipse, then

$$F_1P + PF_2 = 2a$$
$$\sqrt{(x+c)^2 + y^2} + \sqrt{(x-c)^2 + y^2} = 2a$$
$$\sqrt{(x+c)^2 + y^2} = 2a - \sqrt{(x-c)^2 + y^2}$$

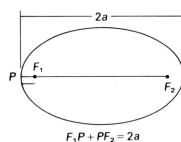

$$F_1P + PF_2 = 2a$$

Let the foci be $F_1(-c, 0)$ and $F_2(c, 0)$, the x-intercepts $\pm a$, and the y-intercepts $\pm b$. We shall define the lengths (i) from $(-a, 0)$ to $(a, 0)$ the major axis, $2a$; (ii) from $(0, -b)$ to $(0, b)$ the minor axis, $2b$.

Squaring both sides

$$(x^2 + 2cx + c^2) + y^2 = 4a^2 - 4a\sqrt{(x-c)^2 + y^2} + (x^2 - 2cx + c^2) + y^2$$
$$4a\sqrt{(x-c)^2 + y^2} = 4a^2 - 4cx$$
$$a\sqrt{(x-c)^2 + y^2} = a^2 - cx$$

Squaring both sides again

$$a^2(x^2 - 2cx + c^2) + a^2y^2 = a^4 - 2a^2cx + c^2x^2$$
$$a^2x^2 - c^2x^2 + a^2y^2 = a^4 - a^2c^2$$

Factoring

$$(a^2 - c^2)x^2 + a^2y^2 = a^2(a^2 - c^2)$$

Substituting $b^2 = a^2 - c^2$,

$$b^2x^2 + a^2y^2 = a^2b^2$$

Dividing both sides by a^2b^2,

$$\boxed{\frac{x^2}{a^2} + \frac{y^2}{b^2} = 1}$$

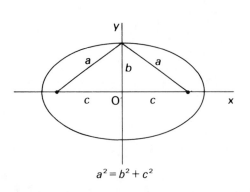

$$a^2 = b^2 + c^2$$

The general equation of an ellipse with centre at the origin is

$$\frac{x^2}{a^2}+\frac{y^2}{b^2}=1$$

where

$2a$ is the major axis
$2b$ is the minor axis

and

$$a^2=b^2+c^2$$

The foci are $(-c, 0)$ and $(c, 0)$.

Ellipses can be long and narrow, or nearly circular. The amount of elongation of an ellipse is measured by a number called the eccentricity

$$e=\frac{c}{a}$$

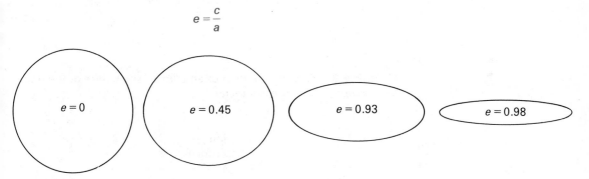

$e = 0$

$e = 0.45$

$e = 0.93$

$e = 0.98$

EXAMPLE 2. *For the ellipse*

$$\frac{x^2}{9}+\frac{y^2}{4}=1$$

state
(a) *the x-intercepts*
(b) *the y-intercepts*
(c) *the length of the major axis*
(d) *the length of the minor axis*
(e) *the location of the foci*
(f) *the eccentricity*
and sketch the ellipse.

A driver sets out on a trip of 30 km at 50 km/h. After 15 km he decides to increase his speed. At what speed must he drive in order to average 100 km/h for the whole trip?

Solution
We write the equation in the form

$$\frac{x^2}{3^2}+\frac{y^2}{2^2}=1$$

$a = 3, b = 2, c^2 = a^2 - b^2$

$$c = \pm\sqrt{9-4} = \pm\sqrt{5}$$

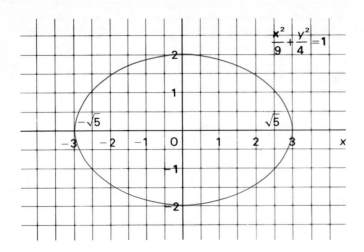

(a) the x-intercepts are ±3
(b) the y-intercepts are ±2
(c) the major axis is $2a = 2(3) = 6$
(d) the minor axis is $2b = 2(2) = 4$
(e) the foci are $(-\sqrt{5}, 0)$ and $(\sqrt{5}, 0)$
(f) the eccentricity is

$$e = \frac{c}{a} = \frac{\sqrt{5}}{3}$$

$$\doteq 0.75$$

EXAMPLE 3. *Find an equation of an ellipse with centre at the origin, x-intercepts ±6, and eccentricity $\frac{2}{3}$.*

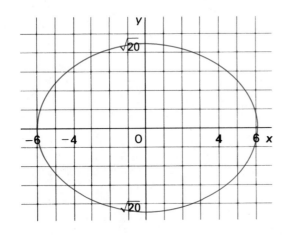

Solution
Eccentricity

$$e = \frac{c}{a}$$

$$e = \frac{2}{3}$$

and

$$a = 6$$

$$\therefore \quad \frac{2}{3} = \frac{c}{6}$$

$$12 = 3c$$

$$\therefore \quad c = 4$$

$$b^2 = a^2 - c^2$$

$$= 6^2 - 4^2$$

$$= 20$$

Substituting into the general equation

$\frac{x^2}{a^2} + \frac{y^2}{b^2} = 1$, we have the required equation

$$\frac{x^3}{36} + \frac{y^2}{20} = 1.$$

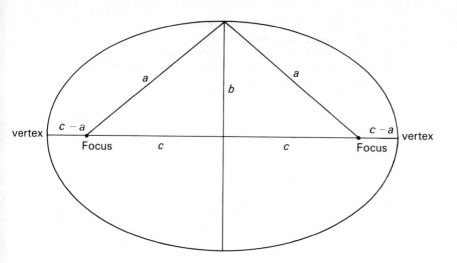

EXERCISE 11-4

1. State the length of the major and minor axes.

(a) $\dfrac{x^2}{25}+\dfrac{y^2}{36}=1$ (b) $\dfrac{x^2}{4}+\dfrac{y^2}{9}=36$ (c) $\dfrac{x^2}{25}+\dfrac{y^2}{16}=1$

2. State the eccentricity of the following ellipses.

(a) $\dfrac{x^2}{25}+\dfrac{y^2}{9}=1$ (b) $\dfrac{x^2}{25}+\dfrac{y^2}{16}=1$ (c) $\dfrac{x^2}{100}+\dfrac{y^2}{36}=1$

3. Locate the foci and graph each of the following.

(a) $\dfrac{x^2}{16}+\dfrac{y^2}{9}=1$ (b) $\dfrac{x^2}{36}+\dfrac{y^2}{4}=1$ (c) $\dfrac{x^2}{49}+\dfrac{y^2}{16}=1$

(d) $\dfrac{x^2}{25}+\dfrac{y^2}{4}=1$ (e) $\dfrac{x^2}{64}+\dfrac{y^2}{100}=1$ (f) $\dfrac{x^2}{49}+\dfrac{y^2}{36}=1$

4. Sketch the graph of the following and find the eccentricity.

(a) $\dfrac{x^2}{25}+\dfrac{y^2}{4}=1$ (b) $\dfrac{x^2}{16}+\dfrac{y^2}{4}=1$ (c) $\dfrac{x^2}{16}+\dfrac{y^2}{9}=1$

(d) $4x^2+9y^2=36$ (e) $4x^2+25y^2=100$ (f) $16x^2+4y^2=64$

5. Find an equation of the following ellipses with centre at the origin.
(a) major axis 10, minor axis 8
(b) minor axis 6, one vertex $(-5, 0)$
(c) foci $(-4, 0)$ and $(4, 0)$, sum of focal radii 10
(d) one vertex $(5, 0)$, one focus $(-4, 0)$
(e) one vertex $(10, 0)$, eccentricity 0.5

The vertices of an ellipse are the end points of the major axis

6. (a) Show that if (m, n) is a point on the ellipse $\dfrac{x^2}{a^2}+\dfrac{y^2}{b^2}=1$ then $(-m, n)$ and $(m, -n)$ are also on the ellipse.
(b) Describe the reflectional symmetries of the ellipse.

7. Show that the ellipse $\dfrac{x^2}{a^2}+\dfrac{y^2}{b^2}=1$ is symmetric with respect to the origin using the point (m, n) on the ellipse.

C **8.** Find the equation of an ellipse with

    (a) foci $(0, 0)$ and $(6, 0)$, and sum of focal radii 10

    (b) foci $(2, 3)$ and $(8, 3)$, and sum of focal radii 10

    (c) foci $(-1, -2)$ and $(7, -2)$ and sum of focal radii 10

9. (a) Sketch the graph of $(x-3)^2 + (y-2)^2 = 9$

    (b) Sketch the graph of $\dfrac{(x-3)^2}{9} + \dfrac{(y-2)^2}{1} = 1$

10. Write the equation

$$4x^2 + 9y^2 - 16x + 54y + 61 = 0$$

in the form

$$\frac{(x-h)^2}{a^2} + \frac{(y-k)^2}{b^2} = 1,$$

and sketch the graph.

11.5 THE EQUATION OF AN HYPERBOLA

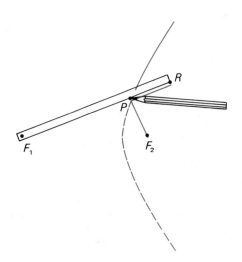

A curve which is found in engineering and navigation is the hyperbola. If we take a length of string and attach it to a fixed point F_2 and the end of a ruler R, permitting the ruler to pivot about a second fixed point F_1, then the figure traced by the pencil at P along the ruler is one branch of an hyperbola.

Hyperbola
   An hyperbola is a locus such that the difference of the distances from any point on the locus to two fixed points, called foci, is constant.

$$|F_1 P - P F_2| = k$$

EXAMPLE 1. *Find an equation of an hyperbola with foci at $F_1(-5, 0)$ and $F_2(5, 0)$ and constant difference between the focal radii is 8*

Solution

Let $P(x, y)$ be any point on the hyperbola.

$$|F_1P - PF_2| = 8$$

Using the distance formula

$$d = \sqrt{(x_2 - x_1)^2 + (y_2 - y_1)^2}$$

$$F_1P = \sqrt{(x + 5)^2 + (y - 0)^2}$$

$$F_2P = \sqrt{(x - 5)^2 + (y - 0)^2}$$

Without loss in generality, we assume $F_1P > PF_2$ and substitute.

$$\sqrt{(x + 5)^2 + y^2} - \sqrt{(x - 5)^2 + y^2} = 8$$

$$\sqrt{(x + 5)^2 + y^2} = 8 + \sqrt{(x - 5)^2 - y^2}$$

Squaring both sides,

$$(x^2 + 10x + 25) + y^2 = 64 + 16\sqrt{(x - 5)^2 + y^2} + (x^2 - 10x + 25) + y^2$$

$$20x - 64 = 16\sqrt{(x - 5)^2 + y^2}$$

Dividing both sides by 4, and then squaring

$$25x^2 - 160x + 256 = 16x^2 - 160x + 400 + 16y^2$$

$$9x^2 - 16y^2 = 144$$

Dividing both sides by 144 we get the equation in a convenient form.

$$\frac{x^2}{16} - \frac{y^2}{9} = 1$$

Some properties of the hyperbola follow from examination of the equation. Setting $y = 0$, we have the x-intercepts ± 4. When we let $x = 0$, we have

$$\frac{0^2}{16} - \frac{y^2}{9} = 1$$

$$y^2 = -9$$

so the hyperbola has no y-intercepts.

Solving the equation for y,

$$\frac{x^2}{16} - \frac{y^2}{9} = 1$$

$$-\frac{y^2}{9} = 1 - \frac{x^2}{16}$$

$$y^2 = \frac{9(x^2 - 16)}{16}$$

$$\therefore \quad y = \pm\tfrac{3}{4}\sqrt{x^2 - 16}$$

y is real if, and only if,

$$x^2 - 16 \geqslant 0$$

$$x^2 \geqslant 16$$

$$|x| \geqslant 4$$

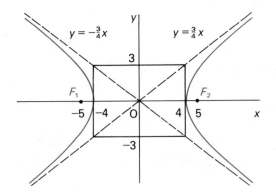

Hence there are no values of y for $-4 \leqslant x \leqslant 4$ and no part of the hyperbola lies between the lines $x = -4$ and $x = 4$. The lines $x = -4$ and $x = 4$ form a rectangle with the lines $y = 3$ and $y = -3$. The graph of the hyperbola lies between the diagonals of this rectangle. The diagonals of this rectangle are called the asymptotes of the hyperbola and their equations are

$$y = \tfrac{3}{4}x \quad \text{and} \quad y = -\tfrac{3}{4}x$$

The method of Example 1 can be used to find a general equation of an hyperbola. We begin in the same manner with

$$|F_1P - PF_2| = 2a$$

The derivation is then similar to that for the ellipse, with $b^2 = c^2 - a^2$.

The equation of the hyperbola with major axis $2a$ and foci $(-c, 0)$ and $(c, 0)$ is

$$\frac{x^2}{a^2} - \frac{y^2}{b^2} = 1$$

where

$$a^2 + b^2 = c^2$$

and the equations of the asymptotes are

$$y = -\frac{b}{a}x \quad \text{and} \quad y = \frac{b}{a}x$$

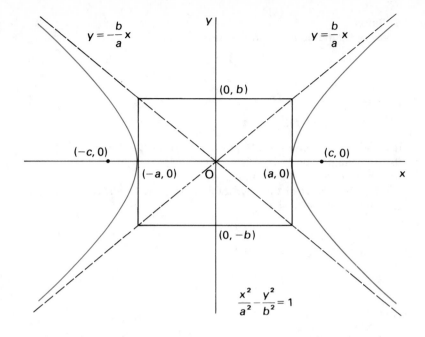

Our discussion has centred on the hyperbola defined by $\frac{x^2}{a^2} - \frac{y^2}{b^2} = 1$.

The graph of $\frac{y^2}{a^2} - \frac{x^2}{b^2} = 1$ is also the graph of an hyperbola but with a vertical major axis.

The eccentricity of an hyperbola is defined the same as for an ellipse.

$$e = \frac{c}{a}$$

EXAMPLE 2. *For the hyperbola*

$$\frac{x^2}{25} - \frac{y^2}{16} = 1$$

state
(a) the intercepts
(b) the length of the major axis
(c) location of the foci
(d) the equations of the asymptotes
(e) the eccentricity
and sketch the graph.

Solution

We write the equation in the form

$$\frac{x^2}{5^2} - \frac{y^2}{4^2} = 1$$

$a = 5, \; b = 4, \; c^2 = a^2 + b^2$

$$c = \pm\sqrt{25 + 16} = \pm\sqrt{41}$$

(a) The x-intercepts are ± 5 and there are no y-intercepts.
(b) The major axis is $2a = 2(5) = 10$
(c) The foci are $(-\sqrt{41}, 0)$ and $(\sqrt{41}, 0)$
(d) The equations of the asymptotes are $y = -\frac{4}{5}x$ and $y = \frac{4}{5}x$
(e) The eccentricity is

$$e = \frac{c}{a} = \frac{\sqrt{41}}{5}$$

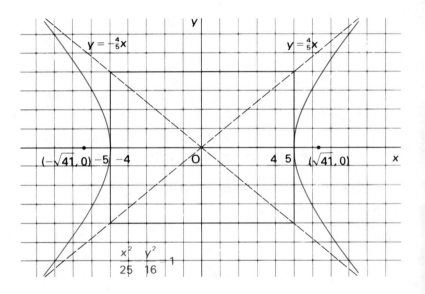

EXAMPLE 3. *Find an equation of an hyperbola with centre at the origin, major axis 8, and eccentricity 1.5*

Solution

Eccentricity

$$e = \frac{c}{a}$$

and

$$2a = 8$$

$$a = 4$$

$$1.5 = \frac{c}{4}$$

$$1.5 \times 4 = c$$

$$\therefore \quad c = 6$$

$$b^2 = c^2 - a^2$$

$$= 6^2 - 4^2$$

$$= 20$$

Substituting into the general equation,

$$\frac{x^2}{a^2} - \frac{y^2}{b^2} = 1$$

we have the required equation

$$\frac{x^2}{16} - \frac{y^2}{20} = 1$$

Hyperbolas such as $x^2 - y^2 = 9$, i.e., $\dfrac{x^2}{9} - \dfrac{y^2}{9} = 1$ where $a = b$ are called equilateral hyperbolas. The asymptotes of an equilateral hyperbola are perpendicular.

The graph of an equation of the form $xy = k$, $k \neq 0$ defines an hyperbola with the coordinate axes as asymptotes.

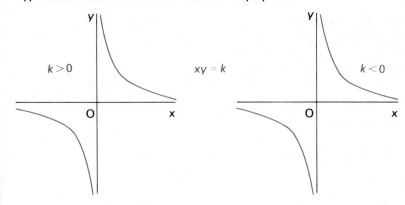

EXERCISE 11-5

1. State the length of the major axis.

(a) $\dfrac{x^2}{25} - \dfrac{y^2}{16} = 1$ (b) $\dfrac{x^2}{9} - \dfrac{y^2}{4} = 1$ (c) $\dfrac{x^2}{20} - \dfrac{y^2}{25} = 1$

2. State the eccentricity of each of the following hyperbolas.

(a) $\dfrac{x^2}{9} - \dfrac{y^2}{16} = 1$ (b) $\dfrac{x^2}{25} - \dfrac{y^2}{144} = 1$ (c) $\dfrac{x^2}{4} - \dfrac{y^2}{12} = 1$

B **3.** Sketch the hyperbolas defined by the following equations, showing (i) intercepts, (ii) length of the major axis (iii) location of the foci (iv) asymptotes.

(a) $\dfrac{x^2}{9} - \dfrac{y^2}{16} = 1$ (b) $\dfrac{x^2}{20} - \dfrac{y^2}{5} = 1$ (c) $\dfrac{x^2}{25} - \dfrac{y^2}{11} = 1$

(d) $\dfrac{x^2}{4} - \dfrac{y^2}{12} = 1$ (e) $\dfrac{x^2}{9} - \dfrac{y^2}{7} = 1$ (f) $\dfrac{x^2}{49} - \dfrac{y^2}{15} = 1$

(g) $3x^2 - 10y^2 = 30$ (h) $2x^2 - 5y^2 = 10$ (i) $7x^2 - 18y^2 = 1$

4. Find an equation of each of the following hyperbolas with centre at the origin.

(a) major axis 10, eccentricity 2

(b) foci $(-5, 0)$ and $(5, 0)$, difference of focal radii 1

(c) one vertex $(5, 0)$, one focus $(6, 0)$

(d) one vertex $(-3, 0)$, eccentricity 1.5

(e) one focus $(-3, 0)$, eccentricity $\frac{5}{4}$

MULTIPLICATION

$$\dfrac{\text{TWO}}{\dfrac{\text{TWO}}{\text{THREE}}}$$

5. Sketch the graphs of

(a) $xy = -4$ (b) $xy = 0$ (c) $xy = 4$

6. Sketch the graphs of

(a) $x^2 - y^2 = 9$ (b) $x^2 - y^2 = 0$ (c) $y^2 - x^2 = 9$

7. (a) Show that if (m, n) is a point on the hyperbola $\dfrac{x^2}{a^2} - \dfrac{y^2}{b^2} = 1$, then

$(-m, n)$ and $(m, -n)$ are also on the hyperbola.

(b) Describe the reflectional symmetries of the hyperbola.

8. Show that the hyperbola $\dfrac{x^2}{a^2} - \dfrac{y^2}{b^2} = 1$ is symmetric with respect to

the origin using the point (m, n) on the hyperbola.

C **9.** Find an equation of an hyperbola with

(a) foci $(0, 0)$ and $(10, 0)$, and difference of focal radii 3

(b) foci $(-3, 2)$ and $(5, 2)$, and difference of focal radii 1

(c) foci $(-2, -2)$ and $(5, -2)$, and difference of focal radii 1.5

10. (a) Sketch the graph of $(x + 2)^2 + (y - 3)^2 = 4$

(b) Sketch the graph of $\dfrac{(x + 2)^2}{25} - \dfrac{(y + 3)^2}{9} = 1$

11. Write the equation

$$7x^2 - 2y^2 - 14x + 12y - 101 = 0$$

in the form

$$\dfrac{(x - h)^2}{a^2} - \dfrac{(y - k)^2}{b^2} = 1$$

and sketch the graph indicating major axis, vertices, and asymptotes.

12. Derive the general equation of the hyperbola $\dfrac{x^2}{a^2} - \dfrac{y^2}{b^2} = 1$ given the major axis is $2a$, the foci are $(-c, 0)$ and $(c, 0)$ and $c^2 = a^2 + b^2$.

11.6 THE CONIC SECTIONS AND THEIR APPLICATIONS

We can obtain the curves of this chapter—circle, parabola, ellipse, and hyperbola—by slicing a cone. Since these curves have this common property—cross sections of a cone—they are appropriately called conic sections.

The following figures show how a cone is sliced to obtain the conic sections.

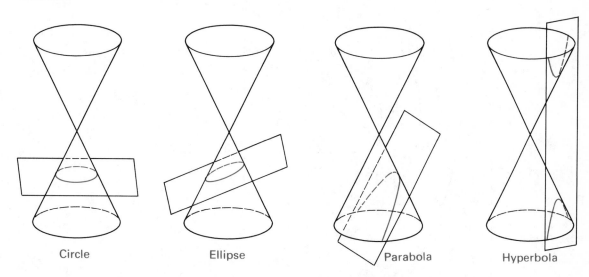

Circle   Ellipse   Parabola   Hyperbola

The extreme cases where we slice the cone and obtain a single point, a line, or a pair of intersecting lines are called degenerate conic sections.

We define the conic sections in terms of a focus and a directrix, as in the case of the parabola (Section 11.3). The ratio of the distances of a point on a conic to the focus and to the directrix is the eccentricity,

$$e = \frac{PF}{PD}$$

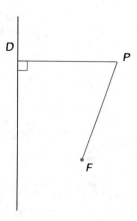

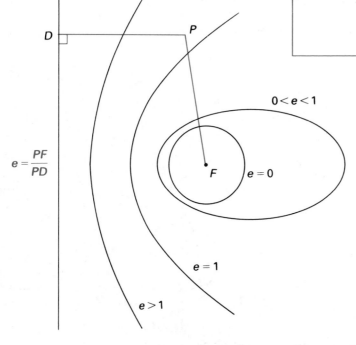

$e = \dfrac{PF}{PD}$

The conic sections occur frequently in science and technology. In the sixteenth century, Galileo discovered that projectiles fired horizontally from the top of a tower fell to the ground along parabolic paths. Later both Kepler and Newton based their theories on the elliptical orbits of the planets. Today, many satellites are launched into elliptical orbits, while it is known that comets travel in parabolic, elliptical or hyperbolic paths.

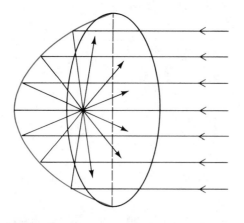

If we take a parabola and rotate it about its axis we have the surface of a paraboloid—the familiar shape of some automobile headlights and also the parabolic reflector used in astronomy and in picking up field-level sounds at football games.

EXAMPLE 1. *A parabolic arch supports a bridge across a stream. The bridge is 24 m wide and the height of the arch is 9 m.*
(a) *Find the equation of the arch.*
(b) *What is the length of a horizontal beam 4 m below the vertex?*
(c) *What is the height of the arch 4 m from either end?*

Solution
(a) Let $P(x, y)$ be any point on the parabola.
The equation of the arch is of the form

$$x^2 = 4cy$$

Since $(12, -9)$ is one point on the parabola,

$$12^2 = 4c(-9)$$

$$\therefore \quad c = -4$$

$\therefore$ the equation of the arch is

$$x^2 = -16y$$

(b) Let $C(x, -4)$ be a point on the parabola 4 units below the vertex.

$$x^2 = -16(-4)$$

$$x^2 = 64$$

$$x = \pm 8$$

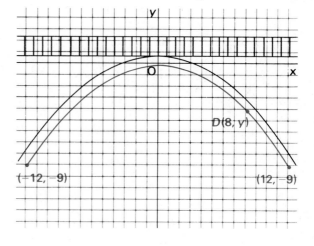

$\therefore$ the length of the beam is 16 m.
(c) Let $D(8, y)$ be a point on the parabola 4 m from one end.

$$8^2 = -16y$$

$$\therefore \quad y = -4$$

$\therefore$ the arch is $9 - 4 = 5$ m high, 4 m from the end.

EXERCISE 11-6

1. Find the equation and sketch the conic with given focus, directrix and eccentricity.
(a) $F(0, 2)$, $y = -2$, $e = 1$
(b) $F(5, 0)$, $x = -5$, $e = 0.5$
(c) $F(4, 0)$, $x = 8$, $e = 0.5$
(d) $F(-3, 0)$, $x = 3$, $e = 2$
(e) $F(2, 0)$, $x = 10$, $e = 1.5$
(f) $F(0, 4)$, $y = -4$, $e = 0.5$
(g) $F(-5, 0)$, $x = 3$, $e = 1$
(h) $F(0, 4)$, $y = 0$, $e = 1$

2. Find the equation of the parabolic arch used to support a bridge. The arch is 80 m wide at the base, and the height of the vertex is 20 m.

3. A ball is thrown horizontally from the top floor of a building 30 m high. It falls in a parabolic path and reaches the ground 50 m from the foot of the building. Find the equation of the parabolic path.

4. The cross-section of a roadway 12 m wide is a parabolic curve. The sides of the roadway are 0.10 m lower than the crown which is in the centre. Find the equation of the cross-section.

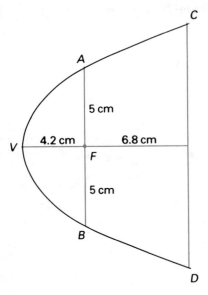

5. The cross-section of a parabolic reflector is as shown. The bulb is located at the focus, 4.2 cm from the vertex and the opening at the focus is 10 cm.
(a) Find an equation of the parabola.
(b) Find the diameter of the opening, *CD*, 11 cm from the vertex.

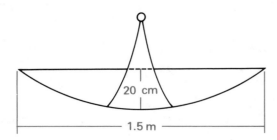

6. A parabolic reflector for picking up sound has a diameter of 1.5 m and 20 cm deep.
(a) Find an equation of the parabola.
(b) Where should the microphone be placed to pick up the sound that is reflected to the focus?

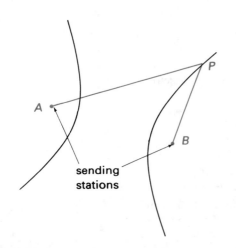

7. Two LORAN (LOng RAnge Navigation) stations at *A* and *B* simultaneously send electronic signals to aircraft. The on-board computer can guide the aircraft by converting the time difference in receiving the signals into a distance difference *PA – PB*. This locates the aircraft on one branch of an hyperbola.

sending stations

(a) Find an equation of an hyperbola determined by the flight path of an aircraft 20 km closer to station *B* than station *A*, if the stations are 100 km apart.

(b) Find an equation of the hyperbola determined by a position 80 km from *B* and 140 km from *A*, if the stations are 100 km apart.

(c) Find an equation of the hyperbola determined by a position 120 km from *B* and 100 km from *A* if the stations are 80 km apart.

8. Earth's orbit around the sun is an ellipse with the sun at one focus. The major axis is 300 million kilometres and the focus is 2.4 million kilometres from the centre of the ellipse.

(a) Find an equation that describes Earth's orbit.

(b) Find the eccentricity of the orbit.

9. An arch in a domed stadium is in the form of a semi-ellipse with a 200 m span and 40 m height.

(a) Find the eccentricity of the ellipse.

(b) Find an equation of the ellipse.

10. The point in an Earth orbit nearest the surface of the Earth is called *perigee* and the point farthest from the surface is called *apogee.*

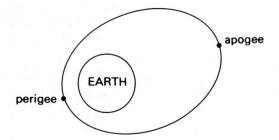

A spacecraft is in a circular orbit 800 km above the Earth. In order to transfer the craft to a lower circular orbit 150 km above the Earth, the spacecraft must be placed in an elliptical orbit as shown with the center of the Earth at one focus.

Find an equation and the eccentricity of the transfer orbit if the radius of the Earth is 6336 km.

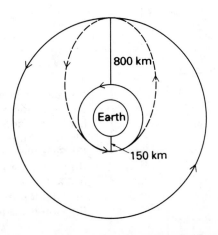

11. The point in a lunar orbit nearest the surface of the moon is called *perilune* and the point farthest from the surface is called *apolune*.

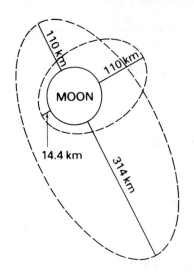

MOON

110 km

110 km

14.4 km

314 km

(a) The Apollo 11 spacecraft was placed in an elliptical lunar orbit with perilune altitude 110 km and apolune altitude 314 km (above the moon). Find an equation of this ellipse if the radius of the moon is 1728 km, and the centre of the moon is at one focus.

(b) The Lunar Module of the Apollo 11 spacecraft was placed in a lunar orbit with perilune altitude 14.4 km and apolune altitude 110 km prior to landing. Find an equation of this ellipse and the eccentricity of the orbit if the centre of the moon is at one focus.

12. The Sputnik I Earth satellite was placed into an elliptical orbit with eccentricity 0.06, reaching a maximum height of approximately 1500 km.
(a) Find the minimum height.
(b) Find an equation of the orbit if the diameter of the Earth is 12 672 km.

13. Find an equation and eccentricity of the elliptical orbit of the Vanguard I mission if the maximum height reached is 6350 km, and the minimum height is 1040 km. The radius of the earth is 6336 km.

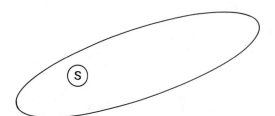

S

14. Comets are generally classified according to the type of orbit in which they move. Comets whose periods can be calculated move in elliptical orbits which are closed curves. Some comets are affected by the gravitational pull of large planets to the extent that they move off into space in hyperbolic orbits.

Astronomical unit

1 AU = 149.6
      million kilometres
   = earth's
      semi-major axis.

(a) Halley's comet (1910) appears every 76 years to move around the sun, one focus of its elliptical orbit. The major axis is 5370 million kilometres and the eccentricity of the ellipse is 0.97
 (i) Find the minor axis.
 (ii) Find the equation of the ellipse.
(b) Faye's comet (1947) appears about every 7.5 years. The major axis is 1140 million kilometres and the eccentricity of the ellipse is 0.56
 (i) Find the minor axis.
 (ii) Find the equation of the ellipse.

11.7 LINEAR-QUADRATIC SYSTEMS

In this section we shall consider the intersection of two loci, where one locus is represented by a linear equation and the other by a quadratic. The point(s) of intersection of the loci satisfy both equations in the system.

Substitution is one method of solving a system of linear equations in two variables. This method is illustrated in the following example.

EXAMPLE 1. *Find the point of intersection of the lines*

$$2x + y = 7$$
$$3x - 4y = 5$$

Solution

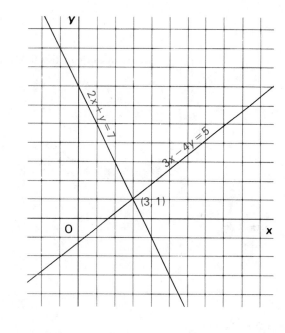

$$2x + y = 7 \quad \text{①}$$
$$3x - 4y = 5 \quad \text{②}$$

Solve for y in ①

$$y = 7 - 2x$$

Substitute in ②

$$3x - 4(7 - 2x) = 5$$
$$3x - 28 + 8x = 5$$
$$11x = 33$$
$$x = 3$$

Substitute $\qquad y = 7 - 2x$

$$= 7 - 2(3)$$
$$= 1$$

∴ $x = 3$ and $y = 1$

You may use the substitution method to solve a system consisting of a linear and a quadratic equation. You do this by solving the linear equation for one of the variables and then substituting into the quadratic equation.

EXAMPLE 2. *Find the points of intersection of the line*

$$x - y = 7 \quad \text{①}$$

and the circle

$$x^2 + y^2 = 25 \quad \text{②}$$

and illustrate with a graph.

Solution

To do this we must solve the linear quadratic system.

$$x + y = 7 \quad ①$$
$$x^2 + y^2 = 25 \quad ②$$

From the linear equation ①

$$y = 7 - x$$

Substituting in the quadratic equation ②

$$x^2 + (7 - x)^2 = 25$$
$$x^2 + 49 - 14x + x^2 = 25$$
$$x^2 - 7x + 12 = 0$$
$$(x - 3)(x - 4) = 0$$

$$x - 3 = 0 \quad \text{or} \quad x - 4 = 0$$
$$x = 3 \qquad\qquad x = 4$$

Substituting in the linear equation

If $x = 3$	If $x = 4$
$y = 7 - 3$	$y = 7 - 4$
$= 4$	$= 3$
$\therefore \ (x, y) = (3, 4)$	$\therefore \ (x, y) = (4, 3)$

$\therefore$ there are two solutions (3, 4) and (4, 3).

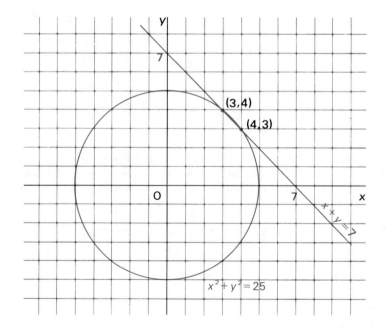

Steps in Solving a Linear-Quadratic System

1. Solve the linear equation for one of the variables.
2. Substitute in the quadratic equation.
3. Solve the quadratic equation.
4. Substitute all values obtained in 3 into the linear equation to find all solutions.

EXERCISE 11-7

B Solve and illustrate with a diagram.

1. $y = x^2 + x$, $y = x + 1$

2. $y = x^2 - 3$, $y = x - 1$

3. $y = x^2 + 4x - 5$, $y = x - 7$

4. $y = x^2 + 3x - 5$, $y = 4x + 1$

5. $y = x^2 - x - 2$, $y = x - 3$

6. $x^2 + y^2 = 25$, $x + y = 5$

7. $x^2 + y^2 = 25$, $y = 3x - 5$

8. $2x + 3y = 6$, $4x^2 + 9y^2 = 36$

9. $y = x^2$, $y = 2x + 3$

10. $x^2 + y^2 = 25$, $3x - 4y = 25$

11. $y^2 = 4x$, $x - 2y = -3$

12. $y^2 + 2x = 16$, $x + y = 9$

13. $x^2 - y^2 = 8$, $y = x + 2$

14. Find the value(s) of k making $y = 4x + k$ tangent to the circle $x^2 + y^2 = 25$

15. Find the value of k making $x + y = k$ a tangent to the parabola $y^2 = 4x$

11.8   QUADRATIC-QUADRATIC SYSTEMS

In this section, we shall find the points of intersection of two conics.

EXAMPLE 1. *Find the points of intersection of the circle*

$$x^2 + y^2 = 25 \quad ①$$

and the parabola

$$x^2 + 4y = 25 \quad ②$$

Solution
  From equation ②

$$x^2 = -4y + 25$$

Substituting $x^2 = -4y + 25$ into equation ①

$$(-4y + 25) + y^2 = 25$$
$$y^2 - 4y = 0$$
$$y(y - 4) = 0$$
$$y = 0 \quad \text{or} \quad y - 4 = 0$$
$$y = 4$$

Determine the pattern.
Find the missing number.

12	8	13	7
13	41	22	51
6	11	7	10
59	47	69	

Substituting $y = 0$ and $y = 4$ in turn into equation ②

$$y = 0 \qquad\qquad y = 4$$
$$x^2 + 4(0) = 25 \qquad x^2 + 4(4) = 26$$
$$x^2 = 25 \qquad\qquad x^2 = 9$$
$$x = \pm 5 \qquad\qquad x = \pm 3$$

∴ the solution set is

$$\{(-5, 0), (5, 0), (-3, 4), (3, 4)\}$$

The results of Example 1 are illustrated in the following diagram.

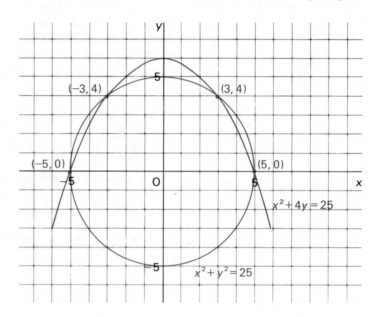

EXERCISE 11-8

Solve the following systems and illustrate with a diagram.

B **1.** $x^2 + y^2 = 25$, $4x + y^2 = 25$ **2.** $x^2 + y^2 = 1$, $y = x^2 - 1$

3. $x^2 + y^2 = 25$, $xy = 12$ **4.** $4x^2 + y^2 = 17$, $xy = 2$

5. $x^2 + y^2 = 10$, $9x^2 + y^2 = 18$ **6.** $x^2 + y^2 = 6$, $y = x^2$

7. $y = x^2$, $y = -x^2 + 2$ **8.** $y = 5 - x^2$, $x^2 + y^2 = 25$

9. $x^2 + y^2 = 9$, $\dfrac{x^2}{9} + \dfrac{y^2}{6} = 1$ **10.** $ax^2 + by^2 = 1$, $bx^2 - ay^2 = 1$

11.9 THREE-DIMENSIONAL ANALYTIC GEOMETRY

To locate a point in space, three coordinates are necessary.

If we take three mutually perpendicular planes which intersect in pairs in the lines OX, OY, OZ, then these lines will also be mutually perpendicular. The three planes are called the coordinate planes (xy-plane, yz-plane, and xz-plane), the three lines are called the coordinate axes (x-axis, y-axis, and z-axis), and the point 0 is the origin.

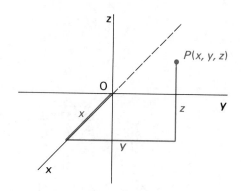

Points in space are located by ordered triples of the form (x, y, z), where

  x is the perpendicular distance from the yz-plane.
  y is the perpendicular distance from the xz-plane, and
  z is the perpendicular distance from the xy-plane.

Since the construction of three-dimensional graphs is often inconvenient, and time-consuming, we must be able to represent these graphs in a plane. One convenient way to represent, in a plane, a point in three dimensional space is to draw the z- and y-axes at right angles coinciding with the rulings on a sheet of rectangular graph paper and to draw the x-axis through the origin along the diagonal of the squares.

The unit on the y- and z-axes is taken as the side of one of the squares, and the unit on the x-axis is one-half of the diagonal of one of these squares.

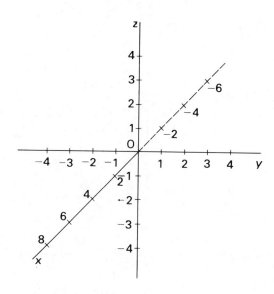

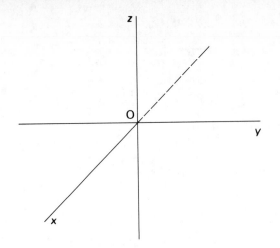

To sketch without graph paper, we can represent three mutually perpendicular axes on a two-dimensional page by drawing the z-and y-axes perpendicular to each other. Then the x-axis will be perpendicular to the page. To make the x-axis appear perpendicular to the page, we draw it bisecting the angle formed by the other axes and reduce the scale on the x-axis by a factor of $\frac{1}{\sqrt{2}} \doteq 0.7$ and give the impression of three-space.

EXAMPLE 1. *Locate the points* $P(2, 3, 5)$, $Q(-4, 3, -4)$ *on a set of three-dimensional axes.*

Solution

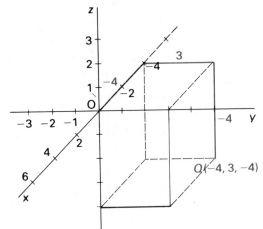

$P \begin{cases} 1. \text{ Move } +2 \text{ along the } x\text{-axis.} \\ 2. \text{ Move } +3 \text{ parallel to the } yz\text{-plane.} \\ 3. \text{ Move } +5 \text{ parallel to the } xz\text{-plane.} \end{cases}$

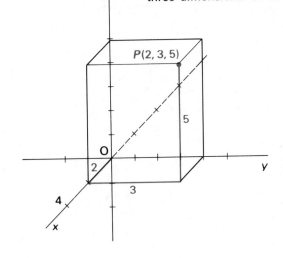

$Q \begin{cases} 1. \text{ Move } -4 \text{ along the } x\text{-axis.} \\ 2. \text{ Move } +3 \text{ parallel to the } yz\text{-plane.} \\ 3. \text{ Move } -4 \text{ parallel to the } xz\text{-plane.} \end{cases}$

Notice that the points *P* and *Q* determine rectangular boxes when the planes through the point are combined with the coordinate planes.

We can use the theorem of Pythagoras to find the length of the diagonal of a rectangular solid. Given a rectangular solid $ABCDEFGH$ with $AB = 3$, $BC = 4$ and $AE = 6$, we wish to find the length of the diagonal EC. Using the theorem of Pythagoras,

$$AC^2 = AB^2 + BC^2$$
$$= 3^2 + 4^2 = 25$$
$$EC^2 = AC^2 + AE^2$$
$$= 25 + 36$$
$$= 61$$
$$\therefore \quad EC = \sqrt{61}$$

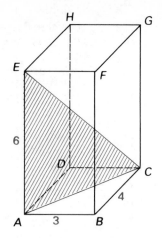

The method of finding the length of the diagonal is used to develop the distance formula for three-dimensions.

If we draw through the point $P_1(x_1, y_1, z_1)$ and $P_2(x_2, y_2, z_2)$ lines, parallel to the axes, forming a rectangular box, then P_1P_2 is one diagonal of the box. The lengths of the edges of this box are $a = |x_2 - x_1|$, $b = |y_2 - y_1|$, $c = |z_2 - z_1|$ as shown in Figure 11-1. Using the theorem of Pythagoras,

$$P_1P = a^2 + b^2$$
$$P_1P_2{}^2 = P_1P^2 + PP_2{}^2$$
$$= (a^2 + b^2) + c^2$$
$$= a^2 + b^2 + c^2$$
$$P_1P_2 = \sqrt{a^2 + b^2 + c^2}$$

Substituting $a = |x_2 - x_1|$, $b = |y_2 - y_1|$, $c = |z_2 - z_1|$

$$P_1P_2 = \sqrt{(x_2 - x_1)^2 + (y_2 - y_1)^2 + (z_2 - z_1)^2}$$

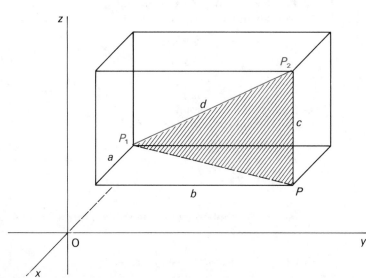

Figure 11-1

For the line segment in space with end-points $P_1(x_1, y_1, z_1)$ and $P_2(x_2, y_2, z_2)$, the length of the segment P_1P_2 is

$$d = \sqrt{(x_2 - x_1)^2 + (y_2 - y_1)^2 + (z_2 - z_1)^2}$$

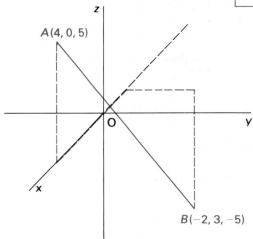

EXAMPLE 2. *Find the distance from* $A(4, 0, 5)$ *to* $B(-2, 3, -5)$.

Solution
Using the distance formula

$$d = \sqrt{(x_2 - x_1)^2 + (y_2 - y_1)^2 + (z_2 - z_1)^2}$$
$$AB = \sqrt{(-2 - 4)^2 + (3 - 0)^2 + (-5 - 5)^2}$$
$$= \sqrt{(-6)^2 + (3)^2 + (-10)^2}$$
$$= \sqrt{36 + 9 + 100}$$
$$= \sqrt{145}$$

SPHERE
A sphere is the locus of points in space which are a constant distance, the radius, from a fixed point called the centre.

We can use the distance formula to find the general form of the equation of the sphere having

Centre $O(0, 0, 0)$, *radius* r
Let $P(x, y, z)$ be any point on the sphere.
P is on the sphere if and only if $OP = r$.

$$\sqrt{(x - 0)^2 + (y - 0)^2 + (z - 0)^2} = r$$
$$x^2 + y^2 + z^2 = r^2$$

Centre $C(h, k, l)$, *radius* r
Let $P(x, y, z)$ be any point on the sphere.
P is on the sphere if and only if $CP = r$.

$$\sqrt{(x - h)^2 + (y - k)^2 + (z - l)^2} = r$$
$$(x - h)^2 + (y - k)^2 + (z - l)^2 = r^2$$

An equation of the sphere with radius r, and centre

$O(0, 0, 0)$ is $x^2 + y^2 + z^2 = r^2$

$C(h, k, l)$ is $(x - h)^2 + (y - k)^2 + (z - l)^2 = r^2$

EXAMPLE 3. *Find the equation of the sphere with*
(a) *Centre* $(0, 0, 0)$, *radius* 5
(b) *Centre* $(2, -3, 4)$, *radius* 4

Solution
(a) Using the formula $x^2 + y^2 + z^2 = r^2$,

$$x^2 + y^2 + z^2 = 5^2$$

$\therefore x^2 + y^2 + z^2 = 25$ is the required equation.
(b) Using the formula $(x - h)^2 + (y - k)^2 + (z - l)^2 = r^2$

$$(x - 2)^2 + (y - (-3))^2 + (z - 4)^2 = {}^2$$

$\therefore (x - 2)^2 + (y + 3)^2 + (z - 4)^2 = 16$ is the required equation.

EXERCISE 11-9

1. Indicate the following points in space on a set of three dimensional axes.
(a) $(4, 2, 3)$ (b) $(2, 3, 4)$ (c) $(4, 2, 5)$ (d) $(-2, 1, 4)$
(e) $(5, -2, -3)$ (f) $(2, 6, 8)$ (g) $(-4, -3, -2)$ (h) $(4, 7, 2)$
(i) $(1, 1, 1)$ (j) $(1, 0, 0)$ (k) $(0, 1, 0)$ (l) $(0, 0, 1)$

2. How far is each of the following points from the origin?
(a) $(2, 3, 5)$ (b) $(-2, 4, 7)$ (c) $(-3, -5, 0)$ (d) $(-8, 1, -4)$

3. Find the distance between the following pairs of points.
(a) $A(3, 5, 7)$ to $B(4, 8, 10)$
(b) $C(0, 0, 5)$ to $D(0, 12, 0)$
(c) $E(-3, -5, 4)$ to. $F(5, -7, 8)$
(d) $G(0, 9, 12)$ to $H(8, 9, 12)$
(e) $I(5, 5, 5)$ to $J(6, 7, 8)$
(f) $K(3, -5, -4)$ to $L(4, -5, 4)$
(g) $M(5, 0, -3)$ to $N(6, -5, 4)$

Write 14 using five 4's.

4. Prove that the triangle whose vertices are $A(2, -1, 2)$, $B(1, 2, 0)$, and $C(4, 0, -1)$ is isosceles.

5. Use the distance formula to prove that the points $A(-1, 3, 0)$, $B(3, -5, 4)$ and $C(-2, 5, -1)$ are collinear.

6. Find the equation of the sphere whose centre and radius are
(a) $(0, 0, 0)$, 5   (b) $(0, 3, 0)$, 3
(c) $(5, 1, 1)$, 6   (d) $(-2, -3, -4)$, 5
(e) $(3, 3, 3)$, 3   (f) $(5, -4, 2)$, 1
(g) $(-2, 0, 5)$, 7   (h) $(3, -2, 4)$, 4

7. Find the centre and radius of the following spheres.
(a) $x^2 + y^2 + z^2 = 49$ (b) $x^2 + y^2 + z^2 = 100$
(c) $(x - 2)^2 + (y - 3)^2 + z^2 = 16$ (d) $(x + 3)^2 + (y - 5)^2 + (z + 1)^2 = 36$

8. Find the centre and radius of the following spheres.
(a) $x^2 + y^2 + z^2 - 8x + 10y + 4z + 29 = 0$
(b) $x^2 + y^2 + z^2 + 12x + 4y + 6z = 0$

REVIEW EXERCISE

B **1.** State the location of the centre and the radius then sketch the graph of the following circles.
(a) $x^2 + y^2 = 36$ (b) $(x-2)^2 + (y+3)^2 = 25$
(c) $x^2 + y^2 + 8x - 6y - 11 = 0$

2. State the equation of the following circles.
(a) centre $(0, 0)$, radius 8 (b) centre $(0, 0)$, radius $\sqrt{5}$
(c) centre $(-3, 5)$, radius 7 (d) centre $(4, -2)$, radius $\sqrt{10}$
(e) centre $(0, 0)$, passing through $(2, 7)$
(f) centre $(3, 3)$, passing through $(0, 0)$

3. (a) Find the length of the chord AB if $A(-2, 4)$ and $B(4, 2)$ lie on the circle $x^2 + y^2 = 20$.
(b) Find the equation of the right bisector of AB.
(c) Show that the right bisector of AB contains the centre.

4. Given the circle $x^2 + y^2 = 25$, find the equation of the tangent at
(a) $(3, 4)$ (b) $(-3, 4)$ (c) $(4, -3)$ (d) $(-4, -3)$

5. Find the length of the tangent to the circle $x^2 + y^2 = 36$ from the points
(a) $(8, 10)$ (b) $(16, 20)$ (c) $(5, -9)$ (d) $(-7, -11)$

6. Find an equation of the parabola with
(a) focus $(0, 4)$, directrix $y = -4$
(b) focus $(-3, 0)$, directrix $y = 3$
(c) focus $(5, 2)$, directrix $x = -2$
(d) focus $(-4, -3)$, directrix $y = 5$

7. Locate the foci, state the eccentricity and sketch the graph of the following.
(a) $\dfrac{x^2}{25} + \dfrac{y^2}{9} = 1$ (b) $\dfrac{x^2}{20} + \dfrac{y^2}{4} = 1$ (c) $\dfrac{x^2}{64} + \dfrac{y^2}{49} = 1$
(d) $9x^2 + 16y^2 = 144$ (e) $\dfrac{(x-3)^2}{36} + \dfrac{(y+2)^2}{25} = 1$

8. Find an equation of the following ellipses.
(a) major axis 12, minor axis 10
(b) major axis 10, one vertex $(4, 0)$
(c) foci $(-3, 0)$ and $(3, 0)$, sum of focal radii 10
(d) vertex $(-8, 0)$, eccentricity 0.75

9. Sketch the hyperbolas defined by the following equations showing
(i) vertices, (ii) major axes, (iii) foci (iv) asymptotes

(a) $\dfrac{x^2}{16} - \dfrac{y^2}{9} = 1$ (b) $\dfrac{x^2}{16} - \dfrac{y^2}{12} = 1$ (c) $\dfrac{x^2}{25} - \dfrac{y^2}{16} = 1$
(d) $5x^2 - 4y^2 = 20$ (e) $\dfrac{(x+4)^2}{9} - \dfrac{(y-2)^2}{16} = 1$

10. Find an equation of the following hyperbolas.
(a) centre $(0, 0)$, major axis 8, eccentricity 1.5
(b) centre $(0, 0)$, one focus $(5, 0)$, one vertex $(4, 0)$
(c) centre $(0, 0)$, one focus $(-4, 0)$, eccentricity 2
(d) foci $(-4, 0)$ and $(4, 0)$, difference of focal radii 2

11. A toy rocket is launched and follows a parabolic path. Find an equation of the trajectory if the rocket reached a height of 80 m and returned to earth 240 m down range.

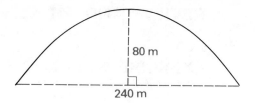

80 m

240 m

12. The Sputnik II satellite was placed in an elliptical orbit with maximum height 939 km and minimum height 215 km. If the diameter of the earth is 12 672 km, find
(a) the major and minor axes.
(b) the eccentricity.
(c) an equation of the ellipse.

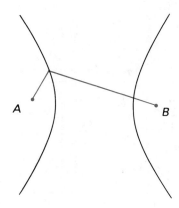

13. Find an equation of an hyperbola determined by the flight path of an aircraft 40 km closer to one of two LORAN stations that are 120 km apart.

A B

14. Solve the following systems.

(a) $x^2 + y^2 = 25$
$3x + 4y = 25$

(b) $2x^2 + 4y^2 = 8$
$x - y + 4 = 0$

(c) $y = x^2$

$x^2 + y^2 = 20$

(d) $\dfrac{x^2}{25} + \dfrac{y^2}{9} = 1$

$25x^2 + 9y^2 = 225$

(e) $\dfrac{x^2}{20} - \dfrac{y^2}{16} = 1$

$x^2 + y^2 = 25$

(f) $\dfrac{x^2}{9} + \dfrac{y^2}{4} = 1$

$\dfrac{x^2}{9} - \dfrac{y^2}{4} = 1$

15. Sketch the graphs of the following.
(a) $x^2 + y^2 > 25$ (b) $x^2 + y^2 \leqslant 9$ (c) $x^2 + y^2 - 4 < 0$
(d) $x^2 + y^2 + 4x - 10y < 0$ (e) $x^2 + y^2 + 2y \geqslant 0$

16. (a) Find the length of the tangent to $x^2 + y^2 = r^2$ from the point (m, n).
(b) Find the equation of the tangent to $x^2 + y^2 = r^2$ at the point (p, q).

17. Write the equation $4x^2 + 9y^2 - 40x + 54y + 145 = 0$ in the form $\dfrac{(x-h)^2}{a^2} + \dfrac{(y-k)^2}{b^2} = 1$

and sketch the graph indicating vertices, centre, major axis and minor axis.

18. Write the equation $9x^2 - 4y^2 - 36x + 24y - 36 = 0$ in the form $\dfrac{(x-h)^2}{a^2} - \dfrac{(y-k)^2}{b^2} = 1$

and sketch the graph indicating vertices, major axis and asymptotes.

REVIEW AND PREVIEW TO CHAPTER 12

EXERCISE 1 PLANE FIGURES

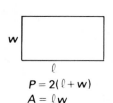

$P = 2(\ell + w)$
$A = \ell w$

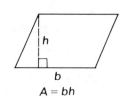

$A = bh$

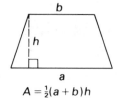

$A = \frac{1}{2}(a + b)h$

$A = \frac{1}{2}bh$

$C = 2\pi r$
$A = \pi r^2$

1. Find the perimeter and area of the following.

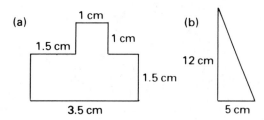

(a) 1 cm, 1.5 cm, 1 cm, 1.5 cm, 3.5 cm

(b) 12 cm, 5 cm

(c) 3 cm, 4 cm, 6 cm

(d) 12 cm

2. Find the area of each shaded region.

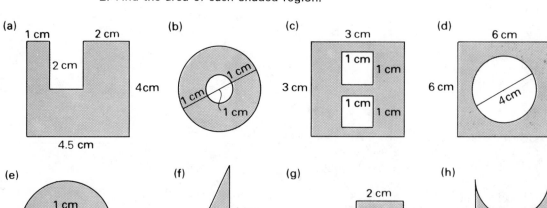

(a) 1 cm, 2 cm, 2 cm, 4cm, 4.5 cm

(b)

(c) 3 cm, 1 cm, 1 cm, 3 cm, 1 cm, 1 cm

(d) 6 cm, 6 cm, 4cm

(e) 1 cm, 1 cm, 1 cm, 1 cm

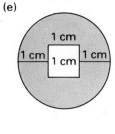

(f) 4 cm, 3 cm, 1.5 cm 2 cm

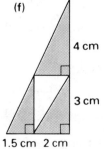

(g) 2 cm, 2 cm, 2 cm, 4 cm

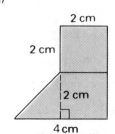

(h) 6 cm, 4 cm

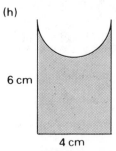

3. Find the area of the shaded region and the perimeter of all edges.

(a)

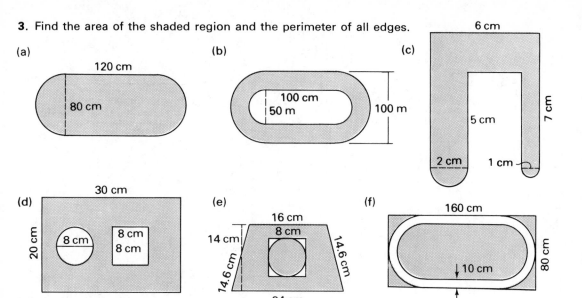

120 cm

80 cm

(b)

100 cm
50 m

100 m

(c)

6 cm

7 cm

5 cm

2 cm   1 cm

(d)

30 cm

20 cm

8 cm

8 cm
8 cm

(e)

16 cm
8 cm

14 cm

14.6 cm   14.6 cm

24 cm

(f)

160 cm

10 cm

80 cm

EXERCISE 2   SOLIDS

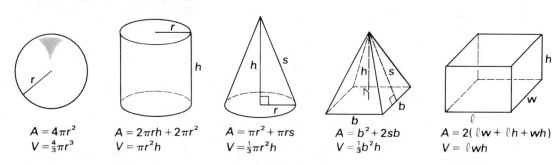

$A = 4\pi r^2$
$V = \frac{4}{3}\pi r^3$

$A = 2\pi rh + 2\pi r^2$
$V = \pi r^2 h$

$A = \pi r^2 + \pi rs$
$V = \frac{1}{3}\pi r^2 h$

$A = b^2 + 2sb$
$V = \frac{1}{3}b^2 h$

$A = 2(\ell w + \ell h + wh)$
$V = \ell wh$

1. Find the total surface area and volume of each of the following.

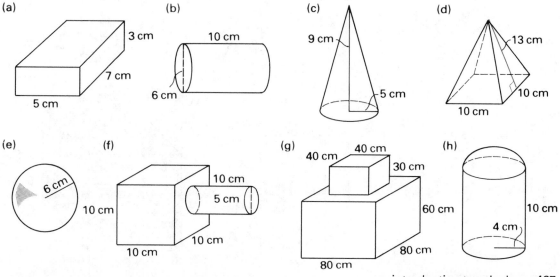

(a)

3 cm

7 cm

5 cm

(b)

10 cm

6 cm

(c)

9 cm

5 cm

(d)

13 cm

10 cm

10 cm

(e)

6 cm

(f)

10 cm

5 cm

10 cm

10 cm

10 cm

(g)

40 cm   40 cm

30 cm

60 cm

80 cm

80 cm

(h)

60 cm   10 cm

4 cm

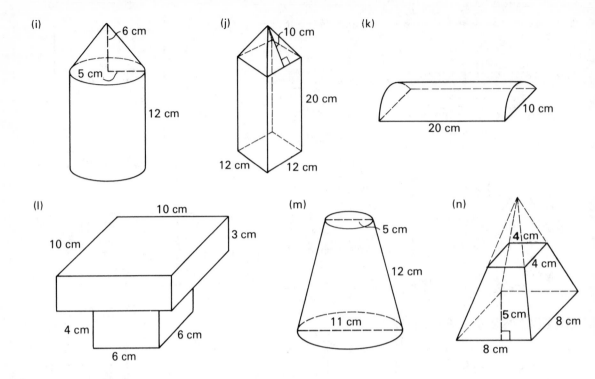

(i) 6 cm, 5 cm, 12 cm

(j) 10 cm, 20 cm, 12 cm, 12 cm

(k) 10 cm, 20 cm

(l) 10 cm, 10 cm, 3 cm, 4 cm, 6 cm, 6 cm

(m) 5 cm, 12 cm, 11 cm

(n) 4 cm, 4 cm, 5 cm, 8 cm, 8 cm

2. Find the volume of each of the following.

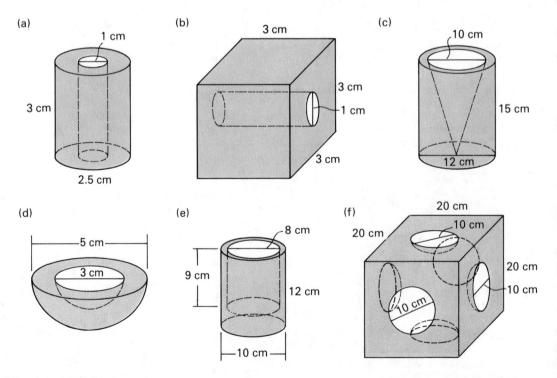

(a) 1 cm, 3 cm, 2.5 cm

(b) 3 cm, 3 cm, 1 cm, 3 cm

(c) 10 cm, 15 cm, 12 cm

(d) 5 cm, 3 cm

(e) 8 cm, 9 cm, 12 cm, 10 cm

(f) 20 cm, 10 cm, 20 cm, 20 cm, 10 cm, 10 cm

Introduction to Calculus

CHAPTER 12

Calculus is the most powerful weapon of thought yet devised by the wit of man.

W. B. Smith

SIR ISAAC NEWTON (1642–1727)

Isaac Newton was born in the small village of Woolsthorpe, England, on Christmas day in 1642, the year of Galileo's death. Newton was not a child prodigy. The signs of genius did not emerge in high school, but while he was a student at Trinity College, Cambridge, he read the works of Euclid and Descartes and these inspired him. In 1665 Cambridge was closed because of the plague and while at home on this enforced vacation Newton made four of his greatest discoveries: (1) the law of gravitation, (2) the nature of colours (white light is composed of the various colours of the spectrum), (3) the method of calculus, and (4) the binomial theorem (not just the expansion of $(a + b)^n$ when n is a positive integer, given in Section 10–4, but the expansion as an infinite series when n is *any* real number.)

It is often said that calculus was invented independently by Newton and the German mathematician Gottfried Wilhelm Leibniz. However integral calculus (the problem of areas) goes back to the ancient Greeks in about 500 B.C. and differential calculus (the problem of tangents) was started by Fermat in the 1630's. Newton's teacher at Cambridge, Isaac Barrow, saw the connection between the two branches of calculus. What Newton and Leibniz did was to exploit this connection and organize calculus into a systematic and powerful method.

Unfortunately a dispute arose between the followers of Newton and the followers of Leibniz as to who had discovered the method of calculus first. Later, Newton and Leibniz themselves were drawn into the priority controversy. It seems clear now that Newton had invented the method first, but Leibniz was the first to publish the method. In spite of the controversy, Leibniz fully recognized Newton's genius. Leibniz said "Taking mathematics from the beginning of the world to the time of Newton, what he has done is much the better half."

12.1 WHAT IS CALCULUS?

The beginnings of calculus go back 2500 years to the ancient Greeks who found areas using the "method of exhaustion." Figure 12-1 illustrates how this method works for the special case of a circle.

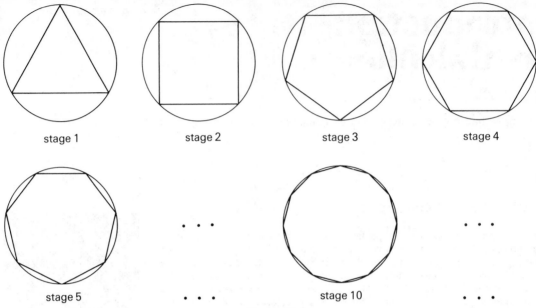

Figure 12-1

As the number of sides of the inscribed polygon increases, its area gets closer and closer to the area of the circle. We say that the area of the circle is the limit of the areas of the inscribed polygons. We can also think of the circle as being the "limiting" figure of the polygons as the number of sides increases indefinitely.

The notion of a limit is the central idea in calculus. Let us look at some other ways in which limits arise.

In Figure 12-2 a sheet of paper is cut in half. One half is thrown away and the other is itself cut in half. The process is repeated indefinitely.

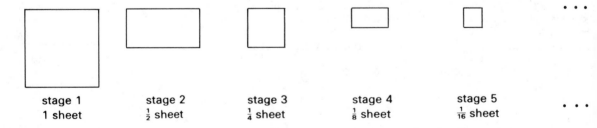

stage 1	stage 2	stage 3	stage 4	stage 5
1 sheet	$\frac{1}{2}$ sheet	$\frac{1}{4}$ sheet	$\frac{1}{8}$ sheet	$\frac{1}{16}$ sheet

Figure 12-2

No matter how many times we repeat this process there will always be some paper left. But you can see that the area of the paper gets closer and closer to 0.

Suppose that we start with a large sheet of paper with area $1\,\text{m}^2$. If t_n is the area of the paper at stage n, in square metres, then

$$t_n = \frac{1}{2^n}$$

This is an infinite geometric sequence. We express the evident geometric fact that the area of the paper approaches 0 by saying that the limit of the sequence $t_n = \frac{1}{2^n}$ is 0 and by writing

$$\lim_{n \to \infty} \frac{1}{2^n} = 0$$

We read the symbol "$\lim_{n \to \infty}$" as "the limit as n approaches infinity of."

Limits also arise when we find tangents to curves. Figure 12-3 shows a curve C, a point P on C, and a tangent t which touches C at P.

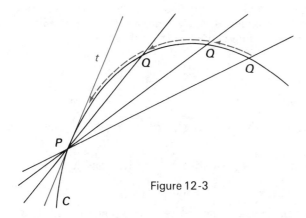

Figure 12-3

The tangent is the limiting position of the secant line PQ as Q approaches P along the curve C. This means that as Q moves closer and closer to P along C, the secant line PQ moves closer and closer to the tangent line t.

In all three examples an infinite process is involved and the desired quantity is a limit.

Calculus is that part of mathematics which involves limits.

In the remaining sections of this chapter we shall use calculus to solve the following types of problems.

1. The tangent problem. Given a curve C and a point P on C, we shall use the branch of calculus called differential calculus to find the equation of the tangent to C at P. This is closely related to the problem of finding velocities.

2. Maximum and minimum problems. We shall see that the methods of differential calculus are the most efficient for finding the maximum and minimum values of various quantities.

3. **The area problem.** The branch of calculus called integral calculus is concerned with the problem of finding the area of a region in a plane. It can also be used to find volumes of solids and lengths of curves.

4. **The sum of an infinite series.** Is it meaningful to talk about the sum of infinitely many numbers? For example do the infinite series

$$1 + \tfrac{1}{2} + \tfrac{1}{3} + \tfrac{1}{4} + \tfrac{1}{5} + \ldots$$

or

$$1 + \tfrac{1}{2} + \tfrac{1}{4} + \tfrac{1}{8} + \tfrac{1}{16} + \ldots$$

exist? Using limits we can make these questions precise and answer them.

12.2 THE LIMIT OF A SEQUENCE

An infinite sequence is a function whose domain is N. If f is an infinite sequence and $n \in N$, we usually write t_n instead of $f(n)$ for the nth term of the sequence and we denote the sequence by $\{t_n\}$. For instance for the infinite sequence $\{t_n\}$ defined by

$$t_n = \frac{n}{n+1}$$

we have

$$t_1 = \tfrac{1}{2}, \quad t_2 = \tfrac{2}{3}, \quad t_3 = \tfrac{3}{4}, \quad t_4 = \tfrac{4}{5},$$

and so on.

This sequence can be described simply by listing its terms:

$$\tfrac{1}{2}, \tfrac{2}{3}, \tfrac{3}{4}, \tfrac{4}{5}, \tfrac{5}{6}, \ldots$$

where the dots indicate that the sequence never ends. Thus a sequence can be regarded as a list of numbers given in a definite order.

Part of the graph of this sequence is shown in Figure 12-4.

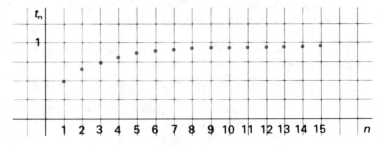

Figure 12-4

Notice that the terms in the sequence are all less than 1 (because $n < n+1$) but they get closer and closer to 1 as n increases. In fact we can make the terms t_n as close as we like to 1 by making n large enough.

We say that the limit of this sequence $t_n = \dfrac{n}{n+1}$ is 1 and we indicate this by writing

$$\lim_{n \to \infty} \frac{n}{n+1} = 1$$

> We say that the sequence $\{t_n\}$ has the limit L and we write
>
> $$\lim_{n \to \infty} t_n = L$$
>
> or
>
> $$t_n \to L \quad \text{as} \quad n \to \infty$$
>
> if the terms t_n are as close as we like to the number L for sufficiently large n.

GOOGOL

Dr. Edward Kasner (Columbia) called the number 10^{100} a googol. Which is larger

$$10^{\text{googol}} \text{ or googol}^{10}?$$

EXAMPLE 1. *Find* $\lim\limits_{n \to \infty} \dfrac{1}{n}$

Solution

The sequence defined by $t_n = \dfrac{1}{n}$ is

$$1, \tfrac{1}{2}, \tfrac{1}{3}, \tfrac{1}{4}, \tfrac{1}{5}, \tfrac{1}{6}, \ldots$$

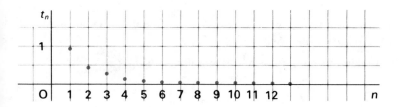

You can see from the graph that as n becomes large, $\dfrac{1}{n}$ becomes small.

We can make $\dfrac{1}{n}$ as close as we like to 0 by making n sufficiently large. For instance we have

$$\frac{1}{n} < 0.001 \quad \text{if} \quad n > \frac{1}{0.001} = 1000$$

As

$$n \to \infty, \frac{1}{n} \to 0,$$

i.e.,

$$\lim_{n \to \infty} \frac{1}{n} = 0$$

EXAMPLE 2. *Find the following limits if they exist.*

$$\text{(a) } \lim_{n \to \infty} n^2 \qquad \text{(b) } \lim_{n \to \infty} (-1)^n \qquad \text{(c) } \lim_{n \to \infty} \frac{2n-1}{5n+4}$$

Solution

(a) The terms of the sequence $t_n = n^2$ are

$$1, 4, 9, 16, 25, 36, \dots$$

The terms become large and do not approach any limit.
$\therefore \lim_{n \to \infty} n^2$ does not exist.

(b) The terms of the sequence $t_n = (-1)^n$ are

$$-1, 1, -1, 1, -1, 1, \dots$$

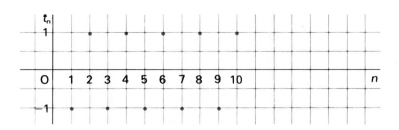

As n increases the terms t_n do not approach any particular number.
$\therefore \lim_{n \to \infty} (-1)^n$ does not exist.

(c) Divide the numerator and denominator of $t_n = \dfrac{2n-1}{5n+4}$ by n.

$$\frac{2n-1}{5n+4} = \frac{2 - \dfrac{1}{n}}{5 + \dfrac{4}{n}}$$

From Example 1 we know that $\lim_{n \to \infty} \dfrac{1}{n} = 0$

$$\therefore \quad \lim_{n \to \infty} \frac{4}{n} = 0$$

$$\therefore \quad \lim_{n \to \infty} \frac{2n-1}{5n+4} = \lim_{n \to \infty} \frac{2 - \dfrac{1}{n}}{5 + \dfrac{4}{n}}$$

$$= \frac{2-0}{5+0}$$

$$= \tfrac{2}{5}$$

In Example 2(c) we used some of the following rules for finding limits.

$$\lim_{n \to \infty} (a_n + b_n) = \lim_{n \to \infty} a_n + \lim_{n \to \infty} b_n$$

$$\lim_{n \to \infty} (a_n b_n) = \left(\lim_{n \to \infty} a_n\right)\left(\lim_{n \to \infty} b_n\right)$$

$$\lim_{n \to \infty} \frac{a}{b_n} = \frac{\lim_{n \to \infty} a_n}{\lim_{n \to \infty} b_n}$$

These facts are proved in advanced courses where more precise definitions of limit are given.

The idea of a sequence having a limit is implicit in the decimal representation of real numbers. For instance if

$$t_1 = 3.1$$
$$t_2 = 3.14$$
$$t_3 = 3.141$$
$$t_4 = 3.141\ 5$$
$$t_5 = 3.141\ 59$$
$$t_6 = 3.141\ 592$$
$$\vdots$$

then $\lim_{n \to \infty} t_n = \pi$

The terms in this sequence are rational approximations to π.

EXERCISE 12-2

A **1.** State the limits of the following sequences if they exist.

(a) $\frac{1}{2}, \frac{1}{4}, \frac{1}{8}, \frac{1}{16}, \frac{1}{32}, \ldots, \frac{1}{2^n}, \ldots$

(b) $5, 4\frac{1}{2}, 4\frac{1}{3}, 4\frac{1}{4}, 4\frac{1}{5}, \ldots, 4 + \frac{1}{n}, \ldots$

(c) $1, 2, 3, 4, 5, \ldots, n, \ldots$

(d) $3, 3, 3, 3, 3, \ldots, 3, \ldots$

(e) $1, 0, \frac{1}{2}, 0, \frac{1}{3}, 0, \frac{1}{4}, 0, \ldots$

(f) $5, 6\frac{1}{2}, 5\frac{2}{3}, 6\frac{1}{4}, 5\frac{4}{5}, 6\frac{1}{6}, \ldots, 6 + \frac{(-1)^n}{n}, \ldots$

(g) $1, \frac{1}{2}, 1, \frac{1}{3}, 1, \frac{1}{4}, 1, \frac{1}{5}, \ldots$

2. Find the following limits if they exist.

(a) $\lim_{n \to \infty} \frac{1}{n^2}$

(b) $\lim_{n \to \infty} \frac{1}{5 + n}$

(c) $\lim_{n \to \infty} \left(6 + \frac{1}{n^2}\right)$

(d) $\lim_{n \to \infty} \frac{n}{3n - 1}$

(e) $\lim_{n \to \infty} \frac{6n + 9}{3n - 2}$

(f) $\lim_{n \to \infty} 5n$

(g) $\lim\limits_{n\to\infty} \dfrac{n^2+1}{2n^2-1}$ (h) $\lim\limits_{n\to\infty} \dfrac{(n+1)^2}{n(n+2)}$

(i) $\lim\limits_{n\to\infty} \dfrac{(-1)^{n+1}}{n}$ (j) $\lim\limits_{n\to\infty} \dfrac{1}{3^n}$

(k) $\lim\limits_{n\to\infty} \dfrac{n}{n^2+1}$ (l) $\lim\limits_{n\to\infty} (-1)^{n+1}n$

(m) $\lim\limits_{n\to\infty} 5^{-n}$ (n) $\lim\limits_{n\to\infty} (n^3+n^2)$

(o) $\lim\limits_{n\to\infty} \dfrac{1+n-2n^2}{1-n+n^2}$ (p) $\lim\limits_{n\to\infty} \dfrac{1}{\sqrt{n}}$

(q) $\lim\limits_{n\to\infty} \dfrac{1}{n^3}$ (r) $\lim\limits_{n\to\infty} \dfrac{1-n^3}{1+2n^3}$

(s) $\lim\limits_{n\to\infty} \left(\tfrac{2}{3}\right)^n$ (t) $\lim\limits_{n\to\infty} \left(\tfrac{4}{3}\right)^n$

(u) $\lim\limits_{n\to\infty} \sin \pi n$ (v) $\lim\limits_{n\to\infty} \sin \dfrac{\pi n}{2}$

3. For what values of r does $\lim\limits_{n\to\infty} r^n$ exist?

4. If $t_1 = 0.3$, $t_2 = 0.33$, $t_3 = 0.333$, $t_4 = 0.3333$ and so on, what is $\lim\limits_{n\to\infty} t_n$?

5. Find $\lim\limits_{n\to\infty} \dfrac{n^2}{2^n}$

6. Find $\lim\limits_{n\to\infty} \sqrt[n]{n}$

C **7.** Find the limit of the sequence

$$\sqrt{2}, \sqrt{\sqrt{2}}, \sqrt{2\sqrt{2\sqrt{2}}}, \sqrt{2\sqrt{2\sqrt{2\sqrt{2}}}}, \dots$$

by expressing each term as a power of 2.

12.3 THE SUM OF AN INFINITE SERIES

Does it make sense to add infinitely many numbers? For instance is it possible for us to assign a meaningful sum to an infinite series such as

(1) $$1 + \tfrac{1}{2} + \tfrac{1}{4} + \tfrac{1}{8} + \tfrac{1}{16} + \dots$$

You may think of replying that to add an infinite number of terms would take an infinite amount of time and so infinite sums are impossible. But observe that in our decimal notation the symbol $0.\dot{6} = 0.666\,666\dots$ means

$$\frac{6}{10} + \frac{6}{100} + \frac{6}{1000} + \frac{6}{10\,000} + \dots$$

and so, in some sense,

$$\frac{6}{10} + \frac{6}{100} + \frac{6}{1000} + \frac{6}{10\,000} + \dots = \frac{2}{3}$$

Thus some infinite series have a meaning, but we must define carefully what the sum of an infinite series is.

Let us begin by trying to see what the sum of the series (1) should be. If we let S_n be the sum of the first n terms of the series

$$1+\frac{1}{2}+\frac{1}{4}+\frac{1}{8}+\frac{1}{16}+\ldots+\frac{1}{2^{n-1}}+\ldots$$

then

$$S_1 = 1$$
$$S_2 = 1.5$$
$$S_3 = 1.75$$
$$S_4 = 1.875$$
$$S_5 = 1.937\,5$$
$$S_6 = 1.968\,75$$
$$S_7 = 1.984\,375$$
$$S_8 = 1.992\,187\,5$$

.
.
.

$$S_{12} = 1.999\,511\,718\,75$$

.
.
.

$$S_{17} \doteq 1.999\,984\,741\,21$$

.
.
.

Notice that as we add more and more terms, the partial sum of the series becomes closer and closer to 2. In fact by adding sufficiently many terms of the series we can make the partial sum as close as we wish to the number 2. It seems reasonable, therefore, to say that the sum of the infinite series is 2 and to write

$$1+\tfrac{1}{2}+\tfrac{1}{4}+\tfrac{1}{8}+\tfrac{1}{16}+\ldots = 2$$

The nth partial sum of this series is

$$S_n = 1+\frac{1}{2}+\frac{1}{4}+\frac{1}{8}+\ldots+\frac{1}{2^{n-1}}$$

This is a geometric series with $a = 1$ and $r = \frac{1}{2}$. Using the formula

$$S_n = \frac{a(1-r^n)}{1-r}$$

from Chapter 8, we have

$$S_n = \frac{1(1-(\frac{1}{2})^n)}{1-\frac{1}{2}} = 2\left(1-\frac{1}{2^n}\right)$$

Since $\lim\limits_{n \to \infty} \dfrac{1}{2^n} = 0$, we have

$$\lim_{n \to \infty} S_n = \lim_{n \to \infty} 2\left(1 - \frac{1}{2^n}\right)$$

$$= 2(1 - 0)$$

$$= 2$$

Thus the sum of the series is the limit of the sequence $\{S_n\}$ of partial sums.

In general if we have an infinite series

(2) $\qquad\qquad\qquad\qquad t_1 + t_2 + t_3 + \cdots t_n + \ldots$

we define the partial sums as follows

$$S_1 = t_1$$
$$S_2 = t_1 + t_2$$
$$S_3 = t_1 + t_2 + t_3$$
$$S_4 = t_1 + t_2 + t_3 + t_4$$

Write 9 using four 7's.

$$\cdot$$
$$\cdot$$
$$\cdot$$

$$S_n = t_1 + t_2 + t_3 + \ldots + t_n$$

$$\cdot$$
$$\cdot$$
$$\cdot$$

S_n is the sum of the first n terms of the series.

> If the infinite sequence $\{S_n\}$ of partial sums of the series (2) has a limit L, then we say that the sum of the series is L and we write
> $$t_1 + t_2 + t_3 + \ldots + t_n + \ldots = L$$

Using sigma notation, this becomes

$$\sum_{n=1}^{\infty} t_n = L$$

If a series has a sum, it is called a convergent series.

EXAMPLE 1. *Determine whether the following series have a sum.*
(a) $1 + 1 + 1 + 1 + \ldots + 1 + \ldots$
(b) $1 - 1 + 1 - 1 + \ldots + (-1)^{n+1} + \ldots$

Solution
$\quad$ (a) $S_n = \underbrace{1 + 1 + 1 + \ldots + 1}_{n \text{ terms}} = n$

$\therefore \lim\limits_{n \to \infty} S_n = \lim\limits_{n \to \infty} n$ does not exist
$\therefore$ the series $1 + 1 + 1 + \ldots$ does not have a sum
Series which do not have a sum are called divergent.

(b) $S_1 = 1$, $S_2 = 1 - 1 = 0$, $S_3 = 1 - 1 + 1 = 1$, $S_4 = 1 - 1 + 1 - 1 = 0, \ldots$
The sequence of partial sums is

$$1, 0, 1, 0, 1, 0, \ldots$$

which has no limit.
$\therefore$ the series $1 - 1 + 1 - 1 + \ldots$ does not have a sum, i.e., it is divergent.

EXAMPLE 2. *Find the sum of the geometric series*

$$a + ar + ar^2 + \ldots + ar^{n-1} + \ldots$$

when it exists.

Solution

The nth partial sum of the geometric series is

$$S_n = a + ar + ar^2 + \ldots + ar^{n-1}$$

$$= \frac{a(1 - r^n)}{1 - r} \quad (r \neq 1)$$

If $|r| < 1$, then $\lim\limits_{n \to \infty} r^n = 0$ and so

$$\lim\limits_{n \to \infty} S_n = \lim\limits_{n \to \infty} \frac{a(1 - r^n)}{1 - r}$$

$$= \frac{a(1 - 0)}{1 - r}$$

$$= \frac{a}{1 - r}$$

$\therefore$ if $|r| < 1$, the geometric series is convergent and its sum is $\dfrac{a}{1-r}$.

If $|r| > 1$, then $\lim\limits_{n \to \infty} r^n$ does not exist. Therefore $\lim\limits_{n \to \infty} S_n$ does not exist and the geometric series does not have a sum.
If $r = 1$, the geometric series becomes

$$a + a + a + a + \ldots$$

which does not have a sum. (See Example 1(a).)
If $r = -1$, the geometric series becomes

$$a - a + a - a + a - a + \ldots$$

which does not have a sum. (See Example 1(b).)
If $-1 < r < 1$, the infinite geometric series

$$a + ar + ar^2 + \ldots + ar^{n-1} + \ldots$$

is convergent and its sum is $S = \dfrac{a}{1-r}$, i.e.,

$$a + ar + ar^2 + \ldots + ar^{n-1} + \ldots = \frac{a}{1-r}, \quad |r| < 1$$

If $|r| \geq 1$, the geometric series is divergent, i.e., it does not have a sum.

Using sigma notation we can write

$$\sum_{n=1}^{\infty} ar^{n-1} = \frac{a}{1-r}, \quad |r| < 1$$

EXAMPLE 3. *Find the sum of the series*

$$25 - 5 + 1 - \tfrac{1}{5} + \tfrac{1}{25} - \tfrac{1}{125} + \ldots$$

Solution

The given series is a geometric series with $a = 25$ and $r = -\tfrac{1}{5}$. Note that $|r| = \tfrac{1}{5}$ which is < 1.

∴ the sum of the series is

$$S = \frac{a}{1-r} = \frac{25}{1 - (-\tfrac{1}{5})}$$

$$= \frac{25}{\tfrac{6}{5}}$$

$$= 25 \times \tfrac{5}{6}$$

$$= \tfrac{125}{6}$$

∴ $25 - 5 + 1 - \tfrac{1}{5} + \tfrac{1}{25} - \tfrac{1}{125} + \ldots = 20\tfrac{1}{6}$

EXAMPLE 4. *Express the repeating decimal* $1.10\dot{3}\,6\dot{5}$ *as a fraction.*

Solution

$$1.10\dot{3}\,6\dot{5} = 1.103\,653\,653\,653\ldots$$

$$= 1.10 + \frac{365}{100\,000} + \frac{365}{100\,000\,000} + \ldots$$

$$= 1.10 + \frac{365}{10^5} + \frac{365}{10^8} + \frac{365}{10^{11}} + \ldots$$

After the first term the series is a geometric series with

$$a = \frac{365}{10^5} \quad \text{and} \quad r = \frac{1}{10^3} = 0.001$$

Since $|r| < 1$ the sum of the geometric part of the series is

$$S = \frac{a}{1-r}$$

$$= \frac{\dfrac{365}{10^5}}{1 - 0.001}$$

$$= \frac{365}{10^5 \times 0.999}$$

∴ $1.10\dot{3}\,6\dot{5} = 1.10 + \dfrac{365}{99\,900}$

$$= \frac{109\ 890 + 365}{99\ 900}$$

$$= \frac{110\ 255}{99\ 900}$$

$$= \frac{22\ 051}{19\ 980}$$

EXERCISE 12-3

B **1.** Find the sums of the following series if they exist.

(a) $1 - \frac{1}{2} + \frac{1}{4} - \frac{1}{8} + \frac{1}{16} + \ldots$

(b) $1 + 3 + 9 + 27 + 81 + \ldots$

(c) $4 + 1 + \frac{1}{4} + \frac{1}{16} + \frac{1}{64} + \ldots$

(d) $3 + 2 + \frac{4}{3} + \frac{8}{9} + \frac{16}{27} + \ldots$

(e) $100 + 10 + 1 + \frac{1}{10} + \frac{1}{100} + \ldots$

(f) $0.1 + 0.05 + 0.025 + 0.0125 + \ldots$

(g) $1 - 2 + 4 - 8 + 16 - \ldots$

(h) $100 - 40 + 16 - \frac{32}{5} + \frac{64}{25} - \ldots$

(i) $\pi - \pi + \pi - \pi + \pi - \pi + \ldots$

2. Express the following repeating decimals as fractions.

(a) $0.\dot{8}$ (b) $0.1\dot{7}$ (c) $0.\dot{6}\dot{4}$

(d) $0.\dot{1}2\dot{3}$ (e) $1.8\dot{3}$ (f) $8.\dot{5}0\dot{1}$

(g) $0.12\dot{3}\dot{4}$ (h) $0.4\dot{3}9\dot{5}$ (i) $20.1\dot{2}1\dot{6}$

3. Find the sum of the series

$$\frac{1}{1 \times 2} + \frac{1}{2 \times 3} + \frac{1}{3 \times 4} + \ldots + \frac{1}{n(n+1)} + \ldots$$

which is not a geometric series.

[*Hint*: Use the identity $\dfrac{1}{k(k+1)} = \dfrac{1}{k} - \dfrac{1}{k+1}$ to find an expression for the nth partial sum.]

4. Find the first 11 partial sums of the series

$$1 - \frac{1}{16} + \frac{1}{81} - \frac{1}{256} + \ldots + \frac{(-1)^{n-1}}{n^4} + \ldots$$

Does it appear that this series is convergent? If so, find its sum correct to 3 decimal places.

5. Find the first 10 partial sums of the series

$$\frac{1}{3} + \frac{2}{5} + \frac{3}{7} + \frac{4}{9} + \ldots + \frac{n}{2n+1} + \ldots$$

Does it appear that this series is convergent or divergent?

6. The number *e* (used as the base of natural logarithms) can be defined as the sum of the infinite series

$$1+\frac{1}{1!}+\frac{1}{2!}+\frac{1}{3!}+\frac{1}{4!}+\ldots+\frac{1}{n!}+\ldots$$

$n! = 1 \times 2 \times 3 \times \ldots \times (n-1) \times n$

Compute *e* correct to 5 decimal places by finding the first 12 partial sums of this series.

7. For what values of *x* are the following geometric series convergent? In each case find the sum of the series for those values of *x*.
(a) $1+x+x^2+x^3+x^4+\ldots$
(b) $1+(x-1)+(x-1)^2+(x-1)^3+(x-1)^4+\ldots$
(c) $1+\dfrac{x}{2}+\dfrac{x^2}{4}+\dfrac{x^3}{8}+\ldots$
(d) $1+2x+4x^2+8x^3+\ldots$
(e) $1+\dfrac{1}{x}+\dfrac{1}{x^2}+\dfrac{1}{x^3}+\ldots$

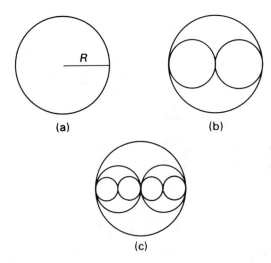

(a)

(b)

8. A circular disc with radius *R* is cut out of paper as in Figure 12-5(a). Two discs with radius $\frac{1}{2}R$ are cut out of paper and placed on top of the first disc as in (b). Four discs of radius $\frac{1}{4}R$ are placed as in (c). Assume that this process can be repeated indefinitely. Find the total area of all the discs.

(c)

Figure 12-5

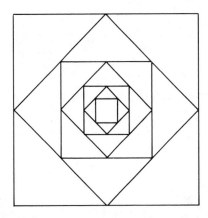

9. The midpoints of a square of side *L* are joined to form a new square. This procedure is repeated for each square.
Find
(a) the sum of the perimeters of all the squares,
(b) the sum of the areas of all the squares.

10. The midpoints of a square of length L are joined to form a new square and the process is repeated as in question 9. A portion of each square is coloured as shown. Assume thte pattern of coloured regions continues indefinitely. What is the total area of the coloured region?

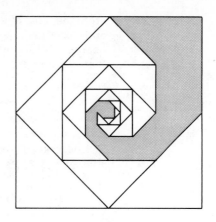

12.4 THE LIMIT OF A FUNCTION

The function $f(x) = \dfrac{\sin x}{x}$ is not defined when $x = 0$, but we can investigate its behaviour as x approaches 0. Using a calculator or tables (and remembering that, if $x \in R$, $\sin x$ means the sine of the angle whose *radian* measure is x) we construct the following table of values correct to 5 decimal places.

x	$f(x) = \dfrac{\sin x}{x}$
1.0	0.841 47
0.5	0.958 85
0.4	0.973 55
0.3	0.985 07
0.2	0.993 35
0.1	0.998 33
0.05	0.999 58
0.01	0.999 98

x	$f(x) = \dfrac{\sin x}{x}$
−1.0	0.841 47
−0.5	0.958 85
−0.4´	0.973 55
−0.3	0.985 07
−0.2	0.993 35
−0.1	0.998 33
−0.05	0.999 58
−0.01	0.999 98

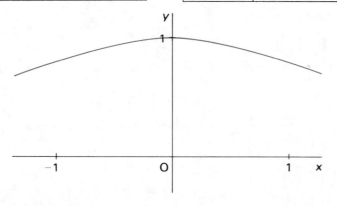

From the table of values and the graph it appears that as x gets closer and closer to 0, $f(x)$ gets closer and closer to 1. We could make $f(x)$ as near as we like to 1 by taking x near enough to 0 (but $x \neq 0$). We say that the limit of $f(x)$ is 1 as x approaches 0 and we write

$$\lim_{x \to 0} \frac{\sin x}{x} = 1$$

> If the values of $f(x)$ get closer and closer to a number L as x gets closer and closer to a number a (but $x \neq a$), then we say that the limit of $f(x)$, as x approaches a, is equal to L and we write
>
> $$\lim_{x \to a} f(x) = L$$

EXAMPLE 1. *Find the following limits.*

$$\text{(a)} \quad \lim_{x \to 2} x^3 \qquad \text{(b)} \quad \lim_{x \to 3} (x^2 - 2x + 5)$$

Solution

(a) As x gets closer and closer to 2, the value of x^3 approaches $2^3 = 8$

$$\therefore \quad \lim_{x \to 2} x^3 = 8$$

(b) As x approaches 3, x^2 approaches $3^2 = 9$ and $2x$ approaches $2 \times 3 = 6$.

$$\lim_{x \to a} (f(x) + g(x))$$

$$= \lim_{x \to a} f(x) + \lim_{x \to a} g(x)$$

$$\therefore \quad \lim_{x \to 3} (x^2 - 2x + 5) = 3^2 - 2 \times 3 + 5$$

$$= 9 - 6 + 5$$

$$= 8$$

In Example 1, we found the limits by substituting the value of a in the expression for $f(x)$. This worked because the functions in Example 1 are continuous functions which are defined at $x = a$. However not all limits are as easy to evaluate because sometimes the functions are not defined at $x = a$.

EXAMPLE 2. *Evaluate*

$$\lim_{x \to 2} \frac{x^2 - 6x + 8}{x - 2}$$

Solution

Let

$$f(x) = \frac{x^2 - 6x + 8}{x - 2}$$

Then $f(x)$ is not defined when $x = 2$, but we can still find the limit of $f(x)$ as x approaches 2.

$$\lim_{x \to 2} \frac{x^2 - 6x + 8}{x - 2} = \lim_{x \to 2} \frac{(x-4)(x-2)}{x - 2}$$

$$= \lim_{x \to 2} (x - 4)$$

$$= 2 - 4$$

$$= -2$$

Remember that the definition of $\lim_{x \to a} f(x)$ says that we consider values of x which are close to a but not equal to a. Thus in Example 2 we have $x \neq 2$ and so we can divide by $x - 2$.

EXAMPLE 3. *Find*

$$\lim_{h \to 0} \frac{(c + h)^2 - c^2}{h}$$

Solution

When $h = 0$ the given expression is undefined. However in finding a limit as $h \to 0$ we consider only values of $h \neq 0$.

$$\lim_{h \to 0} \frac{(c + h)^2 - c^2}{h} = \lim_{h \to 0} \frac{c^2 + 2ch + h^2 - c^2}{h}$$

$$= \lim_{h \to 0} \frac{2ch + h^2}{h}$$

$$= \lim_{h \to 0} (2c + h)$$

$$= 2c + 0$$

$$= 2c$$

Solve for n

$$21\binom{n}{3} = 4\binom{n+1}{4}$$

There are some functions for which $\lim_{x \to a} f(x)$ does not exist. For example

$$\lim_{x \to 0} \frac{1}{x^2}$$

does not exist because the values of $\frac{1}{x^2}$ become arbitrarily large as x approaches 0. (Note that the line $x = 0$ is a vertical asymptote.) Also

$$\lim_{x \to 0} \sin \frac{1}{x}$$

does not exist because the values of $\sin \frac{1}{x}$ oscillate between 1 and -1 indefinitely often as x approaches 0.

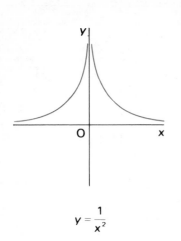

$$y = \frac{1}{x^2}$$

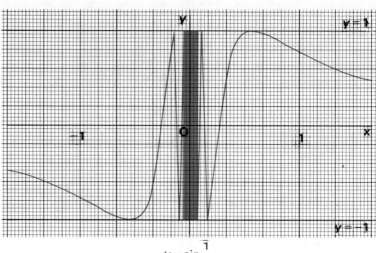

$$y = \sin \frac{1}{x}$$

EXERCISE 12-4

A **1.** State the values of the given limits.

(a) $\lim\limits_{x \to 1} 3x$

(b) $\lim\limits_{x \to 2} x^2$

(c) $\lim\limits_{x \to 0} (x^2 + 5)$

(d) $\lim\limits_{x \to 1} (x^3 + 5x)$

(e) $\lim\limits_{x \to 0} \dfrac{2 - x}{3 + x}$

(f) $\lim\limits_{x \to 4} \sqrt{x}$

(g) $\lim\limits_{h \to 0} (3 + 6h)$

(h) $\lim\limits_{x \to 4} x(x - 1)$

(i) $\lim\limits_{x \to 2} \dfrac{x}{3 + x}$

(j) $\lim\limits_{h \to 0} (h^2 + 3h - 5)$

B **2.** Evaluate the following limits if they exist.

(a) $\lim\limits_{x \to 3} (x^4 - x^2 + 6)$

(b) $\lim\limits_{x \to 7} \dfrac{x^2 + 6x}{x^3 - 3x + 1}$

(c) $\lim\limits_{x \to 1} \dfrac{x}{x - 1}$

(d) $\lim\limits_{x \to 1} \dfrac{x^2 - 1}{x - 1}$

(e) $\lim\limits_{x \to 3} \dfrac{x^2 - x - 6}{x - 3}$

(f) $\lim\limits_{x \to 3} \dfrac{2}{(x - 3)^2}$

(g) $\lim\limits_{x \to 2} \dfrac{2}{(x - 3)^2}$

(h) $\lim\limits_{x \to a} (x^5 - x^3 + x)$

(i) $\lim\limits_{x \to 1} \dfrac{x^2 - 2x - 3}{x + 1}$

(j) $\lim\limits_{x \to -1} \dfrac{x^2 - 2x - 3}{x + 1}$

(k) $\lim\limits_{x \to 1} \dfrac{x^2 + x - 2}{x^2 - 1}$

(l) $\lim\limits_{x \to 4} \dfrac{x - 4}{x^2 - 7x + 12}$

3. Find the following limits.

(a) $\lim\limits_{x \to 0} \cos x$

(b) $\lim\limits_{t \to 0} t \cos t$

(c) $\lim\limits_{y \to 2} \dfrac{y^2 + 8}{y^2 - 8}$

(d) $\lim\limits_{h \to 0} \dfrac{(1 + h)^3 - 1}{h}$

(e) $\lim_{t \to 0} 2^t$

(f) $\lim_{x \to 1} \log_{10} x$

(g) $\lim_{h \to 0} \dfrac{h}{3h + 2h^2}$

(h) $\lim_{h \to 0} \dfrac{h(h+1)}{h^3 - h}$

4. Define $f(x) = \dfrac{1 - \cos x}{x^2}$, $x \neq 0$, x in radians.

Make a guess as to the value of

$$\lim_{x \to 0} \frac{1 - \cos x}{x^2}$$

by first evaluating $f(x)$ for $x = 1$, 0.5, 0.4, 0.3, 0.2, 0.1, 0.05, 0.01.

5. Define $f(x) = \dfrac{2^x - 1}{x}$, $x \neq 0$.

(a) Evaluate $f(x)$, correct to 6 decimal places, for $x = 1$, 0.5, 0.4, 0.3, 0.2, 0.1, 0.05, 0.01, 0.005, 0.001, 0.0005, 0.0001.

(b) Find

$$\lim_{x \to 0} \frac{2^x - 1}{x}$$

correct to 3 decimal places.

12.5 TANGENTS

The word tangent comes from the Latin word *tangens* which means *touching*. Thus a tangent is a line which touches a curve. How can we make this idea precise?

For a simple curve such as a circle we could simply say that a tangent is a line which intersects the circle once and only once, as in Section 8.2.

But for more complicated curves this definition is not good enough. Figure 12-6 shows a point P on a curve C and two lines l and t passing through P.

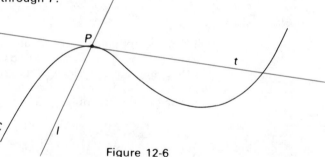

Figure 12-6

The line *l* intersects *C* only once, but it does not look like what we think of as a tangent. On the other hand the line *t* looks like a tangent but it intersects *C* twice.

To give a general definition of tangent we must use limits. Figure 12-7 shows a point *P* on a curve *C* and a sequence of points $Q_1, Q_2, Q_3 \ldots$ which approach *P* along *C*. The secant lines PQ_1, PQ_2, $PQ_3, \ldots$ are also drawn.

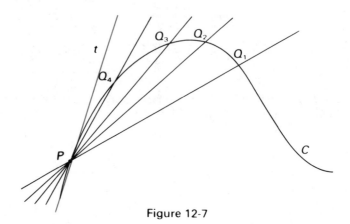

Figure 12-7

As the points *Q* get closer and closer to *P*, the corresponding secant lines *PQ* get closer and closer to what we think of as the tangent line *t* at *P*. Therefore we define the tangent as the limit of the secant lines.

> The tangent to a curve *C* at a point *P* on *C* is the limiting position of the secant line *PQ* as *Q* approaches *P* along the curve.

In order to find the equation of the tangent *t* to *C* at *P* we need to know the coordinates of *P* and the slope of *t*. Since the secant lines *PQ* approach *t*, the slopes of the secant lines must approach the slope of *t*. Therefore we can calculate the slope of *t* as the limit of the slopes of the secant lines *PQ*.

EXAMPLE 1. *Find the equation of the tangent to the parabola $y = x^2$ at the point* (1, 1).

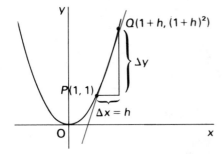

Solution

If *Q* is another point on the parabola, let its *x*-coordinate be $1 + h$ (*h* can be positive or negative but not 0). Since *Q* lies on the parabola $y = x^2$, its *y*-coordinate is $(1 + h)^2$. The slope of the secant line *PQ* is

$$m_{PQ} = \frac{\Delta y}{\Delta x} = \frac{(1+h)^2 - 1}{(1+h) - 1}$$

$$= \frac{1 + 2h + h^2 - 1}{h}$$

$$= \frac{2h + h^2}{h}$$

$$= 2 + h$$

Let the slope of the tangent at $P(1, 1)$ be m. Then m is the limit of the slope m_{PQ} as Q approaches P. But as Q approaches P, h approaches 0.

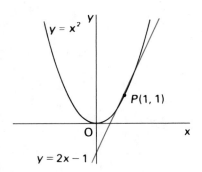

$$\therefore \quad m = \lim_{h \to 0} m_{PQ}$$

$$= \lim_{h \to 0} (2 + h)$$

$$= 2$$

The equation of the tangent to $y = x^2$ at $P(1, 1)$ is

$$y - y_1 = m(x - x_1)$$

$$y - 1 = 2(x - 1)$$

or $$y = 2x - 1$$

From Example 1 we see that the general procedure for finding the equation of the tangent t at $P(x_1, y_1)$ to a curve is as follows:
1. Let $x_1 + h$ be the x-coordinate of another point Q on C.
2. Calculate the slope m_{PQ}.
3. The slope m of t is the limit of the slope of the secant PQ.

$$\therefore \quad m = \lim_{h \to 0} m_{PQ}$$

4. The equation of t is $y - y_1 = m(x - x_1)$.

EXAMPLE 2. *Find the equation of the tangent to the hyperbola $xy = 1$ at the point $P(2, \frac{1}{2})$.*

Solution
If Q is another point on the hyperbola, let its x-coordinate be $2 + h$.
Since Q lies on the hyperbola $y = \frac{1}{x}$, its y-coordinate is $\frac{1}{2+h}$. The slope of PQ is

$$m_{PQ} = \frac{\Delta y}{\Delta x} = \frac{\frac{1}{2+h} - \frac{1}{2}}{2 + h - 2}$$

$$= \frac{\frac{2 - (2+h)}{(2+h)2}}{h}$$

$$= \frac{-h}{(2+h)2} \times \frac{1}{h}$$

$$= -\frac{1}{4+2h}$$

∴ the slope of the tangent at P is

$$m = \lim_{h \to 0} m_{PQ} = \lim_{h \to 0} -\frac{1}{4+2h}$$

$$= -\tfrac{1}{4}$$

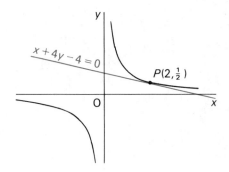

The equation of the tangent to $xy = 1$ at $(2, \tfrac{1}{2})$ is

$$y - y_1 = m(x - x_1)$$

$$y - \tfrac{1}{2} = -\tfrac{1}{4}(x - 2)$$

$$4y - 2 = -x + 2$$

$$x + 4y - 4 = 0$$

EXERCISE 12-5

B 1. For each of the following curves,
   (i) find the slope of the tangent at the given point,
   (ii) find an equation of the tangent at the given point,
   (iii) graph the curve and the tangent.

(a) $y = x^2$ at $(3, 9)$

(b) $y = x^2$ at $(-2, 4)$

(c) $y = \tfrac{1}{4}x^2$ at $(1, \tfrac{1}{4})$

(d) $y = 1 - x^2$ at $(1, 0)$

(e) $y = x^2 + x$ at $(1, 2)$

(f) $y = x^2 + x$ at $(-\tfrac{1}{2}, -\tfrac{1}{4})$

(g) $y = x^3$ at $(1, 1)$

(h) $y = x^3$ at $(0, 0)$

(i) $y = x^3 - x$ at $(1, 0)$

(j) $y = x^3 - x$ at $(0, 0)$

(k) $y = 2x^3 - 6x$ at $(-1, 4)$

(l) $y = \dfrac{1}{x}$ at $(-1, -1)$

(m) $xy = 12$ at $(3, 4)$

(n) $y = \dfrac{1}{x-1}$ at $(4, \tfrac{1}{3})$

(o) $y = x^2$ at $(x_1, x_1{}^2)$

(p) $y = x^3$ at $(x_1, x_1{}^3)$

12.6 DERIVATIVES

In the last section we found the slope of the tangent to the parabola $y = x^2$ at the point $(1, 1)$.

Let us now find the slope of the tangent at a *general* point $P(x, x^2)$ on the curve.

Let $x+h$ be the x-coordinate of another point Q on the parabola. Then the y-coordinate of Q is $(x+h)^2$.

The slope of PQ is

$$m_{PQ} = \frac{\Delta y}{\Delta x} = \frac{(x+h)^2 - x^2}{(x+h) - x}$$

$$= \frac{x^2 + 2xh + h^2 - x^2}{h}$$

$$= \frac{2xh + h^2}{h}$$

$$= 2x + h$$

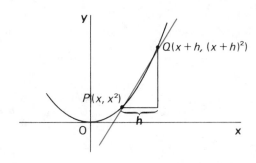

∴ the slope of the tangent at $P(x, x^2)$ is

$$m = \lim_{h \to 0} m_{PQ} = \lim_{h \to 0} (2x + h)$$

$$= 2x$$

Since the slope depends on x it is a function of x. This function $g(x) = 2x$ is called the *derivative* of the original function $f(x) = x^2$.

In general if f is a given function, its graph is a curve C. If C has a tangent at a point $P(x, f(x))$, we denote the slope of this tangent by $f'(x)$. Then f' is a function called the derivative of f.

> If f is a function, its derivative is the function f' such that $f'(x)$ is the slope of the tangent to the graph of f at the point $(x, f(x))$.

The preceding example shows that if $f(x) = x^2$, then $f'(x) = 2x$.

Let PQ be a secant line of a general curve C whose equation is $y = f(x)$. If the x-coordinate of Q is $x + h$, then since Q lies on $y = f(x)$ its y-coordinate is $f(x + h)$.

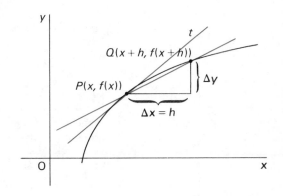

$$\therefore \quad \Delta y = f(x+h) - f(x)$$

$$\Delta x = (x+h) - x = h$$

The slope of the secant line PQ is

$$m_{PQ} = \frac{\Delta y}{\Delta x} = \frac{f(x+h) - f(x)}{h}$$

∴ the slope of the tangent at $P(x, f(x))$ is

$$f'(x) = \lim_{h \to 0} m_{PQ} = \lim_{h \to 0} \frac{f(x+h) - f(x)}{h}$$

Thus the value of the derivative function f' at x is given by the formula

$$f'(x) = \lim_{h \to 0} \frac{f(x+h) - f(x)}{h}$$

If $y = f(x)$, other notations for the derivative are $\dfrac{dy}{dx}$ and y'.

EXAMPLE 1. (a) *Find the derivative of the function* $f(x) = x^3 - 3x$.
(b) *Use the derivative to find the equations of the tangents to the curve* $y = x^3 - 3x$ *at the points*

$$\text{(i)} \quad (0, 0) \qquad \text{(ii)} \quad (1, -2)$$

Solution
(a)

$$f(x) = x^3 - 3x$$
$$f(x+h) = (x+h)^3 - 3(x+h)$$
$$\therefore \quad f(x+h) - f(x) = [(x+h)^3 - 3(x+h)] - [x^3 - 3x]$$
$$= x^3 + 3x^2h + 3xh^2 + h^3 - 3x - 3h - x^3 + 3$$
$$= 3x^2h + 3xh^2 + h^3 - 3h$$
$$= h(3x^2 + 3xh + h^2 - 3)$$

$$\therefore \quad \frac{f(x+h) - f(x)}{h} = \frac{h(3x^2 + 3xh + h^2 - 3)}{h}$$

$$= 3x^2 + 3xh + h^2 - 3$$

$$\therefore \quad f'(x) = \lim_{h \to 0} \frac{f(x+h) - f(x)}{h}$$

$$= \lim_{h \to 0} (3x^2 + 3xh + h^2 - 3)$$

$$= 3x^2 + 0 + 0 - 3$$

$$= 3x^2 - 3$$

The derivative of the function $f(x) = x^3 - 3x$ is

$$f'(x) = 3x^2 - 3$$

(b) (i)

$$f'(0) = 3 \times 0^2 - 3 = -3$$

$\therefore$ the slope of the tangent to $y = x^3 - 3x$ at $(0, 0)$ is $m = -3$ and the equation of the tangent is

$$y - y_1 = m(x - x_1)$$
$$y - 0 = -3(x - 0)$$
$$3x + y = 0$$

(b) (ii)

$$f'(1) = 3 \times 1 - 3 = 0$$

∴ the slope of the tangent at $(1, -2)$ is $m = 0$ and the equation of the tangent is

$$y - y_1 = m(x - x_1)$$

$$y - (-2) = 0(x - 1)$$

$$y + 2 = 0$$

The derivative of a function is useful not only in finding tangents to curves but also in determining where a function is increasing or decreasing. Figure 12-8 shows a curve $y = f(x)$ with several tangents drawn to it.

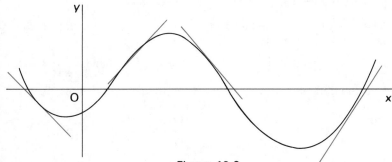

Figure 12-8

You can see that on the intervals where the function is decreasing, the tangents have negative slopes, i.e., the derivative is negative. On the intervals where f is increasing, the tangents have positive slopes, i.e., f has a positive derivative.

If $f'(x) < 0$, then f is a decreasing function.

If $f'(x) > 0$, then f is an increasing function.

EXAMPLE 2. *Use the derivative to find where $f(x) = x^3 - 3x$ is increasing or decreasing.*

Solution
From Example 1 we have $f'(x) = 3x^2 - 3$.
f is increasing when $f'(x) > 0$

$$\therefore \quad 3x^2 - 3 > 0$$

$$3x^2 > 3$$

$$x^2 > 1$$

$$\therefore \quad |x| > 1$$

∴ f is increasing when $x > 1$ or $x < -1$

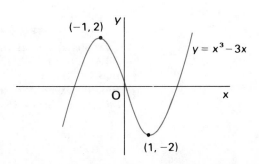

Also f is decreasing when $f'(x) < 0$

$$3x^2 - 3 < 0$$
$$x^2 < 1$$
$$\therefore \ |x| < 1$$

$\therefore \ f$ is decreasing when $-1 < x < 1$.

EXERCISE 12-6

B **1.** (a) Find the derivative of the function $f(x) = x^2 + 2x$.
(b) Use the derivative to find the equations of the tangents to the parabola $y = x^2 + 2x$ at the following points.
(i) $(0, 0)$ (ii) $(1, 3)$ (iii) $(-1, -1)$ (iv) $(-4, 8)$

2. (a) Find the derivative of the function $f(x) = \dfrac{1}{x}$.

(b) Use the derivative to find the equations of the tangents to the hyperbola $xy = 1$ at the following points.

(i) $(1, 1)$ (ii) $(3, \frac{1}{3})$ (iii) $(-\frac{1}{2}, -2)$ (iv) $\left(a, \dfrac{1}{a}\right)$

3. Find the derivative $f'(x)$ of each of the following functions.
(a) $f(x) = x$ (b) $f(x) = x^3$
(c) $f(x) = x^4$ (d) $f(x) = x^3 + 2x^2$
(e) $f(x) = x + \dfrac{1}{x}$ (f) $f(x) = (x - 3)^2$
(g) $f(x) = 6x^2 + 1$ (h) $f(x) = \pi$

4. Copy the following table and fill it in using question 3(a), (b), (c).

$f(x)$	x	x^2	x^3	x^4
$f'(x)$		$2x$		

Do you see a pattern? Make a guess as to the derivative of the function $f(x) = x^5$. Then calculate the derivative to see if your guess is correct.

5. At what point on the curve $y = x^4$ does the tangent have a slope of $\frac{1}{2}$?

6. Use the rules
(i) $(cf)' = cf'$ [The derivative of a constant times a function is equal to the constant times the derivative of the function]
(ii) $(f + g)' = f' + g'$ [The derivative of a sum is the sum of the derivatives]
together with the table of derivatives in question 4 to find the derivatives of the following functions.
(a) $f(x) = 27x^3$ (b) $f(x) = -\frac{1}{2}x^4$
(c) $f(x) = x^4 + x^2$ (d) $f(x) = 6x - x^3$
(e) $f(x) = 16x^4 - 3x^2 + 9x$ (f) $f(x) = 2x^2 + 3x^3 - 8x^4$

7. By the same method as in question 6, find the indicated derivatives.

(a) $y = 3x^2 + 2x$ Find $\dfrac{dy}{dx}$.

(b) $y = t^3 - t^2$ Find $\dfrac{dy}{dt}$.

(c) $s = t^4 + 2t^3$ Find $\dfrac{ds}{dt}$.

(d) $S = 4\pi r^2$ Find $\dfrac{dS}{dr}$.

(e) $h = 180t - 7t^2$ Find $\dfrac{dh}{dt}$.

8. (a) Find the derivative of the function $f(x) = 3x^2 + 2x - 1$.
(b) Use the derivative to find the intervals on which f is increasing or decreasing.
(c) Use this information to sketch the curve $y = 3x^2 + 2x - 1$.

9. (a) Find the derivative of the function $f(x) = 1 + 12x - 3x^3$.
(b) Use the derivative to find the intervals on which f is increasing or decreasing.
(c) Use this information to sketch the graph of f.

10. A manufacturer of cartridges for stereo systems has proposed a needle with parabolic cross-section as shown. The equation of the parabola is $y = 4x^2$ where x and y are measured in millimetres. The needle sits in a record groove whose sides make an angle θ with the horizontal direction, where $\tan \theta = 1.5$. Find the coordinates of the points of contact P_1 and P_2 of the needle with the groove.

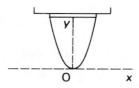

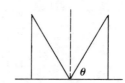

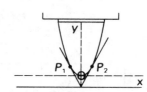

12.7 APPLICATION: VELOCITIES AND OTHER RATES OF CHANGE

If you watch the speedometer of a car while travelling in city traffic you will see that the needle does not stay still for very long, i.e., the speed of the car is not constant. We assume from watching the speedometer that the car has a definite speed at each moment. But how is the "instantaneous" speed defined?

Suppose that a ball is dropped from a balcony on the 25th floor of an apartment building. If the distance to the ground is 80 m and the ball lands there 4 s later, then the average speed of the ball, in m/s, is

$$\frac{\text{distance travelled}}{\text{time elapsed}} = \frac{80}{4} = 20$$

But it would be more important to know the speed of the ball at the instant it hits the ground.

It is known that the distance y, in metres, that the ball falls in t seconds is

$$y = \tfrac{1}{2}gt^2$$
$$= \tfrac{1}{2}(9.8)t^2$$
$$\doteq 5t^2$$

$$y = f(t) = 5t^2$$

Let us first try to find the velocity of the ball after 1 second.

The average velocity in the time period from $t = 1$ to $t = 2$ is

$$\frac{\text{distance travelled}}{\text{time elapsed}} = \frac{\text{change in distance}}{\text{change in time}}$$

$$= \frac{\Delta y}{\Delta t}$$

$$= \frac{f(2) - f(1)}{2 - 1}$$

$$= \frac{5 \times 2^2 - 5 \times 1^2}{1}$$

$$= 15$$

Similar calculations give the average velocities over smaller time periods.

time period	$1 \leqslant t \leqslant 2$	$1 \leqslant t \leqslant 1.5$	$1 \leqslant t \leqslant 1.1$	$1 \leqslant t \leqslant 1.05$	$1 \leqslant t \leqslant 1.01$
average velocity	15	12.5	10.5	10.25	10.05

As we take smaller and smaller time periods starting at $t = 1$, the average velocity approaches 10 m/s. Therefore we *define* the velocity (or instantaneous velocity) at $t = 1$ to be 10 m/s.

If we take the time period to be $1 \leq t \leq 1 + h$, then the average velocity over this time period is

$$\frac{\Delta y}{\Delta t} = \text{slope of secant } PQ$$

$$= m_{PQ}$$

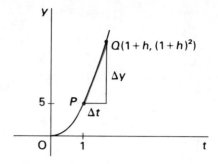

As h approaches 0, m_{PQ} approaches the slope of the tangent to $y = 5t^2$ at $P(1, 5)$. On the other hand $\frac{\Delta y}{\Delta t}$ approaches the velocity at $t = 1$.

$$\therefore \quad \text{velocity after 1 s} = \text{slope of tangent at } P(1, 5)$$

In general, suppose the distance in metres travelled in a straight line by an object in t seconds is given by a function $y = f(t)$. The velocity at time $t = t_1$ is defined to be the limit as h approaches 0 of the average velocity over the time period $t_1 \leq t \leq t_1 + h$. The velocity when $t = t_1$ is equal to the slope of the tangent to the curve $y = f(t)$ at the point $(t_1, f(t_1))$. Therefore it is equal to $f'(t_1)$, the value of the derivative when $t = t_1$.

> If the distance function is given by $y = f(t)$, then the velocity at time t is given by
>
> $$v = f'(t) = \frac{dy}{dt}$$

Now let us return to the ball which was dropped off the balcony.

$$f(t) = 5t^2$$

$$\therefore \quad f'(t) = 5 \times 2t = 10t$$

When the ball hits the ground we have

$$f(t) = 5t^2 = 80$$

$$\therefore \quad t^2 = 16$$

$$\therefore \quad t = 4$$

$$f'(4) = 10 \times 4 = 40$$

$\therefore$ the ball hits the ground with a velocity of 40 m/s.

EXAMPLE 1. *A particle moves in a straight line according to the law $s = t^3 - t^2 + t - 1$ where s is the displacement (signed distance from the origin) in metres and t is measured in seconds. Find the velocity after 5 s.*

Solution

$$s = t^3 - t^2 + t - 1$$

$$\therefore \quad \frac{ds}{dt} = 3t^2 - 2t + 1$$

When $t = 5$,
$$\frac{ds}{dt} = 3 \times 5^2 - 2 \times 5 + 1$$

$$= 75 - 10 + 1$$

$$= 66$$

$\therefore$ after 5 s the velocity of the particle is 66 m/s.

A velocity is the rate of change of position with respect to time. We have seen that it is the derivative of the position function.

In general, if a quantity y depends on another quantity x according to an equation $y = f(x)$, then we can interpret the derivative $f'(x)$ as the (instantaneous) rate of change of y with respect to x because

$$f'(x) = \lim_{h \to 0} \frac{\Delta y}{\Delta x} = \lim_{h \to 0} \frac{f(x+h) - f(x)}{h}$$

and $\dfrac{\Delta y}{\Delta x}$ is the average rate of change of y with respect to x.

EXAMPLE 2. *When a balloon is being blown up its volume V depends on the radius r. find the rate of change of the volume with respect to the radius when r = 10 cm.*

Solution

$$V = \tfrac{4}{3}\pi r^3$$

$$\therefore \quad \frac{dV}{dr} = \frac{4}{3}\pi \times 3r^2 = 4\pi r^2$$

When $r = 10$,
$$\frac{dV}{dr} = 4\pi \times 10^2 = 400\,\pi$$

$\therefore$ when $r = 10$ cm, the rate of change of V with respect to r is 400π cm^3/cm.

Find at least one solution for

$$_nP_3 = k!$$

EXERCISE 12-7

B **1.** The displacement in metres of a particle moving in a straight line is given by $s = t^2 + t$ where the time t is measured in seconds.
(a) Find the average velocity for the time period beginning when $t = 2$ and lasting
(i) 1 s   (ii) 0.5 s   (iii) 0.01 s   (iv) 0.001 s
(v) 0.000 01 s
(b) Find the velocity when $t = 2$.

2. If a ball is thrown vertically into the air with a velocity of 50 m/s, its height in metres after t seconds is given by $y = 50t - 5t^2$.
(a) When does the ball hit the ground?
(b) What is the speed of the ball after 1 s? 2 s? 5 s? 8 s?

(c) When the ball hits the ground what is its speed?

3. If an arrow is shot upward on the moon with a velocity of 58 m/s, its height in metres after t seconds is $h = 58t - 0.83t^2$.
(a) What is the velocity of the arrow after 5 s? 10 s? 20 s?
(b) When will the arrow hit the moon?
(c) With what velocity will it hit the moon?

4. A particle moves in a straight line according to the following laws of motion, where s is the displacement in metres and t is the time in seconds. In each case find
 (i) the velocity as a function of t,
 (ii) the velocity after 6 s.
(a) $s = t + 2$ (b) $s = t - 2t^2$
(c) $s = 10t^2 + 3t$ (d) $s = \frac{1}{2}at^2 + v_0t$
(e) $s = t^3 + 2t^2 + 3$ (f) $s = 8 - 2t + t^3$

5. Find the rate of change of the volume of a cubic box with respect to the length of an edge when the edge is 6 cm.

6. Find the rate of change of the area of a circle with respect to its radius when the radius is 3 cm.

7. Find the rate of change of the total surface area of a cylinder of height 12 cm with respect to the radius of its base when the radius is 4 cm.

12.8 APPLICATION: MAXIMUM AND MINIMUM PROBLEMS

There are many practical problems which require us to find the largest or smallest value of some quantity. The derivative is very useful in finding such maximum and minimum values.

Figure 12-9 shows the graph of a function which has 2 minimum values at the points A and C and a maximum value at B. The function

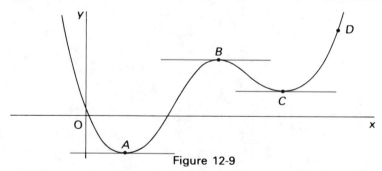

Figure 12-9

has an absolute minimum at A since A is the lowest point on the graph. If we are only interested in the part of the graph from B to D, then C is the lowest point and so we call C a local minimum. Similarly, if we are only interested in the part from A to C, then B is the highest point and we call it a local maximum. You can see from the graph that at each of the points A, B, and C the tangent is horizontal and so its slope is 0. Therefore the derivative must be 0 at these points.

If a function f has a maximum or minimum value when $x = a$ and it has a derivative at a, then

$$f'(a) = 0$$

To find a maximum or minimum value of a function f we find its derivative $f'(x)$, then we solve the equation $f'(x) = 0$.

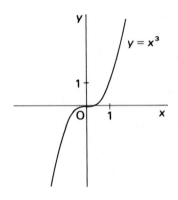

However we have to be careful because there are some functions whose derivatives are 0 at a point where there is no maximum or minimum. For example if $f(x) = x^3$, then $f'(x) = 3x^2$ and so $f'(0) = 0$, but you can see that the curve $y = x^3$ has no maximum or minimum.

If we have a point a with $f'(a) = 0$ and we are not sure if this gives a maximum or a minimum, we can look at the sign of $f''(x)$ to the left and right of a.

If $f'(x) < 0$ to the left of a and $f'(x) > 0$ to the right of a, f decreases and then increases, so it has a minimum at a. If $f'(x) > 0$ to the left of a and $f'(x) < 0$ to the right of a, f increases and then decreases, so it has a maximum at a.

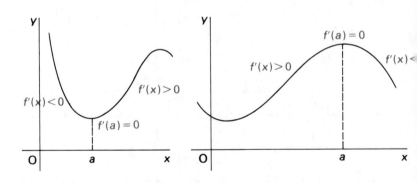

EXAMPLE 1. *An open box with a square base is to be made from a square piece of cardboard with side 2 m by cutting out a square from each corner and then bending up the sides. Find the maximum volume of such a box.*

Solution

We begin by drawing a diagram. Let x be the side of the square cut out from each corner (in metres). When the sides are folded up the result will be an open box with height x and a square base with side $2-2x$.

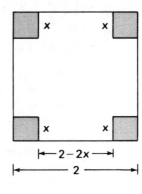

$\therefore$ the volume of the box is

$$V = x(2-2x)^2$$
$$= 4x(1-2x+x^2)$$
$$= 4(x^3-2x^2+x)$$

From the diagram we can see that $0<x<1$.
$\therefore$ the domain of V is $\{x \mid 0<x<1\}$

$$V(x) = 4(x^3-2x^2+x)$$
$$\therefore \quad V'(x) = 4(3x^2-4x+1)$$

To find where V is a maximum we set $V'(x)=0$ and solve for x.

$$V'(x) = 0$$
$$\therefore \quad 3x^2-4x+1 = 0$$
$$(3x-1)(x-1) = 0$$

$\therefore$ $x = \frac{1}{3}$ or $x = 1$

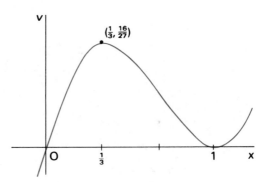

But $x = 1$ is not in the domain of V.
$\therefore$ $x = \frac{1}{3}$ is the only possibility.
This is confirmed by the graph of V.

[Instead of drawing a graph we could observe that since $V'(x) = 4(3x-1)(x-1)$ we have $V'(x)>0$ if $x<\frac{1}{3}$ and $V'(x)>0$ if $\frac{1}{3}<x<1$.]
Since

$$V(\tfrac{1}{3}) = 4[(\tfrac{1}{3})^3 - 2(\tfrac{1}{3})^2 + \tfrac{1}{3}]$$
$$= 4[\tfrac{1}{27} - \tfrac{2}{9} + \tfrac{1}{3}]$$
$$= 4 \times \tfrac{4}{27}$$

the maximum volume of the box is $\frac{16}{27} m^3$.

EXERCISE 12-8

1. Find two numbers whose sum is 68 and whose product is a maximum.

2. Find two numbers whose sum is 68 such that the sum of their squares is a minimum.

3. Find the maximum and minimum values of the following functions.

(a) $f(x) = 5 - 16x - 4x^2$ (b) $f(x) = 2x^2 - 12x + 17$

(c) $f(x) = x - x^3, -1 \leqslant x \leqslant 1$ (d) $f(x) = x^3 - 12x + 1, -3 \leqslant x \leqslant 3$

(e) $f(x) = 2x^3 - 9x^2 + 12x + 1, x \geqslant 1$ (f) $f(x) = x + \dfrac{1}{x}, x > 0$

4. If an arrow is shot upward on the moon with a velocity of 58 m/s, its height in metres after t seconds is $h = 58t - 0.8t^2$. Find the maximum height reached by the arrow.

5. A farmer wants to fence in 60 000 m² of land in a rectangular field along a straight road. The fencing that he plans to use along the road costs $10 per metre and the fencing that he plans to use for the other 3 sides costs $5 per metre.

(a) How much of each type of fence should he buy to keep expenses to a minimum?

(b) What is the minimum expense?

6. A farmer wants to fence in 60 000 m² of land in a rectangular field and then divide it in half with a fence parallel to one pair of sides. What are the dimensions of the rectangular field that requires the least amount of fencing?

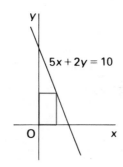

7. What is the area of the largest rectangle with base on the x-axis and one vertex at the origin that can be fitted inside the triangle whose sides are the axes and the line $5x + 2y = 10$?

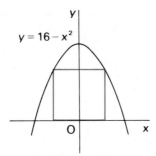

8. What is the area of the largest rectangle with its base on the x-axis and its other 2 vertices above the x-axis and on the parabola $y = 16 - x^2$?

9. A box with a square base with side x metres is open at the top.

(a) If its volume is to be 4000 cm³, show that its surface area is

$$S = x^2 + \frac{16\,000}{x}.$$

(b) Find the dimensions of the box so that its surface area is a minimum.

C **10.** A cylindrical can is to be made to hold 250 cm³. Find the radius and the height of the can which will minimize the amount of metal used. [Leave your answer in terms of π.]

12.9 AREAS

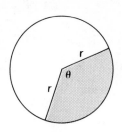

In the first section of this chapter we saw how areas of regions can be regarded as limits of areas of inscribed polygons. Let us use this idea to find a formula for the area of a sector of a circle with radius r and central angle θ.

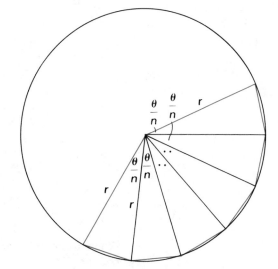

We approximate the area of the sector by the area of a polygon P_n as shown in figure 12-10.

Figure 12-10

P_n has been divided into n congruent triangles with central angle $\dfrac{\theta}{n}$. The area of one of these triangles is

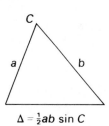

$$\Delta = \tfrac{1}{2}r^2 \sin \frac{\theta}{n}$$

$\therefore$ the area of the polygon P_n is

$$n\Delta = \tfrac{1}{2}r^2 n \sin \frac{\theta}{n}$$

$$\Delta = \tfrac{1}{2}ab \sin C$$

Recall from Section 13.4 that

$$\lim_{x \to 0} \frac{\sin x}{x} = 1$$

As $n \to \infty$, we have $\dfrac{\theta}{n} \to 0$

$$\therefore \quad \lim_{n \to \infty} \frac{\sin \dfrac{\theta}{n}}{\dfrac{\theta}{n}} = 1$$

The area of the sector is the limit of the area of the inscribed polygon P_n as $n \to \infty$.

$$\text{area of sector} = \lim_{n \to \infty} (\text{area of } P_n)$$

$$= \lim_{n \to \infty} \tfrac{1}{2}r^2 n \sin \frac{\theta}{n}$$

$$= \lim_{n \to \infty} \tfrac{1}{2}r^2 \frac{\sin \dfrac{\theta}{n}}{\dfrac{1}{n}}$$

$$= \lim_{n \to \infty} \tfrac{1}{2}r^2\theta \frac{\sin \dfrac{\theta}{n}}{\dfrac{\theta}{n}}$$

$$= \tfrac{1}{2}r^2\theta \times 1$$

The area of a sector of a circle with radius r and central angle θ is

$$A = \tfrac{1}{2}r^2\theta$$

When using this formula it must be remembered to express θ in radians.

In particular when $\theta = 2\pi$ the sector is the whole circle and we have the familiar formula for the area of a circle of radius r: $A = \pi r^2$.

EXAMPLE 1. *A sector of a circle has radius 12 cm and the central angle is 45°.*
(a) *Find the area of the sector.*
(b) *Find the area of the segment between the arc PQ and the chord PQ.*

Solution

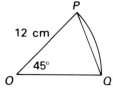

(a) $r = 12$ and $\theta = \dfrac{\pi}{4}$

$$A = \tfrac{1}{2}r^2\theta$$

$$= \tfrac{1}{2}(12)^2 \frac{\pi}{4}$$

$$= \frac{144\pi}{8}$$

$$= 18\pi$$

The area of the sector is 18π cm^2.

(b) The area of triangle OPQ is

$$\triangle OPQ = \tfrac{1}{2}r^2 \sin \theta$$

$$= \tfrac{1}{2}(12)^2 \sin 45°$$

$$= \tfrac{1}{2}(144)\,\frac{1}{\sqrt{2}}$$

$$= 36 \times \frac{2}{\sqrt{2}}$$

$$= 36\sqrt{2}$$

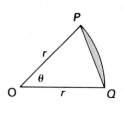

$\therefore$ area of segment $=$ area of sector $- \triangle OPQ$

$$= 18\pi - 36\sqrt{2}$$

$$= 18(\pi - 2\sqrt{2})$$

The area of the segment is $18(\pi - 2\sqrt{2})$ cm^2.

Unfortunately the method we used for finding the area of a sector of a circle does not work for other areas.

Let us try to find the area A of the region under the parabola $y = x^2$ and above the x-axis between $x = 0$ and $x = 1$.

We can approximate the region under the parabola by rectangles.

(a)

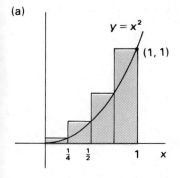

(b)

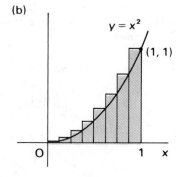

(c)

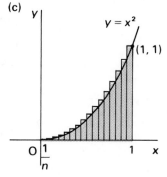

Figure 12-11

Figure 12-11(a) shows an approximation using 4 rectangles of equal width. Let A_4 be the sum of the areas of those 4 rectangles. Each rectangle has width $\tfrac{1}{4}$ and the heights are the values of the function $f(x) = x^2$ at the points $\tfrac{1}{4}, \tfrac{1}{2}, \tfrac{3}{4}, 1$, i.e., the heights are $(\tfrac{1}{4})^2, (\tfrac{2}{4})^2, (\tfrac{3}{4})^2, (\tfrac{4}{4})^2$.

$$\therefore \quad A_4 = \tfrac{1}{4}(\tfrac{1}{4})^2 + \tfrac{1}{4}(\tfrac{2}{4})^2 + \tfrac{1}{4}(\tfrac{3}{4})^2 + \tfrac{1}{4}(\tfrac{4}{4})^2$$

$$= \tfrac{1}{4}(\tfrac{1}{4})^2[1^2 + 2^2 + 3^2 + 4^2]$$

$$= \tfrac{30}{64} = \tfrac{15}{32}$$

By using more rectangles we get a better approximation. Figure 12-11(b) shows an approximation by 8 rectangles of width $\frac{1}{8}$. Their sum is

$$A_8 = \tfrac{1}{8}(\tfrac{1}{8})^2 + \tfrac{1}{8}(\tfrac{2}{8})^2 + \tfrac{1}{8}(\tfrac{3}{8})^2 + \ldots + \tfrac{1}{8}(\tfrac{8}{8})^2$$

$$= \tfrac{1}{8}(\tfrac{1}{8})^2[1^2 + 2^2 + 3^2 + \ldots + 8^2]$$

$$= \frac{1}{8^3} \times 204 = \tfrac{7}{16}$$

In general let us approximate using n rectangles as in (c). The ith rectangle has width $\dfrac{1}{n}$ and height $\left(\dfrac{i}{n}\right)^2$ and so the sum of the areas of the n rectangles is

$$A_n = \frac{1}{n}\left(\frac{1}{n}\right)^2 + \frac{1}{n}\left(\frac{2}{n}\right)^2 + \frac{1}{n}\left(\frac{3}{n}\right)^2 + \ldots + \frac{1}{n}\left(\frac{n}{n}\right)^2$$

$$= \frac{1}{n}\left(\frac{1}{n}\right)^2 [1^2 + 2^2 + 3^2 + \ldots + n^2]$$

Using the formula for the sum of the squares of the first n natural numbers

[See Example 4 in Chapter 13]

$$1^2 + 2^2 + 3^2 + \ldots + n^2 = \frac{n(n+1)(2n+1)}{6}$$

we have

$$A_n = \frac{n(n+1)(2n+1)}{6n^3}$$

You can see from Figure 12-11 that as n increases the approximation of A_n to the true area A becomes better and better. The area A is the limit of the sequence $\{A_n\}$.

$$A = \lim_{n \to \infty} A_n$$

$$= \lim_{n \to \infty} \frac{n(n+1)(2n+1)}{6n^3}$$

$$= \lim_{n \to \infty} \frac{1}{6} \cdot \frac{n}{n} \cdot \frac{n+1}{n} \cdot \frac{2n+1}{n}$$

$$= \lim_{n \to \infty} \frac{1}{6}\left(1 + \frac{1}{n}\right)\left(2 + \frac{1}{n}\right)$$

$$= \tfrac{1}{6}(1+0)(2+0)$$

$$= \tfrac{1}{3}$$

$\therefore$ the area under the parabola $y = x^2$ between 0 and 1 is $\frac{1}{3}$.

In general if $f(x) \geq 0$ and R is the region which lies under the curve $y = f(x)$ and above the x-axis between a and b (i.e., R is bounded by $y = f(x)$, $y = 0$, $x = a$, and $x = b$), then the area of R is defined as a limit of areas A_n of approximating rectangles similar to the procedure for $y = x^2$.

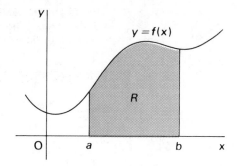

The area of R is denoted by the symbol

$$\int_a^b f(x)\, dx \qquad \text{or} \qquad \int_a^b f$$

and is called the integral of f from a to b.
(An integral can also be defined for a function f that takes on positive and negative values, but such an integral cannot be interpreted as an area.) In this notation, our calculation for the parabola becomes

$$\int_0^1 x^2\, dx = \tfrac{1}{3}$$

Integrals are much harder to evaluate than derivatives, i.e., areas are much harder to find than tangents. In fact until the 1660's so much ingenuity was required to find areas that only a genius could do it. Then Newton's teacher Isaac Barrow discovered that the processes of finding the derivative and finding the integral are inverse processes. Newton quickly exploited this discovery which is called the Fundamental Theorem of Calculus and is proved in more advanced courses.

Fundamental Theorem of Calculus

If f is a continuous function and F is a function such that $F'(x) = f(x)$, then

$$\int_a^b f(x)\, dx = F(b) - F(a)$$

In other words to find an area $\int_a^b f$ all you have to do is think of a function F whose derivative is f, then evaluate F at b and at a, and subtract.

EXAMPLE 2. *Evaluate*

$$\int_0^1 x^2\, dx$$

using the Fundamental Theorem of Calculus.

Solution
If $F(x) = \tfrac{1}{3}x^3$, then $F'(x) = \tfrac{1}{3} \times 3x^2 = x^2$

$$\therefore \quad \int_0^1 x^2\, dx = F(1) - F(0) = \tfrac{1}{3} \times 1^2 - \tfrac{1}{3} \times 0^3 = \tfrac{1}{3}$$

This is much easier than the method we used earlier. In fact the Fundamental Theorem of Calculus is one of the most powerful methods in all of mathematics.

EXERCISE 12-9

B **1.** Find the areas of the sectors or segments shown.

(a)

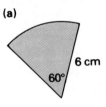

6 cm

60°

(b)

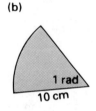

1 rad

10 cm

(c)

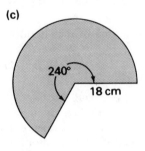

240°

18 cm

(d)

30°
12 cm

(e)

70°

9 cm

(f)

110°

3 cm

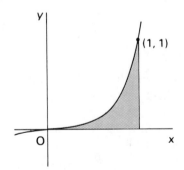

(1, 1)

2. Find the area under the curve $y = x^3$ from 0 to 1 using the method of approximating rectangles and the formula

$$1^3 + 2^3 + 3^3 + \ldots + n^3 = \left[\frac{n(n+1)}{2}\right]^2$$

3. Find the area in question 2 using the fundamental Theorem of Calculus.

4. Evaluate the following integrals using the Fundamental Theorem of Calculus.

(a) $\int_2^4 x^2 \, dx$

(b) $\int_3^5 x^3 \, dx$

(c) $\int_0^3 x^4 \, dx$

(d) $\int_1^2 (x^2 + x^4) \, dx$

(e) $\int_1^3 5x^2 \, dx$

(f) $\int_0^1 (4x^3 + 3x^2 + 2x + 1) \, dx$

5. Find the area of the region which lies between the curves $y = x^2$ and $y = x^3$. [*Hint:* Subtract two areas.]

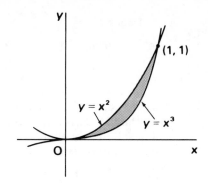

REVIEW EXERCISE

A **1.** State the limits of the following sequences if they exist.
(a) $5, 5\frac{1}{2}, 5\frac{2}{3}, 5\frac{3}{4}, 5\frac{4}{5}, 5\frac{5}{6}, \ldots$
(b) $1, -\frac{1}{2}, \frac{1}{3}, -\frac{1}{4}, \frac{1}{5}, -\frac{1}{6}, \ldots$
(c) $2, 4, 6, 8, 10, 12, \ldots$
(d) $0.9, 0.99, 0.999, 0.9999, 0.999\,99, \ldots$

2. State the values of the given limits.

(a) $\lim_{x \to 2} 3x + 1$

(b) $\lim_{x \to 2} x^2 - 1$

(c) $\lim_{x \to -1} \dfrac{x}{x - 1}$

(d) $\lim_{h \to 0} (h + 3h^2 - 1)$

B **3.** Evaluate the following limits if they exist.

(a) $\lim_{n \to \infty} \dfrac{1}{n^3}$

(b) $\lim_{n \to \infty} \dfrac{n + 1}{2n - 1}$

(c) $\lim_{n \to \infty} \dfrac{1 - n^2}{n + n^2}$

(d) $\lim_{n \to \infty} \left(\dfrac{2}{5}\right)^n$

(e) $\lim_{x \to -3} x^3 + \dfrac{x}{x^2 + 2}$

(f) $\lim_{x \to \pi} \sin x$

(g) $\lim_{x \to 2} \dfrac{x + 2}{x - 2}$

(h) $\lim_{x \to 2} \dfrac{3x^2 - 7x + 2}{x - 2}$

4. Find the sums of the following series if they exist.
(a) $1 + \frac{1}{3} + \frac{1}{9} + \frac{1}{27} + \frac{1}{81} + \ldots$
(b) $25 - 5 + 1 - \frac{1}{5} + \frac{1}{25} + \ldots$
(c) $1 - \frac{3}{2} + \frac{9}{4} - \frac{27}{8} + \frac{81}{16} - \ldots$
(d) $1 + 0.2 + 0.04 + 0.08 + 0.0016 + \ldots$

5. Express the following repeating decimals as fractions.
(a) $0.1\dot{5}$ (b) $1.13\dot{6}$ (c) $2.10\dot{5}$

6. Find the first 10 partial sums of the series

$$1 - \frac{1}{64} + \frac{1}{729} - \frac{1}{4096} + \ldots + \frac{(-1)^{n-1}}{n^6} + \ldots$$

Does it appear that this series is convergent? If so, find its sum correct to 5 decimal places.

7. Define $f(x) = \dfrac{\tan x - \sin x}{x^3}$, $x \neq 0$, x in radians. Evaluate $f(x)$ for $x = 1, 0.5, 0.4, 0.3,$ 0.2, 0.1, 0.05, and guess the value of

$$\lim_{x \to 0} \frac{\tan x - \sin x}{x^3}$$

8. For each of the following functions,
  (i) find its derivative (from first principles),
  (ii) find the equation of the tangent to the curve at the given point,
  (iii) graph the curve and the tangent.

(a) $y = x^2 + 1$ at $(2, 5)$ (b) $y = \dfrac{16}{x}$ at $(2, 8)$

(c) $y = x^4$ at $(-1, 1)$ (d) $y = x^3 - x^2$ at $(1, 0)$

9. Find the derivatives of the following functions using the rules for differentiation. (See Exercise 12-6, questions 4, 6.)
(a) $f(x) = 3x^3 + x$ (b) $f(x) = 8x^2 - 9x + 12$
(c) $f(x) = 1 + x - x^4$ (d) $y = t^3 - 87t^2 + 3t$

10. (a) Find the derivative of the function $f(x) = x^4 - 2x^2 + 1$
(b) Use the derivative to find the intervals on which f is increasing or decreasing.
(c) Use this information to sketch the graph of f.

11. A particle moves in a straight line according to the law $s = 6 + 25t + 32t^2$ where s is the displacement in metres and t is the time in seconds.
(a) Find the velocity of the particle as a function of t.
(b) Find the velocity
(i) at the start   (ii) after 1 s   (iii) after 10 s

12. Find the maximum and minimum values of the following functions.

(a) $f(x) = 4x^2 + 2x + 63$ (b) $f(x) = 2x + \dfrac{32}{x}$, $x > 0$.

13. The pages in a book are to have 3 cm margins at the top and bottom and 2 cm margins at the sides. If the area of the printed portion is to be 200 cm², what should the dimensions of the page be to use the least amount of paper?

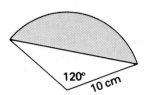

14. Find the area of the given segment.

120°   10 cm

15. Use the Fundamental Theorem of Calculus to find the areas of the shaded regions.

(a)

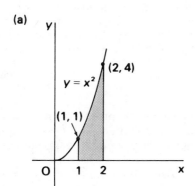

(b)

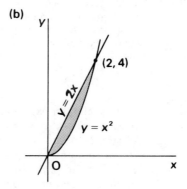

16. A right triangle ABC is given with $\angle A = \theta$ and $AC = b$. CD is drawn perpendicular to AB, DE is drawn perpendicular to BC, $EF \perp AB$, and this process is continued indefinitely. Find the total length of all the perpendiculars

$$CD + DE + EF + FG + \ldots$$

in terms of b and θ.

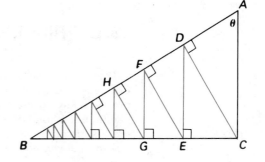

Determine the pattern.
Find the missing number.

32	5	78	15
48	12	59	14
71	8	98	

Problem-Solving

A great discovery solves a great problem but there is a grain of discovery in the solution of any problem. Your problem may be modest; but if it challenges your curiosity and brings into play your inventive faculties, and if you solve it by your own means, you may experience the tension and enjoy the triumph of discovery.

George Polya

In this chapter we present a collection of problems from many different areas of mathematics. To solve them you will have to draw upon the facts that you have learned during the past years, but none of them requires calculus.

Some of the problems are quite challenging and require a certain amount of ingenuity. However it is possible to improve your problem-solving abilities by following the steps outlined in Section 13-1 and by practicing on as many problems as possible.

13.1 PRINCIPLES OF PROBLEM-SOLVING

There are no hard and fast rules that will ensure success in solving problems. However it is possible to outline some general steps in the problem-solving process and to give some principles which may be useful in the solution of certain problems. These steps and principles are just common sense made explicit. They have been adapted from George Polya's book *How to Solve It*.

1. Understand the Problem. The first step is to make sure that the problem is clearly understood. Ask yourself the following questions. *What is the unknown? What are the given quantities? What are the given conditions?* For many problems it is useful to *draw a diagram* and identify the given and required quantities on the diagram.

2. Introduce suitable notation. In many (but not all) problems it is necessary to give names to some of the unknown quantities. In choosing symbols we often use letters such as $a, b, c, \ldots, m, n, \ldots, x, y, \ldots$, but in some cases it helps to use initials as suggestive symbols, e.g., V for volume, t for time.

3. Think of a plan. Find a connection between the given information and the unknown which will enable you to calculate the unknown. If the connection is not immediately seen, the following ideas may be helpful in devising a plan.

(a) Try to recognize something familiar. Relate the given situation to previous knowledge. Look at the unknown and try to recall a more familiar problem having a similar unknown.

(b) Try to recognize patterns. Some problems are solved by recognizing that some kind of pattern is occurring. The pattern could be geometrical, or numerical, or algebraic. If you can see that there is some sort of regularity or repetition in a problem, then you might be able to guess what the continuing pattern is, and then prove it.

(c) Use analogy. Try to think of an analogous problem, i.e., a similar problem, a related problem, but one which is easier than the original problem. If you can solve the similar, simpler problem, then it might give you the clues you need to solve the original, more difficult problem. For instance if a problem involves very large numbers, you could first try a similar problem with smaller numbers. (See Example 2.) Or if the problem is in 3-dimensional geometry, you could look for a similar problem in 2-dimensional geometry. (See Example 3.) Or if the problem you start with is a general one, you could first try a special case.

(d) Introduce something extra. It may sometimes be necessary to introduce something new, an auxiliary aid, to help make the connection between the given and the unknown. For instance in geometry the auxiliary aid could be a new line drawn in a diagram. In algebra it could be a new unknown which is related to the original unknown.

(e) Take cases. You may sometimes have to split a problem into several cases and give a different argument for each of the cases. (See Example 1.) For instance in a question in algebra involving a variable x you might have to treat the three cases $x < 0$, $0 \leq x \leq 1$, $x > 1$ separately.

(f) Work backwards. Sometimes it is useful to imagine that your problem is solved and work backwards, step by step, till you arrive at the given data. Then you may be able to reverse your steps and thereby construct a solution to the original problem.

4. Carry out the plan. In step 3 a plan was devised. In carrying out that plan you have to check each stage of the plan and write down the details that prove that each stage is correct. In checking your solution you may see an easier way of solving the problem.

5. Let your subconscious work. If you have tried very hard to solve a difficult problem without success, do not give up. Take a rest and come back to the problem the next day or after a few days. You will often find that a good idea occurs easily to you. The reason for this is that, while your were resting or thinking about other things, the mental processes which occur in your subconscious mind have been working on the problem by sorting out the various possibilities inherent in the problem. When you return to the problem, the clearer ideas emerge from your subconscious and you are sometimes able to solve the problem.

6. Imitate and practice. The best way to become proficient at solving problems is first to observe other people solving problems (e.g., a teacher or the following examples) and imitate what other people do in solving problems. Secondly one has to gain experience by solving a large number of problems. You will find that after you have solved some of the problems in Exercise 13-1 you will have the necessary insight and technique to solve many other problems.

EXAMPLE 1.   *Find a positive integer which gives a perfect square if 100 is added to it and another perfect square if 168 is added to it.*

Solution
Let x be the required integer.
Then $x + 100$ is a perfect square.

$$\therefore \quad x + 100 = m^2 \qquad \text{①}$$

where $m \in N$.
Also $x + 168$ is a perfect square.

$$\therefore \quad x + 168 = n^2 \qquad \text{②}$$

where $n \in N$.
We can eliminate x by subtracting equation ① from equation ②:

$$68 = n^2 - m^2$$

$$\therefore \quad 68 = (n - m)(n + m) \qquad \text{③}$$

Remember that $n - m$ and $n + m$ are integers, and so equation ③ must express a possible way of factoring 68.
But there are just 3 ways of factoring 68:

$$\text{(a)} \quad 68 = 1 \times 68$$

$$\text{(b)} \quad 68 = 2 \times 34$$

$$\text{(c)} \quad 68 = 4 \times 17$$

Thus there are three possible cases.

Case (1) $68 = 1 \times 68$ gives

$$n - m = 1$$

$$n + m = 68$$

$$\therefore \quad 2n = 69$$

$$n = 34.5$$

Case (1) is impossible since n must be an integer.

Case (2) $68 = 2 \times 34$ gives

$$n - m = 2$$

$$n + m = 34$$

$$\therefore \quad 2n = 36$$

$$n = 18$$

$$m = 16$$

Case (3) $68 = 4 \times 17$ gives

$$n - m = 4$$

$$n + m = 17$$

$$\therefore \quad 2n = 21$$

$$n = 10.5$$

Case (3) is impossible since n must be an integer.

Therefore the only possibility is

$$n = 18, \qquad m = 16$$

$$\therefore \quad x = m^2 - 100 \qquad \text{(from equation ①)}$$

$$= 256 - 100$$

$$= 156$$

The only number which satisfies the given conditions is 156.

EXAMPLE 2. *The positive integers are written down in order starting with* 1: 12345678910111213141516...
What digit is in the 319 468*th position?*

Solution

Since the problem looks complicated, we work by analogy and first solve an easier but similar problem:

What digit is in the 68th position?

Since there are 9 1-digit numbers and $68 - 9 = 59$, the 68th position must be in the 59th position among the 2-digit numbers. So we divide 59 by 2:

Try a simpler problem.

$$\frac{59}{2} = 29\tfrac{1}{2}$$

∴ the required digit must be the first digit of the 30th 2-digit number. Now the 30th 2-digit number is $9 + 30 = 39$. So the required digit is the first digit of 39, i.e., 3.
Now let's try a slightly harder problem:

What digit is in the 356th position?

Try another related problem.

There are $99 - 9 = 90$ 2-digit numbers which occupy $2 \times 90 = 180$ positions. So the 1-digit and 2-digit numbers occupy the first $9 + 180 = 189$ positions. Since $356 - 189 = 167$, the 356th position is the 168th position among the 3-digit numbers. So we divide 167 by 3:

$$\frac{167}{3} = 55\tfrac{2}{3}$$

∴ the required digit must be the second digit of the 56th 3-digit number. But the 56th 3-digit number is $99 + 56 = 155$. So the required digit is the second digit of 155, i.e., 5.
Armed with the clues from solving these two problems we are ready to tackle the original problem.
We have seen that the 1- and 2-digit numbers occupy the first 189 positions. There are $999 - 99 = 900$ 3-digit numbers which occupy $3 \times 900 = 2700$ positions. There are $9999 - 999 = 9000$ 4-digit numbers which occupy $4 \times 9000 = 36\,000$ positions. There are $99\,999 - 9999 = 90\,000$ 5-digit numbers which occupy $5 \times 90\,000 = 450\,000$ positions. Thus the 319 468th position must occur among the 5-digit numbers.

The 1-, 2-, 3-, and 4-digit numbers occupy the first

$$9 + 180 + 2700 + 36\,000 = 38\,889$$

positions. Since

$$319\,468 - 38\,889 = 280\,579$$

the 319 468th position is in the 280 579th position among the 5-digit numbers. So we divide 280 579 by 5:

$$\frac{280579}{5} = 56\,115\tfrac{4}{5}$$

∴ the required digit must be the 4th digit of the 56 116th 5-digit number. But the 56 116th 5-digit number is

$$9999 + 55\,116 = 65\,115$$

∴ the required digit is the 4th digit of 65 115, namely 1.

EXAMPLE 3. *Each edge of a cubical box has length 1 m. The box contains 9 spherical balls with the same radius r. The centre of one ball is at the centre of the cube and it touches the other 8 balls. Each of the other 8 balls touches 3 sides of the box, i.e., the balls are tightly packed in the box. Find r.*

Solution

analogy

Since 3-dimensional situations are often difficult to visualize and work with, let us first try to find an analogous problem in 2 dimensions.

The analogue of a cube is a square and the analogue of a sphere is a circle. Thus a similar problem in 2 dimensions is the following.

If 5 circles with the same radius r are contained in a square of side 1 m so that the circles touch each other and 4 of the circles touch 2 sides of the square, find r.

Draw a diagram

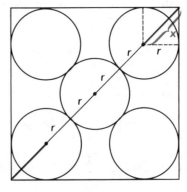

The diagonal of the square is $\sqrt{2}$.

The diagonal is also $4r + 2x$

But x is the diagonal of a smaller square of side r.

$$\therefore \quad x = \sqrt{2}r$$

$$\therefore \quad \sqrt{2} = 4r + 2x$$

$$= 4r + 2\sqrt{2}r$$

$$= (4 + 2\sqrt{2})r$$

$$\therefore \quad r = \frac{\sqrt{2}}{4 + 2\sqrt{2}}$$

Let us use these ideas to solve the original 3-dimensional problem.

The diagonal of the cube is $\sqrt{1^2 + 1^2 + 1^2} = \sqrt{3}$

The diagonal of the cube is also $4r + 2x$ where x is the diagonal of a smaller cube with edge r.

$$\therefore \quad x = \sqrt{r^2 + r^2 + r^2} = \sqrt{3}r$$

$$\therefore \quad \sqrt{3} = 4r + 2x$$

$$= 4r + 2\sqrt{3}r$$

$$= (4 + 2\sqrt{3})r$$

$$\therefore \quad r = \frac{3}{4 + 2\sqrt{3}} = \frac{2\sqrt{3} - 3}{2}$$

The radius of each ball is $\sqrt{3} - \frac{3}{2}$ m.

EXAMPLE 4. *Find the sum S of the squares of the first n positive integers.*

$$S = 1^2 + 2^2 + 3^2 + \ldots + n^2$$

Solution

Start with the identity

$$(n + 1)^3 = n^3 + 3n^2 + 3n + 1$$

or $\qquad\qquad (n + 1)^3 - n^3 = 3n^2 + 3n + 1$

This is true for any $n \in N$; write it down for $n = 1, 2, 3, \ldots$ successively.

$$2^3 - 1^3 = 3 \times 1^2 + 3 \times 1 + 1$$

$$3^3 - 2^3 = 3 \times 2^2 + 3 \times 2 + 1$$

$$4^3 - 3^3 = 3 \times 3^2 + 3 \times 3 + 1$$

$$\cdot$$
$$\cdot$$
$$\cdot$$

$$n^3 - (n - 1)^3 = 3(n - 1)^2 + 3(n - 1) + 1$$

$$(n + 1)^3 - n^3 = 3n^2 + 3n + 1$$

If we add all of these equations, then most of the terms on the left side will cancel and we get

$$(n+1)^3 - 1 = 3(1^2 + 2^2 + 3^2 + \ldots + n^2)$$
$$+ 3(1 + 2 + 3 + \ldots + n)$$
$$+ n$$

$$\therefore \quad (n+1)^3 - 1 = 3S + 3\frac{n(n+1)}{2} + n$$

Solve this equation for S.

$$2(n^3 + 3n^2 + 3n) = 6S + 3n^2 + 5n$$
$$6S = 2n^3 + 3n^2 + n$$
$$= n(n+1)(2n+1)$$
$$\therefore \quad S = \frac{n(n+1)(2n+1)}{6}$$
$$1^2 + 2^2 + 3^2 + \ldots + n^2 = \frac{n(n+1)(2n+1)}{6}$$

You may regard the solution of Example 4 as unsatisfactory because it depends on a trick that very few people would think of. But having seen that trick you are now in a position to use similar tricks in similar situations. (See question 43.)

EXERCISE 13-1

B **1.** How can you bring up from a river exactly 6 L of water when you have only two containers, a 9 L pail and a 4 L pail?

2. Mary buys a hockey stick on sale for $4.33 (including tax) which she pays for with a five dollar bill. The clerk gives her 10 coins as change, consisting of pennies, nickels, and quarters. Did she get the correct change?

3. If 3093 digits were used to number the pages of a book, how many pages are in the book?

4. What is the final digit in the number 4567^{535} (when multiplied out)?

5. $\triangle ABC$ is isosceles with $AB = AC$. P lies on AC and Q lies on AB in such a way that $BC = BP = PQ = QA$. Find $\angle B$.

6. A man must transport a goat, a wolf, and some cabbage across a river in a boat so small that he can only take one at a time. Furthermore, he must be on hand to keep the wolf from eating the goat and the goat from eating the cabbage. How does he do it?

7. Al gives Bob as many cents as Bob has and Cindy as many cents as Cindy has. Bob gives Al and Cindy as many cents as each then has. Cindy gives Al and Bob as many cents as each then has. Each of them ends up with 16 cents. How many cents did each have to start with?

8. Suppose that you start at a point P on the earth's surface and walk 1 km south, then 1 km east, then 1 km north and find yourself back at the same point P. Describe all points P for which this is possible. (There are infinitely many.)

9. $ABCD$ is a square with side 8 cm. A circle is drawn through A and D and is tangent to the side BC. Find the radius of the circle.

10. A clock has just struck 04:00. At what time in the next hour will the hands coincide?

11. The population of the town of Elk Horn in 1976 was a perfect square. By 1978 the population had increased by 100 and was one more than a perfect square. With a further increase of 100 the population was again a perfect square in 1980. Find the population of Elk Horn in 1976.

12. Show that the product of any 4 consecutive integers is one less than a perfect square.

13. Five married couples had to cross a river in a boat that would only hold 3 people at a time. Each husband would not allow his wife to be in a boat or on either bank with another man unless he was himself present. What is the quickest way of getting the five couples across the river? (Being at a bank but still in the boat counts as being on the bank.)

14. A point P is located in the interior of a rectangle so that the distance from P to one corner of the rectangle is 5 cm, from P to the opposite corner 14 cm, and from P to a third corner 10 cm. What is the distance from P to the fourth corner?

15. If n men working n hours a day (at the same rate) for each of n days produce n articles, how many articles are produced by m men working m hours a day for each of m days?

16. An aircraft makes a regular reconnaissance flight every day from the airport to Skull Island and back. Skull Island is 200 km from the airport. The flight is always made at the same airspeed. If there is no wind, the same amount of fuel is used each day. On a particular day the pilot starts his trip with a tail wind. If the wind does not change, will the total flight require more, equal or less fuel than on a day with no wind?

17. Two circles are concentric and the area of the shaded region in 25π cm^2. Find the length of a chord of the larger circle which is tangent to the smaller circle.

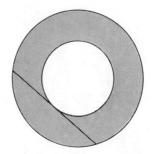

18. A rhombus is given with one diagonal twice the length of the other diagonal. If the area of the rhombus is A, find the length of the side of the rhombus in terms of A.

19. The positive integers are written down in order starting with 1. What digit is in the millionth position?

20. Suppose that in counting a set of n balls, some blue and some green, it was found that 49 of the first 50 balls were blue and of the remainder 7 out of every 8 were blue. If at least 90% of the balls were blue, find the maximum value of n.

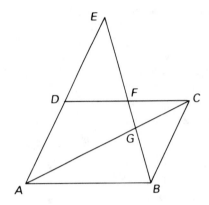

21. $ABCD$ is a parallelogram, E is on AD produced, BE intersects CD at F and AC at G. If $EF = 18$ cm and $FG = 6$ cm, find GB.

22. The integers from 1 to 1000 are written in order around a large circle. Starting at 1, every fifteenth number is crossed out $(1, 16, 31, 46, \ldots)$. This is continued until a number is reached which has already been crossed out. How many numbers are left?

23. Three containers hold 19 L, 13 L, and 7 L respectively. The 19 L container is empty. The other two are full. How can you measure out 10 L using no other container?

24. Find the number of solutions of the equation $2x + 3y = 715$ if x and y must be positive integers.

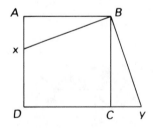

25. $ABCD$ is a square with area 256 cm². X lies on AD and BY is drawn perpendicular to BX meeting DC produced at Y. The area of $\triangle XBY$ is 200 cm². Find the length of CY.

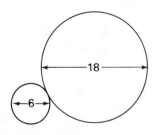

26. Two poles with diameters 6 cm and 18 cm are placed as in the diagram and are bound together with wire. What is the length of the shortest wire that will go around them?

27. You are given 80 similar coins and are told that one of the coins is counterfeit and is lighter than the others. How can you locate the counterfeit coin using a balance 4 times?

28. A sequence is given by

$$10^{\frac{1}{n}}, 10^{\frac{2}{n}}, 10^{\frac{3}{n}}, 10^{\frac{4}{n}}, \ldots$$

Find the smallest value of n such that the product of the first n terms is greater than 100 000.

29. How many positive integers less than 1000 are divisible neither by 5 nor by 7?

30. $ABCD$ is a square whose side has length 4 cm. If a point E on AB and a point F on AD are chosen so that $AE = AF$ and the quadrilateral $CDFE$ has maximum area, find this maximum area.

31. A regular polygon with n sides is inscribed in a circle with radius r. The area of the polygon is $3r^2$. What is n?

32. Let n be the product of the first 100 positive integers, i.e., $n = 100!$ How many zeros are at the end of the number n?

33. If $S = 1! + 2! + 3! + 4! + \ldots + 99!$ what is the last digit in the value of S?

34. In how many ways can ten dollars be changed into dimes and quarters?

35. (a) Three tangent circles of radius 10 cm are drawn. All centres lie on the line AB. The tangent AC to the right hand circle is drawn, intersecting the middle circle at D and E. Find the length DE.

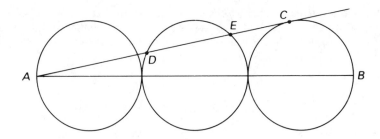

(b) Given that the radius of each circle is r, find an expression for DE in terms of r.

36. Find the value of $x + y + z$ if

$$\log_3 (\log_4 x) = \log_4 (\log_2 y) = \log_2 (\log_3 z) = 1$$

37. Find an integer n such that $\dfrac{n}{2}$ is a perfect square and $\dfrac{n}{3}$ is a perfect cube.

38. George has 44 quarters and 10 pockets. He wants to put the quarters into his pockets in such a way that each pocket contains a different amount of money. Can he do it?

39. Among 12 similar coins there is one counterfeit. It is not known whether the counterfeit coin is lighter or heavier than a genuine coin. Using a balance 3 times, how can the counterfeit be identified and in the process determined to be lighter or heavier than a genuine coin?

40. The perimeter of a right triangle is 60 cm and the altitude perpendicular to the hypotenuse is 12 cm. Find the three sides of the triangle.

41. Solve the following system of equations.

$$x + 5y + 3z + 7t = -16$$
$$6x + 4y + 8z + 2t = 16$$
$$2x + 8y + 4z + 6t = -16$$
$$7x + 3y + 5z + \ \ t = 16$$

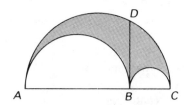

42. Semicircles are constructed on diameters AB, BC, AC so that they are tangent to each other. If $BD \perp AC$, find the ratio of the area of the shaded region to the area of the circle with BD as radius.

43. Use a method similar to that of Example 4 to find a formula for the sum of the cubes of the first n positive integers.

44. A man walked across the city at a constant rate. If he had gone 0.5 km/h faster, he would have walked the distance in 0.8 of the time. If he had gone 0.5 km/h slower, he would have taken 2.5 h longer. What is the distance from one end of the city to the other?

45. Show that

$$1 - \frac{1}{2} + \frac{1}{3} - \frac{1}{4} + \ldots + \frac{1}{199} - \frac{1}{200} = \frac{1}{101} + \frac{1}{102} + \frac{1}{103} + \ldots + \frac{1}{200}$$

46 In $\triangle ABC$, $a = b = \sqrt{3}$ and $c > 3$. Show that $\angle C > 120°$.

47. A paper rectangle is 10 cm long and less than 8 cm wide. It is folded so that two diagonally opposite corners coincide. The length of the crease is $2\sqrt{6}$ cm. How wide is the rectangle?

48. Show that if $a + b + c = 0$, then $a^3 + b^3 + c^3 = 3abc$.

49. Express the length of the hypotenuse of a right triangle in terms of its area A and its perimeter P.

50. Place 8 Queens on a chessboard in such a way that none of the Queens is attacking another Queen. All 12 solutions are required. (Solutions that are the result of rotations or reflections are considered equivalent.)

51. The current in a river flows steadily at 3 km/h. A boat which travels at a constant speed in still water goes downstream 4 km and then returns to its starting point. The trip takes one hour. Find the ratio of the downstream speed to the upstream speed.

52. Two people are seated at a square-topped table. One places a playing card flat on the table, then the other does the same, and so on alternately. The condition is that no card can touch another card. Assuming that each person plays in the best possible manner, and there are an unlimited number of cards, who should play the last card?

53. Bob, Dave, and Ed, when working together, do a job in 6 h less time than Bob alone, in 1 h less time than Dave alone, and in half the time needed by Ed when working alone. How long does it take Bob and Dave to do the job together?

54. Find the sum of the digits of all the numbers in the sequence $1, 2, 3, 4, \ldots, 100\,000$.

55. Five men and their pet monkey Sarah live on a desert island. One afternoon the men gathered a large pile of coconuts which they decided to divide equally among themselves the next morning. During the night one man awoke and helped himself to his share of the coconuts. He divided them into five equal parts and found there was one coconut left over which he gave to Sarah. He hid his share, left the remainder in a single pile, and went back to sleep. Later that night a second man awoke and had the same idea. He divided the pile into five equal parts, found there was one coconut left over which he also gave to Sarah, hid his share, left the remainder in a single pile and went back to sleep. That same night each of the other three men awoke and, not realizing what had happened, followed exactly the same procedure as the first two men. The next morning all five men went to the depleted pile, divided it into five equal parts and found there was one coconut left over. What is the smallest number of coconuts that the original pile could have contained?

56. If the integers from 1 to 222 222 222 are written down, what is the total number of 0's that have been written?

57. If c is the hypotenuse of a right triangle and a, b are the other two sides, prove that $c^n > a^n + b^n$ if $n \in N$ and $n > 2$. [*Hint:* Write $c^n = c^2 \times c^{n-2}$.]

58. Let P be a point outside a given square, but in the same plane as the square. The smallest angle θ with vertex P and containing the square is called "angle under which the square is seen" from P. Find the locus of points from which the square is seen under an angle of
(a) 90°   (b) 45°

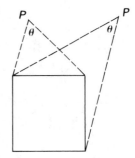

59. Prove that the product of the first n positive integers is divisible by their sum if and only if $n + 1$ is not an odd prime.

60. Given a point P on one side of a triangle, construct a line through P which will divide the area of the triangle in half.

61. A rectangular floor is composed of square tiles of the same size. There are 84 along one side and 52 along the other. If a straight line is drawn diagonally across the floor from corner to corner, how many tiles will it cross?

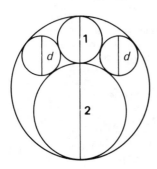

62. A foreman noticed an inspector checking a 3 cm hole with a 2 cm plug and a 1 cm plug and suggested that 2 more gauges be inserted to be sure that the fit was snug. If the new guages are the same size with diameter d, find d.

63. One way to write 100 in the form of a mixed number, using all the nine digits once and only once, is

$$91\frac{5823}{647}$$

Find the ten other ways of doing this.

64. An escalator has n steps visible at any given time and it descends at constant speed. Sue and Ann walk down the escalator steadily as it moves, Sue taking twice as many steps per minute as Ann.

  Sue reaches the bottom after taking 27 steps, while Ann reaches the bottom after taking 18 steps. Find n.

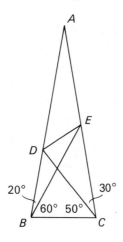

65. Find $\angle BED$.

ANSWERS

CHAPTER 1

Exercise 1-1

1. **(a)** -1 **(b)** -3 **(c)** 31 **(d)** -9
   (e) -2 **(f)** 0 **(g)** -21 **(h)** 197
   (i) $2a-3$ **(j)** $-2a-3$
2. **(a)** 1 **(b)** $\frac{1}{24}$ **(c)** -1 **(d)** $-\frac{1}{3}$
   (e) $\dfrac{1}{\pi-1}$
3. **(a)** 24 **(b)** 10 **(c)** 5 **(d)** 10
   (e) 64 **(f)** 8 **(g)** $\frac{1}{4}$ **(h)** 3
   (i) $\frac{1}{16}$
4. **(a)** $\{1, 2, 3, 4\}$, $\{0, 3, 6, 9\}$, onto
   (b) $\{-2, -1, 0, 1, 2\}$, $\{2, 6, 8, 10\}$
   (c) $\{a, b, c\}$, $\{3\}$
   (d) $\{1, 2, 3, 4\}$, $\{1, 2, 3\}$, onto
5. **(a)** $\{x \mid -4 \leqslant x \leqslant 4\}$ $\{y \mid -4 \leqslant y \leqslant 3\}$
   (b) $\{x \mid x \neq 0\}$ $\{y \mid y > 0\}$
   (c) $\{x \mid -3 \leqslant x \leqslant 3\}$ $\{-1, 1, 3\}$
6. **(b)** and **(c)**
7. **(a)** 5 **(b)** 29 **(c)** 0.71 **(d)** 109
   (e) t^2-3t+1 **(f)** x^2-x-1 **(g)** t^4-3t^2+1 **(h)** x^2+3x+1
8. **(a)** 0 **(b)** -4 **(c)** 104 **(d)** -1.248
   (e) $3\sqrt{2}-3$ **(f)** $-t^3+2t^2-2t$ **(g)** $x^6-x^4+x^2-1$ **(h)** $3x^2+x+1$
9. **(a)** 1 **(b)** $\sqrt{17}$ **(c)** $\sqrt{17}$ **(d)** $5\sqrt{2}$
   (e) 5 **(f)** $\sqrt{x^2+1}$ **(g)** $\sqrt{x^4+1}$ **(h)** $\sqrt{9x^2+1}$
10. **(a)** 6 **(b)** 2 **(c)** 384 **(d)** $\frac{3}{14}$
    (e) $\frac{2}{3}$ **(f)** 256
11. **(a)** R **(b)** R **(c)** $\{x \mid x \geqslant 0\}$ **(d)** $\{x \mid x \leqslant 8\}$
    (e) $\{x \mid x \neq \frac{5}{3}\}$ **(f)** $\{x \mid x > -4\}$ **(g)** $\{x \mid x \neq 1, 3\}$ **(h)** $\{x \mid -2 \leqslant x \leqslant 2\}$
    (i) R **(j)** $\{x \mid |x| \geqslant 2\}$ **(k)** R **(l)** $\{x \mid x \neq -3, 2\}$
12. **(a)** R **(b)** $\{y \mid 0 \leqslant y \leqslant 25\}$ **(c)** $\{y \mid y \geqslant 5\}$
    (d) $\{y \mid y \leqslant 0\}$ **(e)** $\{y \mid -27 \leqslant y \leqslant 8\}$ **(f)** $\{y \mid y \geqslant -1\}$
13. **(a)**, **(c)**, **(e)**
15. **(a)** 1 **(b)** 4 **(c)** 7 **(d)** 12 **(e)** 4
16. **(a)** 5 s   **(c)** 30.625 m
17. **(a)** 146 **(b)** -52 **(c)** 171 **(d)** -27 **(e)** $25x^2-30x+11$
    (f) $-5x^2-7$
18. **(a)** 3 **(b)** $-\frac{1}{2}$ **(c)** 0 **(d)** 1 **(e)** $\dfrac{1-2x}{1-x}$ **(f)** $\dfrac{1-x}{x}$
19. **(a)** (i) 0 (ii) 1 (iii) 1
    (b) (i) 1 (ii) 0 (iii) 1
    (c) (i) -1 (ii) -1 (iii) -1
    (d) (i) -1 (ii) 0 (iii) 1
    (e) (i) 0 (ii) 1 (iii) 0
    (f) (i) 0 (ii) 0 (iii) 0
20. **(a)** $P(t) = \begin{cases} 6t & \text{if } 0 \leqslant t \leqslant 40 \\ 240+9(t-40) & \text{if } t > 40 \end{cases}$ **(b)** \$210, \$285
21. **(a)** $23.851\,41$ **(b)** $0.157\,56$ **(c)** $10.374\,49$ **(d)** $0.090\,16$

Exercise 1-2

1. **(a)** increasing when $-5 \leqslant x \leqslant -2$ and when $0 \leqslant x \leqslant 2$
   decreasing when $-2 \leqslant x \leqslant 0$ and when $2 \leqslant x \leqslant 5$
   (b) decreasing when $-6 \leqslant x \leqslant -4$, $-2 \leqslant x \leqslant 0$, and $2 \leqslant x \leqslant 4$
   increasing when $4 \leqslant x \leqslant 8$
2. **(a)** odd   **(b)** even   **(c)** even   **(d)** neither   **(e)** odd   **(f)** even

3. (a) and (d)

6. (a) decreasing when $-5 \leqslant x \leqslant -2$, increasing when $-2 \leqslant x \leqslant 1$
    (b) increasing when $-1 \leqslant x \leqslant 3$, decreasing when $3 \leqslant x \leqslant 7$
    (c) decreasing when $x \leqslant 2$, increasing when $x \geqslant 2$
    (d) increasing when $x \leqslant -2$, decreasing when $x \geqslant -2$
    (e) increasing when $-3 \leqslant x \leqslant 1$ and when $2 \leqslant x \leqslant 3$,
    decreasing when $1 \leqslant x \leqslant 2$

8. (i) $2x^2 + 5$, even   (ii) $2x^2 + x$, neither   (iii) x^4, even   (iv) $-x^3 + x$, odd

    (v) $x^4 + x^3$, neither   (vi) $\dfrac{1}{x^2}$, even   (vii) $-x^5$, odd   (viii) $|1 - x^2|$, even

9. (a) even   (b) neither   (c) even   (d) odd   (e) odd   (f) odd

Exercise 1-3

1. (a) (i) $x^2 + 4x + 1$ (ii) $x^2 + 2x + 1$ (iii) $-x^2 - 2x - 1$ (iv) $x^3 + 3x^2 + x$ (v) $x + 3 + \dfrac{1}{x}$
    (b) (i)–(iv) R (v) $\{x \mid x \neq 0\}$

2. (i)(a) $x^3 + x + 1$ (b) $-x^3 + x + 3$ (c) B
    (ii)(a) $9x^7 - x$ (b) $7x^7 + x$ (c) $\{x \mid 0 \leqslant x \leqslant 4\}$
    (iii)(a) $2x^3 - x^2 + 2x$ (b) $-x^2 + 2x - 2$ (c) $\{x \mid 1 < x < 2\}$

3. (i)(a) $x^2 - 1$ (b) R (c) $\dfrac{x+1}{x-1}$ (d) $\{x \mid x \neq 1\}$

    (ii)(a) $x^3 - 4x$ (b) A (c) $\dfrac{x}{x^2 - 4}$ (d) $\{x \mid -3 < x < 3, x \neq 2, -2\}$

    (iii)(a) $\sqrt{x^2 + x}$ (b) B (c) $\sqrt{\dfrac{x+1}{x}}$ (d) $\{x \mid x > 0\}$

4. (i)(a) $2x^2 - 3x + 4$ (b) $3x$ (c) $-3x$
    (d) $x^4 - 3x^3 + 4x^2 - 6x + 4$ (domain = R)   (e) $\dfrac{x^2 + 2}{x^2 - 3x + 2}$ (domain = $\{x \mid x \neq 1, 2\}$)

    (ii)(a) $x^3 + x^2 + 3$ (b) $x^3 - x^2 - 5$ (c) $-x^3 + x^2 + 5$
    (d) $x^5 - 4x^3 - x^2 - 4$ (domain = B)   (e) $\dfrac{x^3 - 1}{x^2 + 4}$ (domain = B)

    (iii)(a) $2x^4 + x^2 + 1$ (b) $x^2 + 1$ (c) $-x^2 - 1$
    (d) $x^8 + x^6 + x^4$ (domain = R)   (e) $1 + \dfrac{1}{x^2} + \dfrac{1}{x^4}$ (domain = $\{x \mid x \neq 0\}$)

    (iv)(a) $\sqrt{x^2 - 1} + \sqrt{4 - x^2}$ (b) $\sqrt{x^2 - 1} - \sqrt{4 - x^2}$ (c) $\sqrt{4 - x^2} - \sqrt{x^2 - 1}$
    (d) $\sqrt{-x^4 + 5x^2 - 4}$ (domain = $\{x \mid 1 \leqslant |x| \leqslant 2\}$)
    (e) $\sqrt{\dfrac{x^2 - 1}{4 - x^2}}$ (domain = $\{x \mid 1 \leqslant |x| < 2\}$)

    (v)(a) $x^4 - 3x^3 + 2x^2 - 4x - 16$ (b) $x^4 - 3x^3$ (c) $-x^4 + 3x^3$
    (d) $x^6 - 5x^5 - x^4 + 20x^3 - 12x^2 + 32x + 64$ (domain = B)
    (e) $\dfrac{x^4 - 3x^3 + x^2 - 2x - 8}{x^2 - 2x - 8}$ (domain = $\{x \mid -2 < x < 4\}$)

7. (i) $1 + x$, R (ii) $x^2 + 2x$, R (iii) $x^2 + 1$, $\{x \mid 0 \leqslant x \leqslant 2\}$
    (iv) $x + \sqrt{x}$, $\{x \mid x \geqslant 0\}$ (v) $x^3 - x$, R (vi) $\sqrt{16 - x^2} + x$, $\{x \mid |x| \leqslant 4\}$

9. $2, -3$

10. (a) $\{x \mid x \neq 2, -2\}$, $\{x \mid x \neq 2\}$, $\{x \mid x \neq 2, -2\}$ (b) -2.25

11. (a) $\sin x + \tan x$ (b) $\sin x - \tan x$ (c) $\sin x \tan x = \dfrac{\sin^2 x}{\cos x}$

    (d) $\cos x \left(\text{domain} = \left\{ x \mid 0 \leqslant x < \dfrac{\pi}{2} \right\} \right)$

Exercise 1-4

1. (a) 2   (b) 5   (c) 4   (d) 5   (e) 4   (f) 16   (g) 1   (h) 2

2. (a) Ken   (b) Vera   (c) Ken   (d) Sally   (e) Don
    (f) Ann   (g) Bill   (h) Ann   (i) Jim   (j) Glen
    (k) Vera   (l) Sue   (m) Ken   (n) Mary   (o) Glen

4. $(f \circ g)(x)$ $(g \circ f)(x)$ $(f \circ f)(x)$ $(g \circ g)(x)$
    (a) $40x - 39$ $40x + 39$ $25x + 36$ $64x - 81$
    (b) $2x^3 - 1$ $8x^3 - 12x^2 + 6x - 1$ $4x - 3$ x^9

(c) x	x	$49x - 48$	$\dfrac{x+48}{49}$
(d) 17	280	17	$x^4 - 18x^2 + 72$
(e) x^2	x^2	x	x^4
(f) $x^2 - x + 3$	$-x^2 + x - 2$	$x^4 - 2x^3 + 6x^2 - 5x + 9$	x
(g) $\dfrac{3}{x^2+1} - 4$	$\dfrac{1}{9x^2 - 24x + 17}$	$9x - 16$	$\dfrac{x^4 + 2x^2 + 1}{x^4 + 2x^2 + 2}$
(h) x^2	x^2	$|x|$	x^4
(i) $\sqrt{x^2+1}$	$x + 1$	$\sqrt[4]{x}$	$x^4 + 2x^2 + 2$
(j) $\dfrac{3x^2 + 10x + 9}{2x^2 + 6x + 5}$	$\dfrac{2x^2 + 6x + 5}{3x^2 + 8x + 6}$	$\dfrac{3x^2 + 8x + 6}{2x^2 + 6x + 5}$	$\dfrac{2x^2 + 6x + 5}{3x^2 + 10x + 9}$

5. **(a)** f: domain $= R$, range $= \{y \mid y \geqslant 2\}$

   g: domain $= \{x \mid -1 \leqslant x \leqslant 1\}$, range $= \{y \mid 0 \leqslant y \leqslant 1\}$

   (b) $f \circ g$ is defined but $g \circ f$ is not since the range of f is not contained in the domain of g.

7. $g(x) = 4x - 5$

8. $g(x) = x^2 + x - 1$

9. $g(x) = 4x - 17$

10. $(f \circ f)(x) = \dfrac{x^4 + 3x^2 + 1}{x(x^2 + 1)}$ $(f \circ f \circ f)(x) = \dfrac{x^8 + 7x^6 + 13x^4 + 7x^2 + 1}{x(x^2 + 1)(x^4 + 3x^2 + 1)}$

11. **(a)** $\sin(5x)$ $5 \sin x$ $\sin(\sin x)$ $25x$

  (b) $\cos^2 x + 3$ $\cos(x^2 + 3)$ $x^4 + 6x^2 + 12$ $\cos(\cos x)$

12. **(a)** f: domain $= \{x \mid |x| \geqslant \sqrt{2}\}$, range $= \{y \mid y \geqslant 0\}$

   g: domain $= R$, range $= \{y \mid -1 \leqslant y \leqslant 1\}$

   (b) $g \circ f$ is defined but $f \circ g$ is not.

Exercise 1-5

1. **(a)** shift 6 units upward   **(b)** shift 6 units to the left

  (c) shift 8 units downward   **(d)** shift 8 units to the right

  (e) vertical stretch   **(f)** reflect in x-axis

  (g) stretch and reflect in x-axis   **(h)** vertical shrink

  (i) shrink and reflect in x-axis   **(j)** shift 2 units to the right

  (k) shift 3 units upwards   **(l)** shift 1 unit to the left

  (m) vertical stretch   **(n)** vertical stretch, then shift 1 unit upward

  (o) shift 1 unit to the left   **(p)** shift 1 unit to the left, then stretch vertically

  (q) stretch and reflect in x-axis   **(r)** stretch and reflect in x-axis, then shift 3 units downward

  (s) vertical shrink   **(t)** vertical shrink, then shift 1 unit downward

9. **(a)** 0, 2, 2, 4, 4, 2, 2, 0

11. **(a)** reflect in y-axis

  (b) shrink and reflect in y-axis if $c < -1$

  stretch and reflect in y-axis if $-1 < c < 0$

12. **(a)** vertical stretch, then shift 2 units upward

  (b) reflect in x-axis, then shift 1 unit upward

  (c) shift 5 units to the left

  (d) horizontal shrink

  (e) horizontal shrink, then vertical stretch

  (f) horizontal stretch, then shift 1 unit downward

  (g) reflect in x-axis

  (h) reflect in y-axis

  (i) reflect in both x-axis and y-axis

  (j) horizontal shrink, then vertical shrink, then shift 3 units upward

13. **(a)** shift $\dfrac{d}{c}$ units to the left, then shrink horizontally

  (b) shift $\dfrac{|d|}{c}$ units to the right, then shrink horizontally

  (c) shift $\dfrac{d}{c}$ units to the left, then stretch horizontally

  (d) shift $\dfrac{|d|}{c}$ units to the right, then stretch horizontally

Exercise 1-6

1. (b), (c)
2. (b), (c), (f)
3. (a), (c), (d), (g), (i), (j), (k)

5.

$f^{-1}(x)$	domain	range
(a) $\dfrac{2-x}{5}$	R	R
(b) $\dfrac{x-6}{13}$	R	R
(c) $\sqrt{x}$	$\{x \mid x \geqslant 0\}$	$\{y \mid y \geqslant 0\}$
(d) $\dfrac{1}{x}$	$\{x \mid x \neq 0\}$	$\{y \mid y \neq 0\}$
(e) $\sqrt[3]{x}$	R	R
(f) $\dfrac{x+2}{3}$	$\{x \mid -2 \leqslant x \leqslant 10\}$	$\{y \mid 0 \leqslant y \leqslant 4\}$

6. **(a)** $y = 2x + 7$ **(b)** $y = 36 - 5x$ **(c)** $y = \sqrt[3]{\dfrac{x+6}{5}}$

(d) $y = x^2, x \geqslant 0$ **(e)** $y = x^2 + 3, x \geqslant 0$ **(f)** $y = \dfrac{1}{x-1}$

(g) $y = \dfrac{1}{x} - 1$ **(h)** $y = \dfrac{1-x}{1+x}$ **(i)** $y = \dfrac{-2x-1}{3x-4}$

(j) $y = \dfrac{\pi}{x+3}$ **(k)** $y = \sqrt[4]{x}$ **(l)** $y = \sqrt{\dfrac{x}{3} + 1}$

(m) $y = \sqrt{x^2 - 9}$ **(n)** $y = \sqrt{25 - x^2}, x \geqslant 0$

7. **(a)** $f^{-1}(x) = \dfrac{x+8}{5}$ **(b)** $f^{-1}(x) = x^2$ **(c)** $f^{-1}(x) = \dfrac{1-3x}{2x}$

In each case $(f \circ f^{-1})(x) = x = (f^{-1} \circ f)(x)$

9. (iii)**(a)** $\dfrac{x-1}{2}$ **(b)** $\sqrt{x-2}$ **(c)** $\sqrt[3]{x}$ **(d)** $-\dfrac{1}{x}$

Review Exercise

1. **(a)** 7   **(b)** 0   **(c)** 14   **(d)** 10   **(e)** -1 **(f)** 98
    (g) -10 **(h)** -6 **(i)** -12 **(j)** -2 **(k)** 62   **(l)** $\pi^2 - 2$
2. **(a)** $\{1, 0, -1\}$, $\{5, 6, 7\}$, onto, $1-1$ **(b)** $\{1, 2, 3, 4\}$, $\{\pi, 2\pi, 3\pi\}$, onto
    (c) $\{1, 2, 3\}$, $\{5, 7, 9\}$, $1-1$ **(d)** $\{2, 4, 6\}$, $\{1, 3\}$
3. (a), (c), (d) are functions. (c) is $1-1$.
4. **(a)** 5   **(b)** 3   **(c)** 7   **(d)** 7   **(e)** 2   **(f)** -2 **(g)** 1   **(h)** 10
5. **(a)** shift 4 units downward   **(b)** shift 4 units to the right
    (c) vertical stretch   **(d)** horizontal shrink
    (e) reflect in x-axis
    (f) shift 1 unit to the left, then stretch vertically
    (g) shift 1 unit to the right, then shift 2 units upward
    (h) shrink vertically, then shift 5 units downward
6. **(a)** 52   **(b)** 2.5   **(c)** -1.971 **(d)** 0

    (e) 8.125   **(f)** 1.3   **(g)** $t^3 - 3t$ **(h)** $t - 2 + \dfrac{2}{t}$

8. **(a)** odd   **(b)** even   **(c)** neither   **(d)** even

10.

	$(f \circ g)(x)$	$(g \circ f)(x)$	$(f \circ f)(x)$	$(g \circ g)(x)$
(a)	$x^2 - 4x + 4$	$x^2 - 2$	x^4	$x - 4$
(b)	$x^4 - 2x^2 + 2$	$x^4 + 2x^2$	$x^4 + 2x^2 + 2$	$x^4 - 2x^2$
(c)	$\lvert x \rvert$	x	$\sqrt[4]{x}$	x^4
(d)	$\dfrac{x-1}{2x-1}$	$-\dfrac{1}{x}$	$\dfrac{x+1}{x+2}$	x

11. **(a)** $y = \dfrac{x-9}{2}$ **(c)** $y = x^2 - 1, x \geqslant 0$ **(d)** $y = \sqrt[3]{1-x}$ **(f)** $y = \sqrt{x} - 2$ **(g)** $y = 5\dfrac{x+1}{x-1}$

REVIEW AND PREVIEW TO CHAPTER 2

Exercise 1

1. **(a)** $y = -3x + 1$ **(b)** $y = 2x - 6$ **(c)** $y = -3x + 1$ **(d)** $y = \dfrac{2x - 10}{5}$

2. (a) $2, -3$ **(b)** $-2, 1$ **(c)** $\frac{2}{3}, \frac{5}{3}$ **(d)** $-\frac{3}{2}, 3$ **(e)** $-3, 3$ **(f)** $\frac{3}{2}, -3$

3. (a) $y = 3x - 9$ **(b)** $y = \dfrac{x + 11}{2}$ **(c)** $y = \dfrac{x + 8}{2}$ **(d)** $y = x + 2$ **(e)** $y = 4$ **(f)** $x = -5$

4. (a) $y = mx + 2$ **(b)** $y = 3x + b$ **(c)** $y = -2x + b$ **(d)** $y = -\frac{1}{3}x + b$
(e) $y - 5 = m(x - 2)$ **(f)** $y + 5 = m(x - 2)$ **(g)** $y + 3 = m(x + 1)$ **(h)** $x = k$
(i) $y - 3 = m(x - 1)$ **(j)** $y = -2x + b$ **(k)** $y = mx$

Exercise 3

1. (a) $x + 6$ **(b)** $1 - 2xy$ **(c)** $3c - 2$ **(d)** $2x - \frac{4}{3}$ **(e)** $-3 + \frac{7}{2}m$ **(f)** $\left(1 + \dfrac{5y}{x}\right)$ **(g)** $(x^2 - \frac{9}{5}x)$

(h) $(x^2 - \frac{4}{3}x)$ **(i)** $x - \frac{4}{3}$ **(j)** $(\frac{4}{7} - x)$ **(k)** $x^2 + 6x$ **(l)** $x^2 - 6x$ **(m)** $x^2 - 6x$ **(n)** $x^2 + 6x$

Exercise 2-1

1. (a) $(0, 0)$ **(b)** $(0, 3)$ **(c)** $(0, 0)$ **(d)** $(0, 5)$ **(e)** $(-1, 0)$ **(f)** $(4, 2)$ **(g)** $(-6, 0)$
(h) $(0, -6)$ **(i)** $(1, -6)$ **(j)** $(0, 7)$ **(k)** $(3, 0)$ **(l)** $(-5, 0)$ **(m)** $(0, -7)$ **(n)** $(-6, -10)$
(o) $(3, -3)$ **(p)** $(\frac{1}{2}, 0)$ **(q)** $(3, -0.7)$ **(r)** $(0, -3.4)$ **(s)** $(0, 0)$ **(t)** $(-5, -10)$ **(u)** $(1, 8)$

2. (a) $y = 4x^2$ **(b)** $y = -3x^2$ **(c)** $y = -\frac{1}{2}x^2$ **(d)** $y = x^2 + 4$
(e) $y = -2x^2 - 3$ **(f)** $y = 6x^2 - 4$ **(g)** $y = 2(x - 5)^2$ **(h)** $y = -3(x + 4)^2$
(i) $y = \frac{1}{2}(x + 6)^2$ **(j)** $y = -(x - 3)^2 + 2$ **(k)** $y = -2(x + 3)^2 + 5$ **(l)** $y = 4(x - 4)^2 - 3$
(m) $y = -3x^2 + 6$ **(n)** $y = -5(x + 6)^2 - 7$ **(o)** $y = \frac{1}{3}(x + 5)^2$ **(p)** $y = -\frac{1}{3}x^2$
(q) $y = -\frac{1}{2}(x - 6)^2 + 6$ **(r)** $y = -5(x + 7)^2 + 2$ **(s)** $y = 4x^2 - 7$ **(t)** $y = -7(x + 3)^2 - 4$
(u) $y = -11(x + 6)^2$

4. (a) $y = (x - 3)^2 + 2$ **(b)** $y = -2(x + 1)^2 - 3$ **(c)** $y = 4(x + 3)^2 + 6$ **(d)** $y = -3(x - 2)^2 - 4$
(e) $y = \frac{1}{2}(x - 2)^2 - 6$ **(f)** $y = -(x + 4)^2 + 3$

5. (a) 5 **(b)** $3, -1$ **(c)** -4 **(d)** $1, 3$ **(e)** $2, 6$ **(f)** -7

6. (a) $a = 2, k = 2$ **(b)** $a = -2, k = 5$ **(c)** $a = 3, k = 5$

Exercise 2-3

1. (a) $(3, -25)$ **(b)** $(-3, 31)$ **(c)** $(1, -1)$ **(d)** $(1, -2)$ **(e)** $(6, 15)$
(f) $(-5, -4)$ **(g)** $(3, -\frac{7}{2})$ **(h)** $(\frac{1}{4}, \frac{3}{4})$ **(i)** $(-10, -9)$ **(j)** $(-1, 0.2)$

2. $(16, 16)$ **3.** $(-3, 3)$ **4.** 500 **5.** 150×150 **6.** 200×400 **7.** \$700

8. \$30 **9.** 200×300 **10.** \$29 **11.** 30 **12.** 54 m

Exercise 2-6

2. (a) $(\frac{1}{2}, -\frac{49}{4})$ **(b)** $(-1, 2)$ **(c)** $(1, -3)$ **(d)** $(-1, 6)$ **(e)** $(\frac{1}{4}, -\frac{39}{8})$
(f) $(\frac{1}{6}, \frac{47}{12})$ **(g)** $(2, -1)$ **(h)** $(6, 8)$ **(i)** $(0, -7)$ **(j)** $(\frac{3}{2}, -\frac{9}{2})$

3. (a) $y = x^2 - x + 2$ **(b)** $y = x^2 - 5x + 4$ **(c)** $y = x^2 + 3x - 2$ **(d)** $y = x^2 - 3x + 2$

4. (a), (c), (e), (f)

Review Exercise

5. (a) $(1, 4)$ **(b)** $(2, 6)$ **(c)** $(1, -2)$ **(d)** $(-1, \frac{13}{2})$ **(e)** $(-\frac{1}{4}, -\frac{7}{8})$ **(f)** $(-2, -6)$

6. 300×600

7. 300×600

REVIEW AND PREVIEW TO CHAPTER 3

Exercise 1

1. (a) -22 **(b)** -14 **(c)** -3 **(d)** $\frac{10}{7}$ **(e)** 1 **(f)** 4 **(g)** -5 **(h)** $\frac{9}{5}$
(i) 6 **(j)** 17 **(k)** 0 **(l)** $\frac{14}{3}$ **(m)** $\frac{15}{14}$ **(n)** -2 **(o)** $\frac{19}{11}$ **(q)** $\frac{17}{13}$

2. (a) $x > 1$ **(b)** $w < 6$ **(c)** $t \leq 5$ **(d)** $x \geq -12$ **(e)** $t < \frac{9}{13}$ **(f)** $x < -6$ **(g)** $x \leq \frac{1}{2}$ **(h)** $x \leq 8$

Exercise 2

1. (a) $4\sqrt{2} + 3\sqrt{3}$ **(b)** $-\sqrt{2}$ **(c)** $2\sqrt{3} - 18\sqrt{5}$ **(d)** $16\sqrt{10} - 7\sqrt{3}$
(e) $19\sqrt{7} - 12\sqrt{6}$ **(f)** $-2\sqrt{17} - 13\sqrt{13}$ **(g)** $53\sqrt{3}$ **(h)** $6\sqrt{5}$

2. (a) $15\sqrt{6} - 20\sqrt{3} - 8\sqrt{2} + 12$ **(b)** $14 - 4\sqrt{6}$ **(c)** 147
(d) -14 **(e)** $2\sqrt{15} - 18\sqrt{3}$ **(f)** 67

3. (a) $\dfrac{3\sqrt{2}}{4}$ **(b)** $\dfrac{3\sqrt{6} - \sqrt{3}}{3}$ **(c)** $\dfrac{2\sqrt{5} + 15 - \sqrt{10}}{10}$

(d) $2\sqrt{3} + 2\sqrt{2}$ **(e)** $\dfrac{3 - 3\sqrt{6}}{-17}$ **(f)** $\dfrac{8\sqrt{15} + 12 - 2\sqrt{5} - \sqrt{3}}{17}$

(g) $\dfrac{2\sqrt5-3\sqrt7+2\sqrt{30}-3\sqrt{42}}{-43}$ **(h)** $\dfrac{-3\sqrt{35}-\sqrt7}{44}$ **(i)** $\dfrac{-8\sqrt6-6\sqrt3+4\sqrt2+3}{23}$

4. (a) $x+2\sqrt x-3$ **(b)** $x-8\sqrt x+16$ **(c)** $2x-7\sqrt x+3$
(d) $x+7+5\sqrt{x+1}$ **(e)** $x-4+2\sqrt{x-5}$ **(f)** $9x+19-6\sqrt{x+2}$
(g) $x-2-2\sqrt{x-3}$ **(h)** $x+7-4\sqrt{x+3}$ **(i)** $4x-3+4\sqrt{x-1}$

Exercise 3-1

1. (a) $-4,2$ **(b)** $-5,1$ **(c)** $-7,1$ **(d)** $2,-1$ **(e)** $-3,-1$ **(f)** $4,2$
(g) $-5,4$ **(h)** $-5,-1$ **(i)** $2,-2$ **(j)** $-5,-3$ **(k)** $-4,-2$ **(l)** $5,1$
2. (a) $1,-3$ **(b)** $3,-3$ **(c)** $\frac12,-2$ **(d)** 3 **(e)** $-\frac23,-1$ **(f)** $1,5$
3. $-4\leqslant x\leqslant-3,\ 3\leqslant x\leqslant4$

Exercise 3-2

1. (a) $(x+4)(x+3)$ **(b)** $(x+2)(x+5)$ **(c)** $(y-5)(y-2)$ **(d)** $(w-5)(w-3)$ **(e)** $(x-4)(x+2)$
(f) $(s-7)(s+3)$ **(g)** $(x+5)(x-2)$ **(h)** $(x-4)(x+4)$ **(i)** $(x-5)(x+5)$ **(j)** $(x+5)(x+5)$
(k) $(x-7)(x-7)$ **(l)** $(w+10)(w-7)$ **(m)** $(x+5)(x-3)$ **(n)** $(t-4)(t+3)$ **(o)** $(r+6)(r-4)$
(p) $(w-9)(w+5)$ **(q)** $(t-1)(t-1)$ **(r)** $(x+10)(x-3)$ **(s)** $(x+7)(x+4)$ **(t)** $(w-10)(w-4)$
(u) $(x+9)(x-3)$ **(v)** $(t-5)(t+4)$ **(w)** $(x+11)(x-8)$ **(x)** $(x-10)(x+10)$
2. (a) $-4,3$ **(b)** $5,2$ **(d)** $10,-5$ **(e)** $-9,4$ **(g)** $11,4$
(h) $-10,-2$ **(i)** $-1,-1$ **(j)** $6,-3$ **(k)** $-6,6$ **(l)** $-4,-4$
3. (a) $(2x+1)(x+3)$ **(b)** $(2x-5)(x-1)$ **(c)** $(2w-3)(3w+1)$ **(d)** $(3w+4)(w-5)$
(e) $(3y-1)(2y+1)$ **(g)** $(2x+3)(2x+3)$ **(h)** $(2w-1)(5w+2)$ **(i)** $(2w+5)(w+2)$
(j) $(2x-3)(2x+3)$ **(k)** $(6t+5)(5t-4)$ **(l)** $(7s+3)(2s+5)$ **(m)** $(6x-7)(4x-3)$
(n) $(3w+5)(4w+3)$ **(o)** $(4t-3)(3t-4)$ **(p)** $(2x+5)(2x+5)$ **(q)** $(5-3x)(2-x)$

Exercise 3-3

1. (a) $-3,1$ **(b)** $1,4$ **(c)** $-5,4$ **(d)** $7,-9$ **(e)** $11,7$ **(f)** $-7,-8$
(g) $\frac13,-\frac53$ **(h)** $\frac34,5$ **(i)** $-\frac52,-\frac{10}{3}$ **(j)** $-\frac74,-\frac13$ **(k)** $-\frac38,\frac57$ **(l)** $-\frac{11}{9},-\frac{14}{3}$
2. (a) $4,-3$ **(b)** $-6,-3$ **(c)** $5,-4$ **(d)** $-5,-3$ **(e)** $11,-7$ **(f)** $-9,-13$
(g) $9,14$ **(h)** -4 **(i)** $5,-8$
3. (a) $\frac12,-2$ **(b)** $-\frac13,-2$ **(c)** $\frac52,1$ **(d)** $\frac23,\frac12$ **(e)** $-\frac34,-\frac53$
(f) $\frac32,$ 𝖳$-$ **(g)** $-\frac83,4$ **(h)** $\frac52,-\frac{10}{3}$ **(i)** $-1,-\frac56$ **(j)** $-\frac14,-\frac72$
(k) $5,-\frac94$ **(l)** $-\frac12,7$ **(m)** $\frac32,-\frac53$ **(n)** $\frac32,-\frac54$ **(o)** $-\frac85,-3$
4. (a) $-\frac32,4$ **(b)** $-\frac45,\frac32$ **(c)** $\frac25,5$ **(d)** $-\frac12,5$ **(e)** $-\frac12,-4$
(f) $-\frac45,\frac52$ **(g)** $-\frac{1}{10},-\frac73$ **(h)** $\frac78,\frac27$ **(i)** $\frac95,-6$
5. (a) $\frac52,1$ **(b)** $-3,2$ **(c)** $\frac12,-5$ **(d)** $-5,3$ **(e)** $-\frac45,1$ **(f)** $-\frac37,1$
6. (a) $-\frac32,2$ **(b)** $-\frac34,2$ **(c)** $-\frac{13}{7},2$ **(d)** $-30,15$ **(e)** $\frac43,4$ **(f)** $-\frac37,2$
7. (a) $x^2-7x+12=0$ **(b)** $x^2-3x-10=0$ **(c)** $x^2+11x+28=0$
(d) $6x^2-5x+1=0$ **(e)** $20x^2+19x+3=0$ **(f)** $x^2-(r+s)x+(rs)=0$

Exercise 3-4

1. (a) $0,-\frac72$ **(b)** $-4,4$ **(c)** 0 **(d)** ±2 **(e)** $0,\frac23$ **(f)** $\pm\frac52$ **(g)** 0 **(h)** $0,\frac45$
(i) $\pm\frac{3}{10}$ **(j)** ±9 **(k)** $0,\frac67$ **(l)** $\pm\frac15$ **(m)** $0,\frac23$ **(n)** 0 **(o)** $0,-\frac23$

Exercise 3-5

1. (a) 9 **(b)** 16 **(c)** 25 **(d)** 1 **(e)** 4 **(f)** 36 **(g)** 81 **(h)** 121
(i) $\frac94$ **(j)** $\frac14$ **(k)** $\frac{49}{4}$ **(l)** $\frac{1}{16}$ **(m)** $\frac19$ **(n)** $\frac{1}{100}$ **(o)** $\frac{9}{100}$
2. (a) $-7,-1$ **(b)** $2\pm\sqrt3$ **(c)** $-1\pm\sqrt7$ **(d)** $5\pm2\sqrt2$ **(e)** $-7\pm3\sqrt3$ **(f)** $6\pm2\sqrt3$
(g) $-\frac12\pm\sqrt6$ **(h)** $\dfrac{1\pm\sqrt3}{2}$ **(i)** $\dfrac{-1\pm\sqrt5}{3}$ **(j)** $\dfrac{3\pm\sqrt7}{4}$ **(k)** $\dfrac{-10\pm\sqrt6}{4}$ **(l)** $\dfrac{4\pm\sqrt2}{3}$

3. (a) $4,-2$ **(b)** $2\pm\sqrt3$ **(c)** $-3\pm\sqrt{11}$ **(d)** $\dfrac{-4\pm\sqrt6}{2}$ **(e)** $\dfrac{4\pm\sqrt{10}}{2}$ **(f)** $\dfrac{3\pm\sqrt3}{3}$

(g) $\dfrac{-5\pm\sqrt{65}}{10}$ **(h)** $\frac52,-1$ **(i)** $\dfrac{3\pm\sqrt{13}}{2}$ **(j)** $-1\pm\sqrt3$ **(k)** $\dfrac{-2\pm\sqrt{10}}{3}$ **(l)** $\dfrac{1\pm\sqrt{15}}{7}$

Exercise 3-6

2. (a) $-2,-4$ **(b)** $5,-3$ **(c)** $\frac12,1$ **(d)** $\frac35,\frac32$ **(e)** $0,\frac37$ **(f)** $\pm\dfrac{4\sqrt5}{5}$

(g) $-\frac{1}{2}$ **(h)** $1\pm\sqrt{5}$ **(i)** $\dfrac{1\pm\sqrt{21}}{2}$ **(j)** $-1\pm\sqrt{7}$ **(k)** $\dfrac{-4\pm\sqrt{22}}{2}$ **(l)** $\dfrac{1\pm\sqrt{15}}{7}$

3. (a) $\frac{3}{2}, -1$ **(b)** $-3\pm\sqrt{11}$ **(c)** $\dfrac{1\pm\sqrt{7}}{3}$ **(d)** $4\pm\sqrt{2}$ **(e)** $\dfrac{-4\pm\sqrt{22}}{3}$ **(f)** $\dfrac{1\pm\sqrt{11}}{5}$

(g) $\dfrac{1\pm\sqrt{11}}{5}$ **(h)** $\dfrac{-7\pm3\sqrt{5}}{2}$ **(i)** $\dfrac{-4\pm\sqrt{19}}{3}$ **(j)** $\dfrac{-7\pm\sqrt{61}}{6}$ **(k)** $\pm\dfrac{\sqrt{5}}{5}$ **(l)** $\dfrac{-1\pm\sqrt{15}}{2}$

4. (a) $0.3, -0.2$ **(b)** $2.3, 1.2$ **(c)** $2.6, -5.6$ **(d)** $3.3, -0.2$ **(e)** $4, 0.5$ **(j)** $-9.5, 3$

5. (a) $1\pm\sqrt{6}$ **(b)** $\dfrac{1\pm\sqrt{7}}{2}$ **(c)** $\dfrac{3\pm\sqrt{29}}{2}$ **(d)** $\dfrac{3\pm\sqrt{29}}{2}$ **(e)** $\dfrac{1\pm\sqrt{33}}{4}$ **(f)** $\dfrac{3\pm\sqrt{65}}{4}$ **(g)** $\dfrac{3\pm\sqrt{5}}{2}$

(h) $2\pm\sqrt{7}$ **(i)** $\dfrac{7\pm\sqrt{105}}{4}$ **(j)** $7\pm\sqrt{58}$ **(k)** $\dfrac{3\pm\sqrt{57}}{3}$ **(l)** $\dfrac{-5\pm\sqrt{37}}{2}$ **(m)** $\frac{7}{2}, -1$ **(n)** $4\pm\sqrt{21}$

6. (a) $3.4, -1.4$ **(b)** $2.2, -0.7$ **(c)** $1.7, -1.2$ **(d)** $-0.9, -3.4$ **(e)** $1.3, -0.8$ **(f)** $4.5, -1.6$

7. (a) $\dfrac{3\sqrt{2}}{2}, -\sqrt{2}$ **(b)** $\dfrac{\sqrt{3}\pm\sqrt{11}}{4}$ **(c)** $\dfrac{\sqrt{6}\pm\sqrt{22}}{4}$ **(d)** $(k-1), 1$

Exercise 3-7

1. $(14, 16), (-14, -16)$ **2.** $(17, 19), (-17, -19)$ **3.** $16, -17$
4. $15, 16$ **5.** $(11, 12, 13), (-11, -12, -13)$ **6.** $21, -20$
7. $4, 16$ **8.** $11, 19$ **9.** $(22, 24), (-22, -24)$
10. $13, 15$ **11.** 12 **12.** 9
13. $(4, 6, 8), (-4, -6, -8)$ **14.** $21, -18$ **15.** $(10, 17), (-10, -17)$
16. $9, 12$ **17.** $10, 24$ **18.** 7×13
19. 3.1 **20.** 11.0 **21.** 2.3
22. 20 **23.** 10 **24.** 20
25. 60×40 **26.** 500 **27.** 90
28. 50 **29.** 600 **30.** (a) 45 (b) 6.3 (c) 7.4
31. 6

Exercise 3-8

1. (a) $5+3i$ **(b)** $5+3i$ **(c)** $8+2i$ **(d)** $1+2i$ **(e)** $3-7i$ **(f)** 5
2. (a) $2i$ **(b)** $5i$ **(c)** $i\sqrt{2}$ **(d)** $10i$ **(e)** $i\sqrt{5}$ **(f)** $2i\sqrt{5}$
(g) $2i\sqrt{3}$ **(h)** $3i\sqrt{2}$ **(i)** $4i$ **(j)** -1 **(k)** -2 **(l)** -3
(m) -5 **(n)** $+5$ **(o)** $-i$ **(p)** 1 **(q)** -7 **(r)** -10
(s) 21 **(t)** i
3. (a) -5 **(b)** 2 **(c)** $2i$ **(d)** $7+i$ **(e)** 4 **(f)** $7-3i$
(g) 15 **(h)** 1 **(i)** 0

4. (a) $1\pm i\sqrt{3}$ **(b)** $1\pm i\sqrt{5}$ **(c)** $1\pm i\sqrt{6}$ **(d)** $1\pm\sqrt{7}$ **(e)** $\dfrac{-4\pm i\sqrt{2}}{2}$ **(f)** $\pm3i$

(g) $\pm\dfrac{i\sqrt{14}}{2}$ **(h)** $\dfrac{1\pm3i}{5}$ **(i)** $\dfrac{1\pm i\sqrt{5}}{3}$ **(j)** $\dfrac{1\pm i\sqrt{13}}{7}$ **(k)** $\dfrac{-1\pm i\sqrt{31}}{4}$ **(l)** $5, -\frac{1}{3}$

5. (a) $-1\pm i$ **(b)** $1\pm i$ **(c)** $3\pm\sqrt{7}$ **(d)** $\dfrac{-1\pm i\sqrt{7}}{4}$

Exercise 3-9

2. (a) 2 **(b)** 0 **(c)** 1
3. (a) 0 **(b)** 21 **(c)** -31 **(d)** -24 **(e)** 0 **(f)** 64
(g) -47 **(h)** 41 **(i)** 49 **(j)** 289 **(k)** -11 **(l)** 25
4. (a) Real, distinct   **(b)** Real, distinct   **(c)** Imaginary   **(d)** Real, distinct   **(e)** Real, equal
(f) Real, distinct   **(g)** Real, distinct   **(h)** Real, distinct   **(i)** Real, distinct
5. (a) 4 **(b)** $k<-\frac{9}{8}$ **(c)** $k<1$ **(d)** $k>\frac{3}{4}$ **(e)** $k>8$ or $k<-8$
(f) $\pm\frac{1}{2}$ **(g)** $k<-\frac{4}{3}$ **(h)** 2 **(i)** $-1, -5$ **(j)** $k<-1$ or $k>3$
6. (a) 0 or 4 **(b)** $k<0$ or $k>4$ **(c)** $0<k<4$

Exercise 3-10

1. (a) 8 **(b)** 17 **(c)** $\varnothing$ **(d)** 6 **(e)** 6 **(f)** -3 **(g)** 6 **(h)** 2
(i) $\frac{9}{4}$

2. (a) 26   **(b)** 9   **(c)** 21   **(d)** $\varnothing$ **(e)** 3   **(f)** 8   **(g)** $\varnothing$ **(h)** 25

3. (a) 2   **(b)** 10, 15   **(c)** 12   **(d)** 1, 2   **(e)** 10   **(f)** 2   **(g)** 5   **(h)** $\varnothing$

4. (a) 1   **(b)** 2, 6   **(c)** 0   **(d)** 1   **(e)** $\varnothing$ **(f)** -5

5. (a) 28   **(b)** 10   **(c)** 3   **(d)** 16   **(e)** 2   **(f)** 1, -3 **(g)** 0   **(h)** $\frac{1}{4}$

6. (a) $1+\sqrt{2}$ **(b)** $1+\sqrt{3}$

Exercise 3-11

3. (a) $x<-5$ or $x>-1$ **(b)** $2<x<4$ **(c)** $-5<x<3$ **(d)** $x<-2$ or $x>2$ **(e)** $x<-2$ or $x>0$

   (f) $\varnothing$ **(g)** $x\leqslant-4$ or $x\geqslant3$ **(h)** $3\leqslant x\leqslant4$ **(i)** $-5<x<-4$ **(j)** $x\leqslant-7$ or $x\geqslant2$

4. (a) $x<-4$ or $x>-3$ **(b)** $x<2$ or $x>3$ **(c)** $x\leqslant1$ or $x\geqslant4$ **(d)** $-3\leqslant x\leqslant4$ **(e)** $-3\leqslant x\leqslant3$

   (f) $x\leqslant0$ or $x\geqslant5$ **(g)** $x<-3$ or $x>\frac{1}{2}$ **(h)** $\frac{3}{2}\leqslant x\leqslant5$ **(i)** $-\frac{3}{2}<x<4$ **(j)** $x<1$ or $x>\frac{5}{2}$

5. (a) $-3<x<\frac{5}{2}$ **(b)** $x<1-\sqrt{3}$ or $x>1+\sqrt{3}$ **(c)** $x<1-\sqrt{2}$ or $x>1+\sqrt{2}$

   (d) $-1<x<4$ **(e)** $-\frac{11}{3}\leqslant x\leqslant4$ **(f)** $x<-3$ or $x>1$

   (g) $x<-2$ or $x>6$ **(h)** $2<x\leqslant\frac{10}{3}$

Review Exercise

1. (a) $(x+5)(x+3)$ **(b)** $(4x-3)(4x+3)$ **(d)** $(t-7)(t+5)$ **(f)** $(w+15)(w+12)$

   (g) $(z+12)(z-9)$ **(h)** $(t-10)(t-7)$ **(i)** $(x+13)^2$

2. (a) $6, -7$ **(b)** $-5, -11$ **(c)** $10, -3$ **(d)** $-\frac{1}{2}, 4$

   (e) $\frac{4}{3}, \frac{5}{2}$ **(f)** $-\frac{7}{5}, -\frac{11}{3}$ **(g)** $0, \frac{4}{3}$ **(h)** $0, -\frac{12}{5}$

   (i) $-\frac{5}{4}$

3. (a) $3i$ **(b)** $2i\sqrt{2}$ **(c)** -3 **(d)** $-i$

   (e) -6 **(f)** -14 **(g)** -1 **(h)** -10

4. (a) Real, distinct   **(b)** Real, equal   **(c)** Imaginary   **(d)** Real, distinct

   (e) Real, distinct

5. (a) 7   **(b)** 17   **(c)** -1 **(d)** $\frac{25}{4}$

6. (a) $(3x+1)(2x+3)$ **(b)** $(6t+1)(t-7)$ **(c)** $(5w+6)(3w+2)$ **(d)** $(10x-3)(2x-5)$

   (e) $(14t+3)(2t+3)$ **(f)** $(8x+3)(x-4)$ **(g)** $(6x-5)(2x-7)$ **(i)** $(2t+7)(4t+5)$

7. (a) $6, -\frac{5}{2}$ **(b)** $\pm\frac{2}{3}$ **(c)** $4, \frac{1}{6}$ **(d)** $-\frac{6}{5}, -\frac{3}{2}$

   (e) $\frac{5}{2}, 1$ **(f)** $-3, -5$ **(g)** $-\frac{5}{3}, \frac{1}{3}$ **(h)** $\frac{5}{7}, \frac{1}{2}$

   (i) $\frac{3}{8}, -\frac{5}{2}$

8. (a) $0, -\frac{14}{5}$ **(b)** $\dfrac{5\pm\sqrt{13}}{2}$ **(c)** $-\frac{7}{6}, -1$ **(d)** $\pm\dfrac{i\sqrt{10}}{2}$

   (e) $\dfrac{2\pm\sqrt{2}}{2}$ **(f)** $\dfrac{3\pm i\sqrt{39}}{4}$ **(g)** $-1, 2$ **(h)** $-\frac{1}{2}, -4$

9. (a) $1, -\frac{1}{6}$ **(b)** $\dfrac{-1\pm i\sqrt{3}}{2}$ **(c)** $\frac{5}{2}, -1$ **(d)** $-1\pm i\sqrt{5}$

   (e) $\dfrac{-1\pm\sqrt{13}}{2}$ **(f)** $\dfrac{-1\pm i\sqrt{23}}{4}$ **(g)** $\dfrac{2\pm i\sqrt{5}}{3}$ **(h)** $\dfrac{-3\pm\sqrt{57}}{4}$

10. (a) $1\pm\sqrt{10}$ **(b)** $0.4, -0.5$ **(c)** $-3\pm\sqrt{11}$

   (d) $\dfrac{5\pm i\sqrt{47}}{4}$ **(e)** $-5, 2$ **(f)** $\dfrac{3\pm\sqrt{105}}{24}$

11. $(-9, -8)$ or $(8, 9)$ **12.** $(9, 10, 11)$ or $(-9, -10, -11)$ **13.** 8

14. 18.4   **15.** 100 km/h

16. (a) Real, distinct   **(b)** Real, equal   **(c)** Imaginary

   (d) Real, distinct   **(e)** Imaginary   **(f)** Imaginary

17. (a) $\frac{9}{4}$ **(b)** $k<\frac{7}{16}$ **(c)** $k>-\frac{13}{24}$

18. (a) 3   **(b)** $\varnothing$ **(c)** 3

   (d) 7   **(e)** 10   **(f)** $\varnothing$

19. (a) $-3\leqslant x\leqslant4$ **(b)** $x<0$ or $x>6$ **(c)** $-2<x<5$

   (d) $x\leqq-5$ or $x\geqq-3$ **(e)** $-\frac{1}{2}<x$ or $x>3$ **(f)** $-\frac{2}{3}\leqslant x\leqslant4$

REVIEW AND PREVIEW TO CHAPTER 4

Exercise 1

1. (a) $(2x+3)(x-5)$ **(b)** $(4x-1)(2x-3)$ **(c)** $(3x-5)(x-7)$ **(d)** $(2x+5)(3x+4)$ **(e)** $(6x+7)(x-1)$

(f) $(2x+7)(3x+4)$ **(g)** $2(2x-1)(3x-4)$ **(h)** $3(3x+5)(2x-5)$ **(i)** $x(x-6)(2x+7)$ **(j)** $(6x-1)(3x-8)$

Exercise 2

1. (a) $-3, \frac{1}{2}$ **(b)** $-\frac{5}{3}, -2$ **(c)** $5, \frac{3}{4}$ **(d)** $-\frac{2}{3}, -\frac{1}{2}$ **(e)** $\frac{2}{5}, \frac{3}{2}$ **(f)** $\pm\frac{5}{2}$

(g) $0, \frac{11}{6}$ **(h)** $\dfrac{-3\pm\sqrt{13}}{2}$ **(i)** $\dfrac{1\pm\sqrt{41}}{4}$ **(j)** $\dfrac{-1\pm 3i}{2}$ **(k)** $-3\pm i\sqrt{3}$ **(l)** $\dfrac{1\pm i\sqrt{7}}{20}$

Exercise 3

1. (a) $2x^3-x^2-17x+12$ **(b)** $x^4+4x^3-4x^2-37x-42$ **(c)** $-2x^2+48x-110$
   (d) $8x^2-13x+156$ **(e)** $6x^3+x^2-8x+6$ **(f)** $2x^4-x^3+x^2-3x-15$
   (g) $-x^2+25x+81$ **(h)** $5x^2+39x+6$ **(i)** $3x^5+x^4-6x^3+2x^2+2x-1$
   (j) $4x^3-11x^2-26x-22$ **(k)** $-4x^2+16x-16$ **(l)** $3x^4+8x^3-17x^2-2x+8$
2. (a) x^2-2x+3 **(b)** $2x^3-3x^2+5x$ **(c)** $-3+5xy-6x^4$
   (d) $4xy-2y^2z-5yz$ **(e)** $-9x^2y+12xy^2+6$ **(f)** $-6x^4z^2+5x^3z+1-8x$

Exercise 4.

1. (a) $(0,-4)$ **(b)** $(1,5)$ **(c)** $(-3,-2)$ **(d)** $(-1,-2)$ **(e)** $(2,5)$
   (f) $(\frac{3}{2},\frac{1}{2})$ **(g)** $(3,6)$ **(h)** $(\frac{5}{2},\frac{13}{4})$ **(i)** $(\frac{5}{6},\frac{37}{12})$ **(j)** $(\frac{1}{8},\frac{9}{16})$
   (k) $(-1,0.8)$ **(l)** $(-1,0.2)$ **(m)** $(\frac{1}{4},-\frac{17}{8})$ **(n)** $(-\frac{1}{3},\frac{13}{3})$

Exercise 4-1

3. (a) $\frac{2}{3}, 2$ **(b)** $1, -11$ **(c)** $-2, -3$ **(d)** $-\frac{10}{3}, -\frac{10}{3}$
4. (a) $x^2-11x+28=0$ **(b)** $x^2+3x-18=0$ **(c)** $2x^2+7x-4=0$ **(d)** $12x^2+11x+2=0$
   (e) $5x^2-3x=0$ **(f)** $x^2-36=0$ **(g)** $x^2-2x-2=0$ **(h)** $x^2-6x+1=0$
   (i) $x^2+4=0$ **(j)** $x^2-2x+10=0$ **(k)** $4x^2-8x-1=0$ **(l)** $9x^2-18x+11=0$
5. $\frac{1}{2}, -7$ **6.** $x^2-x-8=0$ **7.** $\frac{1}{5}, -2$
8. $x^2+4x+9=0$ **9.** $2+\sqrt{2}, -4$ **10.** $5x^2+3x+2=0$
11. (a) -2 **(b)** $\frac{5}{14}$ **(c)** 6 **(d)** -10
12. $x^2-12x+4=0$

Exercise 4-2

1. (a) $\pm 3, \pm 2$ **(b)** $\pm 1, \pm 2i$ **(c)** $1, 2, 4$ **(d)** $1, \dfrac{3\pm\sqrt{5}}{2}$ **(e)** 4 **(f)** $\pm 2, \pm 1$

2. (a) $-1, 1, 3$ **(b)** $2, 3, -1, 6$ **(c)** $4, -1, 2, 1,$ **(d)** $\pm 2, \pm i$ **(e)** $\pm\sqrt{6}, \pm 2i$ **(f)** $1, 2$

3. (a) $1\pm\sqrt{7}, 1$ **(b)** $\pm 3, \pm 2$ **(c)** $-2, 3$ **(d)** $\pm\dfrac{\sqrt{2}}{2}, \pm 3i$ **(e)** $\pm 2, \pm 1$ **(f)** $\frac{3}{2}, -2, \frac{1}{2}, -1$

4. (a) $\pm\sqrt{2\pm\sqrt{3}}$ **(b)** $\pm\sqrt{5\pm 8\sqrt{2}}$

Exercise 4-3

2. (a) $0, \pm 3$ **(b)** $-1, 2, -3$ **(c)** $\pm 1, \pm 3$ **(d)** $0, -2, -4$ **(e)** -1
   (f) $1, -1$ **(g)** ± 1 **(h)** $0, -2$ **(i)** -3
3. $x^3+2x^2-11x-12=y$ **4.** $x^3-3x+2=y$ **5.** $y=x^3+x^2-6x$
6. $y=x^4+3x^3-8x^2-12x+16$ **7.** $y=x^4-9x^2+4x+12$ **8.** $y=x^4-6x^3+9x^2$
9. $y=x^3-x^2+x-1$

Exercise 4-4

1. (a) $x^2+x+5, x\neq 3$ **(b)** $x^2-x-5, x\neq -4$ **(c)** $x^2-x-2, R-1, x\neq -3$
   (d) $w^2+6w+2, w\neq 1$ **(e)** $x^2+5x-4, R2, x\neq -6$ **(f)** $t^2+3, t\neq 2$
   (g) $x^2-2x-4, R4, x\neq 5$ **(h)** $x^2-4, x\neq -5$ **(i)** $x^3+2x^2-2x+1, x\neq -2$
   (j) $2w^3+w^2-w-1, w\neq 3$
2. (a) $x^2+x+1, x\neq\frac{1}{2}$ **(b)** $w^2-3w+5, R3, w\neq\frac{2}{3}$ **(c)** $2t^2-t+2, t\neq -\frac{1}{3}$
   (d) $3z^2+2z-3, z\neq -\frac{3}{2}$ **(e)** $4x^2+x-2, R-4, x\neq -2$ **(f)** $2x^2-3x+7, x\neq -\frac{3}{2}$
   (g) $3x^2+2x+2, R3, x\neq\frac{2}{3}$ **(h)** $x^2-2x+13, R-16$
3. (a) x^2-x-12 **(b)** w^2+3w+2 **(c)** t^2+3t+2

Exercise 4-5

1. (a) 18 **(b)** 11 **(c)** -2 **(d)** -58 **(e)** -3 **(f)** 13 **(g)** 35 **(h)** 257
2. Yes a, b, d, f
3. (a) $(x-1)(x+2)(x+3)$ **(b)** $(x+1)(x+2)(x+3)$ **(c)** $(x+2)(x-3)(x+3)$

4. (a) $(w-2)(w-1)(2w+1)$ **(b)** $(t+3)(t+2)(2t-1)$ **(c)** $(x-1)(2x+3)(3x-1)$
(d) $(x-2)(x+3)(x-1)$ **(e)** $(x-3)(x^2+x+5)$ **(f)** $(w-2)(2w^2+2w+3)$
(g) $(x+3)(2x-1)(2x+1)$ **(h)** $(x-4)(2x+5)(3x-1)$
5. -14 **6.** -2
7. (a) $(x+1)(x+2)(x-2)(x+3)$ **(b)** $(x+3)(x-3)(x+2)(x-4)$ **(c)** $(x+3)(x-3)(x^2+x+1)$
8. $a=1, b=-2$ **9.** $2x^3-5x^2-3$

Exercise 4-6

1. (a) $-2, 2, 3$ **(b)** $-1, 2, 3$ **(c)** $-2, 5$ **(d)** $-1, 1, -\frac{1}{3}$
(e) $2, -3, \frac{3}{2}$ **(f)** $3, -2, \frac{3}{4}$ **(g)** $1, 5, -\frac{3}{2}$ **(h)** $3, 4, -4$

2. (a) $2, -1\pm\sqrt{2}$ **(b)** $-1, \dfrac{3\pm\sqrt{5}}{2}$ **(c)** $-2, -1\pm i\sqrt{2}$

(d) $1, \dfrac{-1\pm i\sqrt{3}}{2}$ **(e)** $-2, 1\pm i\sqrt{3}$ **(f)** $-3, \dfrac{1\pm\sqrt{21}}{3}$

3. (a) $-1, 2, \pm3$ **(b)** $4, -3, \pm1$ **(c)** $\pm1, \pm i$ **(d)** $-3, -\frac{2}{3}, \frac{5}{2}$

4. (a) $0, 3, \dfrac{-3\pm 3i\sqrt{3}}{2}$ **(b)** $-2, 3$
5. (a) $2, -2, -3$ **(b)** $\pm1, \pm2, -3$

Review Exercise

3. (a) $x^2+13x+40=0$ **(b)** $12x^2-x-1=0$ **(c)** $x^2-4x-8=0$ **(d)** $x^2-4x+13=0$
4. $-\frac{1}{3}, -4$ **5.** $x^2-2x-5=0$

6. (a) $\pm1, \pm3$ **(b)** $-2, 4, -1, 3$ **(c)** $1, 2\pm\sqrt{3}$ **(d)** $-1, 4, \dfrac{3\pm i\sqrt{7}}{2}$

8. (a) $x^2+4x-2, R1, x\neq2$ **(b)** $3t^2+2t-2, t\neq-\frac{1}{2}$
(c) $2w^2-3w+2, R2, w\neq-\frac{2}{3}$ **(d)** $2x^3-3x^2-x+2, x\neq-3$
9. (a) 3 **(b)** -4 **(c)** -39 **(d)** 37
10. (a) $(w+2)(w-2)(w-3)$ **(b)** $(x+1)(x-3)(x+4)$
(c) $(x-2)(x+3)(2x-1)$ **(d)** $(x-3)(x+3)(2x-3)$
11. -14
12. (a) $-3, -1, -4$ **(b)** $2, 3, 4$ **(c)** $3, -2, -3$ **(d)** $1, -\frac{1}{2}, \frac{3}{2}$ **(e)** $2, -1\pm\sqrt{3}$

(f) $-3, \dfrac{3\pm\sqrt{13}}{2}$ **(g)** $-4, \dfrac{1\pm i\sqrt{3}}{2}$ **(h)** $2, \frac{1}{3}, -\frac{5}{2}$ **(i)** $0, -2, \dfrac{-1\pm\sqrt{13}}{2}$ **(j)** $-3, \dfrac{3\pm 3i\sqrt{3}}{2}$

REVIEW AND PREVIEW TO CHAPTER 5

Exercise 1

1. $\dfrac{2x}{(x+1)(x-1)}$ **2.** $\dfrac{-2}{(x+1)(x-1)}$ **3.** $\dfrac{1}{(x+1)(x-1)}$ **4.** $\dfrac{x-1}{x+1}$

5. $\dfrac{7x-7}{(x-3)(x+4)}$ **6.** $\dfrac{2x+5}{(x-5)(x-2)}$ **7.** $\dfrac{-10x}{(2+3x)(2-3x)}$ **8.** $\dfrac{2b}{(a-b)(a+b)}$

9. $\dfrac{1}{ab^3c}$ **10.** $\dfrac{x^3z^2}{y^2}$ **11.** $\dfrac{3x^2+20x-32}{(7-x)(7+x)}$ **12.** $\dfrac{x^2-2x-1}{(x+2)(x-1)}$

13. 1 **14.** $\dfrac{x}{x+7}$ **15.** $\dfrac{x-2}{3x-1}$ **16.** $\dfrac{4(2x-3)}{(3x-5)}$

17. $\dfrac{-8x-5}{(x-1)(x+1)(x-2)}$ **18.** $\dfrac{2x^2+6x+3}{(x-1)(x^2+x+1)}$ **19.** $a^2b+ab^2+b^3$ **20.** $\dfrac{a^3}{a^2+b^2}$

21. $3ab^2+b^3$ **22.** $\dfrac{a}{a-2}$ **23.** x^2-x **24.** -1

25. $\dfrac{3+2x}{2+x}$ **26.** $\dfrac{10x^3+3x^2+8x+3}{5x^2+4}$

Exercise 5-1

1. (a) 2^4 **(b)** 2^1 **(c)** 2^{28} **(d)** 2^{15} **(e)** 2^5 **(f)** 2^{12}
   (g) 2^{27} **(h)** 2^{10} **(i)** 2^7 **(j)** 2^{4+m} **(k)** 2^{4m} **(l)** 2^{4m}

2. (a) 3^3 **(b)** 3^{10} **(c)** 3^9 **(d)** 3^4 **(e)** 3^{36} **(f)** 3^3 **(g)** 3^{pm} **(h)** 3^7

3. (a) $9^4 \times 13^4$ **(b)** $9^4 x^4$ **(c)** $\dfrac{5^{18}}{6^{18}}$ **(d)** $\dfrac{x^5}{6^5}$ **(e)** 63^8 **(f)** $6^5 \times 72^5$

   (h) $x^3 y^3$ **(i)** π^5 **(j)** π^6 **(k)** $\dfrac{2^{10}}{3^{10}}$ **(l)** $\dfrac{x^6}{y^6}$ **(m)** $(2.78)^8$

   (n) $(-2)^7$ **(o)** $\dfrac{9}{a^2}$ **(p)** $\left(\dfrac{a}{b}\right)^8$ **(r)** $8x^6$ **(s)** x^{15} **(t)** x^{12}

   (u) x^{3n} **(v)** x^{3+n} **(w)** x^{2n} **(x)** x^{n^2}

4. (a) $-27x^{18}$ **(b)** $-12x^9$ **(c)** 3^{18} **(d)** a^{m+n+p} **(e)** 2^{24}
   (f) a^{mnp} **(g)** 4^4 **(h)** x^{3m} **(i)** x^{4n-3}

5. (a) 7 **(b)** $\frac{1}{9}$ **(c)** 256 **(d)** 16 **(e)** 5 **(f)** 1

6. (a) $-a^{3p+q}$ **(b)** x^{6n+8} **(c)** $\frac{1}{810}$ **(d)** 3^{10n} **(e)** 2^{4n-4}

7. (a) $x^7 y^9$ **(c)** $\frac{1}{4}x^{38}y^8$ **(d)** $-x^{39}y^{12}$ **(e)** $\dfrac{5y^3}{6x^4}$ **(f)** $\dfrac{a^{11}}{b^4}$ **(g)** $4y^4$ **(h)** $\dfrac{x}{4y^2}$

   (i) 3^{n-5} **(j)** x^{3n} **(k)** $\dfrac{1}{b^3 c}$ **(l)** b^n **(m)** 1 **(n)** $-8x^8 y^6 z^7$

8. (a) 6 **(b)** 3 **(c)** 3 **(d)** 16 **(e)** 2
   (f) 4 **(g)** 6 **(h)** 2 **(i)** $x \in N$ **(j)** $x \in N$, x even

9. (a) 7^6 **(b)** $\frac{5}{2}(3^n)$ **(c)** 3^n **(d)** $\frac{33}{31}$

Exercise 5-2

1. (a) 1 **(b)** $\frac{1}{9}$ **(c)** $\frac{1}{8}$ **(d)** $\frac{1}{9}$ **(e)** -1 **(f)** 1
   (g) $\frac{1}{1000}$ **(h)** $\frac{1}{837}$ **(i)** 8 **(j)** $\frac{1}{64}$ **(k)** 36 **(l)** 32

2. (a) $\dfrac{1}{x^8}$ **(b)** $\dfrac{x^2}{y^2}$ **(c)** $\dfrac{1}{a^3 b^4}$ **(d)** $\dfrac{1}{a^2}$ **(e)** a^{10} **(f)** $\left(\dfrac{y}{x}\right)^3$ **(g)** $\dfrac{b^3}{a^2}$ **(h)** $x^3 y^5$

3. (a) x^{-3} **(b)** $2ab^{-4}$ **(c)** $\pi x^2 y$ **(d)** $3a^{-2}b^4$ **(e)** $2x^{-1}y^{-2}$ **(f)** $x^2 y^{-2} z^3$

4. (a) $\frac{8}{25}$ **(b)** 1024 **(c)** $\frac{27}{25}$ **(d)** 4 **(e)** 9 **(f)** 2 **(g)** 49
   (h) $\frac{11}{36}$ **(i)** $\frac{5}{4}$ **(j)** $\frac{10}{21}$ **(k)** 2 **(l)** 625 **(m)** $\frac{45}{19}$ **(n)** $\frac{7}{4}$

5. (a) $\dfrac{343x^6}{y^9}$ **(b)** $\dfrac{a^5 b^{10}}{243}$ **(c)** $\dfrac{64a^3 c^9}{b^6 d^{12}}$ **(d)** $\dfrac{a^2}{b^3}$ **(e)** $a^2 b^2 x^2 y^4$

   (f) $\dfrac{a^4}{b^2} - 2\dfrac{a^2}{b} + 1$ **(g)** $a^6 + a^5 - 5a^2$ **(h)** $2x^2 - \dfrac{1}{x^2} - 1$ **(i)** $\dfrac{1}{b^{2n}}$ **(j)** $\dfrac{1}{x^{2n}} - \dfrac{1}{y^{2m}}$

   (k) $\dfrac{b^{2n^2}}{a^{n^2} c^{n^3}}$ **(l)** $\dfrac{y-x}{y+x}$ **(m)** $\dfrac{1}{x} - \dfrac{1}{y} = \dfrac{y-x}{xy}$ **(n)** $\dfrac{x}{y} + \dfrac{y}{x} + 2 = \dfrac{(x+y)^2}{xy}$

   (o) $\dfrac{x^2 + y^2}{x^2 - y^2}$ **(p)** $\dfrac{a^3 b^3}{a+b}$ **(q)** $\dfrac{a^2 b^2 + a^3 b - a^2 b^3}{b^2 - a^2}$

6. (a) 2 **(b)** -7 **(c)** 5 **(d)** $x = 0, \pm 2, \pm 4, \pm 6, \ldots$

Exercise 5-3

1. (a) 2×10^3 **(b)** 3.63×10^2 **(c)** 7.234×10^2 **(d)** 1×10^{-3}
   (e) 7.2×10^{-4} **(f)** 3.5 **(g)** 2.46×10^5 **(h)** 4.5×10^{-2}
   (i) 1.984×10^3 **(j)** 1.23×10^{-1} **(k)** 8×10^{-5} **(l)** 1.2345×10^4
   (m) 1.4061×10^2 **(n)** -1×10^2 **(o)** 8.34×10^{-3} **(p)** 3.7×10^5

2. (a) 2000 **(b)** 740 **(c)** 0.23 **(d)** 0.0037
   (e) $1\,000\,000$ **(f)** $12\,300$ **(g)** 0.0999 **(h)** $0.000\,545\,6$

3. (a) 9.41×10^{12} **(b)** 3×10^{27} **(c)** 5.97×10^{24} **(d)** $\dfrac{1}{3 \times 10^8} \doteq 3.33 \times 10^{-9}$
   (e) 1.5×10^8 **(f)** 4×10^{-13}

4. (a) 6.9×10^{10} **(b)** 6.34×10^{21} **(c)** 7.8×10^{-8} **(d)** 1.983×10^{-5}
   (e) $1.835\,55 \times 10^8$ **(f)** $2.635\,84 \times 10^3$ **(g)** 6.8×10^{-6} **(h)** $1.234\,567\,89 \times 10^{14}$
   (i) 1.7×10^{-5} **(j)** 8.32×10^{-6}

5. (a) $312\,000$ **(b)** $0.008\,57$ **(c)** $0.000\,000\,026\,7$ **(d)** $68\,530\,000\,000$
   (e) $0.000\,000\,000\,149\,5$ **(f)** $9\,000\,000\,000\,000$ **(g)** $0.000\,000\,001\,111\,1$ **(h)** $433\,700\,000\,000$
   (i) $0.000\,000\,65$

6. (a) 2.96×10^{13} **(b)** 5×10^{-8} **(c)** 2.73×10^{6} **(d)** 1.8×10^{-3} **(e)** 9×10^{9} **(f)** 6.4×10^{11}
(g) 8×10^{8} **(h)** 1.1×10^{8} **(i)** 3×10^{-5} **(j)** 8×10^{-14} **(k)** 5.49×10^{5} **(l)** 2×10
7. 4.3×10^{15} **8.** 3.20×10^{12} **9.** 2.213×10^{13}

Exercise 5-4

1. (a) $\sqrt[9]{2}$ **(b)** $\sqrt{37}$ **(c)** $\sqrt[3]{x}$ **(d)** $\sqrt[3]{4}$ **(e)** $\sqrt{8}=2\sqrt{2}$ **(f)** $\sqrt[4]{27}$
(g) $\sqrt[5]{a^{2}}$ or $(\sqrt[5]{a})^{2}$ **(h)** $\sqrt[7]{x^{4}}$ or $(\sqrt[7]{x})^{4}$ **(i)** $\dfrac{1}{\sqrt{2}}$ **(j)** $\dfrac{1}{\sqrt[5]{7}}$ **(k)** $\dfrac{1}{\sqrt{a^{3}}}$ **(l)** $\sqrt[11]{81}$

2. (a) $3^{\frac{1}{2}}$ **(b)** $19^{\frac{1}{2}}$ **(c)** $23^{\frac{1}{3}}$ **(d)** $x^{\frac{1}{4}}$ **(e)** $7^{\frac{2}{3}}$ **(f)** $7^{\frac{2}{3}}$
(g) $6^{\frac{4}{5}}$ **(h)** $13^{\frac{5}{6}}$ **(i)** $a^{\frac{1}{6}}$ **(j)** $a^{\frac{5}{6}}$ **(k)** $5^{-\frac{1}{2}}$ **(l)** $7^{-\frac{3}{4}}$
3. (a) 2 **(b)** 4 **(c)** 27 **(d)** 1 **(e)** $\frac{1}{6}$ **(f)** 4
(g) 3 **(h)** $\frac{1}{2}$ **(i)** $\frac{1}{2}$ **(j)** $\frac{1}{8}$ **(k)** -2 **(l)** 4
4. (a) 16 **(b)** 128 **(c)** 100 **(d)** $\frac{1}{4}$ **(e)** 27 **(f)** $\frac{1}{125}$
(g) 256 **(h)** 3 **(i)** 36 **(j)** 343 **(k)** 2 **(l)** 162
(m) $\frac{2}{3}$ **(n)** $\frac{12}{7}$ **(o)** $\frac{125}{512}$ **(p)** 96 **(q)** 0.08 **(r)** 3
(s) 8 **(t)** 0 **(u)** 7 **(v)** $\frac{5}{6}$ **(w)** 3 **(x)** $\frac{5}{108}$
5. (a) $2^{\frac{5}{6}}$ **(b)** $3\frac{8}{9}$ **(c)** $x^{2}y^{\frac{1}{2}}$ **(d)** $a^{3}b^{4}$ **(e)** $ab^{2}c^{3}$ **(f)** $x+3x^{\frac{2}{3}}$

(g) $2x^{2}y^{\frac{1}{2}}$ **(h)** $\dfrac{16x^{6}}{y^{2}}$ **(i)** $\dfrac{40\sqrt{5}x^{3}y^{\frac{9}{2}}}{z^{\frac{3}{2}}}$ **(j)** $\dfrac{a^{\frac{9}{2}}x}{b^{9}y^{\frac{24}{5}}}$ **(k)** $\dfrac{y^{\frac{1}{4}}}{x^{\frac{1}{24}}}$ **(l)** $a^{\frac{9}{2}}$

6. (a) $3^{\frac{1}{2}}$ **(b)** $7^{\frac{1}{4}}$ **(c)** $3^{\frac{3}{2}}$ **(d)** $14^{-\frac{1}{3}}$

Exercise 5-5

1. (a) 3.2 **(b)** 4.6 **(c)** 8.1 **(d)** 8.1 **(e)** 5.0 **(f)** 0.7
(g) 1.4 **(h)** 0.2 **(i)** 3.2 **(j)** 5.2 **(k)** 0.4 **(l)** 8.6
2. (a) 2.6 **(b)** 0.8 **(c)** -1 **(d)** 2.1 **(e)** 0.6 **(f)** 1.3
(g) -0.1 **(h)** 0.5 **(i)** 0.8 **(j)** -1 **(k)** 0.5 **(l)** 0.7
3. (a) 3.7 **(b)** 56 **(c)** 2.7 **(d)** 832 **(e)** -0.3 **(f)** 4.6 **(g)** 4.9 **(h)** 6.6
4. (a) 7.2 **(b)** 470 **(c)** 147 **(d)** 630 **(e)** 1.2 **(f)** 2.4 **(g)** 3.3 **(h)** 2.0

Exercise 5-6

1. (a) $25\,a$ **(b)** $50\,a$ **(c)** $100\,a$ **(d)** $75\,a$
2. (a) $\frac{1}{2}$ **(b)** $\frac{1}{4}$ **(c)** $\frac{1}{16}$ **(d)** $\frac{1}{64}$
3. (a) 10 000 **(b)** 40 000 **(c)** 80 000 **(d)** 320 000
4. (a) 12 000 **(b)** 24 000 **(c)** 48 000 **(e)** 96 000
5. (a) $5\,000\,000\times2^{\frac{2}{3}}$ **(b)** 320 000 000 **(c)** 327 680 000 000 **(d)** 12 600 000
6. (a) 1250 **(b)** 320 000 **(c)** 5 120 000
7. 45 min **8.** 12 min
9. (a) 7 290 000 **(b)** $10\,000\times3^{\frac{1}{4}}$
10. 72 billion
11. (a) (i) 1 g **(ii)** $4\times2^{-\frac{1}{15}}$ g **(iii)** $\frac{1}{64}$ g **(iv)** $2\sqrt{2}$ g $\doteq2.8$ g
(b) 90 **(c)** 20

12. (a) 12 g **(b)** $6\sqrt{2}\doteq8.5$ g **(c)** $\dfrac{3\sqrt{2}}{4}\doteq1.1$ g

13. 5 h **14.** 270 days **15.** 17 280 years old

Exercise 5-7

1. (a) $\log_{3}9=2$ **(b)** $\log_{2}16=4$ **(c)** $\log_{6}216=3$ **(d)** $\log_{9}(\frac{1}{9})=-1$
(e) $\log_{a}c=b$ **(f)** $\log_{8}1=0$ **(g)** $\log_{4}1024=5$ **(h)** $\log_{49}7=\frac{1}{2}$
(i) $\log_{8}4=\frac{2}{3}$ **(j)** $\log_{5}(\frac{1}{25})=-2$ **(k)** $\log_{10}(10\,000)=4$ **(l)** $\log_{4}(0.125)=-\frac{3}{2}$
2. (a) $7^{2}=49$ **(b)** $3^{6}=729$ **(c)** $4^{4.5}=512$ **(d)** $10^{-1}=0.1$ **(e)** $2^{-4}=\frac{1}{16}$ **(f)** $a^{c}=b$
(g) $12^{3}=1728$ **(h)** $10^{0}=1$ **(i)** $5^{1}=5$ **(j)** $16^{0.5}=4$ **(k)** $8^{\frac{2}{3}}=4$ **(l)** $2^{12}=4096$
3. (a) 2 **(b)** 5 **(c)** 3 **(d)** 3 **(e)** -1 **(f)** 0 **(g)** -2 **(h)** 1
(i) 3 **(j)** 9 **(k)** 87 **(l)** $\sqrt{3}$ **(m)** 1 **(n)** 19 **(o)** 4379
4. (a) 7 **(b)** 4 **(c)** -4 **(d)** -3 **(e)** 4 **(f)** -2
(g) -2 **(h)** -5 **(i)** $\frac{1}{2}$ **(j)** 3.5 **(k)** $\frac{1}{4}$ **(l)** $-\frac{3}{2}$
5. (a) -1, 0, 0.6, 1, 1.3, 1.6, 1.8, 2, 2.2, 2.3, 2.5, 2.6, 2.7, 2.8
6. (a) 1 000 000 **(b)** 256 **(c)** 5 **(d)** 5 **(e)** 16 **(f)** $\frac{1}{3}$
(g) -1 **(h)** -2 **(i)** $\frac{1}{16}$ **(j)** 8 **(k)** 243 **(l)** $\frac{3}{4}$
10. (a) 35 **(b)** $\frac{7}{5}$ **(c)** 343 **(d)** 3
11. $2L$ **12.** $M+N$

Exercise 5-8

1. (a) $\log_{10} 8 + \log_{10} 13$ (b) $\log_2 9.1 + \log_2 6.3$ (c) $\log_5 14 + \log_5 8.1$ (d) $\log_5 11 - \log_5 37$
(e) $\log_8 104 - \log_8 97.2$ (f) $\log_{10} 2 - \log_{10} \pi$ (g) $\log_3 2 + \log_3 \pi$ (h) $\log_2 19 + \log_2 97$
(i) $\log_{12} 16 - \log_{12} 65$ (j) $\log_{10} x + \log_{10} y$ (k) $\log_{10} x - \log_{10} y$ (l) $\log_x A + \log_x B$

2. (a) $\log_{10} (89 \times 14)$ (b) $\log_5 (12.2 \times 2.79)$ (c) $\log_2 \left(\frac{75}{36}\right)$ (d) $\log_3 \left(\frac{634}{149}\right)$ (e) $\log_6 18$

(f) $\log_7 6$ (g) $\log_{10} (xy)$ (h) $\log_2 \left(\frac{x}{y}\right)$ (i) $\log_{10} 9$ (j) $\log_9 60$

3. (a) $2\log_{10} 68$ (b) $5\log_2 3.9$ (c) $10\log_5 \pi$ (d) $\frac{3}{4}\log_{10} 7$ (e) $\frac{1}{2}\log_3 5$ (f) $\frac{1}{2}\log_5 3$
(g) $-\log_{10} 8$ (h) $-\log_{10} 12$ (i) $9\log_{10} x$ (j) $\log_{10} 37^2$ (k) $\log_2 21^8$ (l) $\log_5 8$
(m) $\log_5 \sqrt[3]{97}$ (n) $\log_{10} 3$ (o) $\log_{10} (\frac{1}{5})$ (p) $\log_{10}(\frac{1}{4})$ (q) $y\log_2 x$ (r) $\log_6 A^m$

4. (a) $\log_{12} 82 + \log_{12} 28$ (b) $\log_2 9 + \log_2 13 + \log_2 14$ (c) $20\log_5 9$
(d) $\log_3 \left(\frac{79}{53}\right)$ (e) $\log_{10} 36$ (f) $\log_2 L + \log_2 M + \log_2 N$
(g) $\log_{10} 7$ (h) $\log_2 937 - \log_2 1005$ (i) $-\log_{10} 67$
(j) $\frac{1}{2}\log_5 83$ (k) $\log_a 5 + \log_a x$ (l) $\log_3 (\frac{1}{8})$
(m) $\log_2 42$ (n) $\log_{10} 7$

5. (a) 0.7781   (b) 1.1761   (c) 0.6020   (d) 1.2552   (e) 2.0970
(f) 0.3980   (g) 0.1761   (h) -0.2219 (i) 0.8751   (j) 0.3495
(k) 0.1193   (l) -0.3010 (m) 2.3010   (n) 4.6990   (o) -2.5229

6. (a) 3   (b) 2   (c) 3   (d) 4   (e) 2
(f) $\frac{2}{3}$ (g) $\frac{2}{3}$ (h) 81   (i) $-\frac{1}{2}$ (j) $\frac{3}{2}$

7. (a) 15   (b) 3   (c) $\frac{2}{3}$ (d) 20   (e) 3
(f) 6   (g) 3   (h) 2   (i) 343   (j) 5

8. (a) 3.6   (b) $\dfrac{2(1+\sqrt{10})}{3}$

9. (a) $\log_2 \dfrac{ab}{c}$ (b) $\log_{10} \dfrac{a\sqrt{b}}{c^2}$ (c) $\log_{10} \dfrac{\sqrt{xy}}{c^2}$ (d) $\log_5 \sqrt{\dfrac{ab^2}{c^3}}$ (e) $\log_2 \left(1 - \dfrac{b^2}{a^2}\right)$ (f) $\log_2 \dfrac{ac^b}{e^d}$

Exercise 5-9

1. (a) 10   (b) 10   (c) 100
2. (a) 1000   (b) 10 000 000   (c) 10 000 000 000
3. (a) 3.45×10^5 (b) 0.894   (c) 0.0393   (d) 0.0937   (e) 949
(f) 8.42   (g) 3.61×10^7 (h) 3.68×10^7 (i) 9.00   (j) 8.03×10^{13}

4. $25\log_2 10$ **5.** $30\log_2 20\, s$ **6.** $\dfrac{48}{\log_2 (1.25)}$ **7.** $\dfrac{29}{\log_2 \left(\frac{10}{3}\right)} h$ **8.** $\log_2 100$

9. $40\log_2 6$ **10.** $\dfrac{60}{\log_2 2.5}$ **11.** 3160   **2.** 8.9   **13.** 4000

14. $x = \dfrac{ab(2^{\frac{t}{c}} - 1)}{a2^{\frac{t}{c}} - b}$

Review Exercise

1. (a) 2^5 (b) 2^{15} (c) 2^8 (d) 2^{-1} (e) $2^{\frac{1}{2}}$ (f) $2^{\frac{2}{3}}$ (g) 2^0 (h) 2^{12}
(i) 2^5 (j) 2^{-3} (k) 2^{-1} (l) 2^6

2. (a) 1   (b) $\frac{1}{3}$ (c) $\frac{1}{36}$ (d) 3   (e) 2   (f) 7   (g) 27   (h) $\frac{1}{4}$
(i) $\frac{1}{64}$ (j) 1   (k) $\frac{1}{4}$ (l) 125

3. (a) $8^9 \times 17^9$ (b) 45^6 (c) $\sqrt[7]{4}$ (d) $(\sqrt[4]{7})^3$ or $\sqrt[4]{343}$ (e) $\dfrac{3^8}{17^8}$
(f) 4^6 (g) $x^{\frac{2}{3}}$ (h) π^8 (i) 5^{13} (j) $3^{4.5}$
(k) $16x^8$ (l) $5^{-\frac{2}{3}}$ (m) x^{5n} (n) x^{5+n} (o) $\dfrac{x^4}{16}$
(p) $3^{1.5}$ (q) $5^{2.5}$ (r) x^{a+b+c} (s) 6^3 (t) x^{n+3}

4. (a) 2.34×10^2 (b) 1.8×10^4 (c) 1.6×10^{-2} (d) 6.2×10^{-5}
(e) 1.25×10^6 (f) 1.938×10^2 (g) 6.34×10^5 (h) 7.1×10^{-1}

5. (a) 2   (b) 4   (c) 3   (d) 3
(e) 0   (f) -1 (g) $\frac{1}{2}$ (h) 7

6. (a) $\log_{10} 14 + \log_{10} 29$ (b) $\log_2 11 + \log_2 13 + \log_2 15$ (d) $\log_{10} 61 - \log_{10} 43$
(e) $\frac{1}{2}\log_5 37$ (f) $-\log_{10} 6$ (g) $\log_2 3 + \log_2 \pi$
(h) $\log_3 5$ (i) $\log_2 6$

7. (a) 25   (b) x^5 (c) $\frac{1}{36}$ (d) a^{4n-n^2} (e) $-27x^{14}y^2$ (f) x^6y^4
(g) $\dfrac{y^2z^7}{x^3}$ (h) $\dfrac{b^5}{a^3}$ (i) a^8

8. (a) $\frac{27}{16}$ (b) 729   (c) 27   (d) 32   (e) $\frac{1}{7}$
    (f) 3   (g) 1 000 000 000   (h) 2   (i) 3   (j) $\frac{11}{5}$
    (k) $\frac{3}{2}$ (l) $\frac{9}{16}$ (m) $\frac{6}{7}$ (n) 2.7   (o) $\frac{1}{256}$

9. (a) $\dfrac{5}{x^2y^3}$ (b) $\dfrac{64}{x^3}$ (c) $\dfrac{3y}{4x^2}$ (d) $\dfrac{b^4}{a}$ (e) $\dfrac{81b^8}{a^4c^{16}}$

    (f) $x^7 + x^5 + x^3$ (g) $a^2 - \dfrac{1}{a^2}$ (h) $\dfrac{ab}{b^2 - a^2}$

10. (a) $-\frac{1}{3}$ (b) 6   (c) $\frac{7}{3}$

11. (a) 1.86×10^{-10} (b) 2.685×10^{16} (c) 3.06×10^{15} (d) 8.4×10^{-13} (e) 7×10^9 (f) 8×10^{-13}

12. 2.21×10^{-10}

14. (a) -5 (b) 3   (c) -7 (d) $\frac{1}{2}$ (e) 3   (f) 2.5   (g) 3.7
    (h) 97   (i) 2   (j) 3

15. (a) 32 768   (b) 6   (c) $\frac{1}{5}$ (d) $\frac{1}{625}$ (e) 3   (f) 32   (g) 3   (h) 3

16. (a) $\log_{10} \dfrac{x}{y^2}$ (b) $\log_2 x^3y^6$ (c) $\log_3 MN\sqrt{P}$ (d) $\log_5 \dfrac{A^4}{\sqrt{B}}$

17. (a) 3460   (b) 0.009 42   (c) 8.38

18. (a) 4000   (b) $4000 \times 2^{\frac{1}{20}}$ (c) 11 315   (d) 1 048 576 000

19. $\dfrac{40}{\log_2 3}$

20. (a) (i) $120 \times 2^{-\frac{1}{16}}$ (ii) $\dfrac{15}{8192}$ (iii) $15\sqrt{2}$

    (b) $16 \log_2 120$

21. 31 600

REVIEW AND PREVIEW TO CHAPTER 6

4. (a) $\dfrac{1}{\sqrt{2}}$ (b) $\dfrac{\sqrt{3}}{2}$ (c) 3   (d) $-\dfrac{1}{\sqrt{2}}$ (e) 1

    (f) $-\frac{1}{2}$ (g) 1   (h) -1 (i) $\dfrac{2+\sqrt{2}}{2}$ (j) $\dfrac{1-\sqrt{3}}{2}$

Exercise 2.

1. (a) 16   (b) 17   (c) 14   (d) 16   (e) 10   (f) 31
2. (a) 37°   (b) 36°   (c) 50°   (d) 52°   (e) 37°   (f) 49°
3. (a) 57, 43°, 47°   (b) 196, 220, 27°   (c) 38°, 12, 19
4. 7.2
5. (a) 102   (b) 17   (c) 63.7

Exercise 6-1

1. (a) 25.600°   (b) 54.900°   (c) 33.700°   (d) 40.300°   (e) 50.421°   (f) 27.425°   (g) 47.492°   (h) 17.613°
2. (a) 35°18′   (b) 47°36′   (c) 53°48′   (d) 72°6′   (e) 53°8′35″   (f) 25°22′16″
    (g) 48°12′58″   (h) 83°54′50″
3. (a) 53°36′   (b) 42°21′   (c) 40°24′   (d) 36°36′   (e) 59°31′10″   (f) 4°52′54″
    (g) 75°36′24″   (h) 73°38′   (i) 70°37′10″
5. (a) 0.882 95   (b) -1.0000 (c) $-0.173 65$ (d) 0.669 13   (e) -3.8667 (f) 0.457 09
    (g) $-0.741 98$ (h) $-0.615 20$ (i) 0.977 78   (j) -0.9472 (k) -1.4442
6. (a) 77°32′   (b) 54°30′, 125°30′   (c) 144°24′   (d) 51°42′, 128°18′   (e) 31°36′
    (f) 139°18′   (g) 12°24′, 167°36′   (h) 102°36′
10. (a) $-0.709 57$ (b) 0.773 84   (c) 2.7929   (d) 0.878 82   (e) 0.632 17   (f) $-0.922 54$
    (g) $-0.634 73$ (h) $-0.168 49$ (i) 0.821 15   (j) -1.7054 (k) 5.8164   (l) $-0.713 29$

Exercise 6-2

1. (a) 16.6   (b) 8.49   (c) 176.6
2. (a) 78°30′   (b) 42°18′   (c) 99°12′
3. (a) 44.7   (b) 73.3   (c) 52°42′   (d) 94°42′   (e) 40.4 cm

Exercise 6-3

1. (a) 44.8   (b) 26.2   (c) 38.1 cm   (i) 27.5   (e) 19.2   (f) 64.8

2. (a) 50.2   **(b)** 172   **(c)** 41.6   **(d)** 6.92, 4.61
3. (a) 80°, 14.6, 13.4   **(b)** 126°42′, 85.5, 38.2   **(c)** 58°54′, 106, 119   **(d)** 62°48′, 11.2, 13.5
     (e) 40°48′, 16.9, 8.19
4. (a) 63°54′, 81°, 6.40   **(b)** 21°48′, 47°54′, 15.2   **(c)** 94°42′, 57°30′, 6.08   **(d)** 80°24′, 46°6′, 21.2
     (e) 32°30′, 23°16′, 128

Exercise 6-4

1. (a) 1   **(b)** 2   **(c)** 2   **(d)** 1   **(e)** 0
2. $50 < a < 100$ **3.** $b < 11.9$ **4.** $c = 60.4$ or $c \geqslant 125$
5. 34°24′, 100°36′, 41.7   **6.** 14°30′, 132°48′, 73.3
7. 40.3°, 47.7°, 92.0°, 40.0 cm, 35 cm, 54.1 cm

Exercise 6-5

1. 13.4   **2.** 37.4   **3.** 9°18′   **4.** 509 km
5. Yes   **6.** 57°42′, 76°24′, 45°54′   **7.** 56°18′   **8.** 413.4
9. 267   **10.** 53 or 86
11. (a) (i) 1.414   **(ii)** 1.176   **(iii)** 1.00
12. 22.6 cm   **13.** 122   **14.** 120 m, 59 m   **15.** 12 : 06.5

Exercise 6-6

1. (a) 250   **(b)** 60   **(c)** 21
2. (a) 7824   **(b)** 777   **(c)** 141.0   **(d)** 134.0   **(e)** 481.5
3. (a) 1310   **(b)** 4264   **(c)** 235.4   **(d)** 1342   **(e)** 29 910
4. (a) 26.8   **(b)** 3.80   **(c)** 419.5   **(d)** 121   **(e)** 771.9
5. 77.02
6. 5.881   **(b)** 2.614

Review Exercise

1. (a) 121°   **(b)** 14.71   **(c)** 49.50   **(d)** 64.09
2. (a) 69°6′, 79.44, 122.6   **(b)** 39°30′, 63.83, 50.18   **(c)** 87°6′, 43°54′, 27.20   **(d)** 110°42′, 60.19, 29.78
     (e) 117°6′, 26°42′, 36°12′
3. (a) 67.3, 23°12′, 124°   **(b)** 21.4, 45°42′, 22°
     (c) 63.2, 77°12′, 50°24′ or 102°48′, 24°48′, 34.41   **(d)** 73°30′, 21.58, 11.98
     (e) 67.53, 26°30′, 31°42′
4. (a) 78.78   **(b)** 149.2   **(c)** 513   **(d)** 544   **(e)** 872.8   **(f)** 933.5
5. 7°   **6.** 52.61, 33.77   **7.** 38.79   **8.** 4°48′
9. (a) 10   **(b)** 9°30′, 7.6 cm   **(c)** 63°24′
10. (a) 32.63, 22.92 No

REVIEW AND PREVIEW TO CHAPTER 7

Exercise 2

2. (a) $\frac{1}{2}$ **(b)** $\frac{5}{7}$ **(c)** 3, -2 **(d)** $\frac{1}{5}$, 1   **(e)** $-\frac{1}{3}$, -2 **(f)** $\dfrac{-1 \pm i\sqrt{3}}{2}$ **(g)** $-\frac{5}{3}$, 2   **(h)** 6, -4

Exercise 7-1

3. (a) 20°   **(b)** 71°36′   **(c)** 36°6′   **(d)** 28°36′   **(e)** 143°12′
     (f) 358°6′   **(g)** 100°18′   **(h)** -43°   **(i)** 180°   **(j)** -69°18′
4. (a) 0.70   **(b)** 1.45   **(c)** 2.53   **(d)** 4.01   **(e)** 5.67
     (f) 0.62   **(g)** 0.92   **(h)** 2.24   **(i)** 4.46   **(j)** 5.43
5. (a) 2.4   **(b)** $\frac{5\pi}{6}$ **(c)** 7π **(d)** 3.18   **(e)** 36   **(f)** 9.62
6. (a) 15.71   **(b)** 3534
7. (a) 0.209   **(b)** 3896
8. (a) 95.5   **(b)** 960
9. (a) 53.3 min   **(b)** 14.14 km/s
10. (a) 77.2 rad/s   **(b)** 2315 rad

Exercise 7-3

1. (a) 1   **(b)** 3   **(c)** $\frac{1}{2}$ **(d)** 1   **(e)** 2   **(f)** $\frac{2}{3}$ **(g)** 0.5   **(h)** 1.5   **(i)** 3
2. (a) $\dfrac{2\pi}{3}$ **(b)** π **(c)** 4π **(d)** 6π **(e)** 2π

(f) $\dfrac{2\pi}{k}$ **(g)** $\dfrac{2\pi}{3}$ **(h)** 2π **(i)** $\dfrac{\pi}{2}$ **(j)** 3π

3. (a) π **(b)** $-\dfrac{\pi}{2}$ **(c)** $\dfrac{\pi}{3}$ **(d)** $-\dfrac{\pi}{6}$ **(e)** $\dfrac{\pi}{4}$ **(f)** $-\dfrac{\pi}{4}$

(g) π **(h)** $-\dfrac{2\pi}{3}$ **(i)** $-\dfrac{\pi}{3}$ **(j)** $\dfrac{\pi}{2}$ **(k)** $\dfrac{\pi}{2}$ **(l)** $\dfrac{\pi}{3}$

4.

	amplitude	Period	shift	translation
(a)	2	2π	0	0
(b)	1	π	0	3
(c)	1	2π	$-\dfrac{\pi}{2}$	0
(d)	1	4π	0	0
(e)	3	π	0	2
(f)	2	2π	$-\dfrac{\pi}{3}$	0
(g)	2	$\dfrac{2\pi}{3}$	0	0
(h)	1	2π	$\dfrac{\pi}{6}$	0
(i)	1	π	$\dfrac{\pi}{4}$	0
(j)	$\frac{1}{2}$	2π	0	-5
(k)	1	2π	0	0
(l)	2	2π	$-\pi$	0

Exercise 7-4

1. (a) $y = 7\ \mathrm{Sin}\ \pi t$ **(b)** $y = 170\ \mathrm{Cos}\ 120\pi t$ **(c)** $y = 12\ \mathrm{Sin}\dfrac{\pi t}{2}$

(d) $y = 12\ \mathrm{Sin}\ \pi t$ **(e)** $y = 1.5\ \mathrm{Sin}\ 2\pi t + 1.5$ **(f)** $y = 4\ \mathrm{Sin}\ \dfrac{\pi}{4}t + 2$

2. (c) Answer is $y = 6.9\sin(\pi/2)(t-9) + 22$ **(d) (i)** 15.3 **(ii)** 28.7 **(iii)** 22.9
3. $y = 20\sin(\pi/12)(t-6)$ **4.** $y = 7.5\sin(\pi/6)t$
5. (a) 12 **(b)** $y = 17\sin 50\pi t$ **6.** $y = 10\sin(5\pi/2)t$
7. $y = 2\sin(\pi/6)(t-3.86) + 1.8$ **8.** $y = 12\sin \pi t$
9. $y = 311\sin 120\pi t$ **10.** $y = 6\sin(\pi/6)(t-3) + 16$
11. $y = 8\sin(\pi/6)t + 9$ **12. (a)** 155 v **(b)** $y = 155\sin 120\pi t$
14. (a) $y = 10\sin \pi t/6$ **(b)** $y = 10\sin(\pi/6)(t+2)$ **(c)** $y = 10\sin(\pi/6)(t+3)$

Exercise 7-6

1. (a) $0, \pi, 2\pi$ **(b)** $\dfrac{3\pi}{2}$ **(c)** $\dfrac{\pi}{3}, \dfrac{5\pi}{3}$ **(d)** $\dfrac{\pi}{3}, \dfrac{2\pi}{3}$ **(e)** $\dfrac{2\pi}{3}, \dfrac{4\pi}{3}$ **(f)** $0, \pi, 2\pi$

2. (a) $0, \pi, 2\pi$ **(b)** $\dfrac{\pi}{4}, \dfrac{5\pi}{4}$ **(c)** $\dfrac{\pi}{8}, \dfrac{5\pi}{8}$ **(d)** $\dfrac{3\pi}{4}, \dfrac{5\pi}{4}$ **(e)** $\dfrac{2\pi}{3}, \dfrac{4\pi}{3}$

3. $\dfrac{\pi}{3} + 2k\pi, \dfrac{5\pi}{3} + 2k\pi$ **4.** $\dfrac{7\pi}{6} + 2k\pi, \dfrac{11\pi}{6} + 2k\pi$ **5.** $\dfrac{\pi}{4} + k\pi$

6. $\dfrac{\pi}{4} + k\dfrac{\pi}{2}$ **7.** $\dfrac{\pi}{12} + k\pi, \dfrac{5\pi}{12} + k\pi$ **8.** $\dfrac{3\pi}{8} + \dfrac{k\pi}{2}$

9. $k\pi \pm \dfrac{\pi}{3}$ **10.** $\dfrac{\pi}{6} + k\pi, \dfrac{5\pi}{6} + k\pi$ **11.** $\dfrac{\pi}{4} + k\pi, \dfrac{\pi}{2} + 2k\pi$

12. $k\pi, \dfrac{3\pi}{2} + 2k\pi$ **13.** $\dfrac{\pi}{2} + k\pi$ **14.** $\dfrac{\pi}{3} + 2k\pi, \dfrac{5\pi}{3} + 2k\pi, \pi + 2k\pi$

15. $\dfrac{\pi}{6} + 2k\pi, \dfrac{5\pi}{6} + 2k\pi, \dfrac{3\pi}{2} + 2k\pi$ **16.** $\dfrac{3\pi}{4} + k\pi$ **17.** $k\pi$

18. $\dfrac{\pi}{12} + k\pi, \dfrac{5\pi}{12} + k\pi$ **19.** $(2n-1)\dfrac{\pi}{2}$ or $2(n-1)\pi$ **20.** $\dfrac{\pi}{3} + 4k\pi, \dfrac{5\pi}{3} + 4k\pi$

21. $\dfrac{63°}{2} + k360°, \dfrac{107°}{2} + k360°$

22. $194.5° + k360°, 345.5° + k360°, 90° + k360°$

23. $52°\ 14' + \pi k;\ 127°\ 46' + \pi k$

24. $210° + k360°,\ 330° + k360°,\ 49° + k360°,\ 131° + k360°$

25. $90° + k360°,\ k90°$

Exercise 7-7

1. (a) $\dfrac{\pi}{4}$ **(b)** $\dfrac{\pi}{3}$ **(c)** $\dfrac{\pi}{6}$ **(d)** $\dfrac{\pi}{6}$ **(e)** $-\dfrac{\pi}{4}$ **(f)** $\dfrac{\pi}{4}$ **(g)** $\dfrac{2\pi}{3}$ **(h)** $-\dfrac{\pi}{3}$

2. (a) 0 **(b)** 0 **(c)** $\dfrac{\pi}{4}$ **(d)** $\dfrac{\pi}{4}$ **(e)** 0 **(f)** $-\dfrac{\pi}{4}$ **(g)** $-\dfrac{\pi}{4}$ **(h)** $\dfrac{\pi}{2}$

3. (a) $\dfrac{1}{\sqrt{2}}$ **(b)** 1.7321 **(c)** $\dfrac{1}{\sqrt{2}}$ **(d)** 1 **(e)** -0.5774

    (f) 0.4472 **(g)** 2 **(h)** $\tfrac{1}{2}$ **(i)** 0.8 **(j)** 0.8

Exercise 7-8

7. (a) $\tfrac{63}{65}$ **(b)** $\tfrac{16}{65}$ **(c)** $\tfrac{63}{16}$ **(d)** $-\tfrac{33}{65}$ **(e)** $\tfrac{56}{65}$ **(f)** $-\tfrac{33}{56}$ **(g)** $\tfrac{33}{65}$ **(h)** $\tfrac{5}{13}$ **(i)** $\tfrac{12}{13}$

11. $2.4\,\text{m}$

Exercise 7-9

1. (a) $\left(\dfrac{3\sqrt{3}}{2}, \dfrac{3}{2}\right)$ **(b)** $\left(\dfrac{5\sqrt{2}}{2}, \dfrac{5\sqrt{2}}{2}\right)$ **(c)** $(0, 4)$ **(d)** $\left(\dfrac{-7\sqrt{3}}{2}, \dfrac{7}{2}\right)$ **(e)** $(-2, -2\sqrt{3})$

    (f) $(-3, 0)$ **(g)** $(-\sqrt{2}, -\sqrt{2})$ **(h)** $\left(\dfrac{5\sqrt{3}}{2}, \dfrac{5}{2}\right)$ **(i)** $\left(\dfrac{5\sqrt{3}}{2}, \dfrac{5}{2}\right)$ **(j)** $(-3, 0)$

    (k) $(0, -3)$ **(l)** $\left(\dfrac{5\sqrt{2}}{2}, \dfrac{5\sqrt{2}}{2}\right)$ **(m)** $\left(\dfrac{3\sqrt{2}}{2}, \dfrac{-3\sqrt{2}}{2}\right)$ **(n)** $\left(\dfrac{5\sqrt{2}}{2}, \dfrac{-5\sqrt{2}}{2}\right)$ **(o)** $(\sqrt{2}, -\sqrt{2})$

    (p) $(2, 0)$

2. (a) $(4, 45°)\ (-4, 225°)$ **(b)** $(3, 180°)\ (-3, 0°)$ **(c)** $(4, 90°),\ (-4, -90°)$ **(d)** $(1, 30°),\ (-1, -150°)$

    (e) $(5, 53°)$ **(f)** $(13, 67.5°)$ **(g)** $(13, 112.5°)$ **(h)** $(10, 307°)$

    (i) $(1, 210°)$ **(j)** $(5, 240°)$ **(k)** $(3, -45°)$ **(l)** $(10, 37°)$

6. (a) $r\,\text{Cos}\,\theta - r\,\text{Sin}\,\theta - 1 = 0$ **(b)** $2r\,\text{Cos}\,\theta - 5r\,\text{Sin}\,\theta - 2 = 0$ **(c)** $r^2 = 4$

    (d) $\text{Sin}\,\theta = 2\,\text{Cos}^2\,\theta$

7. (a) $x^2 + y^2 = 2y$ **(b)** $x^2 + y^2 = 3x$

Review Exercise

1. (a) $\dfrac{\pi}{3}$ **(b)** 1.19π **(c)** $\dfrac{41\pi}{18}$ **(d)** 0.474π **(e)** 0.7267π

2. (a) $135°$ **(b)** $330°$ **(c)** $1020°$ **(d)** $252°$ **(e)** $240°$

3. (a) 62.83 **(b)** 188.5

6. (a) $y = \text{Sin}\,2\left(\theta + \dfrac{\pi}{2}\right)$ **(b)** $y = 3\,\text{Sin}\,2\left(\theta - \dfrac{\pi}{3}\right)$ **(c)** $y = 2\,\text{Sin}\,\theta$ **(d)** $y = \tfrac{1}{2}\,\text{Sin}\,4\pi\left(\theta - \dfrac{\pi}{2}\right)$

7. $y = 9.5\,\text{Sin}\,\dfrac{\pi}{5}\left(t - \dfrac{5}{2}\right) + 10.7$

8. (a) $28\,280$ **(b)** $y = 28\,280\,\text{Sin}\,12\,000\pi t$

9. (a) (i) $\dfrac{1}{240} + \dfrac{k}{60}$ **(ii)** $\dfrac{k}{60} - \dfrac{1}{240}$ **(b)** 3.54

11. (a) $\dfrac{\pi}{3} + 2k\pi,\ \dfrac{2\pi}{3} + 2k\pi$ **(b)** $\dfrac{3\pi}{4} + 2k\pi,\ \dfrac{5\pi}{4} + 2k\pi$ **(c)** $\dfrac{3\pi}{4} + k\pi$

    (d) $\dfrac{\pi}{4} + k\pi$ **(e)** $\dfrac{\pi}{6} + 2k\pi,\ \dfrac{5\pi}{6} + 2k\pi$ **(f)** $\dfrac{\pi}{4} + k\pi,\ \dfrac{3\pi}{4} + k\pi$

    (g) $(k-1)\pi,\ \dfrac{\pi}{6} + 2k\pi,\ \dfrac{5\pi}{6} + 2k\pi$ **(h)** $\dfrac{\pi}{2} + k\pi$ **(i)** $\dfrac{\pi}{2} + 2k\pi,\ \dfrac{7\pi}{6} + 2k\pi,\ \dfrac{11\pi}{6} + 2k\pi$

12. (a) $60°$ **(b)** $135°$ **(c)** $-45°$ **(d)** $90°$ **(e)** $120°$ **(f)** $45°$

13. (a) $\left(-\dfrac{7\sqrt{3}}{2}, -\dfrac{7}{2}\right)$ **(b)** $(5\sqrt{2}, 135°)$

14. (b) $r^2 = 25$

REVIEW AND PREVIEW TO CHAPTER 8

Exercise 1

1. (a) $6a^8$ (b) $4x^3$ (c) $8y^{12}$ (d) 1

2. (a) $15x^{-1}$ (b) $2xy^2$ (c) a^6b^9 (d) $\sqrt[3]{3}b$

3. (a) x^6 (b) 1 (c) x^2 (d) $2ab^2$

4. (a) $a^2+2ab+b^2$ (b) 1.0404 (c) 1.0609 (d) 1.0816

5. (a) 5 (b) 18 (c) 26 (d) 9

(e) $\frac{8}{9}$ (f) -5 (g) $\frac{9}{4}$ (h) $\frac{1}{5}$

(i) 4

6. (a) 2 (b) -2 (c) -3 (d) 2

(e) 3 (f) 6 (g) -3 (h) 4

(i) $\frac{7}{2}$ (j) 3 (k) 0 (l) 4

7. (a) $\log \dfrac{ab}{c}$ (b) $\log \dfrac{a^{\frac{1}{2}}}{(ab)^2}$ (c) $\log \dfrac{a^2b^3}{c^5}$

(d) $\log \dfrac{a^3c}{b^2}$ (e) $\log \dfrac{a^xb^v}{a+b}$ (f) $\log \dfrac{(a+b)^2b^2}{a^2}$

Exercise 2

1. (a) \$10 (b) \$405 (c) \$847

2. (a) \$635 (b) \$909.38 (c) \$2400

3. (a) \$19.75 (b) \$24.89 (c) \$61.72

4. (a) 8% (b) 9% (c) 10%

5. (a) $2a$ (b) $3.5a$ (c) 110 days

Exercise 8-1

3. (a) 3, 6, 9, 12, 15 (b) $-3, -1, 1, 3, 5$

(c) 0, 3, 8, 15, 24 (d) $3, 3^2, 3^3, 3^4, 3^5$

(e) $1, 3, 3^2, 3^3, 3^4$ (f) 2, 8, 26, 80, 242

(g) $-1, 1, -1, 1, -1$ (h) $3, -6, 9, -12, 15$

(i) $-1, 1, 3, 5, 7$ (j) $0, \frac{1}{3}, \frac{1}{2}, \frac{3}{5}, \frac{2}{3}$

(k) 1, 3, 6, 10, 15 (l) $0, \frac{2}{5}, \frac{6}{7}, \frac{4}{3}, \frac{20}{11}$

4. (a) 1, 3, 5, 7, 9 (b) 2, 4, 6, 8, 10

(c) $-2, 4, -8, 16, -32$ (d) $2, \frac{4}{3}, \frac{6}{5}, \frac{8}{7}, \frac{10}{9}$

(e) $1, \frac{1}{2}, \frac{1}{3}, \frac{1}{4}, \frac{1}{5}$ (f) $\frac{1}{2}, \frac{1}{4}, \frac{1}{8}, \frac{1}{16}, \frac{1}{32}$

(g) 2, 7, 12, 17, 22 (h) 1, 4, 9, 16, 25

(i) 2, 4, 8, 16, 32 (j) $0, \frac{1}{3}, \frac{1}{2}, \frac{3}{5}, \frac{2}{3}$

(k) 0, 1, 3, 6, 10 (l) $0, \frac{3}{2}, \frac{8}{3}, \frac{15}{4}, \frac{24}{5}$

5. (a) n (b) $5-n$ (c) $2(-\frac{1}{2})^{n-1}$ (d) 2^{n-4}

(e) 2^{n+1} (f) $7-3n$ (g) $(-1)^{n+1}$ (h) $4n-2$

(i) $(2)(3)^{n-1}$ (j) x^{n-1} (k) $(4-n)a+nb$ (l) $a^{4-n}b^n$

6. $3, 1, -3, -11, -27$

7. $t_n = 4n+1$

8. (a) 2, 5, 8, 11, 14 (b) $t_n = 3n-1$ (c) (i) 74 (ii) 2999

9. (a) $3, -2, -7, -12, -17$ (b) $8-5n$ (c) (i) -242 (ii) -2492

10. (a) 3, 5, 7, 9, 11 (b) 1, 6, 16, 36, 76 (c) $3, 1, -1, -3, -5$

(d) 0, 2, 4, 6, 8 (e) 2, 6, 12, 20, 30 (f) 1, 1, 2, 3, 5

Exercise 8-2

1. b, c, e, h, j, l

2. (a) 1, 5, 9, 13, 17 (b) 3, 8, 13, 18, 23

(c) $-8, -11, -14, -17, -20$ (d) $x, x+y, x+2y, x+3y, x+4y$

(e) $x+1, 2x+3, 3x+5, 4x+7,$ (f) $5, 5+x, 5+2x, 5+3x, 5+4x$

$5x+9$

(g) $5m, 8m, 11m, 14m, 17m,$ (h) $3, 4+x, 5+2x, 6+3x, 7+4x$

(i) $5+x, 8+x, 11+x, 14+x, 17+x$ (j) $2a, a, 0, -a, -2a$

(k) 0.5, 2.0, 3.5, 5.0, 6.5 (l) $3a, 2+2a, 4+a, 6, 8-a$

3. (a) 26, 94 (b) 70, 210 (c) 52, 703

(d) $-78, -414$ (e) 4, 232 (f) $a+12b, a+184b$

(g) $21x, 201x$ (h) $a-6b, a-103b$ (i) $67, 1+3n$

(j) $289, -17+6n$ (k) $205, -5+7n$ (l) $a+138, a+(n-1)6$

4. (a)

	a	d	t_n
(a)	4	3	$1+3n$
(b)	-3	5	$-8+5n$
(c)	42	2	$40+2n$
(d)	-19	7	$-26+7n$
(e)	67	-5	$72-5n$
(f)	$\dfrac{-128}{13}$	$\dfrac{-33}{13}$	$\dfrac{-95}{13}-\dfrac{33n}{13}$

(g) $a=-277,\ d=-\dfrac{10}{3}\ tn=-\dfrac{821}{3}-\dfrac{10n}{3}$

(h) $\quad 3-22x \qquad \dfrac{9}{2}x \qquad 3+\dfrac{9nx}{2}-\dfrac{53}{2}x$

5. (a) 64 **(b)** 56 **(c)** 32 **(d)** 31
  (e) 165 **(f)** 27 **(g)** 129 **(h)** 28

6. 146

7. 89

8. 55

9. (a) 1090, 1180, 1270, 1360 **(b)** $4600

10. $\dfrac{1871}{13}$

11. 5

12. 0 or 4

13. 5

14. (a) 7, 9, 11, 13, 15 **(b)** $2k+5$ **(c)** $2k+3$ **(d)** 2

15. (a) 14 **(b)** 11, 17

(c) 18, 21, 24, 27, 30, 33, 36

(d) $\dfrac{9}{7},\dfrac{-45}{7},\dfrac{-99}{7},\dfrac{-153}{7},\dfrac{-207}{7},\dfrac{-261}{7}$

(e) $\dfrac{7x}{4}+5y,\ \dfrac{5x}{2}+8y,\ \dfrac{13x}{4}+11y$

16. 6, 12

17. $7m$

18. $18a$

19. 5

20. $7.20, $1.50

Exercise 8-3

1. b, e, f, g, i, j, k

2. (a) $32, 2^n$ **(b)** $3125, 5^{n-1}$ **(c)** $96, 3(2)^{k-1}$ **(d)** $1, 2^{6-k}$
  (e) $32, 2^n(-1)^{n-1}$ **(f)** $1, (-1)^{n-1}2^{7-n}$ **(g)** $-\frac{1}{27}), (-3)^{5-n}$ **(h)** $\frac{1}{64}, (\frac{1}{2})^n$
  (i) $(2x)^{10}, (2x)^n$ **(j)** $\left(\dfrac{x}{2}\right)^7, \left(\dfrac{x}{2}\right)^{n-1}$ **(k)** x^{44}, x^{94} **(l)** $-3x^{-9}, -3x^{-49}$

3. (a) 6 **(b)** 9 **(c)** 9 **(d)** 10 **(e)** 7 **(f)** 8
  (g) 15 **(h)** 14 **(i)** 7 **(j)** 11 **(k)** 6 **(l)** 19

4.

	a	r	t_n
(a)	4	3	$(4)(3^{n-1})$
(b)	3	2	$(3)(2)^{n-1}$
(c)	±7	±4	$(7)(4)^{n-1}$ or $(-1)^n(7)(4)^{n-1}$
(d)	256	$\frac{1}{2}$	2^{9-n}
(e)	-243	$\frac{1}{3}$	$(-1)^{n-1}3^{6-n}$
(f)	±3	±4	$(3)4^{n-1}$ or $(-1)^n(3)(4)^{n-1}$
(g)	$\pm\frac{4}{3}$	$\pm\sqrt{3}$	$\frac{4}{3}(-1)^{n-1}(3)^{n-1}$
(h)	$\frac{3}{16}$	2	$3(2^{n-5})$
(i)	$\dfrac{(2)(3^{10})}{5^5}$	$\frac{5}{3}$	
(j)	$5x^2$	x^2	$5x^{2n}$
(k)	1	$2x$	$(2x)^{n-1}$
(l)	$\pm128k^{10}$	$\pm\dfrac{1}{2k}$	$(-1)^{n-1}2^{8-n}k^{11-n}$

5. (a) 5 **(b)** 7 **(c)** 9 **(d)** 7 **(e)** 6 **(f)** 10 **(g)** 8 **(h)** 13

6. $-1, 25$

7. $\frac{1}{5}, 6$

8. $1512.63

9. $327, $356.43, $388.50, $300(1+0.09)^n$
10. $680.24
11. 1024
12. **(b)** exponential
13. 10 617
14. 50%
15. 10%
16. (a) 35, 245, 1715 or −35, 245, −1715
  (b) 81, 243, 729 or −81, 243, −729
  (c) 24, 12, 6, 3
  (d) 486, 162, 54, 18, 6
17. (a) ±4 **(b)** ±30 **(c)** $\pm\sqrt{mn}$
18. $a = x + y, r = 2$
19. 64
20. (a) 523.3 **(b)** 350 **(c)** 2

Exercise 8-4

2. (a) $1+0-1-2-3=-5$ **(b)** $-1+4-9+16=10$
  (c) $3-8+15-24=-14$ **(d)** $2+5+8+11+14=40$
  (e) $-1-2-3-4=-10$ **(f)** $1+4+9=14$
  (g) $-1-2-3-4=-10$ **(h)** $-9+16-25+36-49=-31$
  (i) $1+2+4+8+16=31$ **(j)** $\frac{1}{2}+\frac{1}{3}+\frac{1}{4}+\frac{1}{5}+\frac{1}{6}=\frac{87}{60}$
  (k) $3+\frac{3}{2}+1+\frac{3}{4}+\frac{3}{5}=6\frac{17}{20}$ **(l)** $0+1+\frac{4}{3}+\frac{3}{2}+\frac{8}{5}+\frac{5}{3}=\frac{71}{10}$

3. (a) $\sum_{n=1}^{6} 2n$ **(b)** $\sum_{i=1}^{n} i^2$ **(c)** $\sum_{n=0}^{4} 3+2n$

  (d) $\sum_{k=1}^{n} 2^{k-1}$ **(e)** $\sum_{k=1}^{n} 3k-2$ **(f)** $\sum_{k=1}^{n} 3(2)^{k-1}$

  (g) $\sum_{i=0}^{3} 5x^i$ **(h)** $\sum_{k=2}^{5} (k+1)x$ **(i)** $\sum_{k=1}^{5} (-1)^{k+1}x^k$

  (j) $\sum_{k=1}^{4} (k)a^k$ **(k)** $\sum_{k=1}^{4} \frac{1}{k+1}$ **(l)** $\sum_{k=1}^{4} \frac{k}{x^k}$

Exercise 8-5

2. (a) 1 001 000 **(b)** 1 000 000 **(c)** 500 500 **(d)** $\frac{n}{2}[1+n]$ **(e)** 33 975 **(f)** 100 500

3. (a) 1 499 500 **(b)** −989 000 **(e)** 1 503 500 **(d)** −999 000
4. (a) 495 **(b)** 1350 **(c)** 350 **(d)** 1638 **(e)** 50 **(f)** −225 **(g)** 1250 **(h)** 488
5. (a) 20 200 **(b)** 7155 **(c)** 0 **(d)** 42 **(e)** 399 **(f)** −3630 **(g)** 130.5 **(h)** −62.5
6. (a) 10 000 **(b)** 4 002 000 **(c)** 9 560
7. (a) 12 **(b)** 30 **(c)** 20 **(d)** 25 **(e)** 6,10 **(f)** 15
8. 78
9. second, $7.50
10. 925
11. $132 000

12. (a) $\frac{n}{2}[n+1]$ **(b)** 5050 **(c)** 500 500 **(d)** 2001 000

13. (a) k^2 **(b)** $k(k+1)$
14. 93
15. (a) 120 **(b)** 5 **(c)** 11

16. $\frac{n}{2}[3n-1]$
17. $n[-2n-1]$
18. 2, 5, 8, 11, 14
19. (a) 45 **(b)** 360
20. 816

Exercise 8-6

1. (a) 2550   (b) 242   (c) 2343   (d) −3280   (e) 504   (f) 1698
2. (a) 511   (b) 3280   (c) 342   (d) 2735   (e) 364.5   (f) 3000
3. 126
4. 341
5. (a) $3\frac{51}{64}$ (b) $89\frac{7}{32}$
6. 175
7. $19 687.50
8. (a) 150   (b) −109   (c) $363\frac{31}{32}$ (d) $\dfrac{5(5^{1000}-1)}{4}$ (e) $1-(\frac{1}{2})^{96}$

Exercise 8-7

2. (a) $8 144.47   (b) $9 766.95   (c) $2 745.58   (d) $53 065.95   (e) $357.69
3. (a) $7764.85   (b) $2764.85
4. (a) $1430.77   (b) $1425.76   (c) $1418.52
5. (a) 9   (b) 8   (c) 7a
6. 6
7. $1693.85
8. $6381.54
9. 4.44%
10. $53 053.80

Exercise 8-8

1. (a) $6 219.64   (b) $1 682.43   (c) $393.79   (d) $1104.67   (e) $14 167.43
2. $4 419.36
3. $14 213.60
4. (a) $698.92   (b) $701.38   (c) $704.96
5. $1385.22
6. $3280.48
7. $3193.84
8. $8151.36
9. $7651.41
10. $6453.43

Exercise 8-9

1. (a) $14 889.04   (b) $5814.07   (c) $2153.84   (d) $12 577.89
2. (a) $165.56   (b) $232.48   (c) $118.64   (d) $394.45
3. $255.36   4. $1007.46   5. $68 666.25   6. $2148.92   7. $1352.56
8. (a) $7512.90   (b) $12 655.19   (c) $41 689.20   (d) $4 727.60
9. $362.03
10. $28 750.90

Exercise 8-10

1. (a) $4 077.10   (b) $16 935.54   (c) $2 258.06   (d) $38 608.68
2. (a) $505.23   (b) $803.70   (c) $263.61   (d) $867.08
3. $3782.79   4. $166.07   5. $3069.58   6. $65.039.68
7. (a) $42 023.81   (b) $39 023.81
8. $358.94   9. $17 866.35
10. (a) $42 855.07   (b) $162 658.71   (c) $162 658.71 vs $225 000

Review Exercise

1. (a) Arithmetic, $5n-3$ (b) Geometric, 2^n (c) Geometric, x^{2n-1}
   (d) Arithmetic, $x+(n-1)a$ (e) Arithmetic, $9-4n$ (f) Geometric, $3(-2)^{n-1}$

2.

	Type	3 terms	Sum
(a)	Arithmetic	5, 8, 11	124
(b)	Geometric	$\frac{2}{3}$, 2, 6	$2186\frac{2}{3}$
(c)	Arithmetic	4, 7, 10	116
(d)	Arithmetic	18, 15, 12	60
(e)	Geometric	10, 20, 40	2550
(f)	Geometric	$\frac{3}{2}$, $\frac{3}{4}$, $\frac{3}{8}$	$\frac{765}{256}$

3. (a) 24   (b) 9
4. (a) −144, −88, −32, 24   (b) 3, 6, 12, 24

5. (a) 46, 3125 **(b)** 75, 4850
6. (a) 24, 94.5 **(b)** 1250, 7812
7. 9523
8. 9714
9. $2^{64}-1$
10. (a) $2+\frac{3}{2}+\frac{4}{3}+\frac{5}{4}+\frac{6}{5}+\frac{7}{6}$, 8.45 **(b)** $0+\frac{1}{3}+\frac{1}{2}+\frac{3}{5}+\frac{2}{3}$, $\frac{63}{30}$ **(c)** $1+2+4+8+16$, 31
11. (a) $8479.40 **(b)** $405.66
12. (a) $7366.92 **(b)** $6191.79
13. (a) $30 503.54 **(b)** $3042.19
14. (a) $318.76 **(b)** $321.90
15. (a) $1788.50 **(b)** $7721.74
16. (a) 683.04 **(b)** $32.72
19. (b) b^2
20. 1, 3, 9, 27, . . .

REVIEW AND PREVIEW TO CHAPTER 9

Exercise 1

1. (a) (5, 11) **(b)** (−1, 7) **(c)** (3, 8) **(d)** (10, −3)
  (e) (3, 1) **(f)** (−4, 2) **(g)** (1, 1) **(h)** (−2, −3)
  (i) (−5, 6) **(j)** (−5, −1) **(k)** $(\frac{1}{2}, -5)$ **(l)** $(-\frac{1}{3}, \frac{1}{2})$
  (m) (−3, −4) **(n)** (0.4, 0.3) **(o)** (0.2, −0.3) **(p)** (3, 5)
  (q) (12, −18) **(r)** (−3, 4)
2. (a) (2, −2, 3) **(b)** (5, −3, −2) **(c)** (−3, −4, 5) **(d)** (0.5, −1, −3)
  (e) (−3, 0, 5) **(f)** (5, 3, 4) **(g)** (0.1, −0.2, −0.5) **(h)** $(1, -\frac{1}{2}, -\frac{1}{3})$
  (i) (−1, 2, −2, 3) **(j)** (2, −1, 0, −2)

Exercise 9-1

3. (a) $\begin{pmatrix} -2 & 3 & -5 \\ -1 & 3 & 6 \end{pmatrix}$ **(b)** $\begin{pmatrix} 9 & -3 & 2 \\ 1 & 1 & 2 \end{pmatrix}$ **(c)** $\begin{pmatrix} 4 & 1 & -1 \\ -2 & 0 & 8 \end{pmatrix}$ **(d)** $\begin{pmatrix} -6 & 2 & 4 \\ -4 & -8 & 0 \end{pmatrix}$

  (e) $\begin{pmatrix} -11 & 6 & -7 \\ -2 & 2 & 4 \end{pmatrix}$ **(f)** $\begin{pmatrix} 11 & -6 & 7 \\ 2 & -2 & -4 \end{pmatrix}$ **(g)** $\begin{pmatrix} 8 & 2 & 6 \\ -9 & -11 & 18 \end{pmatrix}$ **(h)** $\begin{pmatrix} 14 & -7 & -3 \\ 9 & 13 & -6 \end{pmatrix}$

  (i) $\begin{pmatrix} 27 & -16 & 17 \\ 7 & -3 & -14 \end{pmatrix}$ **(j)** $\begin{pmatrix} 3 & -1 & -6 \\ \frac{9}{2} & \frac{19}{2} & -1 \end{pmatrix}$ **(k)** $\begin{pmatrix} -54 & 32 & -34 \\ -14 & 6 & 28 \end{pmatrix}$ **(l)** $\begin{pmatrix} 17 & -8 & 19 \\ -4 & -16 & 0 \end{pmatrix}$

4. (a) $\begin{pmatrix} -19 & 10 \\ 16 & 11 \end{pmatrix}$ **(b)** $(14 \quad -16 \quad 15 \quad 13)$ **(c)** $\begin{pmatrix} -26 \\ 18 \\ 53 \end{pmatrix}$ **(d)** $\begin{pmatrix} -1 & 12 & -9 \\ -3 & -1 & -11 \\ -2 & 8 & -10 \end{pmatrix}$

5. (a) $\begin{pmatrix} -4 & 9 \\ -3 & -8 \end{pmatrix}$ **(b)** $\begin{pmatrix} 2 & -8 \\ 7 & 5 \end{pmatrix}$ **(c)** $\begin{pmatrix} 11 & 1 \\ 9 & -6 \end{pmatrix}$

  (d) $\begin{pmatrix} -8 & 6 \\ -8 & 10 \end{pmatrix}$ **(e)** $\begin{pmatrix} 7 & 1 \\ 2 & -2 \end{pmatrix}$ **(f)** $\begin{pmatrix} -\frac{1}{2} & -3 \\ -2 & -\frac{9}{2} \end{pmatrix}$

Exercise 9-2

2. (a) $\begin{pmatrix} 8 & 15 \\ 22 & 30 \end{pmatrix}$ **(b)** $\begin{pmatrix} -21 & 7 \\ -20 & 4 \end{pmatrix}$ **(c)** $\begin{pmatrix} 22 & -16 \\ 46 & -11 \end{pmatrix}$ **(d)** $\begin{pmatrix} -42 & 123 \\ 12 & -34 \end{pmatrix}$

  (e) $\begin{pmatrix} 5 & -3 \\ 2 & 9 \end{pmatrix}$ **(f)** $\begin{pmatrix} 53 & -12 & 28 \\ 47 & 19 & -12 \\ 26 & -32 & 46 \end{pmatrix}$ **(g)** $\begin{pmatrix} 3 & 13 & -13 \\ 37 & 5 & -40 \\ -11 & 51 & -20 \end{pmatrix}$ **(i)** $\begin{pmatrix} -24 & -12 & -18 \\ 8 & 4 & 6 \end{pmatrix}$

  (j) $\begin{pmatrix} 3 & 5 & 0 \\ 6 & -1 & 2 \\ 4 & 3 & 0 \end{pmatrix}$ **(k)** $\begin{pmatrix} 3 \\ -5 \\ 2 \end{pmatrix}$ **(m)** $\begin{pmatrix} 58 & 36 \\ 13 & 43 \\ 46 & 53 \end{pmatrix}$

  (n) $\begin{pmatrix} 22 & -9 & 14 & 8 \\ 16 & -11 & -14 & 2 \\ -33 & 17 & -2 & -9 \end{pmatrix}$ **(o)** $\begin{pmatrix} 16 & -6 \\ 1 & -4 \\ 3 & 2 \end{pmatrix}$

3. (a) $1250, $1650, $2200, $1350 **(b)** $350, $450, $600, $400

4. $945, $1065, $630, $1095, $1095
6. (a) (2, 1) **(b)** (2, −3) **(c)** (2, 3) **(d)** (2, 1, 3)

Exercise 9-3

2. (a) 5 **(b)** 1 **(c)** −22 **(d)** −54 **(e)** −21 **(f)** 84 **(g)** 22 **(h)** 13
3. (a) −18 **(b)** 84 **(c)** 8
4. (a) 26 **(b)** −1
5. (a) −4, 2 **(b)** 5, −2

Exercise 9-4

1. (a) $\begin{pmatrix} 2 & -1 \\ -5 & 3 \end{pmatrix}$ **(b)** $\begin{pmatrix} -2 & 3 \\ 3 & -4 \end{pmatrix}$ **(d)** $\begin{pmatrix} -\frac{5}{19} & -\frac{3}{19} \\ -\frac{3}{19} & \frac{2}{19} \end{pmatrix}$ **(e)** $\begin{pmatrix} 1 & 0 \\ 0 & 1 \end{pmatrix}$ **(f)** $\begin{pmatrix} 3 & 1 \\ 1 & 0 \end{pmatrix}$

(g) $\begin{pmatrix} 2 & -\frac{11}{2} \\ -1 & 3 \end{pmatrix}$ **(i)** $\begin{pmatrix} -\frac{1}{2} & 2 \\ 1 & -2 \end{pmatrix}$ **(j)** $\begin{pmatrix} \frac{2}{3} & 1 \\ \frac{1}{3} & 1 \end{pmatrix}$ **(k)** $\begin{pmatrix} \frac{6}{7} & \frac{12}{7} \\ -\frac{1}{21} & \frac{1}{14} \end{pmatrix}$ **(l)** $\begin{pmatrix} \frac{4}{5} & -\frac{3}{5} \\ \frac{1}{5} & \frac{1}{10} \end{pmatrix}$

Exercise 9-5

3. (a) (3, 2) **(b)** (2, 1) **(c)** (−1, 3) **(d)** (−4, −3) **(e)** $(-\frac{1}{2}, 3)$
(f) $(-2, -\frac{1}{3})$ **(g)** (−3, 5) **(h)** $(-\frac{3}{4}, \frac{1}{2})$ **(i)** (−3, −4)
4. (a) (2, 4) **(b)** (−3, 2) **(c)** (4, −2) **(d)** $(-\frac{1}{2}, \frac{1}{4})$ **(e)** (2, 10)
5. 50 km/h

Exercise 9-6

4. (a) $\frac{17}{7}, -\frac{2}{7}$ **(b)** $\frac{52}{17}, -\frac{11}{17}$ **(c)** $-\frac{2}{7}, -\frac{12}{7}$ **(d)** $-\frac{2}{3}, \frac{4}{3}$
(e) $-\frac{8}{43}, \frac{44}{43}$ **(f)** $\frac{13}{7}, \frac{3}{7}$ **(g)** −1, 1 **(h)** $-\frac{8}{5}, -\frac{2}{5}$
5. (a) −4, −2 **(b)** 4, −1 **(c)** −3, −2 **(d)** 2, 3
6. (a) 1, −1, 2 **(b)** 1, 2, 3 **(c)** 2, −1, −1 **(d)** −1, 0, 1 **(e)** 2, 2, −1 **(f)** 0, −2, −3
7. (a) 1, −1, 2, −2 **(b)** 0, 1, −1, 2

Exercise 9-7

1. (2, 1, −1) **2.** (1, 0, 4) **3.** (2, 1, 3) **4.** (2, 3, 7)
5. (2, −2, 1) **6.** (3, −2, 2) **7.** (−2, −1, −3) **8.** (4, 2, −3)
9. (1, −1, 2, 0) **10.** (2, 1, −1, 1) **11.** (1, 2, 3) **12.** (−2, −1, 2)

Exercise 9-8

5. (b) (i) [−5, 3] **(ii)** [5, −1] **(iii)** [2, 9] **(iv)** [7, 8]
(v) [2, 11] **(vi)** [5, −3] **(vii)** [−2, −11] **(viii)** [−3, 12]
6. (a) $\sqrt{74}$ **(b)** $\sqrt{73}$ **(c)** $3\sqrt{17}$ **(d)** $\sqrt{58}$
(e) $\sqrt{53}$ **(f)** $2\sqrt{13}$ **(g)** $3\sqrt{17}$ **(h)** $6\sqrt{2}$
7. (a) 10 **(b)** $3\sqrt{5}$ **(c)** $2\sqrt{5}$ **(d)** $\sqrt{41}$

Exercise 9-9

7. (a) [5, 0] **(b)** [−5, 4] **(c)** [1, −3] **(d)** [−7, 3] **(e)** [−4, 0] **(f)** [11, −3]
8. (a) [−6, −16] **(b)** [−6, −21] **(c)** [−9, −4] **(d)** [−15, −16] **(e)** [−13, 3] **(f)** [1, −4]
9. (a) [2, −5], [1, −9], [−5, 6] **(b)** $\sqrt{10}, \sqrt{29}, \sqrt{17}, \sqrt{29}, \sqrt{82}, \sqrt{61}$

Exercise 9-10

3. (a) 95, 33° **(b)** 87, 17° **(c)** 11, 49° **(d)** 10, 65° **(e)** 15, 37° **(f)** 25, 14°
4. 458, 071° **5.** 427, 232° **6.** -326, 305°
7. 534, 174° **8.** 287, 208° **9.** 398, 290°
10. 11.3, 177°, behind
11. (a) 14.2, 266° **(b)** 14.2, 86.5° **(c)** behind
12. 17.8, 045° **13.** 15.8, 079° **14.** 042° **15.** 208°

Exercise 9-11

1. (a) 3000 **(b)** 30 **2. (a)** 3200 **(b)** 4 **3.** 25.3
4. (a) 114.7, 163.8 **(b)** 469.8, −171 **(c)** −102.6, −281.9
5. (a) 72.5 **(b)** 33.8 **6. (a)** 64.3 **(b)** 76.6
7. (a) 246 **(b)** 5587 **(c)** 14.2
8. ( ) 383 426 **(b)** 334 **(c)** 136 890

Review Exercise

1. (a) $\begin{pmatrix} -1 & 0 & 0 \\ -1 & -1 & 7 \end{pmatrix}$ (b) $\begin{pmatrix} -2 & -3 & 0 \\ 1 & 0 & 5 \end{pmatrix}$ (c) $\begin{pmatrix} 2 & -4 & 2 \\ 4 & 2 & -6 \end{pmatrix}$ (d) $\begin{pmatrix} -2 & 4 & -2 \\ -4 & -2 & 6 \end{pmatrix}$

(e) $\begin{pmatrix} 1 & -11 & 4 \\ 8 & 3 & 0 \end{pmatrix}$ (f) $\begin{pmatrix} -12 & 5 & -10 \\ -7 & -2 & -1 \end{pmatrix}$ (g) $\begin{pmatrix} -10 & -3 & -6 \\ -1 & 0 & 1 \end{pmatrix}$ (h) $\begin{pmatrix} 21 & 0 & 18 \\ 3 & -3 & 33 \end{pmatrix}$

(i) $\begin{pmatrix} 6 & 2 & 2 \\ 2 & 2 & -16 \end{pmatrix}$

2. (a) $\begin{pmatrix} -1 & -4 \\ 6 & -6 \end{pmatrix}$ (b) $\begin{pmatrix} 12 & 11 \\ -6 & -5 \end{pmatrix}$ (d) $\begin{pmatrix} 4 & 3 \\ -1 & 3 \\ 8 & -14 \end{pmatrix}$

(e) $\begin{pmatrix} -4 & 8 & -13 \\ 5 & 3 & -5 \\ 13 & 7 & -12 \end{pmatrix}$ (f) $\begin{pmatrix} 2 & 1 \\ -1 & -2 \\ 3 & 0 \end{pmatrix}$ (g) $\begin{pmatrix} 6 \\ -4 \\ -2 \end{pmatrix}$

3. (a) 22   (b) −10   (c) −45   (d) 8

4. (a) $\begin{pmatrix} \frac{2}{3} & -1 \\ -\frac{1}{3} & 1 \end{pmatrix}$ (b) $\begin{pmatrix} -\frac{4}{11} & -\frac{3}{11} \\ -\frac{1}{11} & \frac{2}{11} \end{pmatrix}$ (c) $\begin{pmatrix} -\frac{1}{3} & \frac{2}{3} \\ 0 & \frac{1}{3} \end{pmatrix}$ (d) $\begin{pmatrix} \frac{1}{8} & -\frac{1}{4} \\ -\frac{3}{16} & -\frac{1}{8} \end{pmatrix}$

5. (a) (2, 3)   (b) (−4, 2)   (c) ($\frac{1}{2}$, −1)

6. (a) (−2, 2)   (b) (−3, −1)   (c) (−2, 3)   (d) (−2, 3)

(e) (1, 1, −2)   (f) (−1, −2, 2)

7. (a) (−2, 2, 3)   (b) (−3, 2, −1)   (c) (−2, 1, 3, 2)   (d) (2, −2, $\frac{1}{2}$)

(e) (−2, −3, 0)   (f) (−3, 4, −2)

8. (a) [1, 3], $\sqrt{10}$ (b) [4, 3], 5   (c) [7, −1], $5\sqrt{2}$

(d) [4, −7], $\sqrt{65}$ (e) [−2, −3], $\sqrt{13}$ (f) [4, −7], $\sqrt{65}$

9. (a) [5, −1]   (b) [2, 2]   (c) [5, −1]   (d) [2, −6]

10. (a) [2, 24]   (b) [−15, 6]   (c) [20, −6]   (d) [10, −12]

11. (a) 75.5, 15°   (b) 13.7, 40°

12. 270.6, 58°   **13.** 200, 209°

14. (a) 10.3, 167°   (b) in front

15. (a) 100 415   (b) 21 072   (c) 131

16. (a) 700   (b) 1

17. (a) 64.3   (b) 76.6

REVIEW AND PREVIEW TO CHAPTER 10

1.
	mean	median	mode
(a)	7	7	7
(b)	15.4	15	12, 16
(c)	22.4	22	21
(d)	55	53.5	
(e)	108.7	106	102, 107

2.
	mean	median	mode
(a)	3.8	4	5
(b)	13.1	12.5	12
(c)	15.8	13	10

3. 54.5, 61, 40   **4.** 33.7, 33, 32   **5.** $32 750, $30 000, $20 000

Exercise 10-1

1. 8   **3.** 21   **4.** (a) 25   (b) 20

5. 36   **6.** 60   **7.** 17 576 000

8. 2730   **9.** (a) 560   (b) 720   **10.** 216 000

11. 16, 2^r **12.** 216   **13.** 720   **14.** 32

Exercise 10-2

1. (a) 120   (b) 5040   (c) 5040   (d) 3 628 800   (e) 11 880   (f) 380

2. (a) 12, *ab, ac, ad, ba, bc, bd, ca, cb, cd, da, db, dc*

(b) 24, *abc, abd, acb, acd, adb, adc, bac, bad, bca, bcd, bda, bdc, cab, cad, cba, cbd, cda, cdb, dab, dac, dba, dbc, dca, dcb*

3. 362 880
6. 6 497 400
10. (a) 40 320
11. (a) 120
    (e) 20 160
    (i) 2 494 800
12. (a) 210
15. (a) 96
    (e) $(n+1)!$
16. (a) 7 484 400

4. 491 400
7. 120
    (b) 5040
    (b) 720
    (f) 840
    (j) 129 729 600
    (b) 35
    (b) n
    (f) $n(n+1)$
    (b) 369 600

5. 997 002 000
8. 360
    (c) 5040
    (c) 60
    (g) 120
    (h) 630
13. 12 600
    (c) 37!

9. 24
    (d) 720
    (d) 120
    (h) 39 916 800
    (i) 34 650

    (d) $n!$

Exercise 10-3

1. (a) 15
    (e) 120
    (i) 60
2. 2300
5. (a) 1287
8. 28

    (b) 495
    (f) 120
    (j) 315
    (b) 13 800
    (b) 495

    (c) 1
    (g) 120
    (k) 4950
3. 792
6. 2 598 960

    (d) 56
    (h) 1
    (l) 700
4. 56
7. 1287

9. (a) 210   **(b)** 5   **(c)** 50   **(d)** 100   **(e)** 50   **(f)** 5
10. 16 380   **11. (a)** 252   **(b)** 140   **(c)** 72
12. 2 402 400   **13.** 24   **14.** 8 211 173 256
15. (d) 56, 56, 84   **16.** 7.91×10^{10} **17. (a)** 924
    (b) 34 650   **(c)** 369 600

Exercise 10-4

1. (a) $a^6 + 6a^5b + 15a^4b^2 + 20a^3b^3 + 15a^2b^4 + 6ab^5 + b^6$
    (b) $a^8 + 8a^7b + 28a^6b^2 + 56a^5b^3 + 70a^4b^4 + 56a^3b^5 + 28a^2b^6 + 8ab^7 + b^8$
    (c) $x^5 + 5x^4y + 10x^3y^2 + 10x^2y^3 + 5xy^4 + y^5$
    (d) $128 + 448x + 672x^2 + 560x^3 + 280x^4 + 84x^5 + 14x^6 + x^7$
    (m) $a^4 - 12a^3 + 54a^2 - 108a + 81$
    (f) $x^{10} - 10x^9y + 45x^8y^2 - 120x^7y^3 + 210x^6y^4 - 252x^5y^5 + 210x^4y^6$
        $- 120x^3y^7 + 45x^2y^8 - 10xy^9 + y^{10}$
    (g) $1 + 9a + 36a^2 + 84a^3 + 126a^4 + 126a^5 + 84a^6 + 36a^7 + 9a^8 + a^9$
    (h) $x^6 + 12x^5y + 60x^4y^2 + 160x^3y^3 + 240x^2y^4 + 192xy^5 + 64y^6$
    (i) $16x^4 + 96x^3 + 216x^2 + 216x + 81$
    (j) $243a^5 - 810a^4b + 1080a^3b^2 - 720a^2b^3 + 240ab^4 - 32b^5$
    (k) $a^{10} + 5a^8b^3 + 10a^6b^6 + 10a^4b^9 + 5a^2b^{12} + b^{15}$
    (l) $x^6 + 6x^4 + 15x^2 + 20 + \dfrac{15}{x^2} + \dfrac{6}{x^4} + \dfrac{1}{x^6}$
    (m) $x^{16} - 16x^{14}y + 112x^{12}y^2 - 448x^{10}y^3 + 1120x^8y^4 - 1792x^6y^5$
        $+ 1792x^4y^6 - 1024x^2y^7 + 256y^8$
    (n) $r^4 + 2r^3 + \frac{3}{2}r^2 + \frac{1}{2}r + \frac{1}{16}$
    (o) $c^{10} - 5c^8\sqrt{d} + 10c^6d - 10c^4d\sqrt{d} + 5c^2d^2 - d^2\sqrt{d}$
2. (a) $a^{12} + 12a^{11}b + 66a^{10}b^2 + 220a^9b^3$
    (b) $x^{12} - 12x^{11}y + 66x^{10}y^2 - 220x^9y^3$
    (c) $x^{14} + 28x^{13} + 364x^{12} + 2912x^{11}$
    (d) $c^{10} - 50c^9d + 1125c^8d^2 - 15\,000c^7d^3$
    (e) $x^{18} - 27x^{16}y + 324x^{14}y^2 - 2268x^{12}y^3$
    (f) $a^{20} + 80\dfrac{a^{19}}{b} + 3040\dfrac{a^{18}}{b^2} + 72\,960\dfrac{a^{17}}{b^3}$

3. (a) $126a^4b^5$ **(b)** $448x^6$ **(c)** $15\,504x^{15}y^5$ **(d)** $70x^{12}y^4$ **(e)** $\frac{35}{64}a^{26}$
4. 98 513 415
5. (a) 1.305   **(b)** 1.049   **(c)** 0.817   **(d)** 260.125
6. 1.10×10^{20}

Exercise 10-5

1. (a) $\frac{1}{13}$ **(b)** $\frac{12}{13}$ **(c)** $\frac{1}{4}$ **(d)** $\frac{3}{4}$ **(e)** $\frac{1}{2}$ **(f)** $\frac{1}{52}$ **(g)** $\frac{3}{13}$ **(h)** $\frac{1}{26}$
2. (a) $\frac{8}{15}$ **(b)** $\frac{7}{15}$ **(c)** $\frac{1}{15}$ **(d)** $\frac{1}{5}$ **(e)** $\frac{1}{3}$ **(f)** $\frac{4}{15}$ **(g)** $\frac{2}{5}$ **(h)** $\frac{2}{5}$
3. (a) 0 **(b)** $\frac{1}{18}$ **(c)** $\frac{5}{36}$ **(d)** $\frac{1}{12}$ **(e)** $\frac{11}{12}$ **(f)** $\frac{1}{2}$
4. (a) $\frac{1}{8}$ **(b)** $\frac{1}{8}$ **(c)** $\frac{3}{8}$ **(d)** $\frac{7}{8}$
5. (a) $\frac{1}{128}$ **(b)** $\frac{127}{128}$ **(c)** $\frac{7}{128}$ **(d)** $\frac{35}{128}$ **(e)** $\frac{21}{128}$ **(f)** $\frac{21}{128}$

6. (a) $\frac{5}{3888}$ **(b)** $\frac{1}{7776}$ **(c)** $\frac{5}{7776}$ **(d)** $\frac{5}{1944}$ **(e)** $\frac{125}{3888}$ **(f)** $\frac{23}{648}$ **(g)** $\frac{5}{1296}$ **(h)** $\frac{5}{54}$

7. (a) $\frac{1}{126}$ **(b)** $\frac{5}{42}$

8. (a) $_{52}C_{13}$ **(b)** $\dfrac{1}{_{52}C_{13}}$ **(c)** $\dfrac{4}{_{52}C_{13}}$ **(d)** $\dfrac{_{48}C_9}{_{52}C_{13}}$ **(e)** $\dfrac{40}{_{52}C_{13}}$ **(f)** $\dfrac{_{32}C_{13}}{_{52}C_{13}}$

9. (a) $\frac{3}{14}$ **(b)** $\frac{1}{28}$ **(c)** $\frac{27}{56}$ **(d)** $\frac{15}{56}$ **(e)** $\frac{27}{28}$ **(f)** $\frac{11}{14}$

10. (a) $\frac{1}{649\,740}$ **(b)** $\frac{33}{66\,640}$ **(c)** $\frac{33}{16\,660}$ **(d)** $\frac{1}{4165}$ **(e)** $\frac{1}{108\,290}$ **(f)** $\frac{6}{4165}$

11. $1 - \frac{990!\,985!}{1000!\,975!}$

Exercise 10-6

1. (a) $\frac{1}{6}$ **(b)** $\frac{1}{3}$ **(c)** $\frac{1}{2}$ **(d)** $\frac{5}{9}$ **(e)** $\frac{4}{9}$ **(f)** $\frac{7}{9}$

2. (a) $\frac{1}{2}$ **(b)** $\frac{15}{52}$ **(c)** $\frac{2}{13}$ **(d)** $\frac{4}{13}$ **(e)** $\frac{11}{26}$ **(f)** $\frac{9}{13}$

3. (a) $\frac{1}{2}$ **(b)** $\frac{1}{4}$ **(c)** $\frac{3}{4}$ **(d)** $\frac{1}{6}$ **(e)** $\frac{7}{12}$ **(f)** $\frac{7}{12}$

4. $\frac{4}{5}$ **5. (a)** $\frac{1}{4}$ **(b)** $\frac{1}{2}$ **(c)** $\frac{5}{8}$

Exercise 10-7

1. (a) $\frac{1}{4}$ **(b)** $\frac{1}{4}$ **2.** $\frac{1}{256}$ **3.** $\frac{1}{2}$

4. (a) $\frac{5}{36}$ **(b)** $\frac{1}{18}$ **5.** $\frac{5}{216}$

6. (a) $\frac{5}{36}$ **(b)** $\frac{1}{16}$ **(c)** $\frac{1}{9}$ **(d)** $\frac{5}{48}$ **(e)** $\frac{5}{48}$ **(f)** $\frac{5}{24}$ **(g)** $\frac{5}{16}$

7. (a) $\frac{1}{16}$ **(b)** $\frac{1}{16}$ **(c)** $\frac{1}{52}$ **(d)** $\frac{1}{26}$ **(e)** $\frac{3}{169}$ **(f)** $\frac{1}{2704}$ **(g)** $\frac{1}{52}$

8. (a) $\frac{1}{2197}$ **(b)** $\frac{1}{64}$ **(c)** $\frac{1}{16}$ **(d)** $\frac{1}{64}$ **(e)** $\frac{1}{104}$ **(f)** $\frac{3}{52}$

Exercise 10-8

1. (a) $\frac{5}{14}$ **(b)** $\frac{3}{7}$ **(c)** $\frac{9}{14}$ **(d)** $\frac{4}{7}$ **2. (a)** $\frac{1}{6}$ **(b)** $\frac{2}{11}$

3. (a) $\frac{3}{8}$ **(b)** $\frac{3}{7}$ **(c)** $\frac{3}{4}$ **(d)** $\frac{1}{2}$ **(e)** $\frac{4}{7}$

4. (a) 0.45   **(b)** 0.6

5. (a) $\frac{13}{51}$ **(b)** $\frac{13}{204}$ **(c)** $\frac{25}{51}$ **(d)** $\frac{25}{204}$ **(e)** $\frac{1}{221}$ **(f)** $\frac{4}{221}$ **(g)** $\frac{1}{17}$ **(h)** $\frac{4}{17}$

6. (a) $\frac{3}{38}$ **(b)** $\frac{3}{38}$ **(c)** $\frac{1}{19}$ **(d)** $\frac{18}{95}$ **(e)** $\frac{91}{190}$ **7.** $\frac{1}{2}$

8. (a) $\frac{1}{5525}$ **(b)** $\frac{11}{850}$ **(c)** $\frac{22}{425}$ **(d)** $\frac{169}{10\,200}$ **(e)** $\frac{169}{1700}$ **(f)** $\frac{8}{16\,575}$ **(g)** $\frac{48}{16\,575}$

9. (a) $\frac{1}{10}$ **(b)** $\frac{4}{7}$ **(c)** $\frac{8}{15}$ **(d)** $\frac{1}{26}$ **(e)** $\frac{1}{3003}$ **(f)** $\frac{131}{143}$ **10.** $\frac{1360}{3003}$

Exercise 10-10

1. (a) 1.12   **(b)** 4.33   **2.** 21.66   **3. (a)** 16%   **(b)** 2%   **(c)** 1500   **(d)** 34%

4. (a) 8400   **(b)** 8200   **5. (a)** 16%   **(b)** 16%   **(c)** 1920

6. (a) 480   **(b)** 60   **7. (a)** 2%   **(b)** 16%   **(c)** 82%

Exercise 10-11

4. 63   **5.** 1.7, −0.3, 0.17   **6.** 66, 81

7. (a) 1.6   **(b)** −0.4   **(c)** 0.6

8. (a) 1.6, 1.14, 0.83, 2.25   **(b)** Social science   **(c)** Business

Exercise 10-12

1. (a) 46.64   **(b)** 21.23   **(c)** 68.26   **(d)** 95.44

    (e) 99.74   **(f)** 12.41   **(g)** 19.81   **(h)** 74.34

2. (a) 0.9713   **(b)** 0.9418   **(c)** 0.9920   **(d)** 0.6293

    (e) 0.0933   **(f)** 0.1234   **(g)** 0.4918   **(h)** 0.2575

3. (a) 0.1587   **(b)** 0.3446   **(c)** 0.3399   **(d)** 0.4068   **(e)** 0.7742

4. 0.6915   **5. (a)** 0.2033   **(b)** 0.5572   **6. (a)** 0.0475   **(b)** 0.2033

7. (a) 0.7486   **(b)** 0.2514   **8. (a)** 0.2514   **(b)** 0.0918

9. 13, 215, 1359, 3413, 215, 13

10. 0.1587   **11.** 59 500

Review Exercise

1. (a) 3024   **(b)** 126   **(c)** 479 001 600   **(d)** 42

    (e) 252   **(f)** 380   **(g)** 4950   **(h)** 4950

2. (a) 625   **(b)** 15 625   **(c)** 13 800

3. 21 340   **4.** 512   **5. (a)** 15 600   **(b)** 2600

6. 5040   **7.** 1128   **8. (a)** 792   **(b)** 120

9. 23 100   **10.** 144   **11. (a)** 5040   **(b)** 840   **(c)** 420

12. (a) $a^9 + 9a^8b + 36a^7b^2 + 84a^6b^3 + 126a^5b^4 + 126a^4b^5 + 86a^3b^6 + 36a^2b^7 + 9ab^8 + b^9$

    (b) $1 - 7x + 21x^2 - 35x^3 + 35x^4 - 21x^5 + 7x^6 - x^7$

    (c) $x^{12} + 12x^{10}y + 60x^8y^2 + 160x^6y^3 + 240x^4y^4 + 192x^2y^5 + 64y^6$

13. (a) $a^{16}+16a^{15}b+120a^{14}b^2+560a^{13}b^3$
  (b) $x^{13}-26x^{12}+312x^{11}-2288x^{10}$

14. 1.110

15. (a) $\frac{1}{13}$ **(b)** $\frac{12}{13}$ **(c)** $\frac{1}{4}$ **(d)** $\frac{2}{13}$ **(e)** $\frac{4}{13}$ **(f)** $\frac{9}{13}$

16. (a) $\frac{1}{64}$ **(b)** $\frac{63}{64}$ **(c)** $\frac{15}{64}$ **(d)** $\frac{5}{16}$

17. (a) $\frac{10}{143}$ **(b)** $\frac{1}{143}$ **(c)** $\frac{60}{143}$ **(d)** $\frac{133}{143}$

18. (a) $\frac{2}{25}$ **(b)** $\frac{1}{100}$ **(c)** $\frac{3}{25}$ **(d)** $\frac{4}{25}$ **(e)** $\frac{1}{100}$

19. (a) $\frac{4}{45}$ **(b)** $\frac{1}{30}$ **(c)** $\frac{2}{15}$ **(d)** $\frac{2}{15}$ **(e)** 0

20. (a) $\frac{7}{18\,278}$ **(b)** $\frac{1}{658\,008}$ **(c)** $\frac{2203}{2812}$ **(d)** $\frac{41\,672}{82\,251}$ **(a)** $\frac{100\,813}{109\,668}$

21. 2.8   **22.** 64, 50   **23.** $-0.7, 0.1, -0.5$

24. (a) 0.1463   **(b)** 0.2955   **(c)** 0.8302

25. (a) 0.3085   **(b)** 0.9599   **(c)** 0.9332   **(d)** 0.3612

26. (a) 0.3085   **(b)** 0.2266   **(c)** 0.7888

REVIEW AND PREVIEW TO CHAPTER 11

Exercise 1.

1. $\sqrt{13}$ **2.** $\sqrt{74}$ **3.** $2\sqrt{17}$ **4.** 5   **5.** $\sqrt{29}$ **6.** $5\sqrt{2}$ **7.** $3\sqrt{5}$
8. (6, 8)   **9.** (1, 0)   **10.** (6, −8)   **11.** (0, 0)   **12.** $\left(-\frac{7}{2}, \frac{9}{2}\right)$ **13.** $\left(\frac{5}{2}, -2\right)$ **14.** $\left(-\frac{1}{2}, 6\right)$

Exercise 2.

1. 31.4, 78.5   **2.** 26, 30.58   **3.** 20.6, 25   **4.** 10.7, 7.07
5. 20.9, 27.3   **6.** 23.5, 34.6   **7.** 43.3, 103   **8.** 34.8, 75.3

Exercise 3.

1. 8   **2.** 9.17   **3.** 13   **4.** 30   **5.** 9.21   **6.** 6.93   **7.** 4.90   **8.** 10.3

Exercise 4.

1. $x=30°, y=60°$ **2.** $x=90°, y=180°$ **3.** $x=95°, y=80°$ **4.** $x=85°, y=95°$
5. $x=140°, y=110°$ **6.** $x=40°, y=40°$ **7.** $x=42°, y=42°$

Exercise 5.

1. $x=13, y=12$ **2.** 12   **3.** 8
4. $a=40°, e=b=90°, d=c=50°$ **5.** 12.2   **6.** 5.20

Exercise 6.

1. $x=55°, y=90°, z=90°$ **2.** $p=60°, q=r=s=65°$ **3.** $a=30°, b=72°=c$
4. 6   **5.** 4   **6.** 6
7. 7.14   **8.** $x=50°, y=100°$ **9.** 9.17

Exercise 11-1

1. (a) (0, 0), 1   **(b)** (0, 0), 7   **(c)** (0, 0), 9   **(d)** (0, 2), 5
  (e) (−3, 0), 6   **(f)** (5, −4), 10   **(g)** (0, 0), $2\sqrt{5}$ **(h)** (0, 0), $\sqrt{17}$

  (i) (0, 0), $5\sqrt{2}$ **(j)** (0, 0), 5   **(k)** (2, −1), $\dfrac{\sqrt{30}}{3}$ **(l)** $(a, b), |c|$

2. (a) $x^2+y^2=9$ **(b)** $x^2+y^2=49$ **(c)** $x^2+y^2=5$
  (d) $(x-2)^2+(y-5)^2=7$ **(e)** $(x+2)^2+(y-3)^2=25$ **(f)** $(x+3)^2+(y+4)^2=25$
  (g) $(x-5)^2+(y+2)^2=9$ **(h)** $x^2+(y-3)^2=36$ **(i)** $(x+4)^2+y^2=32$
  (j) $(x+3)^2+(y+8)^2=100$ **(k)** $(x-a)^2+(y-b)^2=c^2$ **(l)** $(x-a)^2+(y+b)^2=c^2$
3. (a) $y=5$ **(b)** $x=-2$ **(c)** $x^2+y^2=25$
  (d) $(x-2)^2+(y-5)^2=49$ **(e)** $y=2$ **(f)** $y=x-3$
  (g) $3y=x+11$
4. (a) $x^2+y^2=25$ **(b)** $(x-2)^2+(y-5)^2=9$ **(c)** $(x+3)^2+(y+2)^2=100$
  (d) $x^2+(y-5)^2=90$ **(e)** $(x+3)^2+y^2=25$
5. (a) (−3, 0), 6   **(b)** (0, 2), 3   **(c)** (−5, 4), 5   **(d)** (1, 1), $\sqrt{5}$
  (e) (2, 1), 3   **(f)** (5, 6), 8   **(g)** $\left(-\frac{5}{2}, \frac{3}{2}\right), 2\sqrt{2}$
6. (a) $(x-2)^2+y^2=25$ **(b)** $(x-5)^2+(y+1)^2=25$ **(c)** $x^2+y^2=49$
  (d) $x^2+y^2=9$

Exercise 11-2

1. (b) $y = -7x$
2. (b) $(-2, 4)$ (c) -2 (d) $\frac{1}{2}$
3. (b) $4, \sqrt{106}$ (c) $\sqrt{90}$
4. (a) $\sqrt{75}$ (b) $\sqrt{76}$ (c) $2\sqrt{21}$ (d) $\sqrt{10}$ (e) $\sqrt{114}$ (f) 8
   (g) 37 (h) $2\sqrt{33}$
5. (b) $-\frac{4}{3}$ (c) $\frac{3}{4}$ (d) $4y = 3x + 25$
6. (a) $3y = -2x + 13$ (b) $5y = -3x + 34$ (c) $7y = -5x - 74$ (d) $2y = x - 10$
   (e) $y = 6$ (f) $3y = 5x + 34$ (g) $5y = x - 39$ (h) $4y = 3x$
7. (a) $y = \dfrac{a+b}{a-b}x$ 8. (a) $\left(\dfrac{p+q}{2}, \dfrac{q-p}{2}\right)$ (b) $\dfrac{q-p}{p+q}$ (c) $\dfrac{p+q}{q-p}$
9. (a) $r, \sqrt{b^2 + a^2}$ (b) $\sqrt{b^2 + a^2 - r^2}$
10. (a) $\dfrac{b}{a}$ (b) $-\dfrac{a}{b}$ (c) $by = -ax + a^2 + b^2$

Exercise 11-3

1. (a) $y = \frac{1}{12}x^2 - 1$ (b) $y = -\frac{1}{10}x^2 - \frac{1}{2}$ (c) $x = \frac{1}{6}y^2 + \frac{5}{2}$ (d) $x = -\frac{1}{10}y^2 - \frac{1}{2}$
   (e) $y = \frac{1}{6}(x-2)^2 + \frac{1}{2}$ (f) $x = -\frac{1}{4}(y+2)^2 - 2$ (g) $x = \frac{1}{20}(y+1)^2$ (h) $y = -\frac{1}{4}(x+4)^2 + 4$
2. $x = -\frac{1}{12}(y-2)^2 + 4$ 3. $y = -\frac{1}{8}(x+3)^2 - 1$
4. $x = \dfrac{1}{8a}y^2 + a$ 5. $x^2 + 2xy + y^2 - 16y + 32 = 0$

Exercise 11-4

1. (a) $12, 10$ (b) $6, 4$ (c) $10, 8$ 2. (a) 0.8 (b) 0.6 (c) 0.8
4. (a) $\dfrac{\sqrt{21}}{5}$ (b) $\dfrac{\sqrt{3}}{2}$ (c) $\dfrac{\sqrt{7}}{4}$ (d) $\dfrac{\sqrt{5}}{3}$ (e) $\dfrac{\sqrt{21}}{5}$ (f) $\dfrac{\sqrt{3}}{2}$
5. (a) $\dfrac{x^2}{25} + \dfrac{y^2}{16} = 1$ (b) $\dfrac{x^2}{25} + \dfrac{y^2}{9} = 1$ (c) $\dfrac{x^2}{25} + \dfrac{y^2}{9} = 1$ (d) $\dfrac{x^2}{25} + \dfrac{y^2}{9} = 1$ (e) $\dfrac{x^2}{100} + \dfrac{y^2}{75} = 1$
8. (a) $\dfrac{(x-3)^2}{25} + \dfrac{y^2}{16} = 1$ (b) $\dfrac{(x-5)^2}{25} + \dfrac{(y-3)^2}{16} = 1$ (c) $\dfrac{(x-3)^2}{25} + \dfrac{(y-2)^2}{9} = 1$

Exercise 11-5

1. (a) 10 (b) 6 (c) 10 2. (a) $\frac{5}{3}$ (b) $\frac{13}{5}$ (c) 2
4. (a) $\dfrac{x^2}{25} - \dfrac{y^2}{75} = 1$ (b) $4x^2 - \dfrac{4y^2}{99} = 1$ (c) $\dfrac{x^2}{25} - \dfrac{y^2}{11} = 1$ (d) $\dfrac{x^2}{9} - \dfrac{4y^2}{45} = 1$ (e) $\dfrac{25x^2}{144} - \dfrac{25y^2}{81} = 1$
9. (a) $\dfrac{4(x-5)^2}{9} - \dfrac{4y^2}{91} = 1$ (b) $\dfrac{4(x-1)^2}{63} - \dfrac{4(y-2)^2}{63} = 1$ (c) $\dfrac{16(x-1.5)}{9} - \dfrac{16(y+2)^2}{100} = 1$
11. $\dfrac{(x-1)^2}{16} - \dfrac{(y-3)^2}{56} = 1$

Exercise 11-6

1. (a) $y = \frac{1}{8}x^2$ (b) $\dfrac{9(x-\frac{25}{3})^2}{400} + \dfrac{3y^2}{100} = 1$ (c) $\dfrac{9(x-\frac{8}{3})^2}{64} + \dfrac{3y^2}{16} = 1$ (d) $\dfrac{3(x-5)^2}{49} - \dfrac{y^2}{49} = 1$
   (e) $\dfrac{25(x-\frac{82}{5})^2}{2304} - \dfrac{5y^2}{576} = 1$ (f) $\dfrac{3x^2}{64} + \dfrac{9}{256}(y-\frac{20}{3})^2 = 1$ (g) $y^2 = -16(x-1) = 1$ (h) $x^2 = 8(y-2)$
2. $x^2 = -80y$ 3. $x^2 = -\frac{250}{3}y$ 4. $x^2 = -360y$
5. (a) $y^2 = 0.168x$ (b) 16.18 6. (a) $x^2 = \frac{8}{3}y$ (b) 70.3
7. (a) $\dfrac{x^2}{100} - \dfrac{y^2}{2400} = 1$ (b) $\dfrac{x^2}{900} - \dfrac{y^2}{1600} = 1$ (c) $\dfrac{x^2}{100} - \dfrac{y^2}{6300} = 1$
8. (a) $\dfrac{x^2}{(1.50000 \times 10^8)^2} + \dfrac{y^2}{(1.49981 \times 10^8)^2} = 1$ (b) 0.016
4. (a) 0.92 (b) $\dfrac{x^2}{100^2} + \dfrac{y^2}{40^2} = 1$ 10. $\dfrac{x^2}{6811^2} + \dfrac{y^2}{6803^2} = 1, e = 0.048$
11. (a) $\dfrac{x^2}{1940^2} + \dfrac{y^2}{1937^2} = 1$ (b) $e = 0.027, \dfrac{x^2}{1790.2^2} + \dfrac{y^2}{1789.6^2} = 1$
12. (a) $612, \dfrac{x^2}{7392^2} + \dfrac{y^2}{7379^2} = 1$ 13. $\dfrac{x^2}{10\,031^2} + \dfrac{y^2}{9659^2} = 1, e = 0.27$

14. (a) (i) 1305 480 km **(ii)** $\dfrac{x^2}{(2.6850\times10^8)^2}+\dfrac{y^2}{(6.5274\times10^8)^2}=1$

(b) (i) 944 480 000 km **(ii)** $\dfrac{x^2}{(5.7000\times10^8)^2}+\dfrac{y^2}{(4.7224\times10^8)^2}=1$

Exercise 11-7

1. $(1,2)(-1,0)$ **2.** $(-1,-2)(2,1)$ **3.** $(-1,-8)(-2,-9)$
4. $(3,13)(-2,-7)$ **5.** $(1,-2)$ **6.** $(0,5)(5,0)$
7. $(0,-5)(3,4)$ **8.** $(0,2)(3,0)$ **9.** $(-1,1)(3,9)$
10. $(3,-4)$ **11.** $(9,6)(1,2)$ **12.** $(10+i,1+i)(10-i,1-i)$
13. $(-3,-1)$ **14.** $\pm5\sqrt{17}$ **15.** -1

Exercise 11-8

1. $(0,\pm5)(4,\pm3)$ **2.** $(\pm1,0)(0,-1)$
3. $(-4,-3),\ (-3,4-4),\ (3,4),\ (4,3)$
4. $(\tfrac{1}{2},4)(-\tfrac{1}{2},=4)(2,1)(-2,-1)$ **5.** $(1,\pm3)(-1,\pm3)$
6. $(\pm i\sqrt{3},-3)(\pm\sqrt{2},2)$ **7.** $(1,1)(-1,1)$ **8.** $(0,5)(\pm1,-4)$ **9.** $(\pm3,0)$
10. $\left(\pm\sqrt{\dfrac{a+b}{a^2+b^2}},\ \pm\sqrt{\dfrac{b-a}{b^2+a^2}}\right)$

Exercise 11-9

2. (a) $\sqrt{38}$ **(b)** $\sqrt{69}$ **(c)** $\sqrt{34}$ **(d)** 9
3. (a) $\sqrt{19}$ **(b)** 13 **(c)** $2\sqrt{21}$ **(d)** 8 **(e)** $\sqrt{14}$ **(f)** $\sqrt{65}$ **(g)** $5\sqrt{3}$
6. (a) $x^2+y^2+z^2=25$ **(b)** $x^2+(y-3)^2+z^2=9$
   (c) $(x-5)^2+(y-1)^2+(z-1)^2=36$ **(d)** $(x+2)^2+(y+3)^2+(z+4)^2=25$
   (e) $(x-3)^2+(y-3)^2+(z-3)^2=9$ **(f)** $(x-5)^2+(y+4)^2+(z-2)^2=1$
   (g) $(x+2)^2+y^2+(z-5)^2=49$ **(h)** $(x-3)^2+(y+2)^2+(z-4)^2=16$
7. (a) $(0,0,0),\ 7$ **(b)** $(0,0,0),\ 10$ **(c)** $(2,3,0),\ 4$ **(d)** $(-3,5,-1),\ 6$
8. (a) $(4,-5,-2),\ 4$ **(b)** $(-6,-2,-3),\ 7$

Review Exercise

1. (a) $(0,0),\ 6$ **(b)** $(2,-3),\ 5$ **(c)** $(-4,3),\ 6$
2. (a) $x^2+y^2=64$ **(b)** $x^2+y^2=5$ **(c)** $(x+3)^2+(y-5)^2=49$
   (d) $(x-4)^2+(y+2)^2=10$ **(e)** $x^2+y^2=53$ **(f)** $(x-3)^2+(y-3)^2=18$
3. (a) $2\sqrt{10}$ **(b)** $y=3x$
4. (a) $4y=-3x+25$ **(b)** $4y=3x+25$ **(c)** $3y=4x-25$ **(d)** $3y=-4x-25$
5. (a) $8\sqrt{2}$ **(b)** $2\sqrt{155}$ **(c)** $\sqrt{70}$ **(d)** $\sqrt{134}$
6. (a) $x^2=-16y$ **(b)** $y=-\tfrac{1}{6}(x+3)^2+\tfrac{3}{2}$ **(c)** $x=\tfrac{1}{14}(y-2)^2+\tfrac{3}{2}$ **(d)** $y=-\tfrac{1}{16}(x+4)^2+1$
8. (a) $\dfrac{x^2}{36}+\dfrac{y^2}{25}=1$ **(b)** $\dfrac{x^2}{25}+\dfrac{y^2}{9}=1$ **(c)** $\dfrac{x^2}{25}+\dfrac{y^2}{4}=1$ **(d)** $\dfrac{x^2}{64}+\dfrac{y^2}{28}=1$
10. (a) $\dfrac{x^2}{16}-\dfrac{y^2}{20}=1$ **(b)** $\dfrac{a^2}{16}-\dfrac{y^2}{9}=1$ **(c)** $\dfrac{x^2}{4}-\dfrac{y^2}{12}=1$ **(d)** $\dfrac{x^2}{1}-\dfrac{y^2}{15}=1$
11. $x^2=-180y$

12. (a) 14 550 km, 13 102 km   **(b)** 0.43   **(c)** $\dfrac{x^2}{7275^2}+\dfrac{y^2}{6551^2}=1$

13. $\dfrac{x^2}{400}-\dfrac{y^2}{3200}=1$

14. (a) $(3,\pm4)$ **(b)** $\left(\dfrac{-8\pm2i\sqrt{3}}{3},\dfrac{4\pm2i\sqrt{5}}{3}\right)$ **(c)** $(\pm i\sqrt{5},-5)(\pm2,4)$

   (d) $\left(\pm\dfrac{15}{\sqrt{34}},\ \pm\dfrac{15}{\sqrt{34}}\right)$ **(e)** $\left(\pm\dfrac{\sqrt{205}}{3},\ \pm\dfrac{2\sqrt{5}}{3}\right)$ **(f)** $(\pm3,0)$

16. (a) $\sqrt{m^2+n^2-r^2}$ **(b)** $y-q=\dfrac{p}{q}(x-p)$

17. $\dfrac{(x-5)^2}{9}+\dfrac{(y+3)^2}{4}=1$ **18.** $\dfrac{(x-2)^2}{4}-\dfrac{(y-3)^2}{9}=1$

REVIEW AND PREVIEW TO CHAPTER 12

Exercise 1

1. (a) $P = 12$ cm $A = 6.25$ cm^2 (b) $P = 30$ cm $A = 30$ cm^2
   (c) $P = 18$ cm $A = 18$ cm^2 (d) $C = 75.4$ cm $A = 452.4$ cm^2
2. (a) 15 cm^2 (b) 6.28 cm^2 (c) 7 cm^2 (d) 23.4 cm^2
   (e) 6.07 cm^2 (f) 8.25 cm^2 (g) 10 cm^2 (h) 17.7 cm^2
3. (a) $A = 14\,627$ cm^2 $P = 491.3$ cm (b) $A = 10\,890$ m^2 $P = 871$ m
   (c) $A = 28.96$ cm^2 $P = 37.71$ cm (d) $A = 485.7$ cm^2 $P = 157.1$ cm
   (e) $A = 266.3$ cm^2 $P = 126.3$ cm (f) $A = 9000$ cm^2 $P = 1080$ cm

Exercise 2

1. (a) $A = 124$ cm^2 $V = 105$ cm^3 (b) $A = 245$ cm^2 $V = 282.7$ cm^3
   (c) $A = 196$ cm^2 $V = 235.6$ cm^3 (d) $A = 165$ cm^2 $V = 400$ cm^3
   (e) $A = 452$ cm^2 $V = 904.8$ cm^3 (f) $A = 757$ cm^2 $V = 1196$ cm^3
   (g) $A = 38\,400$ cm^2 $V = 432\,000$ cm^3 (h) $A = 402$ cm^2 $V = 636.7$ cm^3
   (i) $A = 507.6$ cm^2 $V = 1100$ cm^3 (j) $A = 1344$ cm^2 $V = 3264$ cm^3
   (k) $A = 592.7$ cm^2 $V = 785.4$ cm^3 (l) $A = 416$ cm^2 $V = 444$ cm^3
   (m) $A = 416.3$ cm^2 $V = 611.4$ cm^3 (n) $A = 200$ cm^2 $V = 127.3$ cm^3
2. (a) 12.37 cm^3 (b) 27.64 cm^3 (c) 1304 cm^3
   (d) 25.66 cm^3 (e) 490 cm^3 (f) 6429 cm^3

Exercise 12-2

1. (a) 0 (b) 4 (d) 3 (e) 0 (f) 6
2. (a) 0 (b) 0 (c) 6 (d) $\frac{1}{3}$ (e) 2 (g) $\frac{1}{2}$ (h) 1 (i) 0 (j) 0
   (k) 0 (m) 0 (o) -2 (p) 0 (q) 0 (r) $-\frac{1}{2}$ (s) 0 (u) 0
3. $-1 < r \leqslant 1$ 4. $\frac{1}{3}$ 5. 0 6. 1 7. 2

Exercise 12-3

1. (a) $\frac{2}{3}$ (c) $\frac{16}{3}$ (d) 9 (e) $\frac{1000}{9}$ (f) 0.2 (h) $\frac{500}{7}$
2. (a) $\frac{8}{9}$ (b) $\frac{17}{99}$ (c) $\frac{64}{99}$ (d) $\frac{41}{333}$ (e) $\frac{182}{99}$ (f) $\frac{2831}{333}$ (g) $\frac{611}{4950}$ (h) $\frac{1465}{3333}$ (i) $\frac{1489}{74}$
3. 1
4. 1, 0.9375, 0.949 846, 0.945 939, 0.947 539, 0.946 768, 0.947 184, 0.946 940, 0.947 093, 0.946 993, 0.947 061; 0.947
5. 0.333 333, 0.733 333, 1.161 905, 1.606 349, 2.060 895, 2.522 433, 2.989 100, 3.459 688, 3.933 372, 4.409 563
6. $e \doteq 2.718\,28$
7. (a) $-1 < x < 1, \dfrac{1}{1-x}$ (b) $0 < x < 2, \dfrac{1}{2-x}$ (c) $-2 < x < 2, \dfrac{2}{2-x}$
   (d) $-\frac{1}{2} < x < \frac{1}{2}, \dfrac{1}{1-2x}$ (e) $|x| > 1, \dfrac{x}{x-1}$
8. $2\pi R^2$
9. (a) $\dfrac{4\sqrt{2}L}{\sqrt{2}-1}$ (b) $2L^2$ 10. $\dfrac{L^2}{4}$

Exercise 12-4

1. (a) 3 (b) 4 (c) 5 (d) 6 (e) $\frac{2}{3}$
   (f) 2 (g) 3 (h) 12 (i) $\frac{2}{5}$ (j) -5
2. (a) 78 (b) $\frac{91}{323}$ (d) 2 (e) 5 (g) 2
   (h) $a^5 - a^3 + a$ (i) -2 (j) -4 (k) $\frac{3}{2}$ (l) 1
3. (a) 1 (b) 0 (c) -3 (d) 3 (e) 1 (f) 0 (g) $\frac{1}{3}$ (h) -1
4. $\frac{1}{2}$
5. (a) 1, 0.828 427, 0.798 770, 0.770 481, 0.743 492, 0.717 735, 0.705 298, 0.695 555, 0.694 350, 0.693 387, 0.693 267, 0.693 171
   (b) 0.693

Exercise 12-5

1. (a) (i) 6 (ii) $y = 6x - 9$ (b) (i) -4 (ii) $4x + y + 4 = 0$
   (c) (i) $\frac{1}{2}$ (ii) $2x - 4y - 1 = 0$ (d) (i) -2 (ii) $2x + y - 2 = 0$

524 fmt: senior

(e) (i) 3   **(ii)** $y = 3x - 1$ **(f) (i)** 0   **(ii)** $y = -\frac{1}{4}$
(g) (i) 3   **(ii)** $y = 3x - 2$ **(h) (i)** 0   **(ii)** $y = 0$
(i) (i) 2   **(ii)** $y = 2x - 2$ **(j) (i)** -1 **(ii)** $y = -x$
(k) (i) 0   **(ii)** $y = 4$ **(l) (i)** -1 **(ii)** $x + y + 2 = 0$
(m) (i) $-\frac{4}{3}$ **(ii)** $4x + 3y - 24 = 0$ **(n) (i)** $-\frac{1}{9}$ **(ii)** $x + 9y - 7 = 0$
(o) (i) $2x_1$ **(ii)** $y = 2x_1 x - x_1^2$ **(p) (i)** $3x_1^2$ **(ii)** $y = 3x_1^2 x - 2x_1^3$

Exercise 12-6

1. (a) $f'(x) = 2x + 2$
  (b) (i) $y = 2x$ **(ii)** $y = 4x - 1$ **(iii)** $y = -1$ **(iv)** $6x + y + 16 = 0$

2. (a) $f'(x) = -\dfrac{1}{x^2}$

  (b) (i) $x + y - 2 = 0$ **(ii)** $x + 9y - 6 = 0$ **(iii)** $4x + y + 4 = 0$ **(iv)** $x + a^2y - 2a = 0$
3. (a) 1   **(b)** $3x^2$ **(c)** $4x^3$ **(d)** $3x^2 + 4x$

  (e) $1 - \dfrac{1}{x^2}$ **(f)** $2x - 6$ **(g)** $12x$ **(h)** 0

5. $(\frac{1}{2}, \frac{1}{16})$
6. (a) $f'(x) = 81x^2$ **(b)** $-2x^3$ **(c)** $4x^3 + 2x$ **(d)** $6 - 3x^2$
  (e) $64x^3 - 6x + 9$ **(f)** $4x + 9x^2 - 32x^3$
7. (a) $6x + 2$ **(b)** $3t^2 - 2t$ **(c)** $4t^3 + 6t^2$ **(d)** $8\pi r$ **(e)** $180 - 14t$
8. (a) $f'(x) = 6x + 2$
  (b) decreasing when $x \le -\frac{1}{3}$, increasing when $x \ge -\frac{1}{3}$

9. (a) $f'(x) = 12 - 9x^2$ **(b)** increasing when $-\dfrac{2}{\sqrt{3}} \le x \le \dfrac{2}{\sqrt{3}}$, decreasing when $x \le -\dfrac{2}{\sqrt{3}}$ and when $x \ge \dfrac{2}{\sqrt{3}}$

10. $(-\frac{3}{16}, \frac{9}{64})$

Exercise 12-7

1. (a) (i) 6 m/s   **(ii)** 5.5 m/s   **(iii)** 5.01 m/s   **(iv)** 5.001 m/s   **(v)** 5.000 01 m/s
  (b) 5 m/s
2. (a) after 10s   **(b)** 40 m/s, 30 m/s, 0 m/s, 30 m/s   **(c)** 50 m/s
3. (a) 49.7 m/s, 41.4 m/s, 24.8 m/s   **(b)** after 69.9 s   **(c)** -58 m/s
4. (a) (i) 1   **(ii)** 1 m/s   **(b) (i)** $1 - 4t$ **(ii)** -23 m/s
  (c) (i) $20t + 3$ **(ii)** 123 m/s   **(d) (i)** $at + v_0$ **(ii)** $6a + v_0$ m/s
  (e) (i) $3t^2 + 4t$ **(ii)** 132 m/s   **(f) (i)** $3t^2 - 2$ **(ii)** 106 m/s
5. 108 cm³/cm   **6.** 6π cm²/cm   **7.** 40π cm²/cm

Exercise 12-8

1. 34, 34   **2.** 34, 34   **3. (a)** 21 (maximum)   **(b)** -1 (minimum)

  (c) $\dfrac{2\sqrt{3}}{9}$ (maximum), $-\dfrac{2\sqrt{3}}{9}$ (minimum)   **(d)** 17 (maximum), -15 (minimum)

  (e) 5 (minimum)   **(f)** 2 (minimum)   **4.** 1051.25 m
5. (a) 800 m of $5 fencing, 200 m of $10 fencing   **(b)** $6000

6. 200 m × 300 m   **7.** 2.5   **3.** $\dfrac{256\sqrt{3}}{9}$

9. (b) 20 cm × 20 cm × 10 cm   **10.** $\dfrac{5}{\sqrt[3]{\pi}}$ cm, $\dfrac{10}{\sqrt[3]{\pi}}$ cm

Exercise 12-9

1. (a) 6π cm²   **(b)** 50 cm²   **(c)** 216π cm²   **(d)** $12(\pi - 3)$ cm²
  (e) $\frac{81}{2}(\frac{7}{18}\pi - \sin 70°) \doteq 9(\frac{7}{4}\pi - 4.23)$ **(f)** $11\pi - 4.23$
2. $\frac{1}{4}$ **4. (a)** $\frac{56}{3}$ **(b)** 136   **(c)** $\frac{243}{5}$ **(d)** $\frac{128}{15}$ **(e)** $\frac{130}{3}$ **(f)** 4   **5.** $\frac{1}{12}$

Review Exercise

1. (a) 6   **(b)** 0   **(d)** 1
2. (a) 7   **(b)** 3   **(c)** $\frac{1}{2}$ **(d)** -1
3. (a) 0   **(b)** $\frac{1}{2}$ **(c)** -1 **(d)** 0   **(e)** $-27\frac{3}{11}$ **(f)** 0   **(h)** 5
4. (a) $\frac{3}{2}$ **(b)** $\frac{125}{6}$ **(d)** $\frac{5}{4}$
5. (a) $\frac{5}{33}$ **(b)** $\frac{25}{22}$ **(c)** $\frac{701}{333}$

6. 1, 0.984 375, 0.985 747, 0.985 503, 0.985 567, 0.985 545, 0.985 554, 0.985 550, 0.985 552, 0.985 551; 0.985 55

7. 0.715 937, 0.535 016, 0.521 482, 0.511 705, 0.505 088, 0.501 255, 0.500 312.

8. (a) (i) $2x$ **(ii)** $y = 4x - 3$ **(b) (i)** $-\dfrac{16}{x^2}$ **(ii)** $4x + y - 16 = 0$

    (c) (i) $4x^3$ **(ii)** $4x + y + 3 = 0$ **(d) (i)** $3x^2 - 2x$ **(ii)** $y = x - 1$

9. (a) $f'(x) = 9x^2 + 1$ **(b)** $f'(x) = 16x - 9$ **(c)** $f'(x) = 1 - 4x^3$ **(d)** $y' = 3t^2 - 174t + 3$

10. (a) $f'(x) = 4x^3 - 4x$ **(b)** increasing when $-1 \leqslant x \leqslant 0$ and when $x \geqslant 1$, decreasing when $x \leqslant -1$ and when $0 \leqslant x \leqslant 1$

11. (a) $v(t) = 25 + 64t$ **(b) (i)** 25 m/s   **(ii)** 89 m/s   **(iii)** 665 m/s

12. (a) 62.75 (minimum)   **(b)** 16 (minimum)

13. $(10\sqrt{3} + 6)$ cm by $\left(\dfrac{20\sqrt{3}}{3} + 4\right)$ cm

14. $\left(\tfrac{100}{3}\pi - 25\sqrt{3}\right)$ cm^2 **15. (a)** $\tfrac{7}{3}$ **(b)** $\tfrac{4}{3}$ **16.** $\dfrac{b \sin \theta}{1 - \sin \theta}$

CHAPTER 13

1. Hint: Work backwards   **3.** 1050   **4.** 3   **5.** $77\tfrac{1}{7}^\circ$

7. 26, 14, 8   **9.** 5 cm   **10.** $21\tfrac{9}{11}$ minutes past four

11. 2401   **14.** 11 cm   **15.** $\dfrac{m^3}{n^2}$ **16.** more   **17.** 10 cm   **18.** $\tfrac{1}{2}\sqrt{5A}$

19. 1   **20.** 210   **21.** 12 cm   **22.** 800   **24.** 119   **25.** 12 cm

26. $12\sqrt{3} + 14\pi$ cm

27. Hint: Divide the coins into 3 groups, two groups of 27 coins and one of 26 coins.

28. 11   **29.** 686   **30.** 10 cm^2 **31.** 12   **32.** 24   **33.** 3

34. 21   **35. (a)** 16 cm **(b)** $\tfrac{8}{5}r$ **36.** 89   **37.** $2^3 \times 3^4 = 648$

40. 15 cm, 20 cm, 25 cm   **41.** $x = 2,\ y = -2,\ z = 2,\ t = -2$ **42.** 1:4

43. $\left[\dfrac{n(n+1)}{2}\right]^2$ **44.** 15 km   **47.** $2\sqrt{5}$ cm   **49.** $\dfrac{P}{2} - 2\dfrac{A}{P}$ **51.** 2:1

52. Hint: Use symmetry   **53.** $\tfrac{4}{3}$ h   **54.** 1 800 001

55. 15 621   **56.** 175 308 642

58. The locus consists of **(a)** 4 semicircles, **(b)** 8 quarter circles.

60. Hint: Consider the midpoint of the side on which P lies.

61. 132   **62.** $\tfrac{6}{7}$ cm   **64.** 54   **65.** 30°

Table I: Squares and Square Roots

n	n^2	$\sqrt{n}$	$\sqrt{10n}$	n	n^2	$\sqrt{n}$	$\sqrt{10n}$
1.0	1.00	1.000	3.162	5.5	30.25	2.345	7.416
1.1	1.21	1.049	3.317	5.6	31.36	2.366	7.483
1.2	1.44	1.095	3.464	5.7	32.49	2.387	7.550
1.3	1.69	1 140	3.606	5.8	33.64	2.408	7.616
1.4	1.96	1.183	3.742	5.9	34.81	2.429	7.681
1.5	2.25	1.225	3.873	6.0	36.00	2.449	7.746
1.6	2.56	1.265	4.000	6.1	37.21	2.470	7.810
1.7	2.89	1.304	4.123	6.2	38.44	2.490	7.874
1.8	3.24	1.342	4.243	6.3	39.69	2.510	7.937
1.9	3.61	1.378	4.359	6.4	40.96	2.530	8.000
2.0	4.00	1.414	4.472	6.5	42.25	2.550	8.062
2.1	4.41	1.449	4.583	6.6	43.56	2.569	8.124
2.2	4.84	1.483	4.690	6.7	44.89	2.588	8.185
2.3	5.29	1.517	4.796	6.8	46.24	2.608	8.246
2.4	5.76	1.549	4.899	6.9	47.61	2.627	8.307
2.5	6.25	1.581	5.000	7.0	49.00	2.646	8.367
2.6	6.76	1.612	5.099	7.1	50.41	2.665	8.426
2.7	7.29	1.643	5.196	7.2	51.84	2.683	8.485
2.8	7.84	1.673	5.292	7.3	53.29	2.702	8.544
2.9	8.41	1.703	5.385	7.4	54.76	2.720	8.602
3.0	9.00	1.732	5.477	7.5	56.25	2.739	8.660
3.1	9.61	1.761	5.568	7.6	57.76	2.757	8.718
3.2	10.24	1.789	5.657	7.7	59.29	2.775	8.775
3.3	10.89	1.817	5.745	7.8	60.84	2.793	8.832
3.4	11.56	1.844	5.831	7.9	62.41	2.811	8.888
3.5	12.25	1.871	5.916	8.0	64.00	2.828	8.944
3.6	12.96	1.897	6.000	8.1	65.61	2.846	9.000
3.7	13.69	1.924	6.083	8.2	67.24	2.864	9.055
3.8	14.44	1.949	6.164	8.3	68.89	2.881	9.110
3.9	15.21	1.975	6.245	8.4	70.56	2.898	9.165
4.0	16.00	2.000	6.325	8.5	72.25	2.915	9.220
4.1	16.81	2.025	6.403	8.6	73.96	2.933	9.274
4.2	17.64	2.049	6.481	8.7	75.69	2.950	9.327
4.3	18.49	2.074	6.557	8.8	77.44	2.966	9.381
4.4	19.36	2.098	6.633	8.9	79.21	2.983	9.434
4.5	20.25	2.121	6.708	9.0	81.00	3.000	9.487
4.6	21.16	2.145	6.782	9.1	82.81	3.017	9.539
4.7	22.09	2.168	6.856	9.2	84.64	3.033	9.592
4.8	23.04	2.191	6.928	9.3	86.49	3.050	9.644
4.9	24.01	2.214	7.000	9.4	88.36	3.066	9.695
5.0	25.00	2.236	7.071	9.5	90.25	3.082	9.747
5.1	26.01	2.258	7.141	9.6	92.16	3.098	9.798
5.2	27.04	2.280	7.211	9.7	94.09	3.114	9.849
5.3	28.09	2.302	7.280	9.8	96.04	3.130	9.899
5.4	29.16	2.324	7.348	9.9	98.01	3.146	9.950
5.5	30.25	2.354	7.416	10	100.00	3.162	10.000

Table II: Trigonometric Ratios

θ degrees	radians	sin θ	cos θ	tan θ	cot θ	sec θ	csc θ		
00°00′	0.0000	0.0000	1.0000	0.0000	—	1.0000	—	1.5708	90°00′
00°06′	0.0017	0.0017	1.0000	0.0017	572.96	1.0000	572.96	1.5691	89°54′
00°12′	0.0035	0.0035	1.0000	0.0035	286.48	1.0000	286.48	1.5673	89°48′
00°18′	0.0052	0.0052	1.0000	0.0052	190.98	1.0000	190.99	1.5656	89°42′
00°24′	0.0070	0.0070	1.0000	0.0070	143.24	1.0000	143.24	1.5638	89°36′
00°30′	0.0087	0.0087	1.0000	0.0087	114.59	1.0000	114.59	1.5621	89°38′
00°36′	0.0105	0.0105	0.9999	0.0105	95.490	1.0001	95.495	1.5603	89°24′
00°42′	0.0122	0.0122	0.9999	0.0122	81.847	1.0001	81.853	1.5586	89°18′
00°48′	0.0140	0.0140	0.9999	0.0140	71.615	1.0001	71.622	1.5568	89°12′
00°54′	0.0157	0.0157	0.9999	0.0157	63.657	1.0001	63.665	1.5551	89°06′
01°00′	0.0175	0.0175	0.9999	0.0175	57.290	1.0002	57.299	1.5533	89°00′
01°06′	0.0192	0.0192	0.9998	0.0192	52.081	1.0002	52.090	1.5516	88°54′
01°12′	0.0209	0.0209	0.9998	0.0209	47.740	1.0002	47.750	1.5499	88°48′
01°18′	0.0227	0.0227	0.9997	0.0227	44.066	1.0003	44.077	1.5481	88°42′
01°24′	0.0244	0.0244	0.9997	0.0244	40.917	1.0003	40.930	1.5464	88°36′
01°30′	0.0262	0.0262	0.9997	0.0262	38.188	1.0003	38.202	1.5446	88°30′
01°36′	0.0279	0.0279	0.9996	0.0279	35.801	1.0004	35.815	1.5429	88°24′
01°42′	0.0297	0.0297	0.9996	0.0297	33.694	1.0004	33.708	1.5411	88°18′
01°48′	0.0314	0.0314	0.9995	0.0314	31.821	1.0005	31.836	1.5394	88°12′
01°54′	0.0332	0.0332	0.9995	0.0332	30.145	1.0006	30.161	1.5376	88°06′
02°00′	0.0349	0.0349	0.9994	0.0349	28.636	1.0006	28.654	1.5359	88°00′
02°06′	0.0367	0.0366	0.9993	0.0367	27.271	1.0007	27.290	1.5341	87°54′
02°12′	0.0384	0.0384	0.9993	0.0384	26.031	1.0007	26.050	1.5324	87°48′
02°18′	0.0401	0.0401	0.9992	0.0402	24.898	1.0008	24.918	1.5307	87°42′
02°24′	0.0419	0.0419	0.9991	0.0419	23.859	1.0009	23.880	1.5289	87°36′
02°30′	0.0436	0.0436	0.9990	0.0437	22.904	1.0010	22.926	1.5272	87°30′
02°36′	0.0454	0.0454	0.9990	0.0454	22.022	1.0010	22.044	1.5254	87°24′
02°42′	0.0471	0.0471	0.9989	0.0472	21.205	1.0011	21.229	1.5237	87°18′
02°48′	0.0489	0.0488	0.9988	0.0489	20.446	1.0012	20.471	1.5219	87°12′
02°54′	0.0506	0.0506	0.9987	0.0507	19.740	1.0013	19.766	1.5202	87°06′
03°00′	0.0524	0.0523	0.9986	0.0524	19.081	1.0014	19.107	1.5184	87°00′
03°06′	0.0541	0.0541	0.9985	0.0542	18.464	1.0015	18.492	1.5167	86°54′
03°12′	0.0559	0.0558	0.9984	0.0559	17.886	1.0016	17.914	1.5149	86°48′
03°18′	0.0576	0.0576	0.9983	0.0577	17.343	1.0017	17.372	1.5132	86°42′
03°24′	0.0593	0.0593	0.9982	0.0594	16.832	1.0018	16.862	1.5115	86°36′
03°30′	0.0611	0.0610	0.9981	0.0612	16.350	1.0019	16.380	1.5097	86°30′
03°36′	0.0628	0.0628	0.9980	0.0629	15.895	1.0020	15.926	1.5080	86°24′
03°42′	0.0646	0.0645	0.9979	0.0647	15.464	1.0021	15.496	1.5062	86°18′
03°48′	0.0663	0.0663	0.9978	0.0664	15.056	1.0022	15.089	1.5045	86°12′
03°54′	0.0681	0.0680	0.9977	0.0682	14.669	1.0023	14.703	1.5027	86°06′
04°00′	0.0698	0.0698	0.9976	0.0699	14.301	1.0024	14.336	1.5010	86°00′
04°06′	0.0716	0.0715	0.9974	0.0717	13.951	1.0026	13.987	1.4992	85°54′
04°12′	0.0733	0.0732	0.9973	0.0734	13.617	1.0027	13.654	1.4975	85°48′
04°18′	0.0750	0.0750	0.9972	0.0752	13.300	1.0028	13.337	1.4957	85°42′
04°24′	0.0768	0.0767	0.9971	0.0769	12.996	1.0030	13.035	1.4940	85°36′
04°30′	0.0785	0.0785	0.9969	0.0787	12.706	1.0031	12.745	1.4923	85°30′
04°36′	0.0803	0.0802	0.9968	0.0805	12.429	1.0032	12.470	1.4905	85°24′
04°42′	0.0820	0.0819	0.9966	0.0822	12.163	1.0034	12.204	1.4888	85°18′
04°48′	0.0838	0.0837	0.9965	0.0840	11.909	1.0035	11.951	1.4870	85°12′
04°54′	0.0855	0.0854	0.9963	0.0857	11.664	1.0037	11.707	1.4853	85°06′
05°00′	0.0873	0.0872	0.9962	0.0875	11.430	1.0038	11.474	1.4835	85°00′
		cos θ	sin θ	cot θ	tan θ	csc θ	sec θ	radians	degrees
									θ

Table II: (Continued)

degrees	radians	sin θ	cos θ	tan θ	cot θ	sec θ	csc θ		
05°00′	0.0873	0.0872	0.9962	0.0875	11.430	1.0038	11.474	1.4835	85°00′
05°06′	0.0890	0.0889	0.9960	0.0892	11.205	1.0040	11.249	1.4818	84°54′
05°12′	0.0908	0.0906	0.9959	0.0910	10.988	1.0041	11.034	1.4800	84°48′
05°18′	0.0925	0.0924	0.9957	0.0928	10.780	1.0043	10.826	1.4783	84°42′
05°24′	0.0942	0.0941	0.9956	0.0945	10.579	1.0045	10.626	1.4765	84°36′
05°30′	0.0960	0.0958	0.9954	0.0963	10.385	1.0046	10.433	1.4748	84°30′
05°36′	0.0977	0.0976	0.9952	0.0981	10.199	1.0048	10.248	1.4731	84°24′
05°42′	0.0995	0.0993	0.9951	0.0998	10.019	1.0050	10.069	1.4713	84°18′
05°48′	0.1012	0.1011	0.9949	0.1016	9.8448	1.0051	9.8955	1.4696	84°12′
05°54′	0.1030	0.1028	0.9947	0.1033	9.6768	1.0053	9.7283	1.4678	84°06′
06°00′	0.1047	0.1045	0.9945	0.1051	9.5144	1.0055	9.5668	1.4661	84°00′
06°06′	0.1065	0.1063	0.9943	0.1069	9.3572	1.0057	9.4105	1.4643	83°54′
06°12′	0.1082	0.1080	0.9942	0.1086	9.2052	1.0059	9.2593	1.4626	83°48′
06°18′	0.1100	0.1097	0.9940	0.1104	9.0579	1.0061	9.1129	1.4608	83°42′
06°24′	0.1117	0.1115	0.9938	0.1122	8.9152	1.0063	8.9711	1.4591	83°36′
06°30′	0.1134	0.1132	0.9936	0.1139	8.7769	1.0065	8.8337	1.4573	83°30′
06°36′	0.1152	0.1149	0.9934	0.1157	8.6427	1.0067	8.7004	1.4556	83°24′
06°42′	0.1169	0.1167	0.9932	0.1175	8.5126	1.0069	8.5711	1.4539	83°18′
06°48′	0.1187	0.1184	0.9930	0.1192	8.3863	1.0071	8.4457	1.4521	83°12′
06°54′	0.1204	0.1201	0.9928	0.1210	8.2636	1.0073	8.3238	1.4504	83°06′
07°00′	0.1222	0.1219	0.9925	0.1228	8.1443	1.0075	8.2055	1.4486	83°00′
07°06′	0.1239	0.1236	0.9923	0.1246	8.0285	1.0077	8.0905	1.4469	82°54′
07°12′	0.1257	0.1253	0.9921	0.1263	7.9158	1.0079	7.9787	1.4451	82°48′
07°18′	0.1274	0.1271	0.9919	0.1281	7.8062	1.0082	7.8700	1.4434	82°42′
07°24′	0.1292	0.1288	0.9917	0.1299	7.6996	1.0084	7.7642	1.4416	82°36′
07°30′	0.1309	0.1305	0.9914	0.1317	7.5958	1.0086	7.6613	1.4399	82°30′
07°36′	0.1326	0.1323	0.9912	0.1334	7.4947	1.0089	7.5611	1.4382	82°27′
07°42′	0.1344	0.1340	0.9910	0.1352	7.3962	1.0091	7.4635	1.4364	82°18′
07°48′	0.1361	0.1357	0.9907	0.1370	7.3002	1.0093	7.3684	1.4347	82°12′
07°54′	0.1379	0.1374	0.9905	0.1388	7.2066	1.0096	7.2757	1.4329	82°06′
08°00′	0.1396	0.1392	0.9903	0.1405	7.1154	1.0098	7.1853	1.4312	82°00′
08°06′	0.1414	0.1409	0.9900	0.1423	7.0264	1.0101	7.0972	1.4294	81°54′
08°12′	0.1431	0.1426	0.9898	0.1441	6.9395	1.0103	7.0112	1.4277	81°48′
08°18′	0.1449	0.1444	0.9895	0.1459	6.8548	1.0106	6.9273	1.4259	81°42′
08°24′	0.1456	0.1461	0.9893	0.1477	6.7720	1.0108	6.8454	1.4242	81°36′
08°30′	0.1484	0.1478	0.9890	0.1495	6.6912	1.0111	6.7655	1.4224	81°30′
08°36′	0.1501	0.1495	0.9888	0.1512	6.6122	1.0114	6.6874	1.4207	81°24′
08°42′	0.1518	0.1513	0.9885	0.1530	6.5350	1.0116	6.6111	1.4190	81°18′
08°48′	0.1536	0.1530	0.9882	0.1548	6.4596	1.0119	6.5366	1.4172	81°12′
08°54′	0.1553	0.1547	0.9880	0.1566	6.3859	1.0122	6.4637	1.4155	81°06′
09°00′	0.1571	0.1564	0.9877	0.1584	6.3138	1.0125	6.3925	1.4137	81°00′
09°06′	0.1588	0.1582	0.9874	0.1602	6.2432	1.0127	6.3228	1.4120	80°54′
09°12′	0.1606	0.1599	0.9871	0.1620	6.1742	1.0130	6.2546	1.4102	80°48′
09°18′	0.1623	0.1616	0.9869	0.1638	6.1066	1.0133	6.1880	1.4085	80°42′
09°24′	0.1641	0.1633	0.9866	0.1655	6.0405	1.0136	6.1227	1.4067	80°36′
09°30′	0.1658	0.1650	0.9863	0.1673	5.9758	1.0139	6.0589	1.4050	80°30′
09°36′	0.1676	0.1668	0.9860	0.1691	5.9124	1.0142	5.9963	1.4032	80°24′
09°42′	0.1693	0.1685	0.9857	0.1709	5.8502	1.0145	5.9351	1.4015	80°18′
09°48′	0.1710	0.1702	0.9854	0.1727	5.7894	1.0148	5.8751	1.3998	80°12′
09°54′	0.1728	0.1719	0.9851	0.1745	5.7297	1.0151	5.8164	1.3980	80°06′
10°00′	0.1745	0.1736	0.9848	0.1763	5.6713	1.0154	5.7588	1.3963	80°00′
		cos θ	sin θ	cot θ	tan θ	csc θ	sec θ	radians	degrees
								θ	

Table II: (*Continued*)

degrees	radians	sin θ	cos θ	tan θ	cot θ	sec θ	csc θ		
10°00′	0.1745	0.1736	0.9848	0.1763	5.6713	1.0154	5.7588	1.3963	**80°00′**
10°06′	0.1763	0.1754	0.9845	0.1781	5.6140	1.0157	5.7023	1.3945	79°54′
10°12′	0.1780	0.1771	0.9842	0.1799	5.5578	1.0161	5.6470	1.3928	79°48′
10°18′	0.1798	0.1788	0.9839	0.1817	5.5026	1.0164	5.5928	1.3910	79°42′
10°24′	0.1815	0.1805	0.9836	0.1835	5.4486	1.0167	5.5396	1.3893	79°36′
10°30′	0.1833	0.1822	0.9833	0.1853	5.3955	1.0170	5.4874	1.3875	79°30′
10°36′	0.1850	0.1840	0.9829	0.1871	5.3435	1.0174	5.4362	1.3858	79°24′
10°42′	0.1868	0.1857	0.9826	0.1890	5.2924	1.0177	5.3860	1.3840	79°18′
10°48′	0.1885	0.1874	0.9823	0.1908	5.2422	1.0180	5.3367	1.3823	79°12′
10°54′	0.1902	0.1891	0.9820	0.1926	5.1929	1.0184	5.2883	1.3806	79°06′
11°00′	0.1920	0.1908	0.9816	0.1944	5.1446	1.0187	5.2408	1.3788	**79°00′**
11°06′	0.1937	0.1925	0.9813	0.1962	5.0970	1.0191	5.1942	1.3771	78°54′
11°12′	0.1955	0.1942	0.9810	0.1980	5.0504	1.0194	5.1484	1.3753	78°48′
11°18′	0.1972	0.1959	0.9806	0.1998	5.0045	1.0198	5.1034	1.3736	78°42′
11°24′	0.1990	0.1977	0.9803	0.2016	4.9594	1.0201	5.0593	1.3718	78°36′
11°30′	0.2007	0.1994	0.9799	0.2035	4.9152	1.0205	5.0159	1.3701	78°30′
11°36′	0.2025	0.2011	0.9796	0.2053	4.8716	1.0209	4.9732	1.3683	78°24′
11°42′	0.2042	0.2028	0.9792	0.2071	4.8288	1.0212	4.9313	1.3666	78°18′
11°48′	0.2059	0.2045	0.9789	0.2089	4.7867	1.0216	4.8901	1.3648	78°12′
11°54′	0.2077	0.2062	0.9785	0.2107	4.7453	1.0220	4.8496	1.3631	78°06′
12°00′	0.2094	0.2079	0.9781	0.2126	4.7046	1.0223	4.8097	1.3614	**78°00′**
12°06′	0.2112	0.2096	0.9778	0.2144	4.6646	1.0227	4.7706	1.3596	77°54′
12°12′	0.2129	0.2113	0.9774	0.2162	4.6252	1.0231	4.7321	1.3579	77°48′
12°18′	0.2147	0.2130	0.9770	0.2180	4.5864	1.0235	4.6942	1.3561	77°42′
12°24′	0.2164	0.2147	0.9767	0.2199	4.5483	1.0239	4.6569	1.3544	77°36′
12°30′	0.2182	0.2164	0.9763	0.2217	4.5107	1.0243	4.6202	1.3526	77°30′
12°36′	0.2199	0.2181	0.9759	0.2235	4.4737	1.0247	4.5841	1.3509	77°24′
12°42′	0.2217	0.2198	0.9755	0.2254	4.4373	1.0251	4.5486	1.3491	77°18′
12°48′	0.2234	0.2215	0.9751	0.2272	4.4015	1.0255	4.5137	1.3474	77°12′
12°54′	0.2251	0.2233	0.9748	0.2290	4.3662	1.0259	4.4793	1.3456	77°06′
13°00′	0.2269	0.2250	0.9744	0.2309	4.3315	1.0263	4.4454	1.3439	**77°00′**
13°06′	0.2286	0.2267	0.9740	0.2327	4.2972	1.0267	4.4121	1.3422	76°54′
13°12′	0.2304	0.2284	0.9736	0.2345	4.2635	1.0271	4.3792	1.3404	76°48′
13°18′	0.2321	0.2300	0.9732	0.2364	4.2303	1.0276	4.3469	1.3387	76°42′
13°24′	0.2339	0.2317	0.9728	0.2382	4.1976	1.0280	4.3150	1.3369	76°36′
13°30′	0.2356	0.2334	0.9724	0.2401	4.1653	1.0284	4.2837	1.3352	76°30′
13°36′	0.2374	0.2351	0.9720	0.2419	4.1335	1.0288	4.2527	1.3334	76°24′
13°42′	0.2391	0.2368	0.9715	0.2438	4.1022	1.0293	4.2223	1.3317	76°18′
13°48′	0.2409	0.2385	0.9711	0.2456	4.0713	1.0297	4.1923	1.3299	76°12′
13°54′	0.2426	0.2402	0.9707	0.2475	4.0408	1.0302	4.1627	1.3282	76°06′
14°00′	0.2443	0.2419	0.9703	0.2493	4.0108	1.0306	4.1336	1.3265	**76°00′**
14°06′	0.2461	0.2436	0.9699	0.2512	3.9812	1.0311	4.1048	1.3247	75°54′
14°12′	0.2478	0.2453	0.9694	0.2530	3.9520	1.0315	4.0765	1.3230	75°48′
14°18′	0.2496	0.2470	0.9690	0.2549	3.9232	1.0320	4.0486	1.3212	75°42′
14°24′	0.2513	0.2487	0.9686	0.2568	3.8947	1.0324	4.0211	1.3195	75°36′
14°30′	0.2531	0.2504	0.9681	0.2586	3.8667	1.0329	3.9939	1.3177	75°30′
14°36′	0.2548	0.2521	0.9677	0.2605	3.8391	1.0334	3.9672	1.3160	75°24′
14°42′	0.2566	0.2538	0.9673	0.2623	3.8118	1.0338	3.9408	1.3142	75°18′
14°48′	0.2583	0.2554	0.9668	0.2642	3.7848	1.0343	3.9147	1.3125	75°12′
14°54′	0.2601	0.2571	0.9664	0.2661	3.7583	1.0348	3.8890	1.3107	75°06′
15°00′	0.2618	0.2588	0.9659	0.2679	3.7321	1.0353	3.8637	1.3090	**75°00′**
		cos θ	sin θ	cot θ	tan θ	csc θ	sec θ	radians	degrees

θ

Table II: (*Continued*)

degrees	radians	sin θ	cos θ	tan θ	cot θ	sec θ	csc θ		
15°00'	0.2618	0.2588	0.9659	0.2679	3.7321	1.0353	3.8637	1.3090	**75°00'**
15°06'	0.2635	0.2605	0.9655	0.2698	3.7062	1.0358	3.8387	1.3073	74°54'
15°12'	0.2653	0.2622	0.9650	0.2717	3.6806	1.0363	3.8140	1.3055	74°48'
15°18'	0.2670	0.2639	0.9646	0.2736	3.6554	1.0367	3.7897	1.3038	74°42'
15°24'	0.2688	0.2656	0.9641	0.2754	3.6305	1.0372	3.7657	1.3020	74°36'
15°30'	0.2705	0.2672	0.9636	0.2773	3.6059	1.0377	3.7420	1.3003	74°30'
15°36'	0.2723	0.2689	0.9632	0.2792	3.5816	1.0382	3.7186	1.2985	74°24'
15°42'	0.2740	0.2706	0.9627	0.2811	3.5576	1.0388	3.6955	1.2968	74°18'
15°48'	0.2758	0.2723	0.9622	0.2830	3.5339	1.0393	3.6727	1.2950	74°12'
15°54'	0.2775	0.2740	0.9617	0.2849	3.5105	1.0398	3.6502	1.2933	74°06'
16°00'	0.2793	0.2756	0.9613	0.2867	3.4874	1.0403	3.6280	1.2915	**74°00'**
16°06'	0.2810	0.2773	0.9608	0.2886	3.4646	1.0408	3.6060	1.2898	73°54'
16°12'	0.2827	0.2790	0.9603	0.2905	3.4420	1.0413	3.5843	1.2881	73°48'
16°18'	0.2845	0.2807	0.9598	0.2924	3.4197	1.0419	3.5629	1.2863	73°42'
16°24'	0.2862	0.2823	0.9593	0.2943	3.3977	1.0424	3.5418	1.2846	73°36'
16°30'	0.2880	0.2840	0.9588	0.2962	3.3759	1.0429	3.5209	1.2828	73°30'
16°36'	0.2897	0.2857	0.9583	0.2981	3.3544	1.0435	3.5003	1.2811	73°24'
16°42'	0.2915	0.2874	0.9578	0.3000	3.3332	1.0440	3.4799	1.2793	73°18'
16°48'	0.2932	0.2890	0.9573	0.3019	3.3122	1.0446	3.4598	1.2776	73°12'
16°54'	0.2950	0.2907	0.9568	0.3038	3.2914	1.0451	3.4399	1.2758	73°06'
17°00'	0.2967	0.2924	0.9563	0.3057	3.2709	1.0457	3.4203	1.2741	**73°00'**
17°06'	0.2985	0.2940	0.9558	0.3076	3.2506	1.0463	3.4009	1.2723	72°54'
17°12'	0.3002	0.2957	0.9553	0.3096	3.2305	1.0468	3.3817	1.2706	72°48'
17°18'	0.3019	0.2974	0.9548	0.3115	3.2106	1.0474	3.3628	1.2689	72°42'
17°24'	0.3037	0.2990	0.9542	0.3134	3.1910	1.0480	3.3440	1.2671	72°36'
17°30'	0.3054	0.3007	0.9537	0.3153	3.1716	1.0485	3.3255	1.2654	72°30'
17°36'	0.3072	0.3024	0.9532	0.3172	3.1524	1.0491	3.3072	1.2636	72°24'
17°42'	0.3089	0.3040	0.9527	0.3191	1.1334	1.0497	3.2891	1.2619	72°18'
17°48'	0.3107	0.3057	0.9521	0.3211	3.1146	1.0503	3.2712	1.2601	72°12'
17°54'	0.3124	0.3074	0.9516	0.3230	3.0961	1.0509	3.2535	1.2584	72°06'
18°00'	0.3142	0.3090	0.9511	0.3249	3.0777	1.0515	3.2361	1.2566	**72°00'**
18°06'	0.3159	0.3107	0.9505	0.3269	3.0595	1.0521	3.2188	1.2549	71°54'
18°12'	0.3176	0.3123	0.9500	0.3288	3.0415	1.0527	3.2017	1.2531	71°48'
18°18'	0.3194	0.3140	0.9494	0.3307	3.0237	1.0533	3.1848	1.2514	71°42'
18°24'	0.3211	0.3156	0.9489	0.3327	3.0061	1.0539	3.1681	1.2462	71°36'
18°30'	0.3229	0.3173	0.9483	0.3346	2.9887	1.0545	3.1515	1.2479	71°30'
18°36'	0.3246	0.3190	0.9478	0.3365	2.9714	1.0551	3.1352	1.2462	71°24'
18°42'	0.3264	0.3206	0.9472	0.3385	2.9544	1.0557	3.1190	1.2444	71°18'
18°48'	0.3281	0.3223	0.9466	0.3404	2.9375	1.0564	3.1030	1.2427	71°12'
18°54'	0.3299	0.3239	0.9461	0.3424	2.9208	1.0570	3.0872	1.2409	71°06'
19°00'	0.3316	0.3256	0.9455	0.3443	2.9042	1.0576	3.0716	1.2392	**71°00'**
19°06'	0.3334	0.3272	0.9449	0.3463	2.8878	1.0583	3.0561	1.2374	70°54'
19°12'	0.3351	0.3289	0.9444	0.3482	2.8716	1.0589	3.0407	1.2357	70°48'
19°18'	0.3368	0.3305	0.9438	0.3502	2.8556	1.0595	3.0256	1.2339	70°42'
19°24'	0.3386	0.3322	0.9432	0.3522	2.8397	1.0602	3.0106	1.2322	70°36'
19°30'	0.3403	0.3338	0.9426	0.3541	2.8239	1.0608	2.9957	1.2305	70°30'
19°36'	0.3421	0.3355	0.9421	0.3561	2.8083	1.0615	2.9811	1.2287	70°24'
19°42'	0.3438	0.3371	0.9415	0.3581	2.7929	1.0622	2.9665	1.2270	70°18'
19°48'	0.3456	0.3387	0.9409	0.3600	2.7776	1.0628	2.9521	1.2252	70°12'
19°54'	0.3473	0.3404	0.9403	0.3620	2.7625	1.0635	2.9379	1.2235	70°06'
20°00'	0.3491	0.3420	0.9397	0.3640	2.7475	1.0642	2.9238	1.2217	**70°00'**
		cos θ	sin θ	cot θ	tan θ	csc θ	sec θ	radians	degrees

θ

θ degrees	radians	sin θ	cos θ	tan θ	cot θ	sec θ	csc θ		
20°00'	0.3491	0.3420	0.9397	0.3640	2.7475	1.0642	2.9238	1.2217	**70°00'**
20°06'	0.3508	0.3437	0.9391	0.3659	2.7326	1.0649	2.9099	1.2200	69°54'
20°12'	0.3526	0.3453	0.9385	0.3679	2.7179	1.0655	2.8960	1.2182	69°48'
20°18'	0.3543	0.3469	0.9379	0.3699	2.7034	1.0662	2.8824	1.2165	69°42'
20°24'	0.3560	0.3486	0.9373	0.3719	2.6889	1.0669	2.8688	1.2147	69°36'
20°30'	0.3578	0.3502	0.9367	0.3739	2.6746	1.0676	2.8555	1.2130	69°30'
20°36'	0.3595	0.3518	0.9361	0.3759	2.6605	1.0683	2.8422	1.2113	69°24'
20°42'	0.3613	0.3535	0.9354	0.3779	2.6464	1.0690	2.8291	1.2095	69°18'
20°48'	0.3630	0.3551	0.9348	0.3799	2.6325	1.0697	2.8161	1.2078	69°12'
20°54'	0.3648	0.3567	0.9342	0.3819	2.6187	1.0704	2.8032	1.2060	69°06'
21°00'	0.3665	0.3584	0.9336	0.3839	2.6051	1.0711	2.7904	1.2043	**69°00'**
21°06'	0.3683	0.3600	0.9330	0.3859	2.5916	1.0719	2.7778	1.2025	68°54'
21°12'	0.3700	0.3616	0.9323	0.3879	2.5782	1.0726	2.7653	1.2008	68°48'
21°18'	0.3718	0.3633	0.9317	0.3899	2.5649	1.0733	2.7529	1.1990	68°42'
21°24'	0.3735	0.3649	0.9311	0.3919	2.5517	1.0740	2.7407	1.1973	68°36'
21°30'	0.3752	0.3665	0.9304	0.3939	2.5386	1.0748	2.7285	1.1956	68°30'
21°36'	0.3770	0.3681	0.9298	0.3959	2.5257	1.0755	2.7165	1.1938	68°24'
21°42'	0.3787	0.3697	0.9291	0.3979	2.5129	1.0763	2.7046	1.1921	68°18'
21°48'	0.3805	0.3714	0.9285	0.4000	2.5002	1.0770	2.6927	1.1903	68°12'
21°54'	0.3822	0.3730	0.9278	0.4020	2.4876	1.0778	2.6811	1.1886	68°06'
22°00'	0.3840	0.3746	0.9272	0.4040	2.4751	1.0785	2.6695	1.1868	**68°00'**
22°06'	0.3857	0.3762	0.9265	0.4061	2.4627	1.0793	2.6580	1.1851	67°54'
22°12'	0.3875	0.3778	0.9259	0.4081	2.4504	1.0801	2.6466	1.1833	67°48'
22°18'	0.3892	0.3795	0.9252	0.4101	2.4383	1.0808	2.6354	1.1816	67°42'
22°24'	0.3910	0.3811	0.9245	0.4122	2.4262	1.0816	2.6242	1.1798	67°36'
22°30'	0.3927	0.3827	0.9239	0.4142	2.4142	1.0824	2.6131	1.1781	67°30'
22°36'	0.3944	0.3843	0.9232	0.4163	2.4023	1.0832	2.6022	1.1764	67°24'
22°42'	0.3962	0.3859	0.9225	0.4183	2.3906	1.0840	2.5913	1.1746	67°18'
22°48'	0.3979	0.3875	0.9219	0.4204	2.3789	1.0848	2.5805	1.1729	67°12'
22°54'	0.3997	0.3891	0.9212	0.4224	2.3673	1.0856	2.5699	1.1711	67°06'
23°00'	0.4014	0.3907	0.9205	0.4245	2.3559	1.0864	2.5593	1.1694	**67°00'**
23°06'	0.4032	0.3923	0.9188	0.4265	2.3445	1.0872	2.5488	1.1676	66°54'
23°12'	0.4049	0.3939	0.9191	0.4286	2.3332	1.0880	2.5384	1.1659	66°48'
23°18'	0.4067	0.3955	0.9184	0.4307	2.3220	1.0888	2.5282	1.1641	66°42'
23°24'	0.4084	0.3971	0.9178	0.4327	2.3109	1.0896	2.5180	1.1624	66°36'
23°30'	0.4102	0.3987	0.9171	0.4348	2.2998	1.0904	2.5078	1.1606	66°30'
23°36'	0.4119	0.4003	0.9164	0.4369	2.2889	1.0913	2.4978	1.1589	66°24'
23°42'	0.4136	0.4019	0.9157	0.4390	2.2781	1.0921	2.4879	1.1572	66°18'
23°48'	0.4154	0.4035	0.9150	0.4411	2.2673	1.0929	2.4780	1.1554	66°12'
23°54'	0.4171	0.4051	0.9143	0.4431	2.2566	1.0938	2.4683	1.1537	66°06'
24°00'	0.4189	0.4067	0.9135	0.4452	2.2460	1.0946	2.4586	1.1519	**66°00'**
24°06'	0.4206	0.4083	0.9128	0.4473	2.2355	1.0955	2.4490	1.1502	65°54'
24°12'	0.4224	0.4099	0.9121	0.4494	2.2251	1.0963	2.4395	1.1484	65°48'
24°18'	0.4241	0.4115	0.9114	0.4515	2.2148	1.0972	2.4300	1.1467	65°42'
24°24'	0.4259	0.4131	0.9107	0.4536	2.2045	1.0981	2.4207	1.1449	65°36'
24°30'	0.4276	0.4147	0.9100	0.4557	2.1943	1.0989	2.4114	1.1432	65°30'
24°36'	0.4294	0.4163	0.9092	0.4578	2.1842	1.0998	2.4022	1.1414	65°24'
24°42'	0.4311	0.4179	0.9085	0.4599	2.1742	1.1007	2.3931	1.1397	65°18'
24°48'	0.4328	0.4195	0.9078	0.4621	2.1642	1.1016	2.3841	1.1380	65°12'
24°54'	0.4346	0.4210	0.9070	0.4642	2.1543	1.1025	2.3751	1.1362	65°06'
25°00'	0.4363	0.4226	0.9063	0.4663	2.1445	1.1034	2.3662	1.1345	**65°00'**
		cos θ	sin θ	cot θ	tan θ	csc θ	sec θ	radians	degrees
									θ

Table II: (*Continued*)

θ degrees	radians	sin θ	cos θ	tan θ	cot θ	sec θ	csc θ		
25°00'	0.4363	0.4226	0.9063	0.4663	2.1445	1.1034	2.3662	1.1345	**65°00'**
25°06'	0.4381	0.4242	0.9056	0.4684	2.1348	1.1043	2.3574	1.1327	64°54'
25°12'	0.4398	0.4258	0.9048	0.4706	2.1251	1.1052	2.3486	1.1310	64°48'
25°18'	0.4416	0.4274	0.9041	0.4727	2.1155	1.1061	2.3400	1.1292	64°42'
25°24'	0.4433	0.4289	0.9033	0.4748	2.1060	1.1070	2.3314	1.1275	64°36'
25°30'	0.4451	0.4305	0.9026	0.4770	2.0965	1.1079	2.3228	1.1257	64°30'
25°36'	0.4468	0.4321	0.9018	0.4791	2.0872	1.1089	2.3144	1.1240	64°24'
25°42'	0.4485	0.4337	0.9011	0.4813	2.0778	1.1098	2.3060	1.1222	64°18'
25°48'	0.4503	0.4352	0.9003	0.4834	2.0686	1.1107	2.2976	1.1205	64°12'
25°54'	0.4520	0.4368	0.8996	0.4856	2.0594	1.1117	2.2894	1.1188	64°06'
26°00'	0.4538	0.4384	0.8988	0.4877	2.0503	1.1126	2.2812	1.1170	**64°00'**
26°06'	0.4555	0.4399	0.8980	0.4899	2.0413	1.1136	2.2730	1.1153	63°54'
26°12'	0.4573	0.4415	0.8973	0.4921	2.0323	1.1145	2.2650	1.1135	63°48'
26°18'	0.4590	0.4431	0.8965	0.4942	2.0233	1.1155	2.2570	1.1118	63°42'
26°24'	0.4608	0.4446	0.8957	0.4964	2.0145	1.1164	2.2490	1.1100	63°36'
26°30'	0.4625	0.4462	0.8949	0.4986	2.0057	1.1174	2.2412	1.1083	63°30'
26°36'	0.4634	0.4478	0.8942	0.5008	1.9970	1.1184	2.2333	1.1065	63°24'
26°42'	0.4660	0.4493	0.8934	0.5029	1.9883	1.1194	2.2256	1.1048	63°18'
26°48'	0.4677	0.4509	0.8926	0.5051	1.9797	1.1203	2.2179	1.1030	63°12'
26°54'	0.4695	0.4524	0.8918	0.5073	1.9711	1.1213	2.2103	1.1013	63°06'
27°00'	0.4712	0.4540	0.8910	0.5095	1.9626	1.1223	2.2027	1.0996	**63°00'**
27°06'	0.4730	0.4555	0.8902	0.5117	1.9542	1.1233	2.1952	1.0978	62°54'
27°12'	0.4747	0.4571	0.8894	0.5139	1.9458	1.1243	2.1877	1.0961	62°48'
27°18'	0.4765	0.4586	0.8886	0.5161	1.9375	1.1253	2.1803	1.0943	62°42'
27°24'	0.4782	0.4602	0.8878	0.5184	1.9292	1.1264	2.1730	1.0926	62°36'
27°30'	0.4800	0.4617	0.8870	0.5206	1.9210	1.1274	2.1657	1.0908	62°30'
27°36'	0.4817	0.4633	0.8862	0.5228	1.9128	1.1284	2.1584	1.0891	62°24'
27°42'	0.4835	0.4648	0.8854	0.5250	1.9047	1.1294	2.1513	1.0873	62°18'
27°48'	0.4852	0.4664	0.8846	0.5272	1.8967	1.1305	2.1441	1.0856	62°12'
27°54'	0.4869	0.4679	0.8838	0.5295	1.8887	1.1315	2.1371	1.0838	62°06'
28°00'	0.4887	0.4695	0.8829	0.5317	1.8807	1.1326	2.1301	1.0821	**62°00'**
28°06'	0.4904	0.4710	0.8821	0.5340	1.8728	1.1336	2.1231	1.0804	61°54'
28°12'	0.4922	0.4726	0.8813	0.5362	1.8650	1.1347	2.1162	1.0786	61°48'
28°18'	0.4939	0.4741	0.8805	0.5384	1.8572	1.1357	2.1093	1.0769	61°42'
28°24'	0.4957	0.4756	0.8796	0.5407	1.8495	1.1368	2.1025	1.0751	61°36'
28°30'	0.4974	0.4772	0.8788	0.5430	1.8418	1.1379	2.0957	1.0734	61°30'
28°36'	0.4992	0.4787	0.8780	0.5452	1.8341	1.1390	2.0890	1.0716	61°24'
28°42'	0.5009	0.4802	0.8771	0.5475	1.8265	1.1401	2.0824	1.0699	61°18'
28°48'	0.5027	0.4818	0.8763	0.5498	1.8190	1.1412	2.0757	1.0681	61°12'
28°54'	0.5044	0.4833	0.8755	0.5520	1.8115	1.1423	2.0692	1.0664	61°06'
29°00'	0.5061	0.4848	0.8746	0.5543	1.8040	1.1434	2.0627	1.0647	**61°00'**
29°06'	0.5079	0.4863	0.8738	0.5566	1.7966	1.1445	2.0562	1.0629	60°54'
29°12'	0.5096	0.4879	0.8729	0.5589	1.7893	1.1456	2.0498	1.0612	60°48'
29°18'	0.5114	0.4894	0.8721	0.5612	1.7820	1.1467	2.0434	1.0594	60°42'
29°24'	0.5131	0.4909	0.8712	0.5635	1.7747	1.1478	2.0371	1.0577	60°36'
29°30'	0.5149	0.4924	0.8704	0.5658	1.7675	1.1490	2.0308	1.0559	60°30'
29°36'	0.5166	0.4939	0.8695	0.5681	1.7603	1.1501	2.0245	1.0542	60°24'
29°42'	0.5184	0.4955	0.8686	0.5704	1.7532	1.1512	2.0183	1.0524	60°18'
29°48'	0.5201	0.4970	0.8678	0.5727	1.7461	1.1524	2.0122	1.0507	60°12'
29°54'	0.5219	0.4985	0.8669	0.5750	1.7391	1.1535	2.0061	1.0489	60°06'
30°00'	0.5236	0.5000	0.8660	0.5774	1.7321	1.1547	2.0000	1.0472	**60°00'**
		cos θ	sin θ	cot θ	tan θ	csc θ	sec θ	radians	degrees
									θ

Table II: (Continued)

degrees	radians	sin θ	cos θ	tan θ	cot θ	sec θ	csc θ		
30°00′	0.5236	0.5000	0.8660	0.5774	1.7321	1.1547	2.0000	1.0472	**60°00′**
30°06′	0.5253	0.5015	0.8652	0.5797	1.7251	1.1559	1.9940	1.0455	59°54′
30°12′	0.5271	0.5030	0.8643	0.5820	1.7182	1.1570	1.9880	1.0437	59°48′
30°18′	0.5288	0.5045	0.8634	0.5844	1.7113	1.1582	1.9821	1.0420	59°42′
30°24′	0.5306	0.5060	0.8625	0.5867	1.7045	1.5194	1.9762	1.0402	59°36′
30°30′	0.5323	0.5075	0.8616	0.5890	1.6977	1.1606	1.9703	1.0385	59°30′
30°36′	0.5341	0.5090	0.8607	0.5914	1.6909	1.1618	1.9645	1.0367	59°24′
30°42′	0.5358	0.5105	0.8599	0.5938	1.6842	1.1630	1.9587	1.0350	59°18′
30°48′	0.5376	0.5120	0.8590	0.5961	1.6775	1.1642	1.9530	1.0332	59°12′
30°54′	0.5393	0.5135	0.8581	0.5985	1.6709	1.1654	1.9473	1.0315	59°06′
31°00′	0.5411	0.5150	0.8572	0.6009	1.6643	1.1666	1.9416	1.0297	**59°00′**
31°06′	0.5428	0.5165	0.8563	0.6032	1.6577	1.1679	1.9360	1.0280	58°54′
31°12′	0.5445	0.5180	0.8554	0.6056	1.6512	1.1691	1.9304	1.0263	58°48′
31°18′	0.5463	0.5195	0.8545	0.6080	1.6447	1.1703	1.9249	1.0245	58°42′
31°24′	0.5480	0.5210	0.8536	0.6104	1.6383	1.1716	1.9194	1.0228	58°36′
31°30′	0.5498	0.5225	0.8526	0.6128	1.6319	1.1728	1.9139	1.0210	58°30′
31°36′	0.5515	0.5240	0.8517	0.6152	1.6255	1.1741	1.9084	1.0193	58°24′
31°42′	0.5533	0.5255	0.8508	0.6176	1.6191	1.1753	1.9031	1.0175	58°18′
31°48′	0.5550	0.5270	0.8499	0.6200	1.6128	1.1766	1.8977	1.0158	58°12′
31°54′	0.5568	0.5284	0.8490	0.6224	1.6066	1.1779	1.8924	1.0140	58°06′
32°00′	0.5585	0.5299	0.8480	0.6249	1.6003	1.1792	1.8871	1.0123	**58°00′**
32°06′	0.5603	0.5314	0.8471	0.6273	1.5941	1.1805	1.8818	1.0105	57°54′
32°12′	0.5620	0.5329	0.8462	0.6297	1.5880	1.1818	1.8766	1.0088	57°48′
32°18′	0.5637	0.5344	0.8453	0.6322	1.5818	1.1831	1.8714	1.0071	57°42′
32°24′	0.5655	0.5358	0.8443	0.6346	1.5757	1.1844	1.8663	1.0053	57°36′
32°30′	0.5672	0.5373	0.8434	0.6371	1.5697	1.1857	1.8612	1.0036	57°30′
32°36′	0.5690	0.5388	0.8425	0.6395	1.5637	1.1870	1.8561	1.0018	57°24′
32°42′	0.5707	0.5402	0.8415	0.6420	1.5577	1.1883	1.8510	1.0001	57°18′
32°48′	0.5725	0.5417	0.8406	0.6445	1.5517	1.1897	1.8460	0.9983	57°12′
32°54′	0.5742	0.5432	0.8396	0.6469	1.5458	1.1910	1.8410	0.9966	57°06′
33°00′	0.5760	0.5446	0.8387	0.6494	1.5399	1.1924	1.8361	0.9948	**57°00′**
33°06′	0.5777	0.5461	0.8377	0.6519	1.5340	1.1937	1.8312	0.9931	56°54′
33°12′	0.5794	0.5476	0.8368	0.6544	1.5282	1.1951	1.8263	0.9913	56°48′
33°18′	0.5812	0.5490	0.8358	0.6569	1.5224	1.1964	1.8214	0.9896	56°42′
33°24′	0.5829	0.5505	0.8348	0.6594	1.5166	1.1978	1.8166	0.9879	56°36′
33°30′	0.5847	0.5519	0.8339	0.6619	1.5108	1.1992	1.8118	0.9861	56°30′
33°36′	0.5864	0.5534	0.8329	0.6644	1.5051	1.2006	1.8070	0.9844	56°24′
33°42′	0.5882	0.5548	0.8320	0.6669	1.4994	1.2020	1.8023	0.9826	56°18′
33°48′	0.5899	0.5563	0.8310	0.6694	1.4938	1.2034	1.7976	0.9809	56°12′
33°54′	0.5917	0.5577	0.8300	0.6720	1.4882	1.2048	1.7929	0.9791	56°06′
34°00′	0.5934	0.5592	0.8290	0.6745	1.4826	1.2062	1.7883	0.9774	**56°00′**
34°06′	0.5952	0.5606	0.8281	0.6771	1.4770	1.2076	1.7837	0.9756	55°54′
34°12′	0.5969	0.5621	0.8271	0.6796	1.4715	1.2091	1.7791	0.9739	55°48′
34°18′	0.5986	0.5635	0.8261	0.6822	1.4659	1.2105	1.7745	0.9721	55°42′
34°24′	0.6004	0.5650	0.8251	0.6847	1.4605	1.2120	1.7700	0.9704	55°36′
34°30′	0.6021	0.5664	0.8241	0.6873	1.4550	1.2134	1.7655	0.9687	55°30′
34°36′	0.6039	0.5678	0.8231	0.6899	1.4496	1.2149	1.7610	0.9669	55°24′
34°42′	0.6056	0.5693	0.8221	0.6924	1.4442	1.2163	1.7566	0.9652	55°18′
34°48′	0.6074	0.5707	0.8211	0.6950	1.4388	1.2178	1.7522	0.9634	55°12′
34°54′	0.6091	0.5721	0.8202	0.6976	1.4335	1.2193	1.7478	0.9617	55°06′
35°00′	0.6109	0.5736	0.8192	0.7002	1.4281	1.2208	1.7434	0.9599	**55°00′**
		cos θ	sin θ	cot θ	tan θ	csc θ	sec θ	radians	degrees
								θ	

Table II: (*Continued*)

θ degrees	radians	sin θ	cos θ	tan θ	cot θ	sec θ	csc θ		
35°00′	0.6109	0.5736	0.8192	0.7002	1.4281	1.2208	1.7434	0.9599	**55°00′**
35°06′	0.6126	0.5750	0.8181	0.7028	1.4229	1.2223	1.7391	0.9582	54°54′
35°12′	0.6144	0.5764	0.8171	0.7054	1.4176	1.2238	1.7348	0.9564	54°48′
35°18′	0.6161	0.5779	0.8161	0.7080	1.4124	1.2253	1.7305	0.9547	54°42′
35°24′	0.6178	0.5793	0.8151	0.7107	1.4071	1.2268	1.7263	0.9529	54°36′
35°30′	0.6196	0.5807	0.8141	0.7133	1.4019	1.2283	1.7221	0.9512	54°30′
35°36′	0.6213	0.5821	0.8131	0.7159	1.3968	1.2299	1.7179	0.9495	54°24′
35°42′	0.6231	0.5835	0.8121	0.7186	1.3916	1.2314	1.7137	0.9477	54°18′
35°48′	0.6248	0.5850	0.8111	0.7212	1.3865	1.2329	1.7095	0.9460	54·12′
35°54′	0.6266	0.5864	0.8100	0.7239	1.3814	1.2345	1.7054	0.9442	54°06′
36°00′	0.6283	0.5878	0.8090	0.7265	1.3764	1.2361	1.7013	0.9425	**54°00′**
36°06′	0.6301	0.5892	0.8080	0.7292	1.3713	1.2376	1.6972	0.9417	53°54′
36°12′	0.6318	0.5906	0.8070	0.7319	1.3663	1.2392	1.6932	0.9390	53°48′
36°18′	0.6336	0.5920	0.8059	0.7346	1.3613	1.2408	1.6892	0.9372	53°42′
36°24′	0.6353	0.5934	0.8049	0.7373	1.3564	1.2424	1.6852	0.9355	53°36′
36°30′	0.6370	0.5948	0.8039	0.7400	1.3514	1.2440	1.6812	0.9338	53°30′
36°36′	0.6388	0.5962	0.8028	0.7427	1.3465	1.2456	1.6772	0.9320	53°24′
36°42′	0.6405	0.5976	0.8018	0.7454	1.3416	1.2472	1.6733	0.9303	53°18′
36°48′	0.6423	0.5990	0.8007	0.7481	1.3367	1.2489	1.6694	0.9285	53°12′
36°54′	0.6440	0.6004	0.7997	0.7508	1.3319	1.2505	1.6655	0.9268	53°06′
37°00′	0.6458	0.6018	0.7986	0.7536	1.3270	1.2521	1.6616	0.9250	**53°00′**
37°06′	0.6475	0.6032	0.7976	0.7563	1.3222	1.2538	1.6578	0.9233	52°54′
37°12′	0.6493	0.6046	0.7965	0.7590	1.3175	1.2554	1.6540	0.9215	52°48′
37°18′	0.6510	0.6060	0.7955	0.7618	1.3127	1.2571	1.6502	0.9198	52°42′
37°24′	0.6528	0.6074	0.7944	0.7646	1.3079	1.2588	1.6464	0.9180	52°36′
37°30′	0.6545	0.6088	0.7934	0.7673	1.3032	1.2605	1.6427	0.9163	52°30′
37°36′	0.6562	0.6101	0.7923	0.7701	1.2985	1.2622	1.6390	0.9146	52°24′
37°42′	0.6580	0.6115	0.7912	0.7729	1.2938	1.2639	1.6353	0.9128	52°18′
37°48′	0.6597	0.6129	0.7902	0.7757	1.2892	1.2656	1.6316	0.9111	52°12′
37°54′	0.6615	0.6143	0.7891	0.7785	1.2846	1.2673	1.6279	0.9093	52°06′
38°00′	0.6632	0.6157	0.7880	0.7813	1.2799	1.2690	1.6243	0.9076	**52°00′**
38°06′	0.6650	0.6170	0.7869	0.7841	1.2753	1.2708	1.6207	0.9058	51°54′
38°12′	0.6667	0.6184	0.7859	0.7869	1.2708	1.2725	1.6171	0.9041	51°48′
38°18′	0.6685	0.6198	0.7848	0.7898	1.2662	1.2742	1.6135	0.9023	51°42′
38°24′	0.6702	0.6211	0.7837	0.7926	1.2617	1.2760	1.6099	0.9006	51°36′
38°30′	0.6720	0.6225	0.7826	0.7954	1.2572	1.2778	1.6064	0.8988	51°30′
38°36′	0.6737	0.6239	0.7815	0.7983	1.2527	1.2796	1.6029	0.8971	51°24′
38°42′	0.6754	0.6252	0.7804	0.8012	1.2482	1.2813	1.5994	0.8954	51°18′
38°48′	0.6772	0.6266	0.7793	0.8040	1.2437	1.2831	1.5959	0.8936	51°12′
38°54′	0.6789	0.6280	0.7782	0.8069	1.2393	1.2849	1.5925	0.8919	51°06′
39°00′	0.6807	0.6293	0.7771	0.8098	1.2349	1.2868	1.5890	0.8901	**51°00′**
39°06′	0.6824	0.6307	0.7760	0.8127	1.2305	1.2886	1.5856	0.8884	50°54′
39°12′	0.6842	0.6320	0.7749	0.8156	1.2261	1.2904	1.5822	0.8866	50°48′
39°18′	0.6859	0.6334	0.7738	0.8185	1.2218	1.2923	1.5788	0.8849	50°42′
39°24′	0.6877	0.6347	0.7727	0.8214	1.2174	1.2941	1,5755	0.8831	50°36′
39°30′	0.6894	0.6361	0.7716	0.8243	1.2131	1.2960	1.5721	0.8814	50°30′
39°36′	0.6912	0.6374	0.7705	0.8273	1.2088	1.2978	1.5688	0.8796	50°24′
39°42′	0.6929	0.6388	0.7694	0.8302	1.2045	1.2997	1.5655	0.8779	50°18′
39°48′	0.6946	0.6401	0.7683	0.8332	1.2002	1.3016	1.5622	0.8762	50°12′
39°54′	0.6964	0.6414	0.7672	0.8361	1.1960	1.3035	1.5590	0.8744	50°06′
40°00′	0.6981	0.6428	0.7660	0.8391	1.1918	1.3054	1.5557	0.8727	**50°00′**
		cos θ	sin θ	cot θ	tan θ	csc θ	sec θ	radians	degrees
								θ	

Table II: (*Continued*)

degrees	radians	sin θ	cos θ	tan θ	cot θ	sec θ	csc θ		
40°00′	0.6981	0.6428	0.7660	0.8391	1.1918	1.3054	1.5557	0.8727	**50°00′**
40°06′	0.6999	0.6441	0.7649	0.8421	1.1875	1.3073	1.5525	0.8709	49°54′
40°12′	0.7016	0.6455	0.7638	0.8451	1.1833	1.3093	1.5493	0.8692	49°48′
40°18′	0.7034	0.6468	0.7627	0.8481	1.1792	1.3112	1.5461	0.8674	49°42′
40°24′	0.7051	0.6481	0.7615	0.8511	1.1750	1.3131	1.5429	0.8657	49°36′
40°30′	0.7069	0.6494	0.7604	0.8541	1.1708	1.3151	1.5398	0.8639	49°30′
40°36′	0.7086	0.6508	0.7593	0.8571	1.1667	1.3171	1.5366	0.8622	49°24′
40°42′	0.7103	0.6521	0.7581	0.8601	1.1626	1.3190	1.5335	0.8604	49°18′
40°48′	0.7121	0.6534	0.7570	0.8632	1.1585	1.3210	1.5304	0.8587	49°12′
40°54′	0.7138	0.6547	0.7559	0.8662	1.1544	1.3230	1.5273	0.8570	49°06′
41°00′	0.7156	0.6561	0.7547	0.8693	1.1504	1.3250	1.5243	0.8552	**49°00′**
41°06′	0.7173	0.6574	0.7536	0.8724	1.1463	1.3270	1.5212	0.8535	48°54′
41°12′	0.7191	0.6587	0.7524	0.8754	1.1423	1.3291	1.5182	0.8517	48°48′
41°18′	0.7208	0.6600	0.7513	0.8785	1.1383	1.3311	1.5151	0.8500	48°42′
41°24′	0.7226	0.6613	0.7501	0.8816	1.1343	1.3331	1.5121	0.8482	48°36′
41°30′	0.7243	0.6626	0.7490	0.8847	1.1303	1.3352	1.5092	0.8465	48°30′
41°36′	0.7261	0.6639	0.7478	0.8878	1.1263	1.3373	1.5062	0.8447	48°24′
41°42′	0.7278	0.6652	0.7466	0.8910	1.1224	1.3393	1.5032	0.8430	48°18′
41°48′	0.7295	0.6665	0.7455	0.8941	1.1184	1.3414	1.5003	0.8412	48°12′
41°54′	0.7313	0.6678	0.7443	0.8972	1.1145	1.3435	1.4974	0.8395	48°06′
42°00′	0.7330	0.6691	0.7431	0.9004	1.1106	1.3456	1.4945	0.8378	**48°00′**
42°06′	0.7348	0.6704	0.7420	0.9036	1.1067	1.3478	1.4916	0.8360	47°54′
42°12′	0.7365	0.6717	0.7408	0.9067	1.1028	1.3499	1.4887	0.8343	47°48′
42°18′	0.7383	0.6730	0.7396	0.9099	1.0990	1.3520	1.4859	0.8325	47°42′
42°24′	0.7400	0.6743	0.7385	0.9131	1.0951	1.3542	1.4830	0.8308	47°36′
42°30′	0.7418	0.6756	0.7373	0.9163	1.0913	1.3563	1.4802	0.8290	47°30′
42°36′	0.7435	0.6769	0.7361	0.9195	1.0875	1.3585	1.4774	0.8273	47°24′
42°42′	0.7453	0.6782	0.7349	0.9228	1.0837	1.3607	1.4746	0.8255	47°18′
42°48′	0.7470	0.6794	0.7337	0.9260	1.0799	1.3629	1.4718	0.8238	47°12′
42°54′	0.7487	0.6807	0.7325	0.9293	1.0761	1.3651	1.4690	0.8221	47°06′
43°00′	0.7505	0.6820	0.7314	0.9325	1.0724	1.3673	1.4663	0.8203	**47°00′**
43°06′	0.7522	0.6833	0.7302	0.9358	1.0686	1.3696	1.4635	0.8186	46°54′
43°12′	0.7540	0.6845	0.7290	0.9391	1.0649	1.3718	1.4608	0.8168	46°48′
43°18′	0.7557	0.6858	0.7278	0.9424	1.0612	1.3741	1.4581	0.8151	46°42′
43°24′	0.7575	0.6871	0.7266	0.9457	1.0575	1.3763	1.4554	0.8133	46°36′
43°30′	0.7592	0.6884	0.7254	0.9490	1.0538	1.3786	1.4527	0.8116	46°30′
43°36′	0.7610	0.6896	0.7242	0.9523	1.0501	1.3809	1.4501	0.8098	46°24′
43°42′	0.7627	0.6909	0.7230	0.9556	1.0464	1.3832	1.4474	0.8081	46°18′
43°48′	0.7645	0.6921	0.7218	0.9590	1.0428	1.3855	1.4448	0.8063	46°12′
43°54′	0.7662	0.6934	0.7206	0.9623	1.0392	1.3878	1.4422	0.8046	46°06′
44°00′	0.7679	0.6947	0.7193	0.9657	1.0355	1.3902	1.4396	0.8029	**46°00′**
44°06′	0.7697	0.6959	0.7181	0.9691	1.0319	1.3925	1.4370	0.8011	45°54′
44°12′	0.7714	0.6972	0.7169	0.9725	1.0283	1.3949	1.4344	0.7994	45°48′
44°18′	0.7732	0.6984	0.7157	0.9759	1.0247	1.3972	1.4318	0.7976	45°42′
44°24′	0.7749	0.6997	0.7145	0.9793	1.0212	1.3996	1.4293	0.7959	45°36′
44°30′	0.7767	0.7009	0.7133	0.9827	1.0176	1.4020	1.4267	0.7941	45°30′
44°36′	0.7784	0.7022	0.7120	0.9861	1.0141	1.4044	1.4242	0.7924	45·24′
44°42′	0.7802	0.7034	0.7108	0.9896	1.0105	1.4069	1.4217	0.7906	45°18′
44°48′	0.7819	0.7046	0.7096	0.9930	1.0070	1.4093	1.4192	0.7889	45°12′
44°54′	0.7837	0.7059	0.7083	0.9965	1.0035	1.4118	1.4167	0.7871	45°06′
45°00′	0.7854	0.7071	0.7071	1.0000	1.0000	1.4142	1.4142	0.7854	**45°00′**
		cos θ	sin θ	cot θ	tan θ	csc θ	sec θ	radians	degrees

θ

Table III: $(1+i)^n$

n	½%	1%	1½%	2%	2½%	3%	3½%	n
1	1.005 00	1.010 00	1.015 00	1.020 00	1.025 00	1.030 00	1.035 00	1
2	1.010 03	1.020 10	1.030 23	1.040 40	1.050 63	1.060 90	1.071 23	2
3	1.015 08	1.030 30	1.045 68	1.061 21	1.076 89	1.092 73	1.108 72	3
4	1.020 15	1.040 60	1.061 36	1.082 43	1.103 81	1.125 51	1.147 52	4
5	1.025 25	1.051 01	1.077 28	1.104 08	1.131 41	1.159 27	1.187 69	5
6	1.030 38	1.061 52	1.093 44	1.126 16	1.159 69	1.194 05	1.229 26	6
7	1.035 53	1.072 14	1.109 84	1.148 69	1.188 69	1.229 87	1.272 28	7
8	1.040 71	1.082 86	1.126 49	1.171 66	1.218 40	1.266 77	1.316 81	8
9	1.045 91	1.093 69	1.143 39	1.195 09	1.248 86	1.304 77	1.362 90	9
10	1.051 14	1.104 62	1.160 54	1.218 99	1.280 08	1.343 92	1.410 60	10
11	1.056 40	1.115 67	1.179 95	1.243 37	1.312 09	1.384 23	1.459 97	11
12	1.061 68	1.126 83	1.195 62	1.268 24	1.344 89	1.425 76	1.511 07	12
13	1.066 99	1.138 09	1.213 55	1.293 61	1.378 51	1.468 53	1.563 96	13
14	1.072 32	1.149 47	1.231 76	1.319 48	1.412 97	1.512 59	1.618 69	14
15	1.077 68	1.160 97	1.250 23	1.345 87	1.448 30	1.557 97	1.675 35	15
16	1.083 07	1.172 58	1.268 99	1.372 79	1.484 51	1.604 71	1.733 99	16
17	1.088 49	1.184 30	1.288 02	1.400 24	1.521 62	1.652 85	1.794 68	17
18	1.093 93	1.196 15	1.307 34	1.428 25	1.559 66	1.702 43	1.857 49	18
19	1.099 40	1.208 11	1.326 95	1.456 81	1.598 65	1.753 51	1.922 50	19
20	1.104 90	1.220 19	1.346 86	1.485 95	1.638 62	1.806 11	1.989 79	20
21	1.110 42	1.232 39	1.367 06	1.515 67	1.679 58	1.860 29	2.059 43	21
22	1.115 97	1.244 72	1.387 56	1.545 98	1.721 57	1.916 10	2.131 51	22
23	1.121 55	1.257 16	1.408 38	1.576 90	1.764 61	1.973 59	2.206 11	23
24	1.127 16	1.269 73	1.429 50	1.608 44	1.808 73	2.032 79	2.283 33	24
25	1.132 80	1.282 43	1.450 95	1.640 61	1.853 94	2.093 78	2.363 24	25
26	1.138 46	1.295 26	1.472 71	1.673 42	1.900 29	2.156 59	2.445 96	26
27	1.144 15	1.308 21	1.494 80	1.706 89	1.947 80	2.221 29	2.531 57	27
28	1.149 87	1.321 29	1.517 22	1.741 02	1.997 50	2.287 93	2.620 17	28
29	1.155 62	1.334 50	1.539 98	1.775 84	2.046 41	2.356 57	2.711 88	29
30	1.161 40	1.347 85	1.563 08	1.811 36	2.097 57	2.427 26	2.806 79	30
31	1.167 21	1.361 33	1.586 53	1.847 59	2.150 01	2.500 08	2.905 03	31
32	1.173 04	1.374 94	1.610 32	1.884 54	2.203 76	2.575 08	3.006 71	32
33	1.178 91	1.388 69	1.634 48	1.922 23	2.258 85	2.652 34	3.111 94	33
34	1.184 80	1.402 58	1.659 00	1.960 68	2.315 32	2.731 91	3.220 86	34
35	1.190 73	1.416 60	1.683 88	1.999 89	2.373 21	2.813 86	3.333 59	35
36	1.196 68	1.430 77	1.709 14	2.039 89	2.432 54	2.898 28	3.450 27	36
37	1.202 66	1.445 08	1.734 78	2.080 69	2.493 35	2.985 23	3.571 03	37
38	1.208 68	1.459 53	1.760 80	2.122 30	2.555 68	3.074 78	3.696 01	38
39	1.214 72	1.474 12	1.787 21	2.164 74	2.619 57	3.167 03	3.825 37	39
40	1.220 79	1.488 86	1.814 02	2.208 04	2.685 06	3.264 04	3.959 26	40

n	4%	4½%	5%	5½%	6%	7%	8%	n
1	1.040 00	1.045 00	1.050 00	1.055 00	1.060 00	1.070 00	1.080 00	1
2	1.081 60	1.092 03	1.102 50	1.113 03	1.123 60	1.144 90	1.166 40	2
3	1.124 86	1.141 17	1.157 63	1.174 24	1.191 02	1.225 04	1.259 71	3
4	1.169 86	1.192 52	1.215 51	1.238 82	1.262 48	1.310 80	1.360 49	4
5	1.216 65	1.246 18	1.276 28	1.306 96	1.338 23	1.402 55	1.469 33	5
6	1.265 32	1.302 26	1.340 10	1.378 84	1.418 52	1.500 73	1.586 87	6
7	1.315 93	1.360 86	1.407 10	1.454 68	1.503 63	1.605 78	1.713 82	7
8	1.368 57	1.422 10	1.477 46	1.534 69	1.593 85	1.718 19	1.850 93	8
9	1.423 31	1.486 10	1.551 33	1.619 09	1.689 48	1.838 46	1.999 00	9
10	1.480 24	1.552 97	1.628 89	1.708 14	1.790 85	1.967 15	2.158 93	10
11	1.539 45	1.622 85	1.710 34	1.802 09	1.898 30	2.104 85	2.331 64	11
12	1.601 03	1.695 88	1.795 86	1.901 21	2.012 20	2.252 19	2.518 17	12
13	1.665 07	1.772 20	1.885 65	2.005 77	2.132 93	2.409 85	2.719 62	13
14	1.731 68	1.851 94	1.979 93	2.116 09	2.260 90	2.578 53	2.937 19	14
15	1.800 94	1.935 28	2.078 93	2.232 48	2.396 56	2.759 03	3.172 17	15
16	1.872 98	2.022 37	2.182 87	2.355 26	2.540 35	2.952 16	3.425 94	16
17	1.947 90	2.113 38	2.292 02	2.484 80	2.692 77	3.158 81	3.700 02	17
18	2.025 82	2.208 48	2.406 62	2.621 47	2.854 34	3.379 93	3.996 02	18
19	2.106 85	2.307 86	2.526 95	2.765 65	3.025 60	3.616 53	4.315 70	19
20	2.191 12	2.411 71	2.653 30	2.917 76	3.207 14	3.869 68	4.660 96	20
21	2.278 77	2.520 24	2.785 96	3.078 23	3.399 56	4.140 56	5.033 83	21
22	2.369 92	2.633 65	2.925 26	3.247 54	3.603 54	4.430 40	5.436 54	22
23	2.464 72	2.752 17	3.071 52	3.426 15	3.819 75	4.740 53	5.871 46	23
24	2.563 30	2.876 01	3.225 10	3.614 59	4.048 93	5.072 37	6.341 18	24
25	2.665 84	3.005 43	3.386 35	3.813 39	4.291 87	5.427 43	6.848 48	25
26	2.772 47	3.140 68	3.555 67	4.023 13	4.549 38	5.807 35	7.396 35	26
27	2.883 37	3.282 01	3.733 46	4.244 40	4.822 35	6.213 87	7.988 06	27
28	2.998 70	3.429 70	3.920 13	4.477 84	5.111 69	6.648 84	8.627 11	28
29	3.118 65	3.584 04	4.116 14	4.724 12	5.418 39	7.114 26	9.317 27	29
30	3.243 40	3.745 32	4.321 94	4.983 95	5.743 49	7.612 26	10.062 66	30
31	3.373 13	3.913 86	4.538 04	5.258 07	6.088 10	8.145 11	10.867 67	31
32	3.508 06	4.089 98	4.764 94	5.547 26	6.453 39	8.715 27	11.737 08	32
33	3.648 38	4.274 03	5.003 19	5.852 36	6.840 59	9.325 34	12.676 05	33
34	3.794 32	4.446 36	5.253 35	6.174 24	7.251 03	9.978 11	13.690 13	34
35	3.946 09	4.667 35	5.516 02	6.513 83	7.686 09	10.676 58	14.785 34	35
36	4.130 93	4.877 38	5.791 82	6.872 09	8.147 25	11.423 94	15.968 17	36
37	4.268 09	5.096 86	6.081 41	7.250 05	8.636 09	12.223 62	17.245 63	37
38	4.438 81	5.326 22	6.385 48	7.648 80	9.154 25	13.079 27	18.625 28	38
39	4.616 37	5.565 90	6.704 75	8.069 49	9.703 51	13.994 82	20.115 30	39
40	4.801 02	5.816 36	7.039 99	8.513 31	10.285 72	14.974 46	21.724 52	40

Table IV: $\dfrac{1}{(1+i)^n}$

i \ n	½%	1%	1½%	2%	2½%	3%	3½%	i \ n
1	0.995 02	0.990 10	0.985 22	0.980 39	0.975 61	0.970 87	0.966 18	1
2	0.990 07	0.980 30	0.970 66	0.961 17	0.951 81	0.942 60	0.933 51	2
3	0.985 15	0.970 59	0.956 32	0.942 32	0.928 60	0.915 14	0.901 94	3
4	0.980 25	0.960 98	0.942 18	0.923 85	0.905 95	0.888 49	0.871 44	4
5	0.975 37	0.951 47	0.928 26	0.905 73	0.883 85	0.862 61	0.841 97	5
6	0.970 52	0.942 05	0.914 54	0.887 97	0.862 30	0.837 48	0.813 50	6
7	0.965 69	0.932 72	0.901 03	0.870 56	0.841 27	0.813 09	0.785 99	7
8	0.960 89	0.923 48	0.887 71	0.853 49	0.820 75	0.789 41	0.759 41	8
9	0.956 10	0.914 34	0.874 59	0.836 76	0.800 73	0.766 42	0.733 73	9
10	0.951 35	0.905 29	0.861 67	0.820 35	0.781 20	0.744 09	0.708 92	10
11	0.946 61	0.896 32	0.848 93	0.804 26	0.762 14	0.722 42	0.684 95	11
12	0.941 91	0.887 45	0.836 39	0.788 49	0.743 56	0.701 38	0.661 78	12
13	0.937 22	0.878 66	0.824 03	0.773 03	0.725 42	0.680 95	0.639 40	13
14	0.932 56	0.869 96	0.811 85	0.757 88	0.707 73	0.661 12	0.617 78	14
15	0.927 92	0.861 35	0.799 85	0.743 01	0.690 47	0.641 86	0.596 89	15
16	0.923 30	0.852 82	0.788 03	0.728 45	0.673 62	0.623 17	0.576 71	16
17	0.918 71	0.844 38	0.776 39	0.714 16	0.657 20	0.605 02	0.557 20	17
18	0.914 14	0.836 02	0.764 91	0.700 16	0.641 17	0.587 39	0.538 36	18
19	0.909 59	0.827 74	0.753 61	0.686 43	0.625 53	0.570 29	0.520 16	19
20	0.905 06	0.819 54	0.742 47	0.672 97	0.610 27	0.553 68	0.502 57	20
21	0.900 56	0.811 43	0.731 50	0.659 78	0.595 39	0.527 55	0.485 57	21
22	0.896 08	0.803 40	0.720 69	0.646 84	0.580 86	0.521 89	0.469 15	22
23	0.891 62	0.795 44	0.710 04	0.634 16	0.566 70	0.506 69	0.453 29	23
24	0.887 19	0.787 57	0.699 54	0.621 72	0.552 88	0.491 93	0.437 96	24
25	0.882 77	0.779 77	0.689 21	0.609 53	0.539 39	0.477 61	0.423 15	25
26	0.878 38	0.772 05	0.679 02	0.597 58	0.526 23	0.463 69	0.408 84	26
27	0.874 01	0.764 40	0.668 99	0.585 86	0.513 40	0.450 19	0.395 01	27
28	0.869 66	0.756 84	0.659 10	0.574 37	0.500 88	0.437 08	0.381 65	28
29	0.865 33	0.749 34	0.649 36	0.563 11	0.488 66	0.424 35	0.368 75	29
30	0.861 03	0.741 92	0.639 76	0.552 07	0.476 74	0.411 99	0.356 28	30
31	0.856 75	0.734 58	0.630 31	0.541 25	0.465 11	0.399 99	0.344 23	31
32	0.852 48	0.727 30	0.620 99	0.530 63	0.453 77	0.388 34	0.332 59	32
33	0.848 24	0.720 10	0.611 82	0.520 23	0.442 70	0.377 03	0.321 34	33
34	0.844 02	0.712 97	0.602 77	0.510 03	0.431 91	0.366 04	0.310 48	34
35	0.839 82	0.705 91	0.593 87	0.500 03	0.421 37	0.355 38	0.299 98	35
36	0.835 64	0.698 92	0.585 09	0.490 22	0.411 09	0.345 03	0.289 83	36
37	0.831 49	0.692 00	0.576 44	0.480 61	0.401 07	0.334 98	0.280 03	37
38	0.827 35	0.685 15	0.567 92	0.471 19	0.391 28	0.325 23	0.270 56	38
39	0.823 23	0.678 37	0.559 53	0.461 95	0.381 74	0.315 75	0.261 41	39
40	0.819 14	0.671 65	0.551 26	0.452 89	0.372 43	0.306 56	0.252 57	40

i \ n	4%	4½%	5%	5½%	6%	7%	8%	i \ n
1	0.961 54	0.956 94	0.952 38	0.947 87	0.943 40	0.934 58	0.925 93	1
2	0.924 56	0.915 73	0.907 03	0.898 45	0.890 00	0.873 44	0.857 34	2
3	0.889 00	0.876 30	0.863 84	0.851 61	0.839 62	0.816 30	0.793 83	3
4	0.854 80	0.838 56	0.822 70	0.807 22	0.792 09	0.762 90	0.735 03	4
5	0.821 93	0.802 45	0.783 53	0.765 13	0.747 26	0.712 99	0.680 58	5
6	0.790 31	0.767 90	0.746 22	0.725 25	0.704 96	0.666 34	0.630 17	6
7	0.759 92	0.734 83	0.710 68	0.687 44	0.665 06	0.622 75	0.583 49	7
8	0.730 69	0.703 19	0.676 84	0.651 60	0.627 41	0.582 01	0.540 27	8
9	0.702 59	0.672 90	0.644 61	0.617 63	0.591 90	0.543 93	0.500 25	9
10	0.675 56	0.643 93	0.613 91	0.585 43	0.558 39	0.508 35	0.463 19	10
11	0.649 58	0.616 20	0.584 68	0.554 91	0.526 79	0.475 09	0.428 88	11
12	0.624 60	0.589 66	0.556 84	0.525 98	0.496 97	0.444 01	0.397 11	12
13	0.600 57	0.564 27	0.530 32	0.498 56	0.468 84	0.414 96	0.367 70	13
14	0.577 48	0.539 97	0.505 07	0.472 57	0.442 30	0.387 82	0.340 46	14
15	0.555 26	0.516 72	0.481 02	0.447 93	0.417 27	0.362 45	0.315 24	15
16	0.533 91	0.494 47	0.458 11	0.424 58	0.393 65	0.338 73	0.291 89	16
17	0.513 37	0.473 18	0.436 30	0.402 45	0.371 36	0.316 57	0.270 27	17
18	0.493 63	0.452 80	0.415 52	0.381 47	0.350 34	0.295 86	0.250 25	18
19	0.474 64	0.433 30	0.395 73	0.361 58	0.330 51	0.276 51	0.231 71	19
20	0.456 39	0.414 64	0.376 89	0.342 73	0.311 80	0.258 42	0.214 55	20
21	0.438 83	0.396 79	0.358 94	0.324 86	0.294 16	0.241 51	0.198 66	21
22	0.421 96	0.379 70	0.341 85	0.307 93	0.277 51	0.225 71	0.183 94	22
23	0.405 73	0.363 35	0.325 57	0.291 87	0.261 80	0.210 95	0.170 32	23
24	0.390 12	0.347 70	0.310 07	0.276 66	0.246 98	0.197 15	0.157 70	24
25	0.375 12	0.332 73	0.295 30	0.262 23	0.233 00	0.184 25	0.146 02	25
26	0.360 69	0.318 40	0.281 24	0.248 56	0.219 81	0.172 20	0.135 20	26
27	0.346 82	0.304 69	0.267 85	0.235 60	0.207 37	0.160 93	0.125 19	27
28	0.333 48	0.291 57	0.255 09	0.223 32	0.195 63	0.150 40	0.115 91	28
29	0.320 65	0.279 02	0.242 95	0.211 68	0.184 56	0.140 56	0.107 33	29
30	0.308 32	0.267 00	0.231 38	0.200 64	0.174 11	0.131 37	0.099 38	30
31	0.296 46	0.255 50	0.220 36	0.190 18	0.164 25	0.122 77	0.092 02	31
32	0.285 06	0.244 50	0.209 87	0.180 27	0.154 96	0.114 74	0.085 20	32
33	0.274 09	0.233 97	0.199 87	0.170 87	0.146 19	0.107 23	0.078 89	33
34	0.263 55	0.223 90	0.190 35	0.161 96	0.137 91	0.100 22	0.073 05	34
35	0.253 42	0.214 25	0.181 29	0.153 52	0.130 11	0.093 66	0.067 63	35
36	0.243 67	0.205 03	0.172 66	0.145 52	0.122 74	0.087 54	0.062 62	36
37	0.234 30	0.196 20	0.164 44	0.137 93	0.115 79	0.081 81	0.057 99	37
38	0.225 29	0.187 75	0.156 61	0.130 74	0.109 24	0.076 46	0.053 69	38
39	0.216 62	0.179 67	0.149 15	0.123 92	0.103 06	0.071 46	0.049 71	39
40	0.208 29	0.171 93	0.142 05	0.117 46	0.097 22	0.066 78	0.046 03	40

Table V:
Areas under the Standard Normal Curve

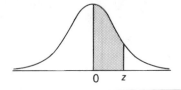

z	0	1	2	3	4	5	6	7	8	9
0.0	0.0000	0.0040	0.0080	0.0120	0.0160	0.0199	0.0239	0.0279	0.0319	0.0359
0.1	0.0398	0.0438	0.0478	0.0517	0.0557	0.0596	0.0636	0.0675	0.0714	0.0754
0.2	0.0793	0.0832	0.0871	0.0910	0.0948	0.0987	0.1026	0.1064	0.1103	0.1141
0.3	0.1179	0.1217	0.1255	0.1293	0.1331	0.1368	0.1406	0.1443	0.1480	0.1517
0.4	0.1554	0.1591	0.1628	0.1664	0.1700	0.1736	0.1772	0.1808	0.1844	0.1879
0.5	0.1915	0.1950	0.1985	0.2019	0.2054	0.2088	0.2123	0.2157	0.2190	0.2224
0.6	0.2258	0.2291	0.2324	0.2357	0.2389	0.2422	0.2454	0.2486	0.2518	0.2549
0.7	0.2580	0.2612	0.2642	0.2673	0.2704	0.2734	0.2764	0.2794	0.2823	0.2852
0.8	0.2881	0.2910	0.2939	0.2967	0.2996	0.3023	0.3051	0.3078	0.3106	0.3133
0.9	0.3159	0.3186	0.3212	0.3238	0.3264	0.3289	0.3315	0.3340	0.3365	0.3389
1.0	0.3413	0.3438	0.3461	0.3485	0.3508	0.3531	0.3554	0.3577	0.3599	0.3621
1.1	0.3643	0.3665	0.3686	0.3708	0.3729	0.3749	0.3770	0.3790	0.3810	0.3830
1.2	0.3849	0.3869	0.3888	0.3907	0.3925	0.3944	0.3962	0.3980	0.3997	0.4015
1.3	0.4032	0.4049	0.4066	0.4082	0.4099	0.4115	0.4131	0.4147	0.4162	0.4177
1.4	0.4192	0.4207	0.4222	0.4236	0.4251	0.4265	0.4279	0.4292	0.4306	0.4319
1.5	0.4332	0.4345	0.4357	0.4370	0.4382	0.4394	0.4406	0.4418	0.4429	0.4441
1.6	0.4452	0.4463	0.4474	0.4484	0.4495	0.4505	0.4515	0.4525	0.4535	0.4545
1.7	0.4554	0.4564	0.4573	0.4582	0.4591	0.4599	0.4608	0.4616	0.4625	0.4633
1.8	0.4641	0.4649	0.4656	0.4664	0.4671	0.4678	0.4686	0.4693	0.4699	0.4706
1.9	0.4713	0.4719	0.4726	0.4732	0.4738	0.4744	0.4750	0.4756	0.4761	0.4767
2.0	0.4772	0.4778	0.4783	0.4788	0.4793	0.4798	0.4803	0.4808	0.4812	0.4817
2.1	0.4821	0.4826	0.4830	0.4834	0.4838	0.4842	0.4846	0.4850	0.4854	0.4857
2.2	0.4861	0.4864	0.4868	0.4871	0.4875	0.4878	0.4881	0.4884	0.4887	0.4890
2.3	0.4893	0.4896	0.4898	0.4901	0.4904	0.4906	0.4909	0.4911	0.4913	0.4916
2.4	0.4918	0.4920	0.4922	0.4925	0.4927	0.4929	0.4931	0.4932	0.4934	0.4936
2.5	0.4938	0.4940	0.4941	0.4943	0.4945	0.4946	0.4948	0.4949	0.4951	0.4952
2.6	0.4953	0.4955	0.4956	0.4957	0.4959	0.4960	0.4961	0.4962	0.4963	0.4964
2.7	0.4965	0.4966	0.4967	0.4968	0.4969	0.4970	0.4971	0.4972	0.4973	0.4974
2.8	0.4974	0.4975	0.4976	0.4977	0.4977	0.4978	0.4979	0.4979	0.4980	0.4981
2.9	0.4981	0.4982	0.4982	0.4983	0.4984	0.4984	0.4985	0.4985	0.4986	0.4986
3.0	0.4987	0.4987	0.4987	0.4988	0.4988	0.4989	0.4989	0.4989	0.4990	0.4990
3.1	0.4990	0.4991	0.4991	0.4991	0.4992	0.4992	0.4992	0.4992	0.4993	0.4993
3.2	0.4993	0.4993	0.4994	0.4994	0.4994	0.4994	0.4994	0.4995	0.4995	0.4995
3.3	0.4995	0.4995	0.4995	0.4996	0.4996	0.4996	0.4996	0.4996	0.4996	0.4997
3.4	0.4997	0.4997	0.4997	0.4997	0.4997	0.4997	0.4997	0.4997	0.4997	0.4998
3.5	0.4998	0.4998	0.4998	0.4998	0.4998	0.4998	0.4998	0.4998	0.4998	0.4998
3.6	0.4998	0.4998	0.4999	0.4999	0.4999	0.4999	0.4999	0.4999	0.4999	0.4999
3.7	0.4999	0.4999	0.4999	0.4999	0.4999	0.4999	0.4999	0.4999	0.4999	0.4999
3.8	0.4999	0.4999	0.4999	0.4999	0.4999	0.4999	0.4999	0.4999	0.4999	0.4999
3.9	0.5000	0.5000	0.5000	0.5000	0.5000	0.5000	0.5000	0.5000	0.5000	0.5000

INDEX